Order Number: T-TURENG-0101

AIRCRAFT TURBINE ENGINES

THOMAS WILD
RONALD STERKENBURG

AVOTEK INFORMATION RESOURCES

Production Staff

Editor Ian McCloskey

Designer/Production Coordinator Emily Clark

Illustrator Amy Siever

International Standard Book Number 1-933189-14-2
ISBN 13: 978-1-933189-14-7
Order # T-TURENG-0101

For Sale by: Avotek
A Select Aerospace Industries company

Mail to:
P.O. Box 219
Weyers Cave, Virginia 24486
USA

Ship to:
200 Packaging Drive
Weyers Cave, Virginia 24486
USA

Toll Free: 1-800-828-6835
Telephone: 1-540-234-9090
Fax: 1-540-234-9399

Printed in the USA

www.avotek.com
www.avotekbooks.com

Preface

This textbook has been written to acquaint powerplant technicians and flight crewmembers with aircraft gas turbine engines. Easy to understand diagrams and images are used to illustrate many concepts and to increase the level of understanding. The fundamentals of gas turbine engines are presented along with turbine engine types, theory and nomenclature. Basic operating principles, the laws of physics and thrust development formulas are presented in simple, easy to understand terms. Engine systems and components are covered in order to allow the reader to easily understand their function as part of the overall operation of the engine. The technician or flight crewmember will benefit from the discussions of safety and engine performance.

Turbine engine maintenance, manufacturing, and overhaul practices are mentioned to provide background information on standard turbine industry practices. Examples of aircraft gas turbine engines, turbofan, turbojet, turboprop and turboshaft are examined and their systems are emphasized. The text covers those areas needed in a powerplant technician training program. Anyone wanting to learn about turbine engines will enjoy this text.

Textbooks, by their very nature, must be general in their overall coverage of a subject area. As always, the manufacturer is the sole source of operation, maintenance, repair, and overhaul information. Manufacturers manuals are approved by the FAA and must always be followed. The material presented in this or any other textbook must not be used as a manual for actual operation, maintenance or repairs.

The writers, individuals and companies which have contributed to the production of this textbook have done so in the spirit of cooperation for the good of the industry. To the best of their abilities, they have tried to provide accurate and pertinent material. However, as with all human endeavors, errors and omissions may occur. If any exist, they are unintentional. Please bring them to our attention.

Email us at corrections@avotekbooks.com for comments or suggestions.

Acknowledgements

The Boeing Company

Sergey Dubikovsky — *Purdue University*

Honeywell International, Inc.

National Aeronautics and Space Administration

Pratt & Whitney

Pratt & Whitney Canada

Rolls-Royce plc

Transformation Technologies, Inc.

Contents

Chapter 1
HISTORY *of turbines*

Gas turbine engines have allowed for the creation of the jet age. Propeller-driven aircraft with reciprocating engines are limited in speed to a maximum of around 400 m.p.h. As the jet age became a reality, the gas turbine engine allowed aircraft to exceed the propeller speed limit. Gas turbine engines have increased the cruising speed of most transport aircraft to approximately 600 m.p.h. or 0.8 Mach.

One of the reasons the gas turbine is able to deliver more power (thrust) for engine weight is that all operating functions take place simultaneously. A reciprocating engine has the functions of intake, compression, combustion and exhaust which take place in the same combustion chamber.

On the other hand, the turbine has a separate section for each function, allowing them all to take place at the same time. This also reduces the overall engine weight to power ratio.

The history and development of the gas turbine engine is an important part of understanding how aviation grew from the reciprocating piston engine and its propeller limits into the air transport aviation of today. Although there are different types of turbine engines, they are divided into the following sections:

- Air inlet section for directing the air into the engine
- Compressor section where inlet air is compressed
- Diffuser section to slow airflow and increase pressure
- Combustion section where heat energy is introduced by burning fuel.
- Turbine section that retrieves enough energy to drive the compressor

Learning Objectives

- *History*
- *Early Jet Propulsion*
- *Engine Development*
- *Advancements*
- *Fuel Economy*

***Left*: The Allison J33 was one of the first production gas turbine engines.**

- Exhaust section that directs exhaust gas not used to drive any type of turbine over board
- Accessory section that is used to drive the accessories needed for engine operation

Each one of these engine sections contains subsections and can differ in construction, but each section performs the same basic functions in each engine type.

Section 1

History and Development of the Gas Turbine Engine

In the 1930s, military and civilian engineers worked to develop a generation of aircraft engines that could produce more power than the piston engine of the time as well as operate at higher altitudes.

This resulted in the development of the jet engine. A jet engine discharges a fast-moving jet of fluid to provide forward thrust. The fluid may be air, water or some other liquid or gas. Aircraft jet engines use air as the working fluid.

The term turbine engine describes a specific type of jet engine. The terms turbine engine and jet engine are often used interchangeably. A turbine engine produces thrust by injecting fuel into compressed air and igniting it. The hot, high-energy gasses are then ejected through a nozzle to produce thrust. A turbine, or fan, is placed in the exhaust. It converts some of the exhaust energy into rotary motion and powers a compressor, hence the name turbine engine. This is the jet engine as we know it today.

All modern turbine aircraft including airliners, business aircraft and helicopters are powered by one of four types of turbine engines. The type of aircraft and its use determines the type of turbine engine. The four basic variants are turbojet, turbofan (also called bypass fan), turboprop (also called prop-jet) and turboshaft.

Figure 1-1-1. Hero's aeolipile is the first known example of jet propulsion.

Turbojet. The earliest production engines were turbojets. All of the early jet airliners used turbojets. They have been phased out of commercial service due to their high fuel consumption and noise levels, but they are still used in many military applications.

Turbofan. Modern commercial passenger aircraft use turbofan engines. These engines produce high thrust levels and can still maintain good fuel efficiency. A version of these engines, designed with lower bypass ratios and sometimes equipped with an afterburner section, is used on many modern military aircraft.

Turboprop. A turboprop engine is a turbine engine that turns a conventional propeller. This type of engine offers high fuel efficiency compared to other turbine engines, however, the propeller limits maximum aircraft speed. It is popular on business aircraft and small, short-range airliners.

Turboshaft. Turboshaft engines, used on helicopters, are gas turbine engines that drive a

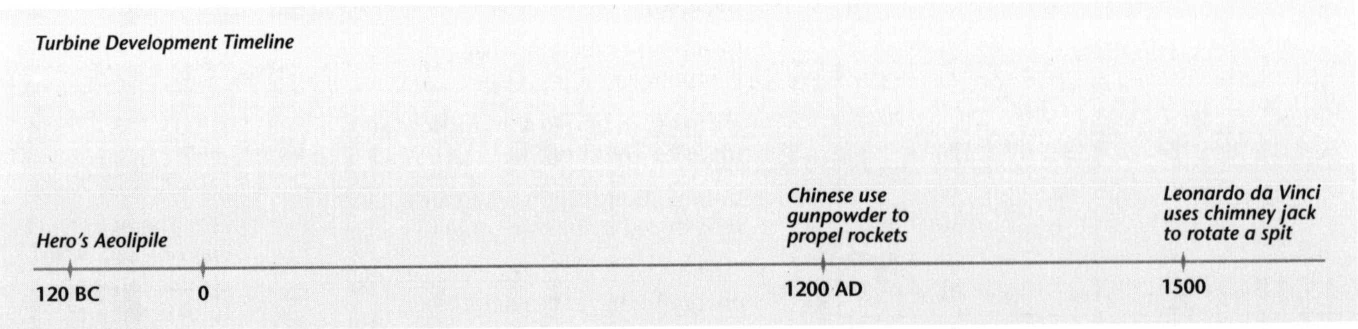

transmission and rotor system. A variation of the turboshaft is the auxiliary power unit (APU). APUs are used to provide power to start the main engines. They are also used to provide electrical power and compressed air for heating and cooling the aircraft on the ground.

Early Jet Propulsion

The first discovery of the jet propulsion principle was made by a man named Hero of Alexandria. He invented an apparatus which was turned by steam, as illustrated in Figure 1-1-1. He called his invention an aeolipile, but apparently it had no practical use at that time.

The aeolipile resembled a primitive form of a jet or reaction engine. It was operated by hot air or steam. It operated by heating air in a tube which forced a flow of air radially around a horizontal wheel which resulted in the creation of an impulse effect. Many other early inventors also worked with several types of propulsion devices which applied the jet principle.

The history of rockets dates back to approximately 1200 A.D. when the Chinese invented gunpowder. From gunpowder, artillery and fireworks were developed. There is a record of the use of rockets in warfare by the Chinese during this period, but for several centuries rockets were used primarily for fireworks.

Travel by rocket has intrigued man for many centuries. The first recorded attempt of rocket-powered flight dates back to the thirteenth century. Wan Hu, Chinese scholar and scientist, intended to hurl himself into space by simultaneously igniting several rockets lashed to a sedan chair in which he was seated. In the blast that followed, both Wan Hu and his sedan chair completely disappeared, thus we can assume that he became the first martyr in man's struggle to achieve jet-propelled flight.

Leonardo da Vinci designed a device called the chimney jack around the year 1500 A.D. The chimney jack was used to turn a roasting spit. This reaction-type turbine worked on the principle of heat. Rising gases from the roasting fire passed through fanlike blades that turned the roast using a series of gears.

Section 2
Turbine Engine Development

Early Pioneers

In 1629 Giovanni Branca perfected a steam turbine that could be used to operate primitive machinery but this was not yet a complete engine. In 1687 Isaac Newton attempted to put his newly formulated laws of motion to the test with his steam wagon. He tried to propel the wagon by directing steam through a nozzle pointed rearward. Steam was produced by a boiler mounted on the wagon. Due to the low power output from the steam, this vehicle could not move itself. A drawing of Newton's carriage is shown in Figure 1-2-1.

The first patent covering a gas turbine was granted to John Barber of England in 1794. This design was the first that used the thermodynamic cycle of the modern gas turbine engine. His design contained the basics of the modern gas turbine in that it had a compressor, a combustion chamber and a turbine. It included all the essential elements of the modern gas turbine except that it had a reciprocating-type compressor.

In 1808 a patent was granted in England to John Bumbell for a gas turbine which had rotating blades but no stationary, guiding elements. A Dr. Franz Stolze designed what was probably the first true gas turbine in 1872 and tested working models between 1900 and 1904. Stolze used both a multistage reaction gas turbine and a multistage axial compressor.

Sir Charles Parsons, the great English inventor, obtained a patent in 1884 for a steam turbine, in which he advanced the theory that a turbine could be converted to a compressor

1629	1687	1794	1808	1872
Giovanni Branca develops steam turbine	*Isaac Newton discovers Three Laws of Motion and designs steam carriage*	*John Barber patents gas turbine*	*John Bumbell patents a turbine engine with rotating blades*	*Dr. Franz Stolze designs first true gas turbine*

1-2-1. Newton's carriage used a steam jet for propulsion.

by driving it in an opposite direction with an external source of power. Parsons believed that compressed air could be discharged into a combustion chamber, fuel injected and the products of combustion expanded through a turbine. This set the basic idea of the makeup of the modern turbine engine.

The period between World War I and World War II was one of active research in the field of jet propulsion. Much original research and development was done by the major world powers. The reciprocating engine for transport aircraft reached the peak of its capabilities in the early 1940s, just as the steam engine had done forty years before. Man needed a new kind of power to further increase the speed of his aircraft and the answer was found in the gas turbine engine.

Sanford A. Moss, who was an engineer at the General Electric Company (GE), conducted experiments that developed the first gas turbine in the United States. The engine was not a success from a practical standpoint because the power required to drive the compressor was greater than the power delivered by the gas turbine. Moss learned enough to enable him to start GE's gas-turbine project, however. Today GE has grown to be one of the largest manufacturers of gas turbine engines.

In the intervening years there were various turbine inventions and developments in the United States and in Europe, but the next outstanding one was the construction of the first General Electric turbosupercharger by Moss.

The turbosupercharger went through a long stage of development and finally the engineers took the knowledge that they acquired from working with the turbosupercharger and applied it to jet propulsion.

Frank Whittle began work on gas turbines and applied for a patent in England in 1930 for a machine having a blower compressor mounted at the forward end and a gas turbine at the rear end of the same shaft, supplied by energy from the combustion chamber.

Sir Charles Parsons patents steam engine — **1884**

Dr. Sanford Moss develops a turbo-supercharger at G.E. — **1917**

Dr. A. A. Griffith develops theory of turbine gas flow past airfoils — **1920**

Frank Whittle patents design for gas turbine engine — **1930**

Von Ohain starts working with Heinkel — **1935**

Discharge jets were located between the annular housings of the rotary elements and in line with several combustion chambers distributed around the circumference. An outstanding pioneer in British turbojet engine development, Whittle, while still a cadet in his teens, proposed the use of a gas turbine for aircraft propulsion.

In 1928 he submitted a thesis on this proposition. In 1931 Whittle was granted a patent on his idea for a centrifugal-flow engine. Development of an engine of his design was begun in 1936 and successfully ground-tested in 1937.

Further development culminated in a successful flight of the Gloster Pioneer, powered by a Whittle jet engine, in May 1941. Continued development of jet aircraft in England during World War II produced the Gloster Meteor fighter, the only allied jet-propelled fighter in service during the war.

While Whittle and his associates were working on the development of a gas turbine engine in England, the Heinkel Aircraft Company was developing a gas turbine engine in Germany. In 1936 Germany began an extensive turbo-jet development program which resulted in the building and successful flight of the world's first turbo-jet-powered airplane in August 1939. The HE178, was equipped with a centrifugal-flow jet engine which developed 1,100 pounds of thrust. A HE178 is shown in Figure 1-2-2.

Subsequent German development of turbojet-powered aircraft produced the ME-262, a 500 mile-per-hour fighter, powered by a two axial-flow engines. More than 1,600 ME-262 fighters were built in the closing stages of World War II, but they reached operational status too late to seriously challenge the overwhelming air superiority gained by the Allies.

During the same period, jet-propelled fighter planes built in England and in the United States by the Bell Aircraft Corporation were powered by a combustion, gas-turbine, jet propulsion powerplant system developed from Frank Whittle's designs and built by the General Electric Company. British development of the turbojet engine had paralleled the work done in Germany.

In the United States, jet engine development was begun after a prototype Whittle W-IX engine was demonstrated to American observers in 1941. This engine was shipped to the United States in June, 1941 and a contract was awarded to the General Electric Company to improve and place this type of engine in production.

General Electric's experience with gas turbines and turbosuperchargers soon led to the development of the I16 engine, the United States' first jet engine. A General Electric I16 is shown in Figure 1-2-3.

Two of these engines, each rated at 1,250 pounds of thrust, were mounted in the XP-59A.

Figure 1-2-2. The earliest jet propelled airplane was the He178.

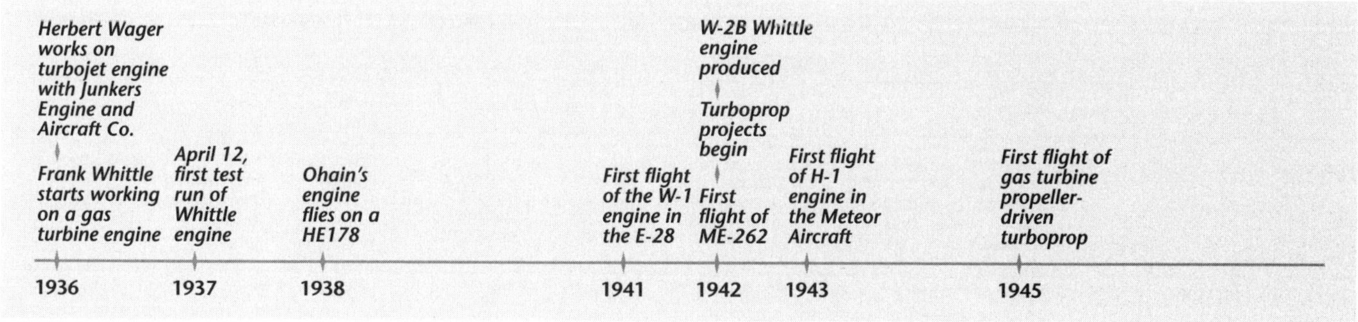

Figure 1-2-3. The General Electric I16 was a license-built version of Frank Whittle's design.

This airplane was test flown in October 1942 and was the first jet-powered aircraft ever to fly in America.

In 1943 The Lockheed Aircraft Company was selected to build the XP-80 jet fighter. This plane was designed and built in the record time of only six months. When the XP-80 was test flown on January 9, 1944, it was powered by a British Halford turbojet engine. The production model, however, was powered by a newly designed I-40 (Air Force GE-J-33) engine which produced 4,000 pounds of thrust. The P-80, later re-designated the F-80 Shooting Star, was capable of speeds in excess of 600 miles per hour. The excellence of this fighter was demonstrated by its performance during the early stages of the Korean War.

Only a few of the many important inventors and engineers who contributed to the modern jet engine program have been mentioned, but the work of every one of them has been based fundamentally on basic jet propulsion principles.

Figure 1-3-1. The modern gas turbine engine has changed over the years. *Image courtesy of General Electric*

1950 — *The British Vickers Viscount first turboprop airliner flies*; *General Electric J-33 developed*

1951 — *J57 developed*; *JT3 one of first dual-spool engines developed*

1952 — *JT36 turbojet engine producing 10,000 lbs*

1953 — *J57 afterburning engine powers aircraft past sound barrier*

1956 — *General Electric J79 and Pratt & Whitney J75 turbojets developed*

1957 — *Jet-powered aircraft flies around world*

The development of the turboprop engine paralleled the development of the turbojet engine. The turboprop engine as it is sometimes called, consists of a small turbojet engine which drives a propeller through suitable reduction gearing. The most noticeable internal difference is the design of a turbine which has the necessary additional stages to extract sufficient energy from the gases in order to rotate a propeller.

Section 3

Turbine Engine Advancements

Modern gas turbine engines have made tremendous progress in improved dependability and reliability. A modern gas turbine engine (turbofan) is shown in Figure 1-3-1. It incorporates new concepts and technologies such as low-emission combustors, fan blade shapes to increase performance, thermal barrier coating, improve monitoring, metallurgy and structural improvement features for high-pressure turbines. These features will increase the overall performance of future engines.

Years of operating experience have provided engine manufacturers with data on engine operation that has extended or improved temperature limits, engine life, fuel economy and thrust ratings. New technology in the manufacturing process and improved metallurgy have allowed engines to operate at much higher temperatures which add to a major increase in gas turbine engine efficiency.

Thermal coatings. Thermal barrier coatings on many of the hot section parts of the engines have also allowed for raising the operating temperatures. By increasing the internal engine temperatures, the amount of thrust the engine can produce has also increased dramatically since the early days of gas turbine engines. Ceramic coatings on components in the high temperature areas of gas turbine engines have contributed to the overall improved engine operation. Figure 1-3-2 is a combustion liner with a ceramic coating.

Figure 1-3-2. Ceramic coating on components is one major advancement in turbine engines.

Improved overhaul, maintenance inspection practices and repair techniques have extended the operating life of many types of current gas turbine engines.

Electronic control of the engine through full authority digital electronic control (FADEC) units have provided more reliable and fuel-efficient engines. Engines are quieter than ever before through the use of new materials and techniques that decrease and absorb the noise created by the engines.

Fuel Economy and Maintenance

Fuel economy will dictate the design and technology in future engine development and manufacturing. In the past 50 years, aviation fuel burn has been reduced by 70% and harmful emissions by 50%. The ability to monitor and record engine parameters through the use of computers has improved the maintainability and maintenance planning for gas turbine engines. Engine condition monitoring systems assure the overall dependability of the gas path components. Engine condition monitoring compares certain engine operating characteristics to that of a new or good engine to determine the condition of many of the internal components.

Oil analysis programs monitor the condition of an engine's bearings and other rotating compo-

JT3D turbofan engine developed
1959

Vectored thrust engines developed
1961

CJ-805-23 aft fan engine
TF-33 Pratt & Whitney turbofan engine 21,000 lbs thrust
1962

Turbo ramjet J58 (JT110-20B) set altitude and speed records
1964

JT9D high bypass fan engine developed
1968

Honeywell TFE731
1969

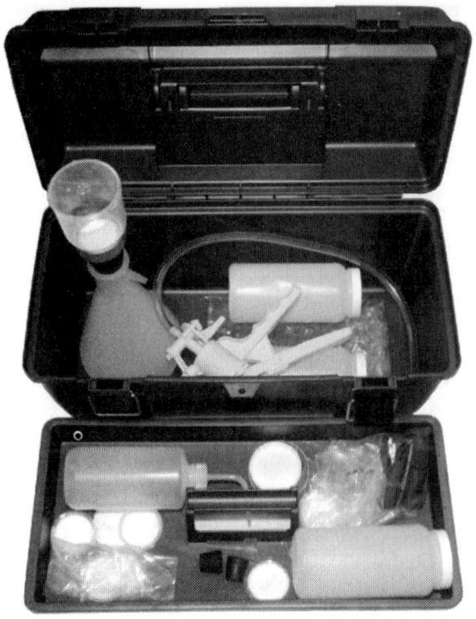

Figure 1-3-3. Oil analysis can spot potential problems before they become serious.

nents by measuring very small amounts of metal present in the oil which can identify early bearing failure. An oil analysis kit is shown in Figure 1-3-3.

Ultra high by-pass engines further increase fuel economy with as much as ten times or more of the air bypassing the core of the engine. The core of the engine is where the fuel is burned, where a small amount of the engine's total airflow is passed through. Real time continuous monitoring of turbine engine parameters along with other engineering improvements provides for extreme reliability and dependability with the new generation of turbine engines.

Technological Advances

Blade design. Advanced technology focuses on new swept fan blades and brings the advantages of better top-of-climb performance derived from increased fan flow capacity and reduced noise levels. This enables engines to meet the increasingly strict rules imposed by airports and regulating bodies. Advanced aerodynamics, new materials and design concepts will continue to increase engine efficiency.

Wide chord blades. Many of the current advanced engines use unique wide chord shroudless, hollow blades. These are manufactured by placing a piece of honeycomb material between two sheets of pre-machined titanium. At high temperatures a diffusion bond is formed between these three pieces of material such that the finished blade is extremely strong with a leading edge that is resistant to damage due to foreign object impact. In addition, the nature of the wide-chord blade centrifuges foreign object damage (FOD) debris and dust into the by-pass duct reducing engine removals. Figure 1-3-4 shows a wide chord blade used by Rolls-Royce.

Combustion chambers. New combustor design has improved fuel consumption and reduced smoke and other emissions. The floatwall combustor is another example of innovative combustor technology. The combustor liner consists of sheet metal shells to which cast turbine alloy segments are attached. The segments 'float' on the cooling air between the segments and the outer shell. The design improves cooling effectiveness, eliminates stresses and the segments can be replaced individually; lowering maintenance cost.

New alloys. A modern turbine blade alloy is complex in that it contains up to ten significant alloying elements, but its microstructure is very simple. Since the 1950s, the evolution from wrought blades through conventionally cast and directionally solidified blades to single crystal turbine blades has yielded a 250°C increase in allowable metal temperatures.

Developments in blade cooling have nearly doubled this increase in terms of turbine entry gas temperature. An important recent contribution has come from the alignment of the alloy grain in the single crystal blade which has allowed the elastic properties of the material to be closely controlled. These properties in turn control the natural vibration frequencies of the blade. A potentially important performance improvement can be exploited by improving the metallurgy of the blades. This helps reduce the quantity of air used for cooling. Some engines use 5% of compressor air to cool its

1970	1972	1973	1974	1977	1979	1980s	1981
First DC-10 APU delivered	*Rolls-Royce RB211 certificated*	*Allison A250-C20B in service*	*CFM56 first run*	*JT8D-209 first turbofan*	*DC-8 CFM56 re-engine program*	*Computer-aided engine fuel controls*	*Space shuttle engine developed*

rows of high pressure turbine blades. Certain single crystal alloy blades are able to run about 35° hotter than their predecessors. This may seem a small increase, but it has allowed some turbine blades to remain uncooled. It is estimated that over the next twenty years a 200°C increase in turbine entry gas temperature will be required to meet the airlines' demand for improved performance. Some of this increase will be made possible by the use of thermal barrier coatings.

The operating temperature at which gas turbine engine blades are able to safely rub against abradable shroud linings has been dramatically increased from 350° to 1200°C. This was achieved by raising the operating temperatures, by the use of efficient aerodynamic design and by the use of lightweight materials.

To further increase efficiency there must be a reduction of the clearance distance between the blade tip and casing. The development of abradables can decrease this clearance. The selection of the optimum thermal spray process is the goal to produce a seal that does not cause blade wear and maintains a smooth shroud surface.

Thermal barrier coatings. Thermal barrier coatings have been used for some years on static parts, initially using magnesium zirconate but more recently yttria-stabilized zirconia. Further increases in temperature are likely to require the development of ceramic matrix composites. The composite ceramic rotor blade is a great challenge.

This technology will eventually become successful for some applications of gas turbine engines. Research work has concentrated on fiber-reinforced ceramics. Some ceramic composites use silicon carbide fibers in a ceramic matrix such as silicon carbide or alumina. These materials can operate at temperatures up to 1,200°C.

Uncooled turbine applications will require an all oxide ceramic material, to ensure stability at the very highest temperatures over the life of the blade.

Emissions and noise. Environmental technology advancements in combustor design strive for reduced emissions and lower jet and fan noise through the use of advanced coatings and baffles. Reducing the environmental impact of gas turbine engine operation will result in quieter, cleaner aircraft that will be able to operate without excessive noise and emissions.

Performance analysis. Another way that advanced technology is helping to lower operator costs is through enhanced operational safety and performance provided by real-time engine health monitoring. The development of advanced health management systems throughout all the engine systems and components will minimize unscheduled maintenance and eliminate premature component replacement. These self-diagnostic component-monitoring devices will be integrated into a propulsion health management system.

Gas turbine engine performance analysis is sometimes accomplished using a Gas Turbine Simulation Program. These programs enable both steady-state and transient simulations. Almost any gas turbine configuration can be performed by establishing specific engine inputs. By varying the normal engine inputs, such as ambient temperature, pressure, power setting and air speed, the engine's parameters can be observed or calculated. This type of program or performance deck can be used to predict present and future engine performance.

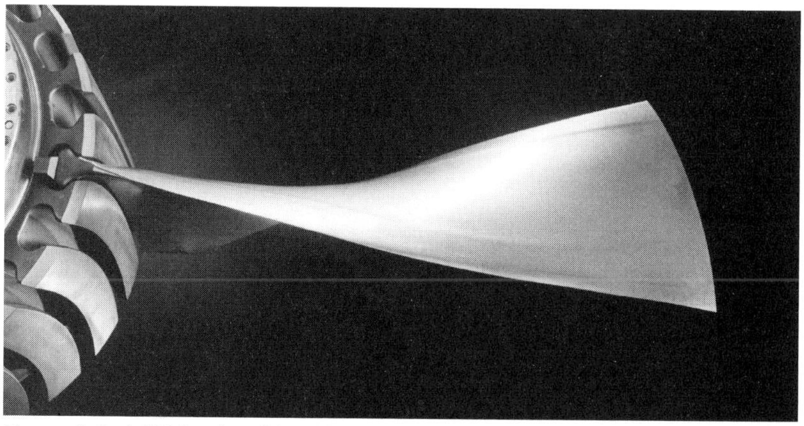

Figure 1-3-4. Wide chord fan blades decrease FOD to the core of the engine

1985	1990s	1994	1995	2002
Advanced single crystal hollow turbine blades developed	*FADECs developed* *PW 4000 and RR Trent series high thrust engines in service*	*Double annular combustor developed*	*GE90 engine 123 inch fan diameter*	*GE90-115 high thrust engine 115,000 lbs thrust*

Chapter 2

TURBINE principles

Thrust is required to propel an aircraft in flight. The most widely used form of propulsion system for modern commercial aircraft is the gas turbine engine. Gas turbine engines have the core components: a compressor, combustion section, and turbine, which combine to drive the compressor. The thermodynamics and basic operating principles of all gas turbine engines are similar.

Learning Objectives:

- *Thermodynamics*
- *Operating Principles*
- *Bernoulli's Principle*
- *Newton's Laws*
- *Brayton Cycle*
- *Efficiencies*

Section 1

Theory, Physics and Operating Principles

To understand how a gas turbine engine operates, the basic thermodynamics of gases must be studied. Gases have properties that can be observed, including pressure (P), temperature (T), mass (M), and volume (V). A thermodynamic process, such as heating or compressing gas, changes the values of the airflow in a manner that is described by the laws of thermodynamics. Air is the gas used in aircraft gas turbines.

The cycle concept is important for understanding engine operational theory. A cycle consists of a series of processes. In each process, the airflow properties are changed; however, the gas eventually returns to its original state.

The mechanical operation of the engine and the thermodynamic processes that enable the engine to produce useful work must both be considered when studying the operation of the gas turbine engine. The mechanical sections of the engine are shown in Figure 2-1-1.

Left: All turbine engines use the same basic principles of operation.

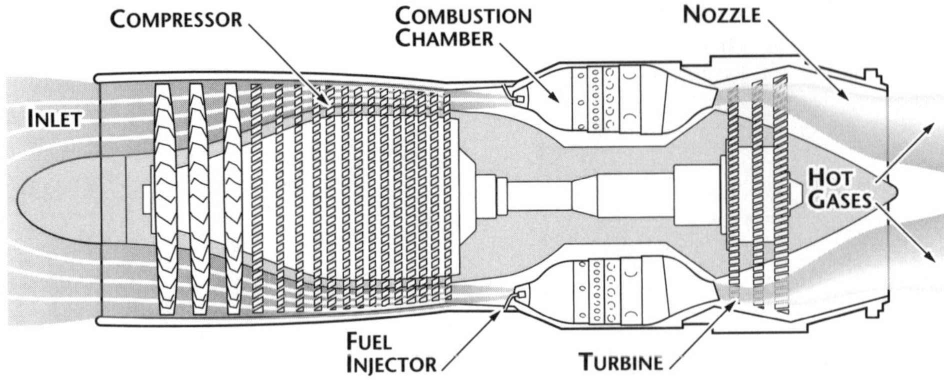

Figure 2-1-1. The major sections of a turbine engine

Thermodynamics

Work accomplished by a gas. The condition of a gas (air) is determined by certain measurable properties such as the pressure, temperature, and volume of the gas. The values of these air properties (pressure, temperature, volume) can be changed. A gas confined in the containers shown in Figure 2-1-2 is in two different conditions. In condition 1 the gas is at a higher pressure and occupies a smaller volume than in condition 2.

The condition of the gas on a graph of pressure versus volume (P-V diagram) is shown in Figure 2-1-3. To change the properties of the gases in Figure 2-1-2, the conditions in the container must be changed by either heating the gas, or physically changing the volume. The latter can be accomplished by moving the piston or by changing the pressure—adding or removing the force on the piston.

Work can be accomplished by changing the condition of the gas. Another change can be adding or removing heat. By compressing the air as in condition 1 of Figure 2-1-2, the force is converted to pressure in the gas.

The gas turbine actually operates by manipulating the pressure, temperature and volume (which can manipulate velocity) of the air flowing through the engine. By adding heat energy (burning fuel) the airflow is further manipulated and air pressure and velocity is changed to provide the optimum values for operation.

Thermodynamics can be used to determine the amount of work and the amount of heat necessary to change the condition of the gas. Thermodynamics deals with the energy and work that a system accomplishes. There are three principal laws of thermodynamics. Each law leads to the definition of thermodynamic properties which are used to predict the changes in pressure, temperature, added heat energy and changes in velocity.

Thermodynamic Laws

The three thermodynamic laws are used to define the thermodynamic operation of a physical system.

First law of thermodynamics. The first law of thermodynamics relates the various forms of

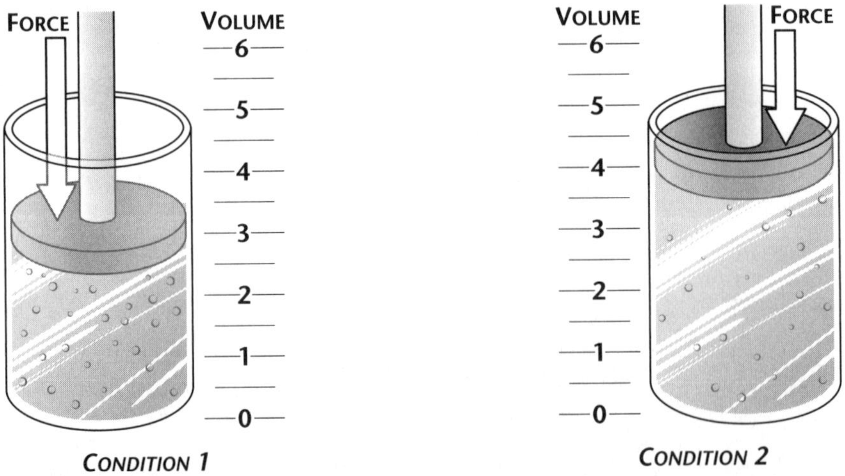

Figure 2-1-2. The contained gas is in two different conditions.

kinetic and potential energy in a system to the work which a system can perform and to the transfer of heat. This law is sometimes taken as the definition of internal energy. It introduces an additional condition variable: enthalpy.

Enthalpy is defined as the sum of the internal energy (E) plus the product of the pressure (P) and volume (V). Using the symbol H for the enthalpy:

$$H = E + P \times V$$

The enthalpy can be made into a specific variable by dividing it by the mass. The specific heat capacity (cp) means the specific heat at constant pressure and is related to the universal gas constant.

Second law of thermodynamics. The second law states that it is impossible to move heat by a cyclic process, from something at a lower temperature to something at a higher temperature, unless work is added to the system.

This law defines the variable condition known as entropy. Thermodynamic equilibrium occurs when two objects have the same temperature. If two objects that are initially at different temperatures are brought into physical contact, they eventually achieve thermal equilibrium, as is shown in Figure 2-1-4. During the process of reaching thermal equilibrium, heat is transferred between the objects. Heat is always transferred from the object at the higher temperature to the object at the lower temperature.

The heat capacity is a constant that tells how much heat is added per unit to the temperature rise. The value of the constant is different for different materials. Heating a gas changes the condition of the gas. For a gas, the heat transfer is related to a change in temperature. The temperature, pressure, and volume of the gas together determine the condition of the gas.

The amount of work that a gas can do depends on both the initial and final conditions, and on the process used to make the change in the gas's condition. In the same way, the amount of heat transferred in changing the condition of a gas also depends on the initial and final condition, plus the exact process used to change that condition. Different processes result in different amounts of heat transfer and work.

The effects of both heat flow and work are combined in the first law of thermodynamics. There are some thermodynamic processes in which there is no heat transfer. This process is an adiabatic process. As stated in the first law of thermodynamics, the internal energy of a gas is also a condition variable of the gas. A useful additional condition variable for a gas is the enthalpy. Enthalpy is used in the evaluation of the work done on the flow by a compressor and

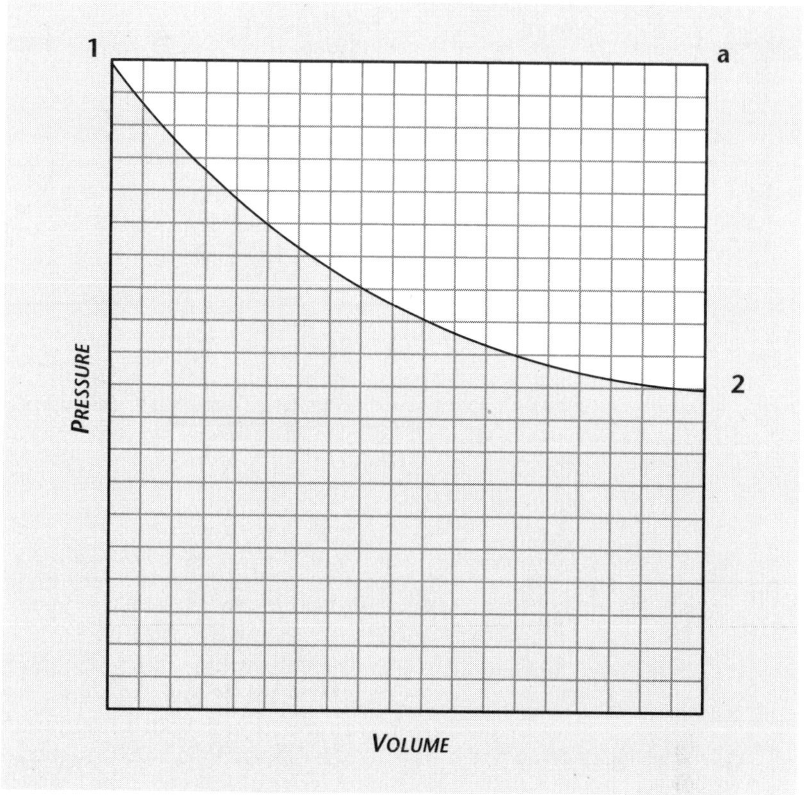

Figure 2-1-3. A representative graph showing one possible relationship between pressure and volume.

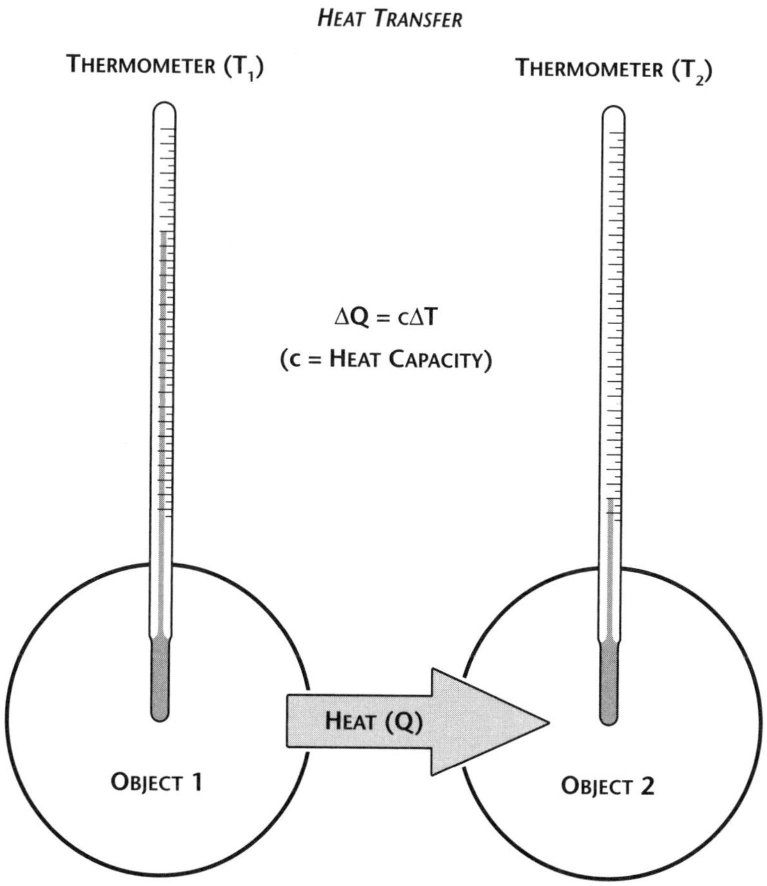

Figure 2-1-4. Heat will move from a warmer object to a cooler object until a point of equilibrium is reached.

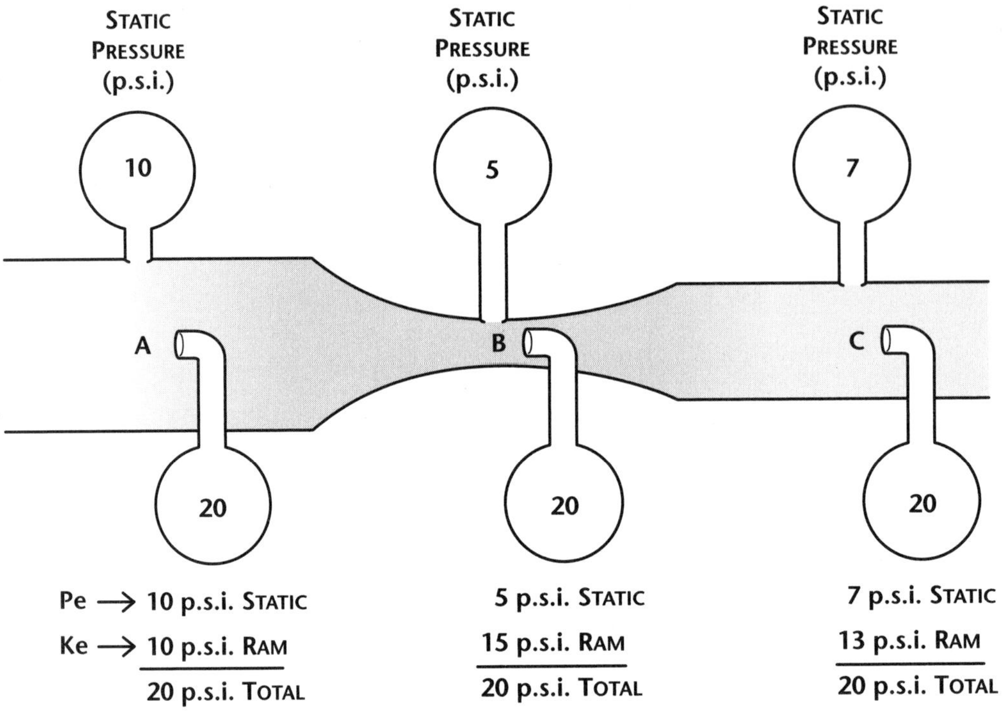

Figure 2-1-5. Pressures include both a static and a ram component

the work available from a turbine. There are several options for changing the condition of a gas from one condition to another. The amount of work done on, or by a gas could be different depending on exactly how the condition is changed. For example, on the graph in Figure 2-1-3, the curved black line indicates the change from point 1 and point 2 of a confined gas as shown in Figure 2-1-2. This line represents a change brought about by reducing the force and decreasing the pressure, thus allowing the volume to adjust according to Boyle's law with no heat addition. The line is curved and the amount of work done on the gas is shown by the shaded area below this curve.

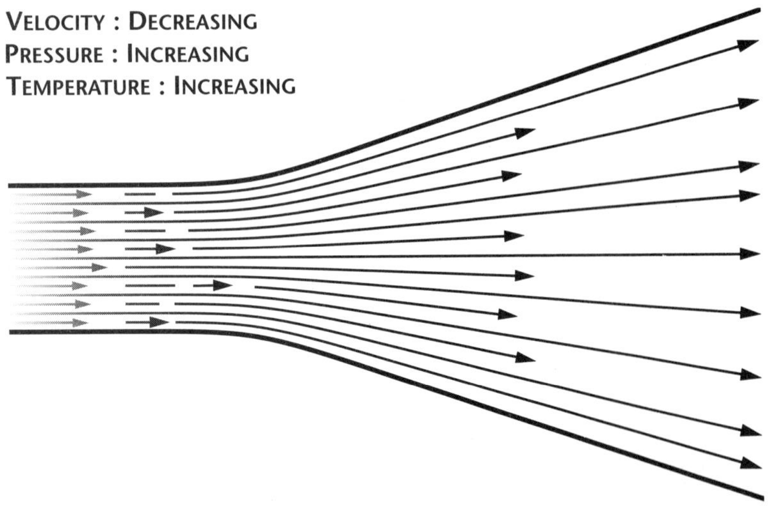

Figure 2-1-6. Subsonic airflow through a divergent duct

By heating the gas, in Figure 2-1-2, using Charles' law and holding the pressure constant, the volume would need to increase. The work done by a gas not only depends on the initial and the final condition of the gas but also on the process used to change the condition. Different processes can produce the same state, but produce different amounts of work.

Third law of thermodynamics. The third law states that if the entropy of each element at absolute zero can be taken as zero, then all elements above absolute zero must have infinite positive entropy.

Pressure and Airflow Principles

A gas is composed of a large number of molecules that are very small relative to the distance between molecules. The molecules of a gas are in constant, random motion; they frequently collide with each other, and with the walls of any container. The molecules possess the physical properties of mass, momentum, and energy. The momentum of a single molecule is the product of its mass and velocity. As the gas molecules collide with the walls of a container, they impart momentum to the walls, producing a force perpendicular to the wall.

The sum of the forces of all the molecules striking the wall, divided by the area of the wall, is defined as the pressure of the gas. Since turbine engines use air as the working gas, gas will be referred to in this case as air. The pressure of air is then a measure of the average linear momentum of the moving molecules of that air.

Static air (static pressure) is one that does not appear to move or flow. While the air as a whole does not appear to move, the individual molecules of the air, which cannot be seen by the naked eye, are in constant random motion. Because the motion of the individual molecules is random in every direction, we do not detect any motion.

If the air is enclosed within a container, we detect pressure in the gas resulting from the molecules colliding with the walls of the container. Anywhere inside the gas container, the force per unit of area (the pressure) is the same. Pressure acts in all directions inside a container. At the surface of a gas, the pressure force acts perpendicular to the surface.

If the air as a whole is moving, the measured pressure is different in the direction of the motion of the airflow. Similarly, the ordered motion of the air produces an ordered component of the momentum in the direction of the motion. An additional pressure component, called dynamic pressure (ram pressure), in the direction of the motion is called the total pressure and is obtained by adding the static and dynamic pressure. This action is shown in Figure 2-1-5.

During the passage of air through the engine, aerodynamic and energy requirements demand changes in the velocity and pressure of the air. For instance, during compression, a rise in the pressure of the air, not an increase in its velocity, is required. After the air has been heated and its internal energy increased by combustion, an increase in the velocity of the gases is necessary to force the turbine to rotate.

At the propelling nozzle, a high exit velocity is required for the change in momentum of the air that provides the thrust on the aircraft. Local decelerations of airflow are also required, such as in the combustion chambers, to provide a low-velocity zone in which the flame can burn.

The various changes of air pressure and velocity are effected by means of the size and shape of the ducts through which the air passes on its way through the engine. Where a conversion from velocity (kinetic energy) to pressure is required, the passages are divergent in shape, as is shown in Figure 2-1-6. Conversely, where it is required to convert the energy stored in the combustion gases to velocity energy, a convergent passage or nozzle as in Figure 2-1-7 is used.

These shapes apply to the gas-turbine engine where the airflow velocity is subsonic (at the local speed of sound). A convergent-divergent nozzle, as shown in Figure 2-1-8, is used where supersonic speeds are encountered, such as

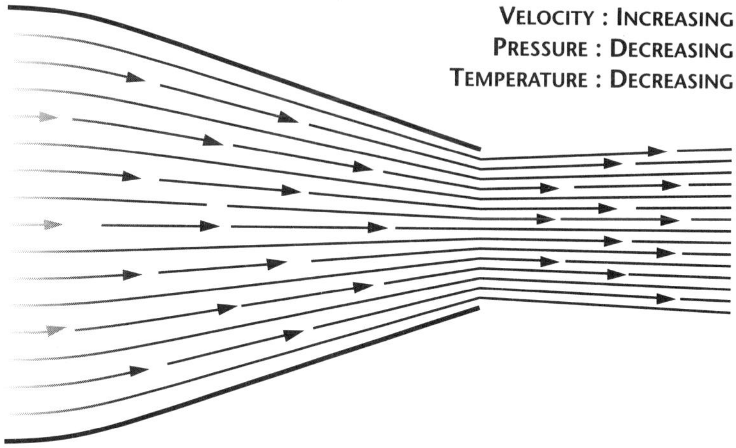

Figure 2-1-7. Subsonic airflow through a convergent duct

in the propelling nozzle of the rocket or some afterburning turbine engines. This nozzle will obtain the maximum conversion of energy in the combustion gases to kinetic energy or thrust. At supersonic speeds the principle reverses and the air velocity is increased passing through a divergent duct. The same reversal takes place for a supersonic convergent duct: as air passes through it, the velocity will decrease.

Bernoulli's principle. Bernoulli's principle states that whenever a flow of air increases in velocity there is a decrease in pressure. Conversely, if air flow decreases its velocity, there is an increase in pressure. In gas turbine engines, pressure and velocity are changed by the shape of the duct the air is flowing through.

By making the engine ducts either divergent or convergent, air flow velocity and pressure can be changed to provide the pressure and velocity for optimum engine operation. This is based on subsonic (air flow less than the speed sound) flows inside the operating engine. This principle is demonstrated in Figures 2-1-6 and 2-1-7.

Pressure is a condition variable of the airflow inside the engine, such as temperature and density. The change in pressure during any process is governed by the laws of thermodynamics. Pressure inside the engine is normally measured in pounds per square inch gauge (lbs/sq. in. g) or p.s.i.g. Gauge pressure normally does not take into account absolute pressure (atmospheric pressure). Standard pressure at mean sea level is 14.679 p.s.i. absolute. To convert gauge to absolute pressure, take the ambient absolute pressure (atmospheric) and add or subtract gauge pressure. Gauge pressure can be negative. For example, if the p.s.i.g. (gauge pressure) is negative, it should be subtracted from ambient absolute pressure. If the p.s.i.g. (gauge pressure) is positive, then it should be added to the ambient absolute pressure.

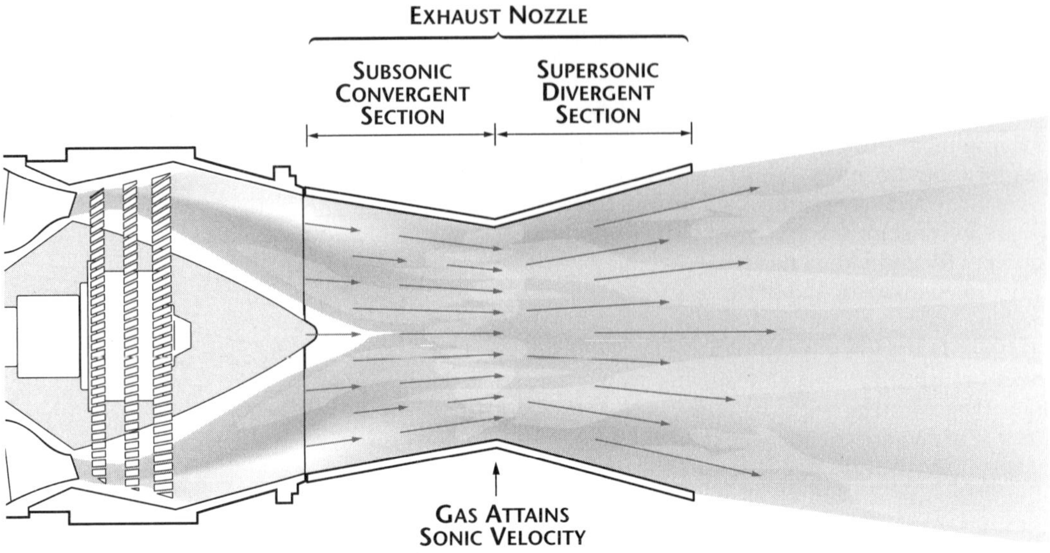

Figure 2-1-8. Airflow through a convergent-divergent exhaust nozzle

Temperature

For the study of gas turbine engines, an important property of any gas (including air) is temperature. It is especially important when determining engine evaluations. It must be very precise because it is a major factor in evaluating the engine's health or condition.

In a hot gas, the molecules move faster than in a cold gas; the mass remains the same, but the kinetic energy, and hence the temperature, is greater because of the increased velocity of the molecules.

A thermometer can be constructed which assigns a number to the temperature of an object. When the thermometer is brought into contact with another object, it quickly establishes a thermodynamic equilibrium.

By measuring the thermodynamic effect on some physical property of the thermometer at some fixed conditions (like the boiling point and freezing point of water), we can establish a scale for assigning temperature values. The number assigned to the temperature depends on what we pick for the reference condition. As a result, several different temperature scales have arisen.

The Celsius scale, designated °C, uses the freezing point of pure water as the zero point and the boiling point as 100°, with a linear scale between these extremes. The Fahrenheit scale, designated °F, originally used the freezing point of sea water as the zero point and the freezing point of pure water as 30°. On this scale, the boiling point of pure water was 212°.

So Fahrenheit constructed a scale making the boiling point of pure water 212° and the freezing point of pure water 32°, which gave 180° between the two reference points. Since the two scales start at different zero points, we can convert from the temperature on the Fahrenheit scale (°F) to the temperature on the Celsius scale (°C).

$$°C = 5/9 + (°F-32)$$

When there are Fahrenheit temperatures below the freezing point of water, these are assigned negative numbers. The coldest possible temperature was determined to be absolute zero at which molecular kinetic energy is a minimum or almost zero. This value was found to be -273.16° C, shown in Figure 2-1-9. This point was set as the new zero point, which can define another temperature scale called an absolute temperature scale. If the size of a single degree is kept the same as the Celsius scale, we get a temperature scale which is absolute. It is designated the Kelvin scale represented by a letter K. To convert Celsius to Kelvin:

$$K = C + 273.16$$

There is a similar absolute temperature scale corresponding to the Fahrenheit scale. It is the Rankine scale and is designated with an R. To convert Fahrenheit to Rankine:

$$R = F + 459.69$$

Absolute temperatures are used in variables such as enthalpy, and entropy. Temperature, like pressure, is a scalar quantity. Temperature has a magnitude but no direction associated with it. It has just a single value at every location in a gas. The value can change from location to location, but again, there is no direction connected to the temperature.

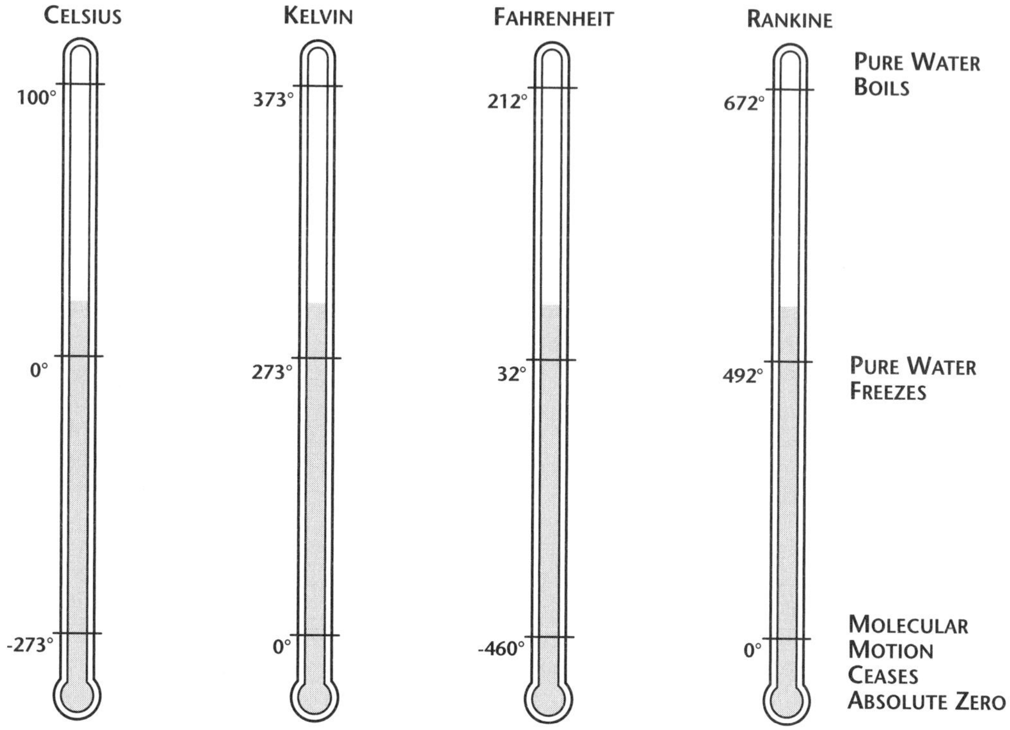

Figure 2-1-9. Common temperatures compared in the temperature measurement systems normally encountered. The Rankine scale is used to convert Fahrenheit to absolute.

With regard to gas turbine engines, temperature is a very important engine variable. Typically two relative temperature scales are used to monitor temperatures in the engine. Celsius and Fahrenheit are used to monitor the engine's exhaust temperatures. Some test installations use Fahrenheit to measure engine temperature during testing. Both of these relative temperature scales have a corresponding absolute scale. Generally, Celsius is converted to Kelvin and Fahrenheit is converted to Rankine as mentioned previously.

Gas turbines produce work in proportion to the amount of heat released internally. Therefore, it is necessary to study the production of heat in the engine, most of which is obtained by the burning of fuel (although some is obtained by compressing the air in the compressor). An ordinary thermometer indicates the temperature of the gases, but does not show the quantity of heat that is available.

Heat cannot be measured directly, but must be calculated from three known quantities: temperature, mass (or weight), and specific heat. Although the exact nature of heat is not known, arbitrary standards have been internationally agreed upon by which changes in heat content can be calculated accurately. The standard in the British system, also accepted internationally, is the British thermal unit (BTU). A BTU is defined as the amount of heat required to increase the temperature of one pound of water one degree Fahrenheit as seen in Figure 2-1-10.

Standard temperatures and absolute temperature scale conversion factors. The gas turbine industry has agreed on standard temperatures to allow comparisons of engine parameters regardless of ambient conditions. Due to operation of engines at many different altitudes and temperatures, the standard temperature can be used to convert all engine temperatures to a common standard. This allows engines to be compared regardless of the operating ambient temperature. The standard temperature is 59° F or 15° C.

Converting relative temperatures measured during engine testing to absolute and standard day allows engine performance to be evaluated at any ambient temperature. To convert from standard day Celsius to Kelvin, just add 273 to 15 for a total of 288° K. This is the standard day absolute temperature in Kelvin that is used for engine comparisons. When using the Fahrenheit scale, convert to Rankine absolute by adding 459.67 to 59 for a total of 518.67° R, the standard day absolute temperature.

Engine temperature gradients. Temperature differences (gradients) occur throughout the gas turbine engine. A temperature gradient occurs whenever one surface of a part differs in temperature across the component or from one end to the other. These temperature gradients can cause thermal fatigue and warping of parts from their original shape. Due to the close clearances inside the engine, warping of engine components can be detrimental to engine operation.

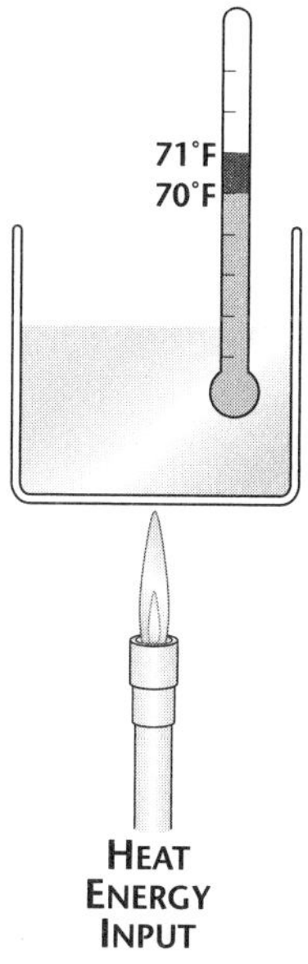

Figure 2-1-10. A BTU is a measure of heat energy and is equal to 778 foot-pounds of mechanical work.

Components are engineered to accept normal operating temperatures, but if the temperature limits are exceeded, warping and burning can occur. This in turn, can lead to internal clearance changes that could cause engine damage or even failure. When the engine is static, just after it is shut down, heat from the engine's components can soak into areas that are otherwise cooled during operation. Such elevated temperature gradients can cause engine components to misalign temporarily. The residual starting temperature limit (highest temperature that the engine should be restarted at) should always be observed.

Density

Another property of any gas (including air) is density. Density is defined as the mass of an object divided by its volume. Some objects are heavier than others, even though they are the same size. A brick and a loaf of bread are about the same size, but a brick is the heavier—has more mass—of the two. For solids, the density of a single element or compound remains constant, because the molecules are bound to one another. But for air, because the molecules are free to move about, density can vary over a wide range. Air at sea level has a very different density than air at high altitudes. Because the molecules are in motion, a gas will expand to fill the container.

Since density is defined as mass divided by volume, density depends directly on the size of the container in which a fixed mass of gas is confined. The variation of the volume is very important for the final value of pressure and temperature. Density is an important variable of a gas, and the change in density during a process is governed by the laws of thermodynamics.

Actual molecules of a gas are incredibly small and move in a completely random motion. Because there are so many molecules and the motion of each molecule is random, the value of the density is the same throughout the container.

Density, like temperature, is a scalar quantity; it has a magnitude but no direction associated with it. In the atmosphere, air molecules near the surface of the earth are held together more tightly than the molecules in the higher atmosphere because of the gravitational pull of the earth. The higher you go in the atmosphere, the fewer the molecules. Therefore, in the atmosphere, density decreases as altitude increases.

Section 2

Newton's Laws of Motion

The thrust produced by a jet engine may be explained to a large extent by Newton's laws of motion. These may be stated as follows:

First law of motion. A body at rest tends to remain at rest, and a body in motion tends to continue in motion in a straight line unless caused to change its state by an external force.

Second law of motion. The acceleration of a body is directly proportional to the force causing it and inversely proportional to the mass of the body.

Third law of motion. For every action, there is an equal and opposite reaction.

Newton's first law states that every object will remain at rest or in uniform motion in a straight line unless compelled to change its motion by the action of an external force. This is the definition of inertia. If there is no net force acting on an object (if all the external forces cancel each other out) then the object will maintain a constant velocity. If that velocity is zero, then the object remains at rest. If an external force is applied, the velocity will change because of the force.

The second law explains how the velocity of an object changes when it is subjected to an external force. The law defines a force (F) to be equal to change in momentum (M) (mass times velocity) per change in time. For an object with a constant mass the second law states that the force is obtained by the object's mass times its acceleration $F = M \times A$.

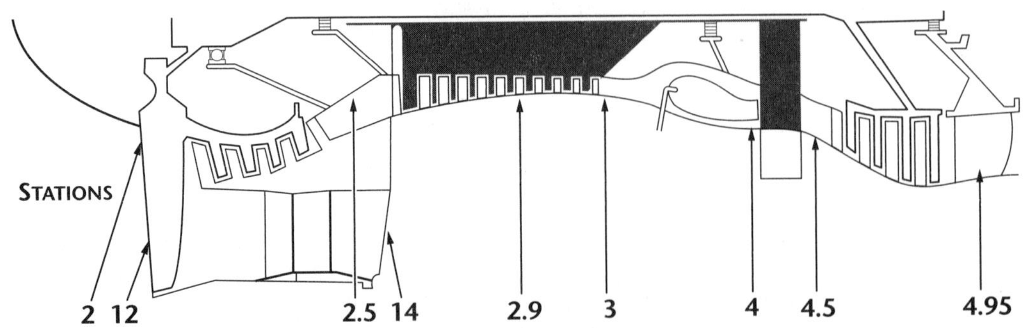

Figure 2-2-1. The gas path through a turbine engine is divided into multiple stations.

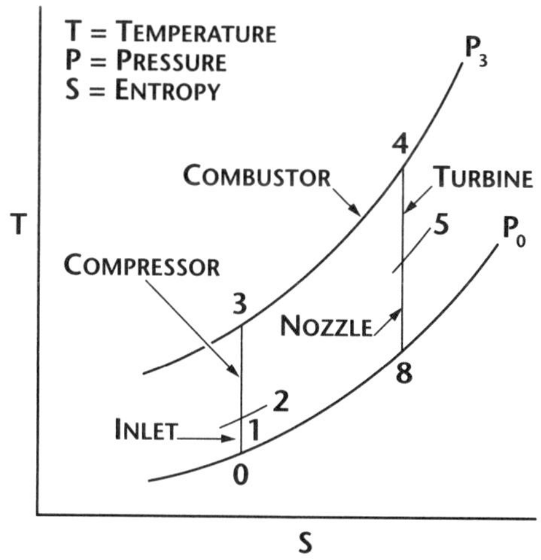

Figure 2-2-2. Brayton thermodynamic cycle

This law can be demonstrated by the use of a simple balloon. When the balloon is blown up and the end is closed, the pressure of the air inside the balloon is equal in all directions. If the air is allowed to escape from the balloon the pressure still in the balloon pushes it in the opposite direction of the escaping air.

This also demonstrates Newton's third law where the air exiting the balloon was the action and the forward movement of the balloon the opposite reaction. When a gun is fired, the kick back is a reaction to the bullet exiting the gun (the action). When water flows from a hose the water exiting the hose is the action and the push against the hose is the reaction. A change in velocity (acceleration) or in the mass will affect the amount of force.

The third law states that for every action (force) there is an equal and opposite reaction. A gas turbine engine produces thrust through action and reaction. The engine produces hot exhaust gases that flow out the back of the engine (action). In reaction, a thrusting force is produced in the opposite direction. The third law can be used to explain the production of thrust by a gas turbine (jet) engine. If the mass is a constant, then using the definition of acceleration as the change in velocity with time, the second law reduces to mass times acceleration.

Brayton Thermodynamic Cycle

The Brayton Thermodynamic Cycle, which is used in all gas turbine engines can be explained by using the turbine engine station numbering system, as shown in Figure 2-2-1. Station numbers are used to locate specific points in the gas path through the engine.

A pressure-velocity (P-V) chart of an ideal Brayton Cycle is shown in Figure 2-2-2. Beginning with conditions at station 0 in cruising flight, the inlet slows the air stream as it is brought to the compressor inlet at station 2. As the flow slows, some of the energy associated with the aircraft's velocity increases the static pressure (ram pressure) of the air and the flow is compressed.

The compressor works on the gas and increases the pressure and temperature to station 3, the compressor exit. The combustion process in the burner occurs at a constant pressure from station 3 to station 4. The hot exhaust is then passed through the turbine in which work is accomplished by the flow from station 4 to station 5. Because the turbine and compressor are on the same shaft, the work done on the turbine is equal to the work done by the compressor. The nozzle then brings the flow to free stream pressure from station 5 to station 8. Externally, the flow conditions return to ambient air-flow condition which completes the cycle.

Turbine Operating Principles

The mass of air is accelerated within the engine by the use of a continuous cycle (Brayton cycle). Air enters the inlet where it is subjected to changes in temperature, velocity, and pressure. As the air is compressed by the compressor section of the engine the pressure increases along with temperature. When the air flow exits the compressor section it flows through the diffuser where the air velocity is slowed down and pressure is increased by a divergent duct.

Twenty-five percent of the air passes into the combustion area (burner) of the engine while 75% of the air flow is used to cool the combustion area. Part of the 75% of air flow is used to dilute the hot gases exiting the combustion section. The air now flows into a turbine inlet guide vane which directs the flow into the turbine wheel.

The air flow turns the turbine wheel which is mechanically connected to the compressor. After the gases flow past the compressor turbine the remaining energy is used to drive more turbine wheels which can turn a propeller, fan, or a shaft. The exhaust gases then pass through the exhaust section which directs the unused exhaust gases overboard.

Thrust

To understand thrust and how it is derived, it is best to use mathematical values to describe the units and forces acting in the engine. Since much of the evaluation of performance and troubleshooting are based on the actual thrust developed by a turbine engine, the need to understand and be able to calculate engine performance is very important to the study of gas turbines.

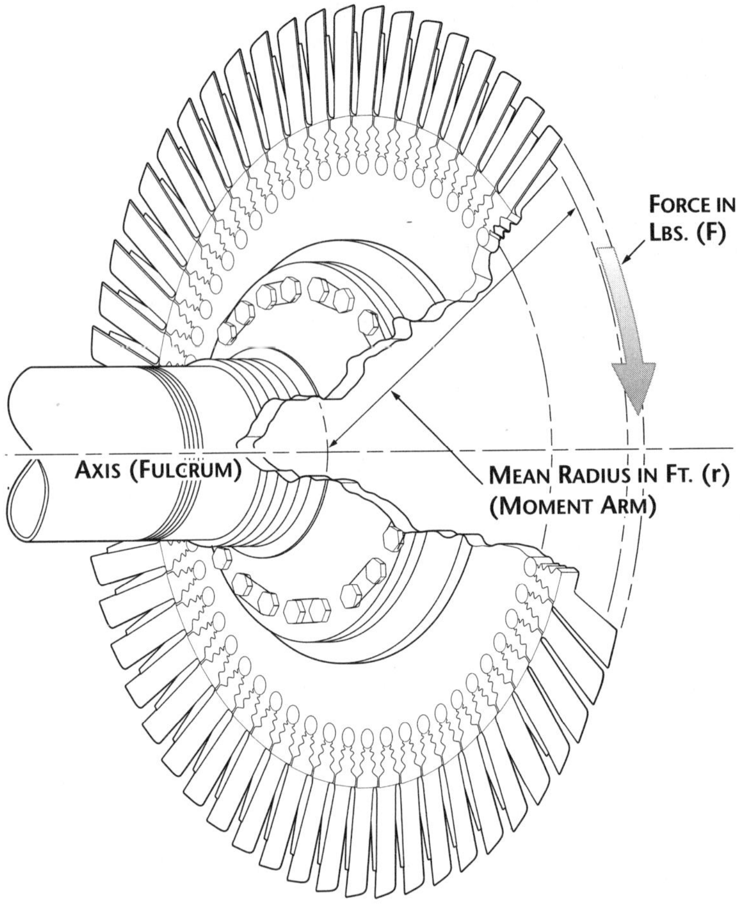

Figure 2-2-3. Point of force and radius on a turbine wheel

The turbine engine and whether it is operating correctly is very dependent on the operating data (temperatures, speeds, thrust produced, and many other engine parameters). To evaluate engine performance the technician must understand where and how thrust is made. Some of the calculations shown here are more for engineering purposes and the average technician would not need to understand all of the calculations presented in the text.

The thrust of a gas-turbine engine depends on the acceleration of a mass (weight) in accordance with Newton's second law. The quantity (mass) of air and gases accelerated plus the amount of acceleration determine the thrust produced. The thrust is determined by the size and type of propulsion system used on the aircraft as well as the throttle setting selected by the pilot.

Mass is a basic property of matter, whereas weight is the effect of gravity on a mass. When we consider matter on the surface of the earth, mass and weight are approximately the same.

From Newton's second law of motion for constant mass, force (F) is equal to mass (M) times acceleration (A), F = M x A.

The formula used may be stated:

$$F = \frac{W \times A}{g}$$

Where:

F = force, in pounds (lbs)

W = weight, in pounds (lbs)

A = acceleration, ft/sec^2

g = acceleration of gravity = 32.2 ft/sec^2

Static thrust or gross thrust is the amount of thrust an engine is producing when the aircraft (engine) is not moving through the air. Net thrust is the amount of force or thrust being developed when the aircraft is in flight. To calculate the net thrust, the speed of the aircraft must be accounted for and used in the computations.

To determine the amount of thrust, the weight of the mass air (normally in lbs/sec) through the engine must be determined. This is can be calculated by knowing the inlet volume (= πr^2 x flow velocity/sec.) multiplied by the weight of the air, in lbs per cu. ft., entering the engine. The weight of the air will vary with temperature. A conversion chart can be used to determine the weight of the air for a given temperature. For example, one cu. ft. of air at 59°F will weigh 0.07467 lbs. To calculate mass air flow the following formula can be used.

$$W_a = \pi r^2 \times \text{airflow velocity per second} \times 0.07647$$

The basic formula for the approximate thrust of a gas-turbine engine is:

$$F = \frac{W_a}{g}(V_2 - V_1)$$

Where:

F = force, lbs

w_a = flow rate of airmass (lbs/sec)

g = acceleration of gravity (32.2 ft/sec^2)

V_2 = final velocity of gases (velocity of exhaust gases at jet nozzle)

V_1 = initial velocity of gases (aircraft speed if calculating for net thrust)

The approximate thrust of an engine may be determined by considering the weight of the air only, because the fuel weight is a very small percentage of the air weight. However, to obtain an accurate indication of thrust produced by the acceleration of the fuel-air mixture, it is necessary to include both fuel and air in the equation. The equation then becomes:

$$F = \frac{W_a}{g}(V_2 - V_1) + \frac{W_f}{g}(V_j)$$

Where:

F= force, lbs

g = acceleration of gravity (32.2 ft/sec^2)

W_f = fuel flow, lbs/sec

V_j = velocity of gases at jet nozzle, ft/sec

In this equation, V_j represents the acceleration of the fuel, because the initial velocity of the fuel is the same as that of the engine. In actual practice, not all the pressure of the gases flowing from the nozzle of a turbine engine can be converted to velocity. This is particularly true of a jet nozzle in which the velocity of the gases reaches the speed of sound (the nozzle becomes choked).

In such cases, the static pressure of the gases at the jet nozzle is above the ambient air pressure. This difference in pressure creates additional thrust proportional to the area of the jet nozzle. The thrust generated at the jet nozzle is indicated by:

$$F = A_j (P_j - P_{amb})$$

Where:

F = force (thrust, because of choked nozzle)

A_j = area of jet nozzle, in^2

P_j = static pressure at jet nozzle, lbs/in^2

P_{amb} = static pressure of ambient air

When the jet nozzle thrust is added to the reaction thrust created by acceleration of gases in the engine, the equation for the net thrust (F_n) becomes:

$$F_n = \frac{W_a}{g}(V_2 - V_1) + \frac{W_f}{g}(V_j) + A_j (P_j - P_{amb})$$

By using calculations similar to those described above, the thrust of a turbofan engine can also be determined. An example of a formula for an engine with an un-choked exhaust nozzle would be:

$$F_n = (\text{Eng}) \frac{W_a (V_2 - V_1)}{g} + \frac{W_f}{g}(V_j) +$$

$$(\text{Fan}) \frac{W_a (V_2 - V_1)}{g}$$

Basic horsepower calculations. Many times with turboshaft and turboprop engines it is necessary to know the horsepower the engine is developing. This is due to limits of horsepower use in the engine and in the reduction gear box. This information is also critical to performance evaluations. Work is defined as:

Work = force (F) applied x distance moved (D) or (W = F x D).

The unit of work is the foot-pound. These calculations demonstrate the development of horsepower created from a turbine wheel by using force applied at a radius.

$$hp = \frac{F \times N \times 2\pi \times R}{33,000}$$

Where:

hp = horsepower

F = force, lbs

N = shaft r.p.m.

2π = circumference multiplier (2 x 3.14)

R = mean radius

In Figure 2-2-3, the point in which the force and radius are taken from the turbine wheel is illustrated.

Horsepower calculation when torque is a known. Sometimes it is helpful to be able to calculate the horsepower being developed by a turboprop engine using the torque reading and propeller r.p.m. from the aircraft instruments. This is because there are limits on horsepower in certain configurations of operation. The horsepower can be calculated by:

hp = torque x r.p.m. x K

Where:

$$K = \frac{2\pi}{33,000}$$

Converting thrust to horsepower. Because power is determined by using the product of a force and a distance, it is not possible to make a direct comparison of thrust and horsepower in a turbine engine. When the engine is driving an airplane through the air, however, we can compute the equivalent horsepower being developed. When we convert the foot-pounds per minute of 1 hp to mile-pounds per hour, we obtain the figure of 375. That is, 1 hp is equal to 33,000 ft. lb/min. or 375 mi. lb/hr. Thrust horsepower (thp) is then obtained by using the following formula:

$$thp = \frac{\text{thrust (lb)} \times \text{airspeed (m.p.h.)}}{375}$$

If a jet engine is developing 800 lb (44,480-N) thrust and is driving an airplane at 500 m.p.h., then:

$$thp = \frac{800 \times 500}{375} = 1{,}066.6$$

Note that thrust in the metric system is measured in newtons. One newton (N) is equal to 0.22482 lb of force.

Turbine horsepower calculations. The formula for finding the amount of horsepower a turbine wheel is absorbing is as follows:

$$hp = \frac{C_p \times \Delta T \times W_a \times 778}{550}$$

Where:

C_p=0.24 amount of BTUs it takes to raise one pound of air one degree F

ΔT = temperature drop from one side of the turbine wheel to the other side or across the wheel.

W_a= mass air flow in lb per second

778= ft lbs per one BTU

550= horsepower constant per second

Section 3

Efficiencies

The efficiency of any engine can be described as the output divided by the input. One of the main measures of turbine engine efficiency is the amount of thrust produced or generated, divided by the fuel consumption. This is called thrust specific fuel consumption (tsfc).

The tsfc is the amount of lbs. of fuel required to produce 1 lb (0.00445 KN) of thrust per hour and can be calculated as follows:

$$tsfc = \frac{W_f}{F_n}$$

Where:

W_f = fuel flow, lb/hour

F_n = net thrust, lb

This leads to the conclusion that the more thrust we obtain per pound of fuel, the more efficient the engine.

Specific fuel consumption is made up of a number of other efficiencies. The two major factors affecting the tsfc are propulsive efficiency and cycle efficiency.

Propulsive Efficiency

Propulsive efficiency (PE) is the amount of thrust developed by the jet nozzle compared to the energy supplied to it in a usable form. In other words, the propulsive efficiency is the percentage of the total energy made available by the engine which is effective in propelling the engine. Propulsive efficiency can also be expressed as:

$$\frac{\text{work completed}}{\text{work completed + work wasted in the exhaust}}$$

A simplified version of this formula for an unchoked engine can be stated as follows:

$$PE = \frac{2V}{V + V_j}$$

Where:

V_j = Jet velocity at propelling nozzle (ft/sec)

V = Aircraft speed (ft/sec)

Example:

If an aircraft was traveling at 300 m.p.h. (V) and its jet velocity was 1,200 m.p.h. (V_j) the propulsive efficiency could be calculated as follows:

$$PE = \frac{2 \times 300}{300 + 1{,}200} = 40\%$$

The propulsive efficiency formula for calculating a turbofan engine using separate exhaust nozzles is listed as follows:

$$\frac{W_{a_1} V(V_{j_1} - V) + W_{a_2} V(V_{j_2} - V)}{W_{a_1} V(V_{j_1} - V) + W_{a_2} V(V_j - V) + \%W_{a_1}(V_{j_1} - V)^2 + \%W_{a_2}(V_{j_2} - V}$$

Where:

W_a = Mass of air passing through engine (lb/sec)

V_j = Jet velocity at propelling nozzle (ft/sec)

V = Aircraft speed (ft/sec)

Cycle Efficiency

Cycle efficiency is the amount of energy put into a usable form as compared to the total amount of energy available in the fuel. Some of the factors involved are combustion efficiency, thermal efficiency, mechanical efficiency, and compressor efficiency. This amounts to the overall efficiency of the engine components starting with the compressor and going through the combustion chamber and turbine. The job of these components is to get the energy in the fuel into a form which the jet nozzle can convert into thrust.

Thermal Efficiency

Thermal efficiency (TE) is defined as the heat value or heat energy output of the engine, divided by the heat energy input (fuel consumed). Thermal efficiency increases as the turbine inlet temperature increases. At low turbine inlet temperatures, the expansion energy of the gases is too low for efficient operation. As the temperature is increased, the gases (molecules) become more energetic and the thermal functions are performed at a rate that suits the engine design.

The thermal efficiency is controlled by the cycle pressure ratio and the combustion temperature. Unfortunately, this temperature is limited by the thermal and mechanical stresses that can be tolerated by the turbine. The development of new materials and techniques to minimize these limitations is continually being pursued.

A turbine engine's thermal efficiency will tend to improve with airspeed due to the ram effect. Ram pressure, when multiplied across the compressor by the compressor ratio, can mean an improvement in the mass of air passing through an engine (W_a) and the combustion chamber pressure. This increases thrust output, with little or no change in shaft energy input to the compressor. The average gas turbine engine has a thermal efficiency under cruise conditions of 45% to 50%. Thermal efficiency is basically a comparison of how well the energy in the fuel is converted to direct power.

Thermal efficiency is expressed as a ratio of the net work produced by the engine to the fuel energy input.

$$TE = \frac{\text{h.p. output of engine}}{\text{h.p. value of fuel consumed}}$$

Thermal efficiency improves with increased aircraft speed due to ram pressure rise effect in the intake.

Example:

A turboshaft engine is producing 750 shaft horsepower and is consuming 325 lbs/hr of fuel containing 18,730 BTU/lb. What is the engine's thermal efficiency?

Solution to finding thermal efficiency:

The fuel flow is 325 lbs/hr. This needs to be converted to lbs/min by dividing by 60.

$$\frac{325 \text{ lbs/hr}}{60} = 5.42 \text{ lbs/min}$$

Using the heat value of the fuel in British thermal units (BTUs) and multiplying it times the lbs/min of fuel flow, the BTUs/min. can be obtained. Since one BTU is equal to 778 ft/lbs, multiplying the BTUs/min by 778 converts to ft lbs/min. By dividing this answer by 33,000 (amount of ft lbs/min for one horsepower) the amount of fuel horsepower can be calculated. Fuel horsepower is the amount of horsepower the fuel would be capable of producing if all the fuel flowing to the engine was converted to horsepower (100% thermal efficiency).

Heat value = 18,730 BTUs/lb x 5.42 lbs/min

Heat value = 101,516.6 BTUs/min (since 1 BTU = 778 ft lbs)

$$\text{Fuel horsepower} = \frac{101{,}516.6 \times 778}{33{,}000 \text{ ft lbs/min/1 horsepower}}$$

Fuel horsepower = 2,393.3 hp

The value of 750 shaft horsepower being developed by the engine represents the actual horsepower being developed by the engine. By dividing the fuel horsepower into the actual horsepower developed by the engine, the thermal efficiency can be calculated.

$$TE = \frac{750}{2{,}393.3} = 0.31 \times 100 = 31\%$$

Example:

A turbofan engine produces 12,000 lbs of net thrust in flight at 600 m.p.h. The fuel being consumed is 5,900 lbs/hr. What is the thermal efficiency if the fuel contains 18,730 BTUs?

Solution to thermal efficiency:

$$\text{Fuel Flow} = \frac{5{,}900 \text{ lbs/hr}}{60} = 98.3 \text{ lbs/min}$$

Heat value = 18,730 x 98.3 = 1,841,159 BTUs/min

$$\text{Fuel h.p.} = \frac{1{,}841{,}159 \times 778}{33{,}000}$$

Fuel hp = 43,406.72

Since the engine is producing thrust instead of horsepower, the thrust must be converted to horsepower. By taking the thrust and multiplying it by the speed of the aircraft and dividing by 375, the thrust horsepower can be obtained. The value of 375 is obtained from 33,000 ft lbs multiplied by 60 and divided by 5,280 ft (feet in a statute mile).

$$\text{thp} = \frac{1{,}200 \times 600}{375}$$

thp = 19,200 hp

$$TE = \frac{19{,}200}{43{,}406.72} = 0.44 \times 100 = 44\%$$

Chapter 3

TERMS & engine types

Gas turbines engines are used in many different aviation and industrial configurations. The nomenclature and abbreviations that are used to describe sections, components, and systems are an important part of the study of gas turbine engines. Drawings of the engine representing the important components parts are labeled, and the corresponding parts on the drawing are indicated, as shown in Figure 3-1-1. Later in this chapter, a study of the basic operation of the turbojet, turbofan, turboshaft, auxiliary power units and turboprop engines will be discussed.

Learning Objectives

- *Nomenclature*
- *Engine Ratios*
- *Turbojets*
- *Turbofans*
- *High Bypass Engines*
- *Turboprops*
- *Turboshafts*

Section 1

Nomenclature

Although most turbine engines share common components, each type or manufacturer has components that are specific to a particular engine. The common components that all turbines share are the compressor, combustion and turbine section. The two main types of compressors used are centrifugal and axial flow. A centrifugal compressor's two major components are the impeller and the diffuser. The impeller increases the velocity of incoming air and the diffuser converts velocity into pressure. The centrifugal type compressor has high-pressure rise per stage. This means the pressure will increase to about eight times the inlet pressure. One limit is that only two stages of compression can be efficiently used. Centrifugal compressors operate well in low airflow conditions.

The compressor that can move great quantities of airflow is the axial compressor. Along with the high flow, the axial compressor can have many stages which can increase the com-

Left: **The Rolls-Royce RB211 illustrates the size and complexity of a modern turbofan engine.**
Photo courtesy of Rolls-Royce

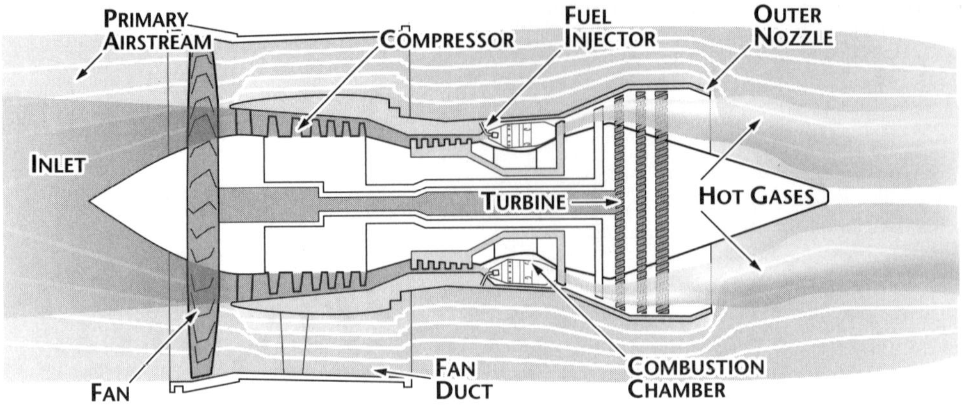

Figure 3-1-1. Ducted turbofan engine

pressor's overall pressure ratio. Many modern engines use more than one axial compressor turning at different speeds. Centrifugal compressors can operate at 8:1 compression ratios while axial flow compressors will have ratios of 1.25:1 or slightly greater. Axial flow compressors are made up of rotating wheels filled with blades to increase airflow velocity, followed by a set of stationary vanes that increase pressure.

A row of blades and vanes make up a compression stage. A stage is defined as an increase in pressure. A rotor blade and a stator vane make a stage. Axial compressors are made up of several stages of compression.

After the airflow is compressed, it passes into the diffuser which slows the flow velocity and increases pressure before flowing into the combustion section. The combustion section is where heat energy is added by burning fuel sprayed into the combustion section by fuel nozzles.

Only about 25% of the airflow is for combustion. The other 75% is used for cooling areas of the combustion section. When heat energy is added to the airflow, it increases its velocity; the air is then directed into another component—the turbine inlet guide vanes. These stationary guide vanes direct the airflow into the turbine blades causing the turbine wheel to rotate.

The disk that the blades are mounted to is part of a common shaft. This shaft is also connected to the compressor. The shaft is mounted to supports with bearings that support the shaft in the engine. This mechanically connects the turbine to the compressor. As the turbine is turned by the heated gases flowing from the combustion section, the shaft in turn rotates the compressor.

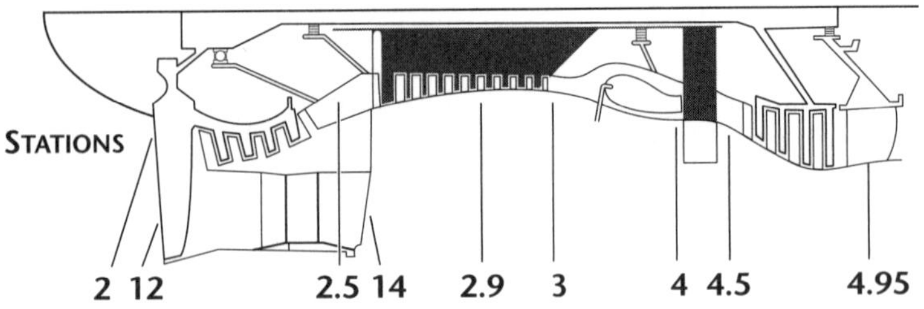

Figure 3-1-2. Engine stations

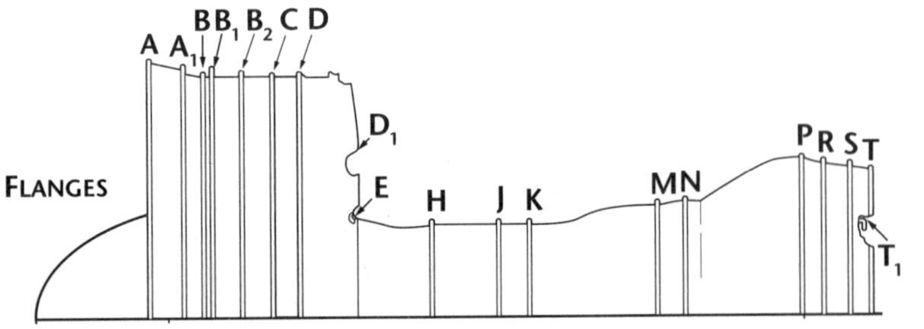

Figure 3-1-3. Engine flanges

To explain a basic gas turbine engine's operation, begin with a long tube with bearing supports at the front and rear to support the rotating components. At the front is a compressor which compresses incoming airflow. In the middle of the tube is the combustion section which is where the fuel is burned. The combustion section is annular around the inside of the tube. After fuel is burned, which greatly expands the airflow, it passes through a turbine that drives the compressor. The remaining gases (hot airflow) flow out a nozzle causing the action and the engine pushes forward, the reaction.

An actual engine changes the shape of the ducts (divergent and convergent) in the airflow path to control or manipulate the airflow through the engine. By changing the pressure and velocity of the airflow as it passes through the engine gas path, optimum efficiency can be attained. All gas turbine engines have a compressor, combustion and turbine section. Often, there are multiples of these components. Some gas turbine configurations have two sets or spools of rotating sections. These spools consist of a high and low-pressure compressor and a high and low-pressure turbine.

The high-pressure compressor is attached to the high-pressure turbines. Most of the time, the compressors are made up of many stages (rotor blade and stator vane per stage). The turbine also has multiple stages (turbine wheels) that drive the corresponding compressor. The engine in Figure 3-1-1 is a multi-spool turbofan engine.

By adding a fan to the low-pressure compressor, the fan air duct is separated into core or primary air flows. Several systems such as the fuel, oil, starter, and ignition are used to control, start and lubricate the engine during operation.

Station numbers. Locations on the engine are assigned station numbers as shown in Figure 3-1-2. These are locations in the gas path (flow of air through the engine from entrance to exit) that the manufacturer assigns to determine specific points in the engine. Each engine model will have its own unique numbering system. Although some engines will have the same numbered locations, they are not standardized.

Usually the ambient air is labeled 0 and the entrance to the inlet is station 1. The exit of the inlet, or just before the compressor, is station 2 on most engines. The compressor exit and burner entrance is generally station 3, and the combustion section exit is most often station 4. Since there can be several turbine sections, the turbine exit station can vary with different manufacturers and engines.

The exhaust nozzle area is generally station 8. Some nozzles have an additional section downstream. Typically, this nomenclature number of the primary (core) flow will not exceed station 10. If an engine has two gas path flows such as a turbofan engine, the fan gas path flow will often start with 12 and end with a station of less than 20.

The station numbers simplify communication when describing the operation of a gas turbine engine. By using station numbers, specific points in the gas path can be identified and referenced without confusion. It makes technical reports, documents, and conversations much more concise and easier to understand. For instance, the compressor discharge temperature can be referred to as simply T3, and the compressor exit pressure can be referred to as P3, with the letters T and P signifying temperature and pressure and the number 3 indicating the station.

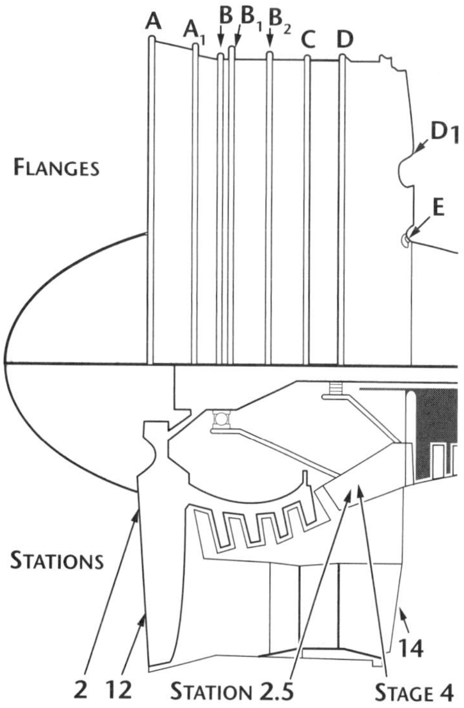

Figure 3-1-4. Stations and stages can be in the same location on the engine.

Flanges. Every turbine engine is divided into sections for assembly and maintenance. These areas are known as flanges and are labeled alphabetically starting with A at the front of the engine, as shown in Figure 3-1-3. Some of the flanges are used for bracket attachments or for securing accessories. They are also designed to stiffen the engine against bending and flexing forces created during operation.

Stages. Stages and stations should not be confused. The components in the compressors and turbines are identified by stages. The station number is a specific point within the engine whereas a stage number represents an increase in pressure within the gas path through the engine. Stages will start with the number 1 and continue through the compressor. Generally, a rotor and a stator make up a stage in an axial flow compressor.

An example of the difference: station 2.5 is stage 4 in an engine, as seen in Figure 3-1-4. The first turbine inlet vane and turbine wheel make up turbine stage 1. Each set of vanes and turbine wheels make up the rest of the turbine stages. Both stations and stages can use decimals when needed to describe a stage. Generally, stage numbers that use decimals are stages added to an engine after initial design, or to designate newer models of the same engine.

Bearing numbering. Engine bearings are also numbered starting with the number 1 bearing

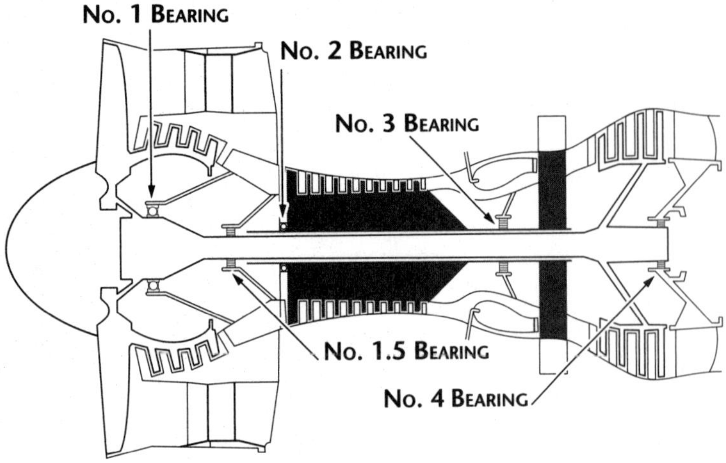

Figure 3-1-5. Engine bearing numbers and locations

and continuing through the number needed in the engine. Bearings can also have decimals if the bearing was added later in the design process. An example of a 1.5 bearing can be seen in Figure 3-1-5.

Most turbine engines use ball and straight roller bearings to support the rotating shafts; an example can be seen in Figure 3-1-6. Turbine engines use anti-friction bearings to support and align the rotating shafts of the engine.

Ball bearings will accept both thrust and radial loads while straight roller bearings can accept only radial loads. The straight roller bearings allow the engine shaft to expand with the heat of operation to prevent the shaft from becoming distorted at certain operating temperatures.

Figure 3-1-7 shows the three ways that bearings can be mounted inside an engine. They can be mounted hydraulically in a film of oil, free within a bearing cavity or mounted rigidly by pressing into the bearing cavity. Hydraulic mounted bearings reduce the amount of vibration transferred to the cabin and increase the life of the bearings. A hydraulic mounted bearing has oil pumped between the outer race and the bearing mounting which allows the bearing to ride on the film of oil.

Engine Ratios

Compressor pressure ratio. Every gas turbine engine has a compressor to increase the pressure of the incoming air. There are currently two principal compressor designs used with gas turbine engines: the axial compressor, in which the air flows parallel to the axis of rotation, and the centrifugal compressor, in which the air is turned perpendicular to the axis of rotation. In either design, the job of the compressor is to increase the pressure of the airflow.

We measure the increase by the compressor pressure ratio (CPR), which is the ratio of total air pressure (pt) exiting the compressor to the total air pressure entering the compressor. This number is always greater than 1.0. Referring to station numbering, the compressor entrance is station 2 and the compressor exit is station 3 in this case. The CPR is equal to P_{T3} divided by P_{T2}, as shown.

$$CPR = \frac{PT_3}{PT_2}$$

Where:

CPR = compressor pressure ratio

P_{T3} = compressor outlet pressure

P_{T2} = compressor inlet pressure

Many turbofan engines have more than one compressor: a low-pressure, or N_1, and a high-pressure, or N_2, compressor. The N_1 includes the fan and a few down-stream compressor stages. The N_2 compressor is second in the order of flow and turns on a different shaft than the N_1. The r.p.m. of the two compressors are different with the N_2 turning at a higher rate. A separate turbine turns each compressor, the N_1 compressor is driven by the N_1 low-pressure turbine. The N_2 compressor is driven by the N_2 high-pressure turbines. Each compressor and turbine combination makes up a spool. A turbofan with both a high and a low-pressure compressor is often called a two-spool engine. Each compressor can have its own CPR or both can be considered as one.

$$N_1\ CPR = \frac{\text{outlet pressure (29.4 p.s.i.a.)}}{\text{inlet pressure (14.7 p.s.i.a.)}}$$

N_1 CPR = 2:1

$$N_2\ CPR = \frac{\text{outlet pressure (300 p.s.i.a.)}}{\text{inlet pressure (29.4 p.s.i.a.)}}$$

N_2 CPR = 10.204:1

Overall compressor ratio would be;

$$N_1 \& N_2 = \frac{\text{outlet pressure (300 p.s.i.a.)}}{\text{inlet pressure (14.7 p.s.i.a.)}}$$

Engine compressor ratio (N_1 & N_2) = 20.408:1

Burner pressure ratio. Another engine ratio is the burner pressure ratio (BPR), which is the burner outlet pressure divided by the burner inlet pressure.

$$BPR = \frac{\text{burner outlet (p.s.i.)}}{\text{burner inlet (p.s.i.)}}$$

Engine pressure ratio. One of the most common turbine engine ratios is the engine pressure ratio (EPR). It is defined as the ratio of the engine inlet pressure to the engine outlet pressure. The EPR is often used as an indicator of developed thrust or the power being produced by the engine. It is common to see an EPR gauge in the aircraft cockpit. EPR is obtained by:

$$EPR = \frac{\text{total pressure outlet}}{\text{total pressure inlet}}$$

One example is:

$$EPR = \frac{P_{T7}\ (20\ \text{p.s.i.a.})}{P_{T2}\ (14\ \text{p.s.i.a.})}$$

$$EPR = 1.428$$

Where:

P_{T7} = pressure total at engine station 7

P_{T2} = pressure total at engine station 2

Some turbofan engines also rely on N_1 speed for an indication of thrust.

Bypass ratio (turbofan engines). The bypass ratio (BPR) is generally associated with turbofan engines. The total mass airflow through the fan duct, divided by the total mass airflow through the core of the engine is called the BPR. A turbofan engine does not have a need for all the airflow to pass through the gas generator-core of the engine. Much of the engine's total mass airflow is through the fan. The core of the engine still requires airflow, because this is where the compressor, burner and turbines are located. With this type of engine, certain turbines drive the fan and others drive the compressor.

To find the BPR:

$$BPR = \frac{W_{AF}}{W_{AC}}$$

Where:

W_{AF} = total mass airflow through the fan duct of the engine

W_{AC} = total mass airflow through the core of the engine

Engines are often categorized by their bypass ratio. These vary from low to ultra-high bypass.

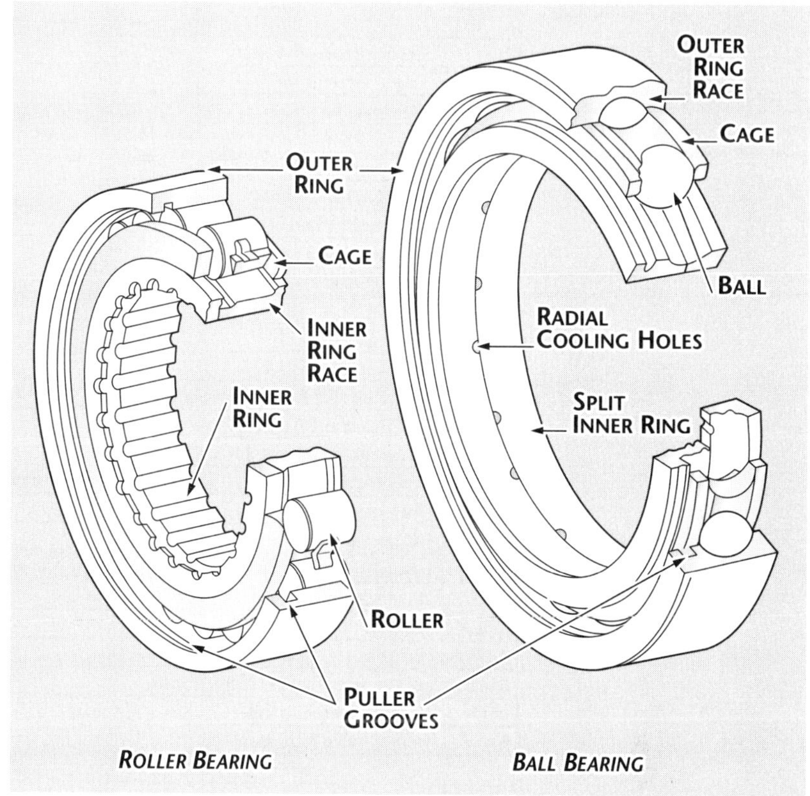

Figure 3-1-6. Roller and ball anti-friction bearings are used in turbine engines.

A high bypass engine is one that has a bypass ratio in excess of 4:1. This means that at least 4 times as much air flows through the fan duct than passes through the engine's core. Twenty percent of the air flows through the core of the engine where the high-pressure compressor, burner, and compressor-turbines are located. The other 80% of air flows through the fan duct. This type of engine often has separate exit nozzles, one nozzle for the fan duct and one for the core.

Low bypass engines have a bypass ratio of less than 2:1. Medium bypass engines have a bypass ratio of greater than 2:1, but less than 4:1. The latest generation of engines in development, known as ultra-high bypass engines, have bypass ratios in excess of 9:1.

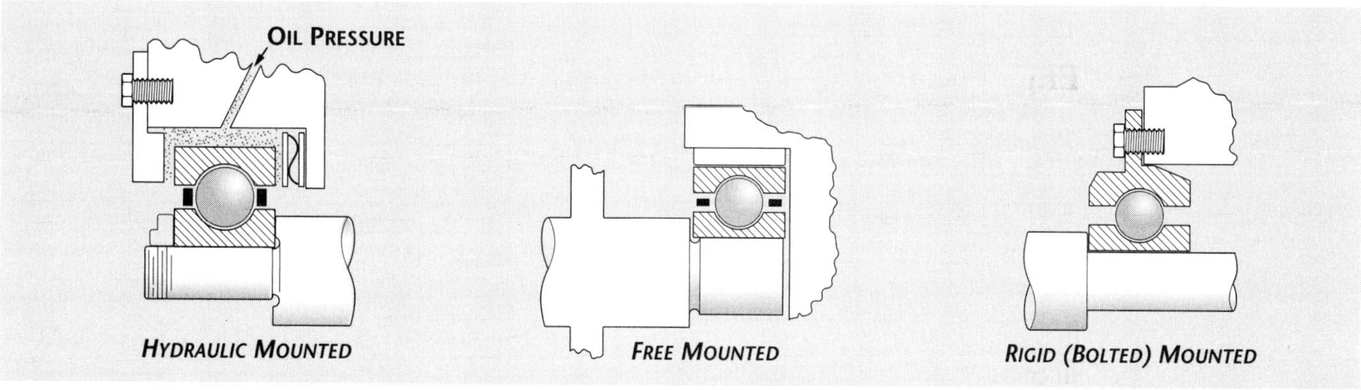

Figure 3-1-7. Three common methods of mounting bearings in turbine engines

	-A-
A	Cross-sectional Area
a	Linear Acceleration
ABBR	Abbreviations
ABMM	Airbus Maintenance Manual
ABS	Absolute
AC	Alternating Current
ACARS	ARINC Communications and Reporting System
ACCEL	Acceleration
AGB	Angle Gearbox
AOX	Air/Oil Heat Exchanger
AP	Access Port
APU	Auxiliary Power Unit
ARINC	Aeronautical Radio Incorporated
ATA	Air Transport Association
ATRC	Automatic Turbine Rotor Clearance
ATS	Autothrottle System
AUTO	Automatic
AVM	Airborne Vibration Monitor
	-B-
BAL	Balance
BPR	Bypass Ratio
BRT	Bright
BSFC	Brake Specific Fuel Consumption
BTU	British Thermal Unit
BVA	Bleed Valve Actuator
	-C-
c	Speed of Sound; Gas Velocity
C	Celsius; Coefficient
CONT	Continuous
c_p	Specific Heats at Constant Pressure
c_v	Specific Heats at Constant Volume
CPR	Compressor Pressure Ratio
CPU	Central Processing Unit
CRT	Cathode Ray Tube
	-D-
D	Diameter
DADC	Digital Air Data Computer
DECEL	Deceleration
°C	Degrees Celcius
°F	Degrees Fahrenheit
DEP	Data Entry Plug
DMU	Data Management Unit
DOT_3	Differential Oil Temperature (No. 3 Bearing Scavenge Oil Temperature Minus Engine Scavenge Oil Temperature)
	-E-
EBU	Engine Buildup Unit (components which configure an engine for an aircraft installation; usually supplied by other than engine manufacturer)
ECAM	Electronic Centralized Aircraft Monitoring
ECS	Environmental Control System
EEC	Electronic Engine Control
EEROM	Electrically Erasable Read Only Memory
EGT	Exhaust Gas Temperature (Also referred to as Tt 4.95 or Tt5)
eng	Engine
EPR	Engine Pressure Ratio
EPR ACT	Actual EPR
EPR COM	Commanded EPR
EPR MAX	Maximum EPR
	-F-
f	Frequency
F	Thrust
FADEC	Full Authority Digital Engine Control
FD	Fuel Drain
FLT	Flight
FLXTOTEMP	Flexible Takeoff Temperature
FMU	Fuel Metering Unit
F_n	Net Thrust
F_{nf}	Fan Net Thrust
F_{np}	Primary Net Thrust
F_{nt}	Total Net Thrust
FP	Fuel Pump
F_r	Ram Drag of Engine Airflow
ft	Feet
	-G-
g	Acceleration Due to Gravity; Mass Conversion Factor
gal	Gallon
GE	General Electric
GND	Ground
	-H-
Hg	Mercury
hp	Horsepower
HPC	High-pressure Compressor
HPT	High-pressure Turbine
hr	Hour
HX	Heat Exchanger
	-I-
ID	Inside Diameter
IDG	Integrated Drive Generator
IDGS	Integrated Drive Generator System
Ign	Ignition
IGV	Inlet Guide Vane
in	Inch
	-K-
K	Constant
Kg	Kilograms
KPa	Kilo Pascal
	-L-
l	Length
L	Left
lb	Pound
lb/hr	Pounds Per Hour
LPC	Low-pressure Compressor
LPT	Low-pressure Turbine
LRU	Line Replaceable Unit
LVDT	Linear Variable Differential Transformer
	-M-
m	Mass
M	Moment; Torque; Mach Number
MAX	Maximum
Mb	Millibars
MGB	Main Gearbox
mils	Thousands of an Inch
Mn	Mach Number
MSG	Message
	-N-
N	Rotational Speed In r.p.m. or Percent r.p.m.
NAC	Nacelle
N_1	Low-pressure Compressor Rotational Speed
N_2	High-pressure Compressor Rotational Speed
N_{2c2}	Corrected High-pressure Rotor Speed (derived from T_{t2})
$N_{2c2.5}$	Corrected High-pressure Rotor Speed (derived from $T_{t2.5}$)
N_{2dot}	Derivative of High-pressure Rotor Speed With Respect to Time

Table 3-4-1. Index of turbine engine abbreviations, terms and symbols

ND	Navigation Display
No.	Number
	-O-
OAT	Outside Air Temperature
OD	Outside Diameter
	-P-
p	Pressure
P_{amb}	Ambient Pressure
P_b	Burner Pressure
P_{bl}	Pressure Bleed
P_{br}	Breather Pressure
P_{cr}	Pressure Critical
PDU	Pneumatic Drive Unit
P_f	Fine Filtered Supply Pressure
PD	Pressurization and Dump
PFD	Primary Flight Display
P_{fr}	Fuel Pump Interstage Pressure
PLA	Power Level Angle
PMA	Permanent Magnet Alternator
PNAC	Nacelle Pressure
PNEU	Pneumatic
PMG	Permanent Magnet Generator
PO	International Standard Day Sea Level Pressure
pph	Pounds Per Hour
PRI	Primary
P_s	Static Pressure
p.s.i.	Pounds Per Square Inch
p.s.i.a.	Pounds Per Square Inch Absolute
p.s.i.d.	Pounds Per Square Inch Differential (Differential Pressure)
p.s.i.g.	Pounds Per Square Inch Gauge
P_{s3}	High-pressure Compressor Discharge Static Pressure
P_t	Total Pressure
P_{t2}	Compressor Inlet Total Air Pressure
$P_{t2.5}$	Low-pressure Compressor Exit Total Air Pressure (also referred to as intercompressor pressure)
$P_{t4.95}$	Exhaust Gas Pressure (also referred to as $P_{t4.9}$ or P_{t5})
PW	Pratt & Whitney
	-Q-
Q	Volume Rate of Flow; Heating Value of Fuel
QEC	Quick Engine Change
qt	Quart
Qty	Quantity
	-R-
r	Radius
R	Right
Re	Reynolds number
REF	Reference
REV	Reverse
REV UNLK	Reverse Unlock
r.p.m.	Revolutions Per Minute
RR	Rolls-Royce
RVDT	Rotational Variable Differential Transformer
	-S-
s	Entropy
SEC	Secondary
SFC	Specific Fuel Consumption
SVA	Stator Vane Actuator
	-T-
T	Absolute Temperature
T_{amb}	Ambient Temperature

TAT	Total Air Temperature
T_{av}	Temperature Average
TBD	To Be Determined
TBV	Thrust Balance Vent
TCC	Thrust Control Computer
T_{cr}	Temperature Critical
TEC	Turbine Exhaust Case
TIT	Turbine Inlet Temperature
TLA	Thrust Lever Angle
TNGV	Turbine Nozzle Guide Vane
T_{oil}	Temperature Engine Oil
TOT	Turbine Outlet Temperature
T/R	Thrust Reverser
TRA	Thrust Lever Resolver Angle
TRC	Thermatic Rotor Control
TRP	Thrust Rating Panel
T_s	Temperature Static
tsfc	Thrust Specific Fuel Consumption
T_t	Total Temperature
T_{t2}	Compressor Inlet Total Air
$T_{t2.5}$	Low-pressure Compressor Exit Total Air Temperature
T_{t3}	High-pressure Compressor Exit Total Air Temperature
$T_{t4.95}$	Exhaust Gas Total Temperature (also referred to as $T_{t4.9}$ and T_{t5})
TVBCA	Turbine Vane and Blade Cooling Air
	-U-
u	Internal Energy; Rotor Linear Velocity
US	United States
	-V-
V	Velocity; Volume
VAC	Volts, Alternating Current
VDC	Volts, Direct Current
VIB	Vibration
	-W-
W	Weight (Force) Rate of Flow (Expressed as Weight of Flow)
W_a	Rate of Airflow
W_{af}	Rate of Fan Airflow
W_{ap}	Rate of Primary Airflow
W_{at}	Rate of Total Airflow ($W_{at} + W_{af}$)
W_f	Rate of Fuel Flow
W_{fl}	Fuel Flow Temperature
	-SYMBOLS-
$<$	Less Than
$>$	Greater Than
ΔP	Delta, Differential, Finite Difference
∂	Theta: Relative Temperature Ratio
Δ	Delta: Relative Pressure Ratio
η	Efficiency
Θ	Relative Absolute Temperature
μ	Absolute Viscosity
π	3.141592653589793
=	Equal, Equivalent
≈	Approximately
%	Percent
↑	Above or Higher
↓	Below or Lower
:	Proportional To
→	No Change

Jet engine symbols and abbreviations. Individuals who deal with gas turbine engines have found it advantageous to use a common set of symbols and abbreviations to refer to particular engine areas or attributes. The more common abbreviations and symbols for turbine engines are listed in Table 3-1-1.

Section 2

Types of Jet Propulsion Engines

Jet propulsion engines provide thrust by accelerating a mass through the engine. The mass used is usually air. Some jet propulsion engines contain both the mass to be accelerated and the accelerant (or fuel) within the engine; others only carry fuel and must intake the mass from an external source.

Figure 3-2-1. Rockets do not require external oxidizers for combustion.

Rockets, ramjets, pulse jets and gas turbine engines are all considered jet propulsion engines. Rocket fuel contains both the reaction mass and the accelerant. The other types take in air and mix it with an accelerant, exhausting the combined mass.

Rocket. The simplest form of rocket is a tube which can be made of metal or even paper, filled with gunpowder or some other sort of rapid-burning mixture of chemicals. As the fuel burns, gases are expelled from the back of the tube and the rocket is pushed forward (reaction) through the action of the exhaust gases passing out the end of the tube. Modern rocket engines that propel spacecraft use the action/reaction principle.

In a rocket, no external air is brought on board since the oxidizer is carried in the rocket. Rockets can generate thrust in a vacuum where there is no other source of oxygen. Stored fuel and stored oxidizer are pumped into a combustion chamber where they are mixed and burned. The rocket engine produces thrust by burning liquid fuel that has been mixed with an oxidizer, usually liquid oxygen. These are typically pumped into and mixed in the combustion chamber where the mixture is ignited, as illustrated in Figure 3-2-1.

The combustion process that takes place in the engine produces large amounts of exhaust gas at high temperature and pressure. As the flow rate of the hot gas approaches the speed of sound (Mach 1) the nozzle becomes choked. The nozzle is designed to be convergent-divergent in order to accelerate the gas to a high velocity and produce a maximum of thrust. Thrust is produced according to Newton's third law of motion. The amount of thrust produced by the rocket depends on the mass flow rate through the engine, the exit velocity of the exhaust, and the pressure at the nozzle exit. All of these variables are governed by the design of the engine and nozzle.

The smallest cross-sectional area of the nozzle is called the throat of the nozzle. The hot exhaust is passed through a nozzle which accelerates the mass flow. This type of nozzle is required in rockets in order to achieve extremely high-velocity (highly accelerated) exhaust gases.

Gas turbine engines rely on the atmosphere to provide air for mass flow and oxygen in the air as oxidizer for combustion. Since there is no need for carrying oxygen in the atmosphere, gas turbine engines are suitable for operation in the atmosphere.

Ramjet. The ramjet engine in Figure 3-2-2 is a unique jet propulsion engine that has no internal moving parts. Compression of the air is created by the ram air effect produced by the forward speed of the aircraft. To maintain the flow through the engine, the combustion must occur at a higher pressure than the pressure at the exhaust nozzle. The inlet pressure must be produced by ram air pressure entering into the inlet of the engine.

The source of ram air can be produced by the forward speed of the aircraft. The atmospheric air that is rammed into the inlet of the engine becomes the working fluid (mass air and fuel flow), much like a gas turbine engine. The shape of the inlet compresses the air as it enters the combustion chamber.

Passing the hot exhaust flow from the combustion section through an exhaust nozzle produces the thrust. The nozzle accelerates the airflow through the engine, which produces thrust.

In a gas turbine engine, the high-pressure in the engine's inlet is generated by the compressor; however there are no compressors in a ramjet. Therefore, ramjet engines are lighter and simpler than gas turbine engines.

Ramjets produce thrust only when an aircraft is already moving; they cannot produce thrust when the engine is stationary or static. Since a ramjet cannot produce static thrust, another type of propulsion system must be used to accelerate the vehicle to a speed where the ramjet begins to produce thrust. The higher the aircraft's speed, the better a ramjet works, until aerodynamic losses become too great.

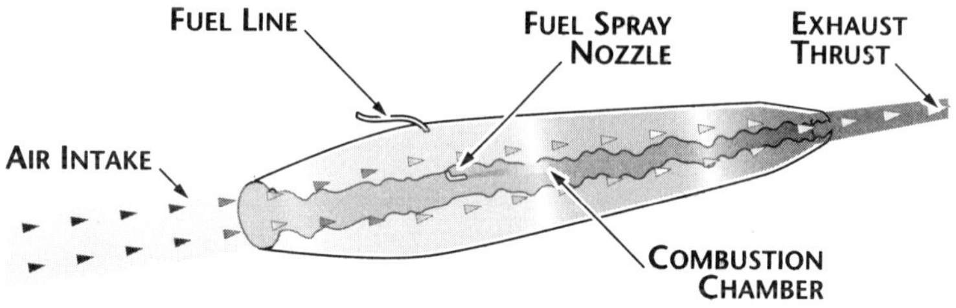

Figure 3-2-2. The ramjet engine cannot produce static thrust

The combustion process that produces thrust in the ramjet occurs at a subsonic speed in the combustor. When an aircraft is traveling supersonically, the air entering the engine must be slowed to subsonic speeds by the aircraft inlet. Shock waves present in the inlet cause performance losses, and above a high Mach speed number, ramjet propulsion becomes very inefficient.

Pulse jet engines. The pulse jet engine, as shown in Figure 3-2-3, is somewhat more complex than the ramjet since it has a grill of shutters located at the inlet of the engine. However, the operation of the pulse jet is easier to understand. The shutters, which are kept open with springs, allow air to enter the combustion chamber. As the air is packed into the combustion chamber, it is mixed with fuel and ignited.

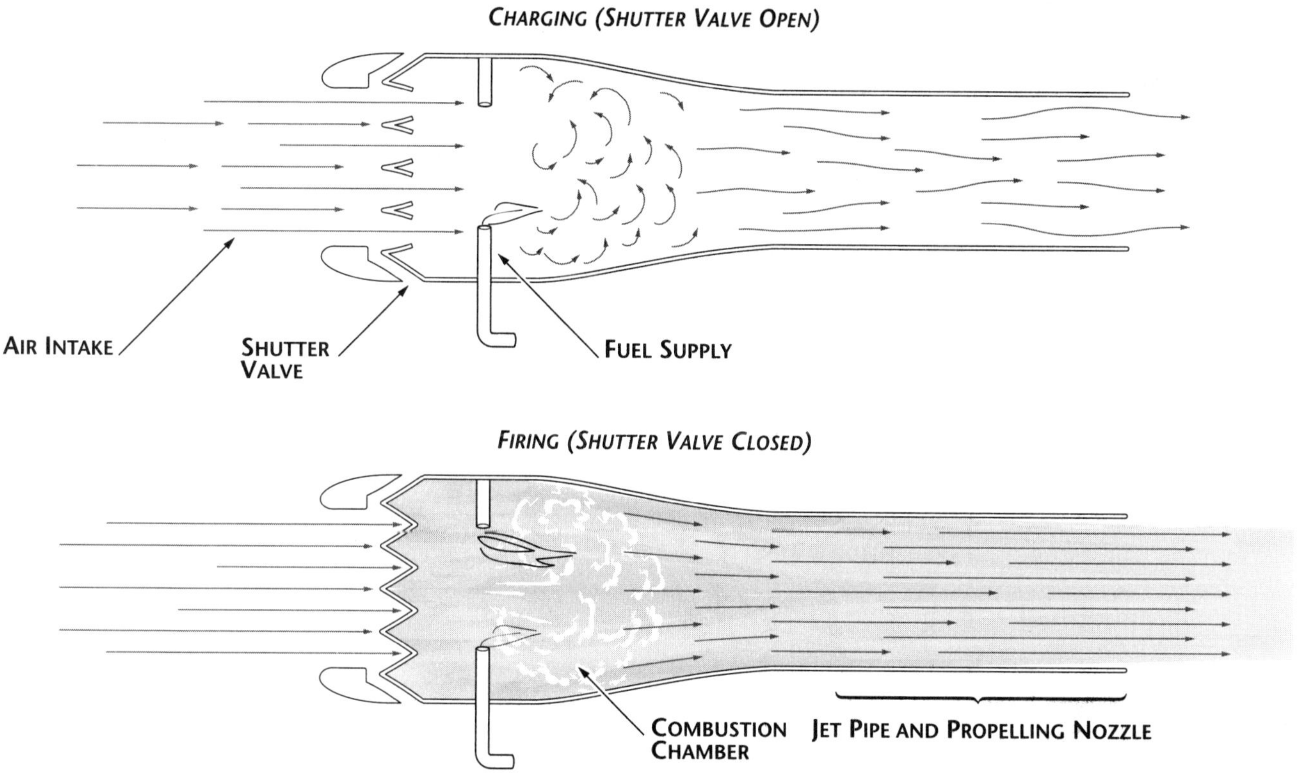

Figure 3-2-3. A pulse jet engine operates on intermittent power impulses

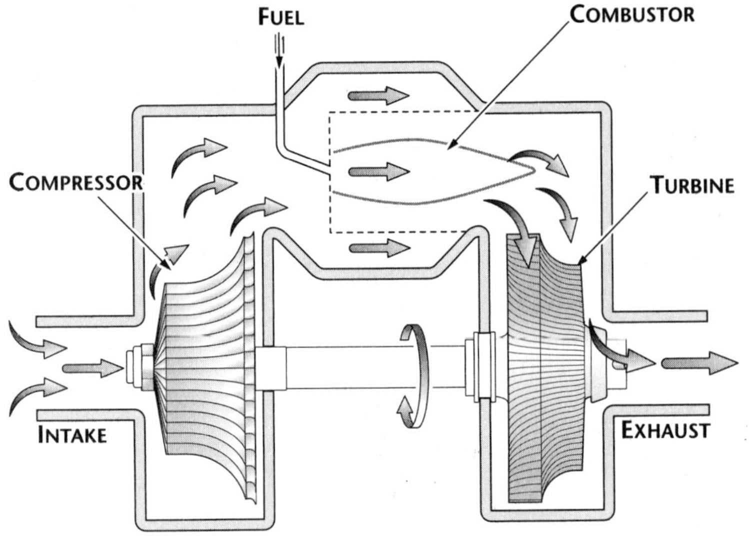

Figure 3-2-4. A turbine engine in its most basic form

The shutters are forced closed by the pressure of the exhaust gases when combustion takes place. Consequently, the exhaust gases can only move down the tailpipe and out the exhaust. Then the springs force the shutters to reopen, allowing more fresh air to enter, and the cycle repeats.

The length of the tailpipe of the pulse jet regulates the frequency of ignition. Fuel flow is continuous, but flame propagation is intermittent, since the pulse jet operates in a step-by-step cycle. This is the only form of jet propulsion that operates by intermittent power surges, utilizing explosive rather than progressive or continuous combustion. However, in most pulse jet engines, the cycles per second are rather high, and the net effect is practically continuous thrust. Pulse jet engines provided thrust for some early unguided missiles.

Gas turbine engine. The earliest turbine engines resembled modern turbochargers in their construction. (See Figure 3-2-4). The turbine engine can be compared to the four-cycle reciprocating engine in terms of its basic operation. There is an intake event, a compression event, a power event and an exhaust event. The difference is that in the turbine engine all of these events happen continuously and simultaneously.

Air enters the engine through an air intake. This is often placed to take advantage of pressure created by the forward motion of the aircraft. This ram air continuously enters the compressor. The compressor performs the same function as the compression stroke in a reciprocating engine. It takes the intake air and compresses it into a smaller space. The intake air is then fed into the combustor. High-pressure fuel is injected into the combustion chamber where it mixes with the moving air.

The compressed fuel/air mixture is then ignited. In practice, once started, the engine operates with a constant flame in the combustion chamber. The combustion process creates both heat and pressure. The combustion gases are then directed onto the turbine.

A significant percentage of the energy of the exhaust stream gases is absorbed by the turbine, causing a high rotational speed. The turbine wheel transmits energy to the compressor through connecting shafts. The remaining energy of the exhaust stream produces thrust.

The compressor, burner and turbine are called the core of the engine, since all gas turbine engines have these components. The core is also referred to as the gas generator, since the output of the core is hot exhaust gas. The gas is passed through a turbine that in turn drives the compressor. In the simplest application the exhaust gas is directed through a nozzle and directly produces forward thrust.

Section 3

Types of Gas Turbine Engines

Gas turbine engines are the most complex jet propulsion engines used in aviation. They are also the most numerous. They can self-start, they do not need to carry their own reaction mass, and they are very reliable. A number of variants of gas turbine engines have been developed over the years. Versions have been developed to power almost any type of aircraft, from jet fighters, airliners, small personal aircraft, helicopters and even blimps.

Although there are four basic types of gas turbine engines, they all contain a compressor, combustion and turbine section. Each engine differs because according to its mission. Turboshaft and turboprop engines generally have lower airflow than turbofan engines.

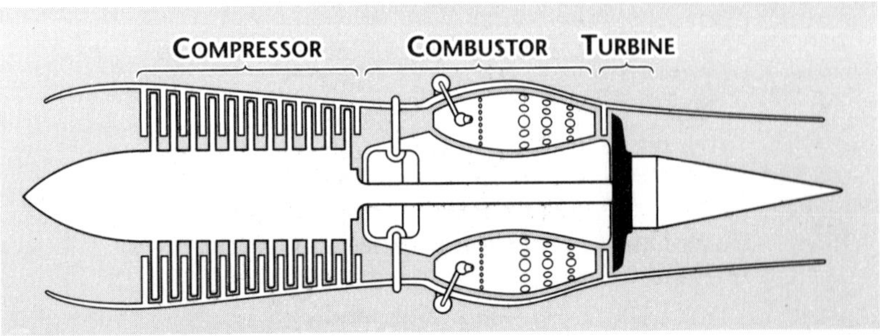

Figure 3-3-1. Basic single stage rotor turbine

Figure 3-3-2. A basic bypass turbofan engine with an enclosed bypass duct *Photo courtesy of Pratt & Whitney*

This allows for varying gas path flows during operation which makes the components differ in size and shape.

Turbofan engines tend to pass air straight through the engine while turboshaft and turboprop engines turn the airflow several times to allow a smaller overall engine dimension. Even though each engine type has a different mission, all of them use either a centrifugal or axial compressor.

Another common item is the combustion section. Modern engines tend to use an annular shaped combustion section. The use of turbine inlet guide vanes and turbine wheels is also very common to each type of engine. One of the variables is the number of turbine stages (guide vane and turbine wheel). Several stages are used to drive fans, propellers, and shafts (helicopter).

Basic turbojet engine. The basic turbojet engine, shown in Figure 3-3-1, was the original type of gas turbine engine developed. All other gas turbine engines are a further development of this basic engine.

The basic engine includes a compressor, combustion section (burner), and a turbine to drive the compressor. The compressor is used to increase the pressure and velocity of the air drawn into the engine. The air flows into the burner sections where fuel is injected and mixed with some of the airflow. As the fuel burns, its velocity increases with only a slight drop in pressure. The high velocity gases pass through the turbine section, which is connected to the compressor by a shaft. This action provides the power needed to drive the compressor. This basic turbojet engine provided thrust through a nozzle in the exhaust section. It provides high velocity airflow at a lower mass flow (amount of air flowing through the engine).

These early turbojet engines are very noisy and have very high fuel consumption compared to the amount of thrust produced. Because of their poor combustion efficiency, they produce a significant amount of hydrocarbon emissions, seen as smoke from the exhaust. Due to these drawbacks, the basic turbojet engine has been mostly replaced with new derivatives.

All derivatives contain the original turbojet engine (core engine) with numerous technological improvements. By building on the original core engine (turbojet), the turbofan, turboshaft and turboprop engines were developed and have proven to be more efficient in most operations.

Turbofan engine. Most modern airliners use turbofan engines because of their high thrust and good fuel efficiency. A turbofan engine is a variation of the basic gas turbine engine, as can be seen in Figure 3-3-2.

The basic construction of the turbofan engine consists of a core engine with a large diameter fan in the front of the engine. The fan is attached to the turbines that drive it, through a shaft, which passes through and inside the core engine's shaft. This shaft runs from the low-pressure turbines behind the compressor turbines to the fan. This assembly is called the low-pressure spool. The core compressor and turbine assembly form the high-pressure spool.

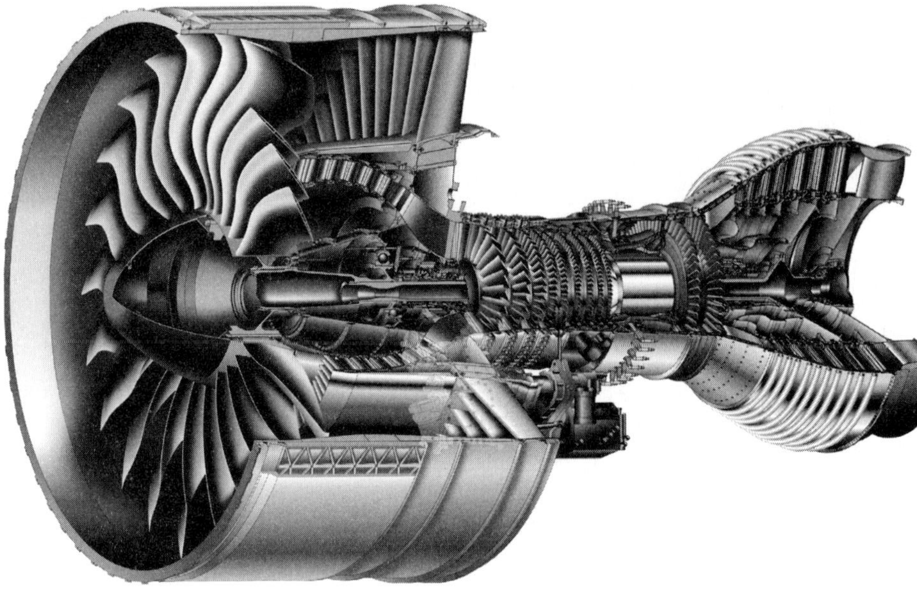

Figure 3-3-3. High bypass turbine engine cutaway

Photo courtesy of General Electric

This type of arrangement is called a two-spool engine (one spool for the fan, one spool for the core).

The operation of a turbofan engine starts with the incoming air being drawn into the engine inlet. A portion of the airflow passes through the fan and continues around the engine core, bypassing the core of the engine. The remaining air flows into the core of the engine where the compressor increases its pressure and velocity. It then flows into the burner, where it is mixed with fuel, and combustion takes place. The ratio of air flowing around the core compared to the air flowing through the core varies according to engine model. The turbofan gets some of its thrust from the core, but the majority of the thrust is from the fan. The hot exhaust passes through the core (high-pressure turbines) and fan turbines (low-pressure turbines), then out the core nozzle, producing part of the total engine's thrust. The airflow that passes through

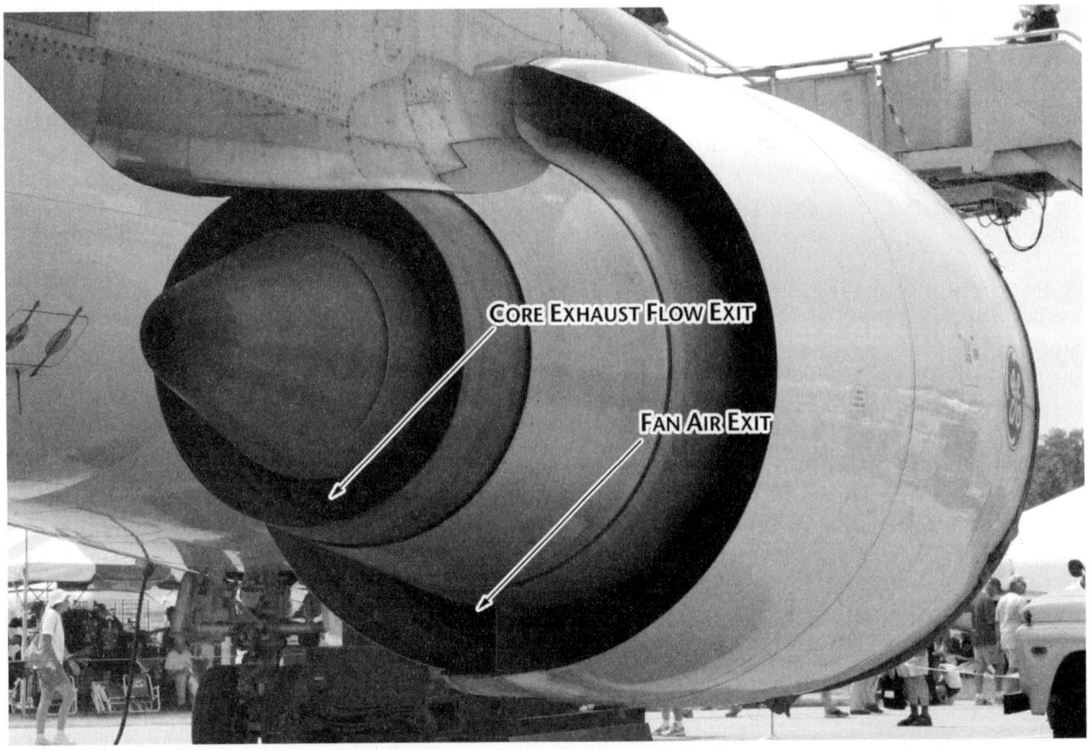

Figure 3-3-4. Core nozzle and fan nozzle

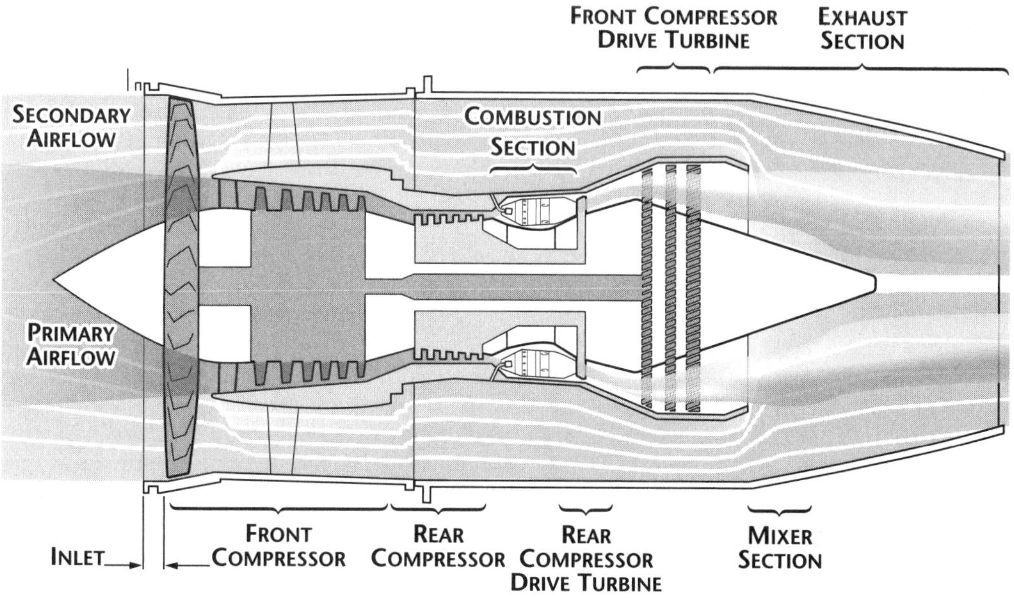

Figure 3-3-5. Core and bypass air mixing in a common nozzle

the fan has a velocity increase that produces most of the engine's thrust. The bypass ratio is an indirect indication of the ratio of thrust produced by the fan and the engine core. A higher percentage of the thrust is produced by the fan in higher bypass ratio engines. A modern high bypass turbofan typically generates 85% of the total thrust with the fan.

A turbofan is very fuel-efficient. The fuel flow rate for the core is changed only a small amount by the addition of fan turbine stages. A turbofan generates more thrust proportionally for the small amount of extra fuel used by the core.

Because the fan is enclosed by the inlet and composed of many blades, it can operate efficiently at higher air speeds. Turbofans are found on most modern jet aircraft, both commercial and military.

Many modern military aircraft use low bypass ratio turbofans equipped either with an afterburner or with augmenters. Such aircraft can then cruise efficiently but still have high thrust when needed. Low bypass ratio turbofans are still more fuel efficient than basic turbojets.

Low bypass engines are more efficient at high aircraft speeds than a high bypass turbofan engine. Even though some military aircraft can exceed the speed of sound, the air flowing through the engine must be kept subsonic. The design of the engine inlet slows the incoming air before it enters the compressor section of the engine.

High-bypass turbofan engine. The high-bypass turbofan engine, shown in Figure 3-3-3, has become one of the principal sources of power for large transport aircraft. A high-bypass engine utilizes the fan section of the compressor to bypass a large volume of air compared with the amount that passes through the engine. An engine with a bypass ratio of 4:1 or higher is considered a high bypass engine. This means that the bypassed airflow is at least four times the flow of the air passed through the core of the engine.

The principal advantages of the high-bypass engines are greater fuel efficiency and reduced noise. The high-bypass engine has the advantages of the turboprop engine but does not have the problems of propeller limits or angle control. The design is such that the fan can rotate at its most efficient speed, depending on the speed of the aircraft and the power demanded from the engine.

On engines with the fan at the front of the engine, the bypass air-stream is ducted directly from the fan through a short fan exhaust nozzle. This type of engine uses two separate exhaust nozzles, as can be seen in Figure 3-3-4, one for the core exhaust and one for the bypass fan air. When the fan air-stream is ducted through longer ducts, which direct the fan air-stream around the outside of the core, it is generally termed a ducted fan engine. At the aft end of the engine, the core air-stream and fan air combine in a common (or mixed) exhaust nozzle. This mixes the core and fan air before it exits through the exhaust nozzle. A mixed or common nozzle is shown in Figure 3-3-5.

Turboprop. A turboprop engine, illustrated in Figure 3-3-6, is a gas turbine engine with a reduction gearbox that is normally mounted on the forward end to drive a standard aircraft propeller. This engine uses almost all the exhaust

Figure 3-3-6. The Rolls-Royce AE2100 is a modern, fuel efficient turboprop available in versions producing from 3,600 shp to 6,100 shp.

gas energy to drive the propeller. It therefore provides very little thrust through the ejection of exhaust gases. The exhaust gases represent only about 10% of the total amount of energy available through the exhaust nozzle. The other 90% of the energy is extracted by the set of turbines that drive the compressor plus a turbine that drives the propeller.

The basic components of the turboprop engine are identical to those of the turbojet; that is, compressor, combustor, and turbine. The only difference is the addition of the gear-reduction box, which reduces the rotational speed to a value suitable for propeller r.p.m. ranges. Many low speed (up to 400 m.p.h.) transport, business, and small commuter aircraft use turboprop engines for propulsion. These engines develop thrust by moving a large mass of air through a small change in velocity.

Figure 3-3-7. PT6 turboprop propeller reduction gearbox

The turboprop uses a gas turbine core, called the gas generator, to turn turbines that drive the propeller. Turbines that provide power to the propeller are called power turbines. When these two sections, gas generator and power turbine, are linked mechanically, the engine is called a fixed turbine engine. With this type of engine, the propeller must be in flat (or zero pitch) to the plane of rotation for starting. This will decrease the load on the engine and starter during the start sequence.

If there is no mechanical connection between the compressor turbine and the power turbine, the engine is referred to as a free turbine engine. In the free turbine engine the only connection between the two turbine sections (compressor turbine and power turbine) is a link of hot gases flowing from the compressor turbine into the power turbine. A free turbine allows the gas generator to be turned with only the air link between the turbines. This configuration has the advantage of allowing the gas generator to start by itself and, as the air link gets stronger, then the propeller will start to rotate.

The two main parts of a turboprop propulsion system are the core engine and the propeller system. The core engine is used to produce the expanding hot exhaust gases that pass through the power turbines. Most of the energy of the exhaust is used to turn the power turbine and, in turn, the propeller system. The exhaust velocity of a turboprop is low and contributes little thrust because most of the energy of the core exhaust has gone into turning the drive shaft of the power turbine.

There can be multiple power turbines depending upon the type of turboprop engine. The power turbine drives a shaft at very high speed. This shaft is connected to a speed reduction gearbox which can be seen in Figure 3-3-7. The gearbox is then connected to a propeller that produces around 90% of the thrust. The speed of the power turbine is reduced so the propeller can continue to turn at an optimum speed as the speed of the aircraft changes.

Turboshaft. A variation of the turboprop engine is the turboshaft engine. A turboshaft engine, shown in Figure 3-3-8 is a gas turbine engine which delivers power through an output shaft. As in the turboprop, this engine uses almost all the exhaust energy to drive the output shaft. The primary difference between a turboprop and a turboshaft engine is the r.p.m. of the output shaft. Turboshaft engines typically turn between 6,000 and 7,000 r.p.m. at the output shaft while turboprop engines typically turn about one third of that at the propeller shaft.

These turboshaft engines are used mainly on helicopters and as auxiliary power units on large transport aircraft. In a helicopter, the gearbox is not connected to a propeller but to a transmission that drives the main and tail rotors on helicopters.

Turboshaft engines are gas turbine engines (core) that use an extra set of turbine stages to drive an output shaft. There is a set of turbine stages that drives the compressor and a set that drives the output shaft, the latter are called the power turbines. The power turbines are located down stream of the compressor turbines. Since the engine powers a turning shaft, the output is measured in shaft horsepower.

Turboshaft engines can also be used for industrial purposes, providing power to generators, large pumps and production machinery. These engines can range from 400 h.p. to several thousand horsepower. The engines are made as compact as possible, and the air stream may change direction several times as it flows through the engine, as shown in Figure 3-3-9.

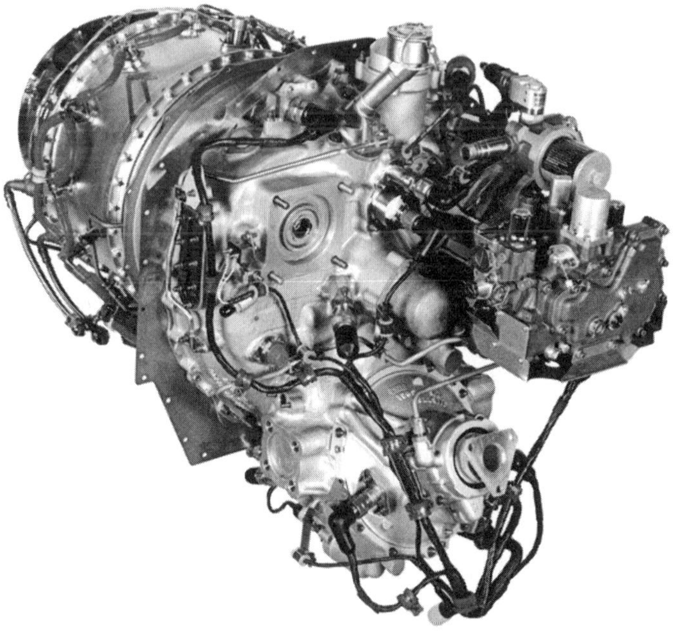

Figure 3-3-8. PW 206 turboshaft engine *Photo courtesy of Pratt & Whitney*

Auxiliary power unit. Another application of the gas turbine engine is the auxiliary power unit (APU) shown in Figure 3-3-10. An APU is a special type of turboshaft engine. The main purpose of this type of turbine is to provide electrical power and a high volume of compressed air. The APU can be used to drive hydraulic pumps or provide the power for electric motors that drive the pumps. In some cases, it can function as an inflight back-up generator, but its main use is for starting the main engines on the ground.

APUs can come in several sizes and capacities from small APUs used on business aircraft to

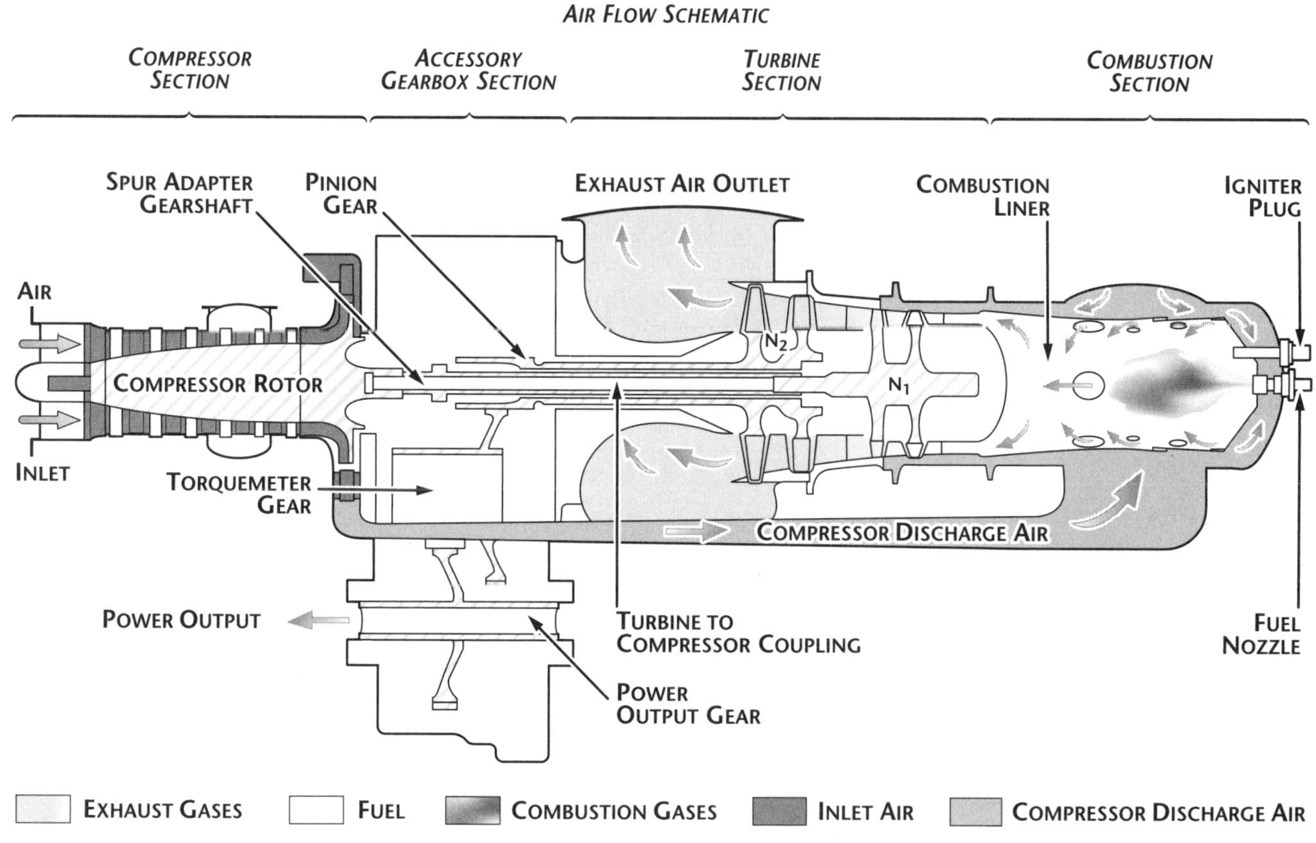

Figure 3-3-9. Rolls-Royce 250 turboshaft engine

Figure 3-3-10. Auxiliary power units provide electrical power and compressed air. *Image courtesy of Honeywell*

large wide-body airliner aircraft. Large aircraft require high power output in order to drive as many as two generators for electrical power.

Bleed air from the APU compressor is ducted to an air turbine starter mounted on the engine. This compressed air from the APU is directed onto a set of turbine blades that rotate at a high r.p.m.. This high rotational speed is then converted to a lower r.p.m. with high torque that is used to turn the main engine compressor spool to start the engine.

The APU's bleed air can also be used to heat and cool the aircraft cabin on the ground. The APU must be able to provide enough compressed air to operate the onboard air-conditioning or heating packages on the ground.

In its simplest form, the APU consists of a single stage compressor burner, and a centrifugal in-flow turbine. Larger APUs can have several stages in the compressor and extra turbine stages that turn separately from the compressor turbine. Smaller APUs generally use a centrifugal compressor that flows compressed air into a burner, then into a torus that directs the hot gases into the turbine to drive the compressor. The torus, shown in Figure 3-3-11, starts at about the same cross sectional area as the burner, but as it circles around the turbine inlet vanes in a radial direction (these direct the hot gases into the turbine), it reduces in size to provide an even flow into the turbine vanes.

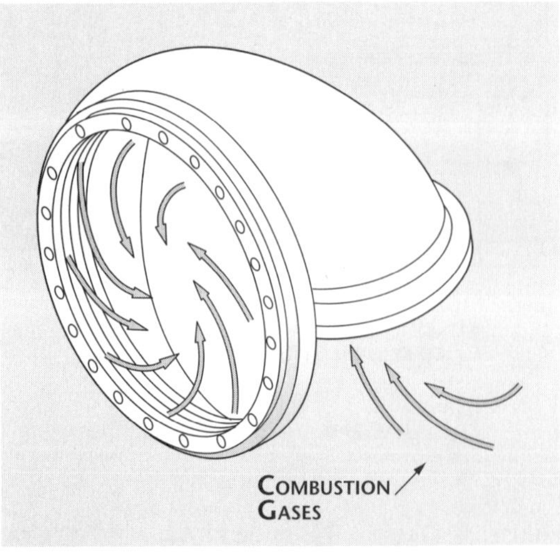

Figure 3-3-11. APU torus directs combustion gases into a radial flow turbine.

A thermostat is placed in the exhaust stream. It is set to reduce fuel flow if the engine's maximum temperature is exceeded. This protects the APU from overheating while in operation. The bleed airflow valve can also be partially closed by a thermostat if the engine temperature is exceeded. When bleed air is taken from the engine for aircraft systems, there is less air in the APU for cooling; hence the higher temperatures. The most common placement of the APU in transport aircraft is in the tail area shown in Figure 3-3-12. This provides for the exhaust to be directed out the rear of the aircraft, reducing noise level in the cabin.

Turbojet or turbofan with afterburner. Most modern fighter aircraft employ an afterburner or augmenter on either a low bypass turbofan or a turbojet. When fighter aircraft fly faster than sound (supersonic), they have to overcome a sharp rise in drag near the speed of sound. A simple way to get the necessary thrust is to add an afterburner (augmenter) to a core turbojet or turbofan. Turbine engines intake more air than is used for combustion.

Figure 3-3-12. A typical APU engine used on large transport aircraft.

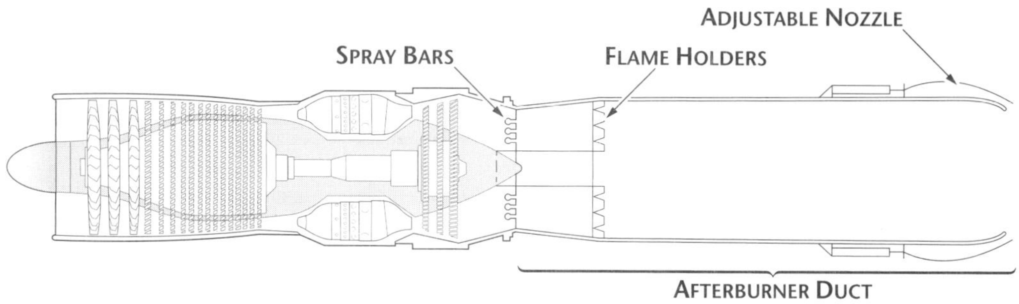

Figure 3-3-13. An afterburner augments the thrust of the basic turbojet.

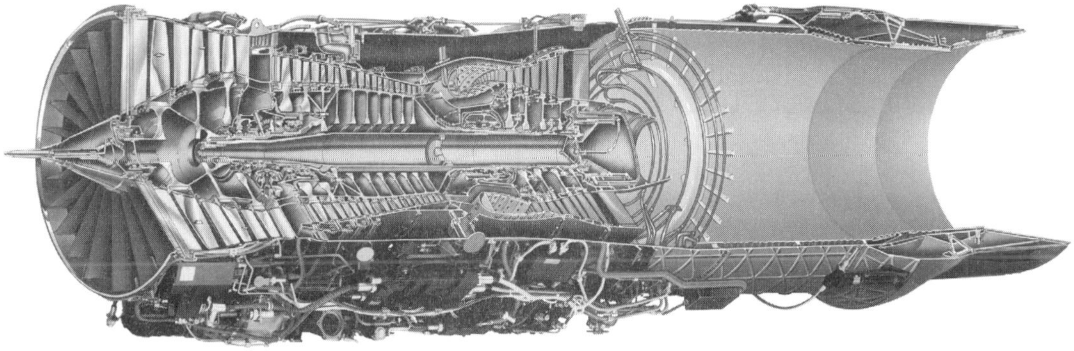

Figure 3-3-14. A turbofan engine equipped with afterburners and flame holder

Image courtesy of Pratt & Whitney

The excess air provides cooling to the engine. Hot turbine exhaust contains enough oxygen to support significant additional combustion. The afterburner takes advantage of this to add thrust.

In Figure 3-3-13, the nozzle of the basic turbojet has been extended and there is now a flame holder, after the turbine stages, in the nozzle. When the afterburner is activated, additional fuel is injected through a series of fuel nozzles into the hot exhaust stream of the engine. The fuel burns and produces additional thrust, but it doesn't burn as efficiently as it does in the combustion section of the engine. More thrust is produced, but the amount of fuel used increases dramatically.

The engine performs like a basic turbojet engine when the afterburner is turned off. Afterburners are a simple way to augment thrust and are used on both turbojets and low bypass turbofans. The low bypass turbofan engine uses the bypassed air to increase the oxygen flow from fresh air flowing past the core of the engine. This airflow is remixed with the core flow and exits the engine from a common exhaust nozzle. This can be seen in Figure 3-3-14. When the afterburner or augmenter is employed and activated, the exhaust nozzle must open wider to allow the extra mass to flow through the engine. A variable exhaust nozzle is needed with an augmenter, because of the change in flow from the engine at intermediate power (just the engine) to full augmented power. A variable nozzle is shown in Figure 3-3-15.

Figure 3-3-15. A variable exhaust nozzle

Photo courtesy of Pratt & Whitney

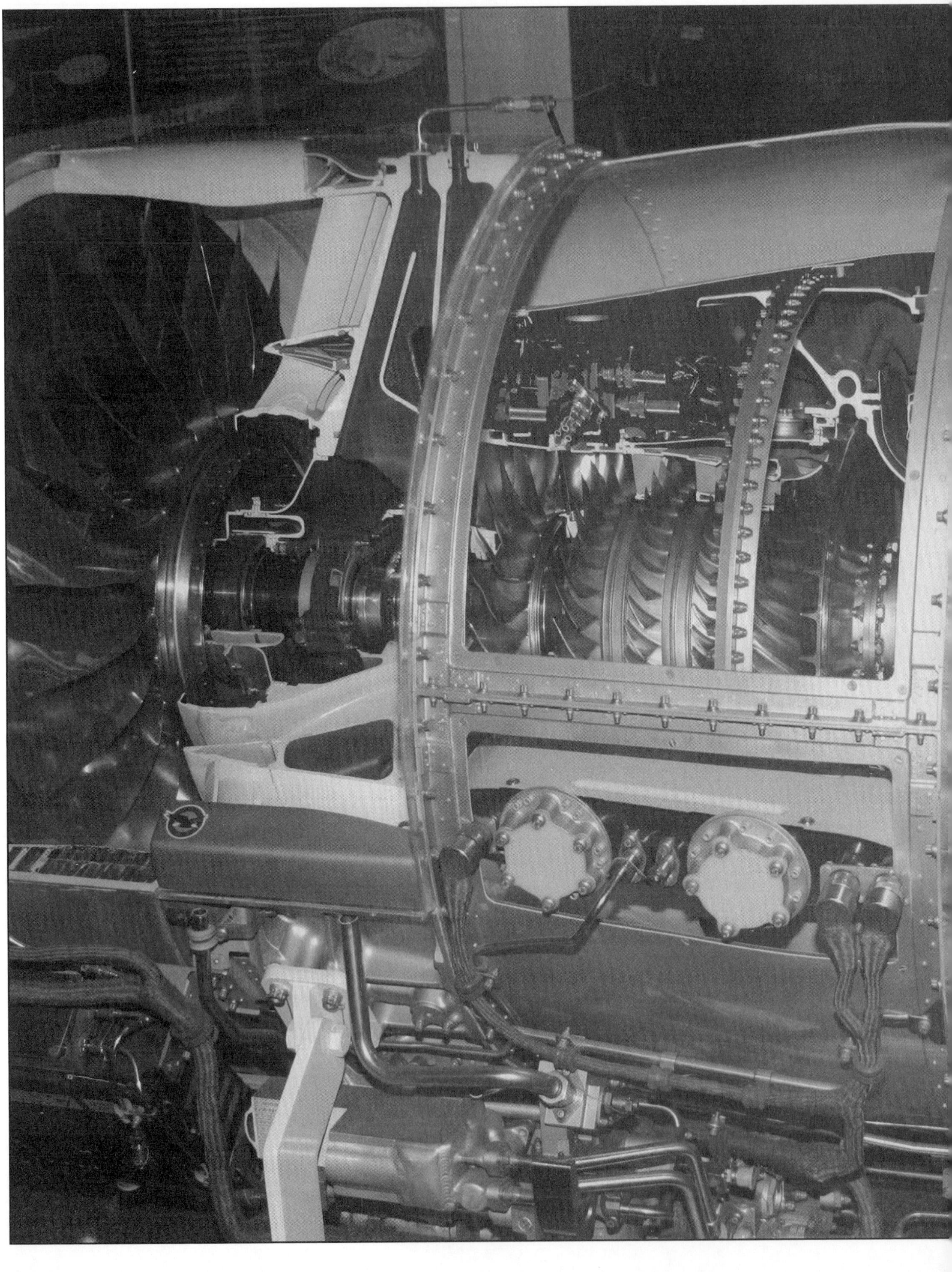

Chapter 4

TURBINE design

The study of gas turbine engines must include the details of each engine section and information on the materials used in its construction. Many of the specific alloys used are proprietary in nature. Engine manufacturers keep this information closely guarded. Still, the many different types of materials used will be discussed in this chapter. Factors such as strength, light weight, heat resistance and fatigue life are just some of the important considerations when selecting materials. Along with materials, this chapter will also discuss the nomenclature of the components that make up each section.

Learning Objectives:

- *Construction Materials*
- *Engine Inlets*
- *Compressor Section*
- *Combustion Section*
- *Turbine Blades*
- *Exhaust Section*
- *Noise and Emissions*
- *Accessory Gearboxes*

Section 1

Turbine Engine Construction Materials

Gas turbine engines are constructed of a variety of materials. Much work has been done to integrate the lightest materials into engine designs. The development of advanced materials for aircraft gas turbines continues to be directed at improving materials for both the fan and compressor (low temperature) section and the turbine (high temperature) section of the engine.

The type of material used is related to the amount of heat and load the parts will be subjected to. Among metals, aluminum is less dense than most other metals. Since weight savings are very important in engine design, the search for stronger, lighter and more heat-resistant materials is ongoing.

The cold section of the engine consists of the inlet, compressor and diffuser sections. It contains many different materials such as alumi-

Left: Today's turbine engine is a sophisticated machine that uses aerodynamics, advanced metallurgy and complex manufacturing techniques.

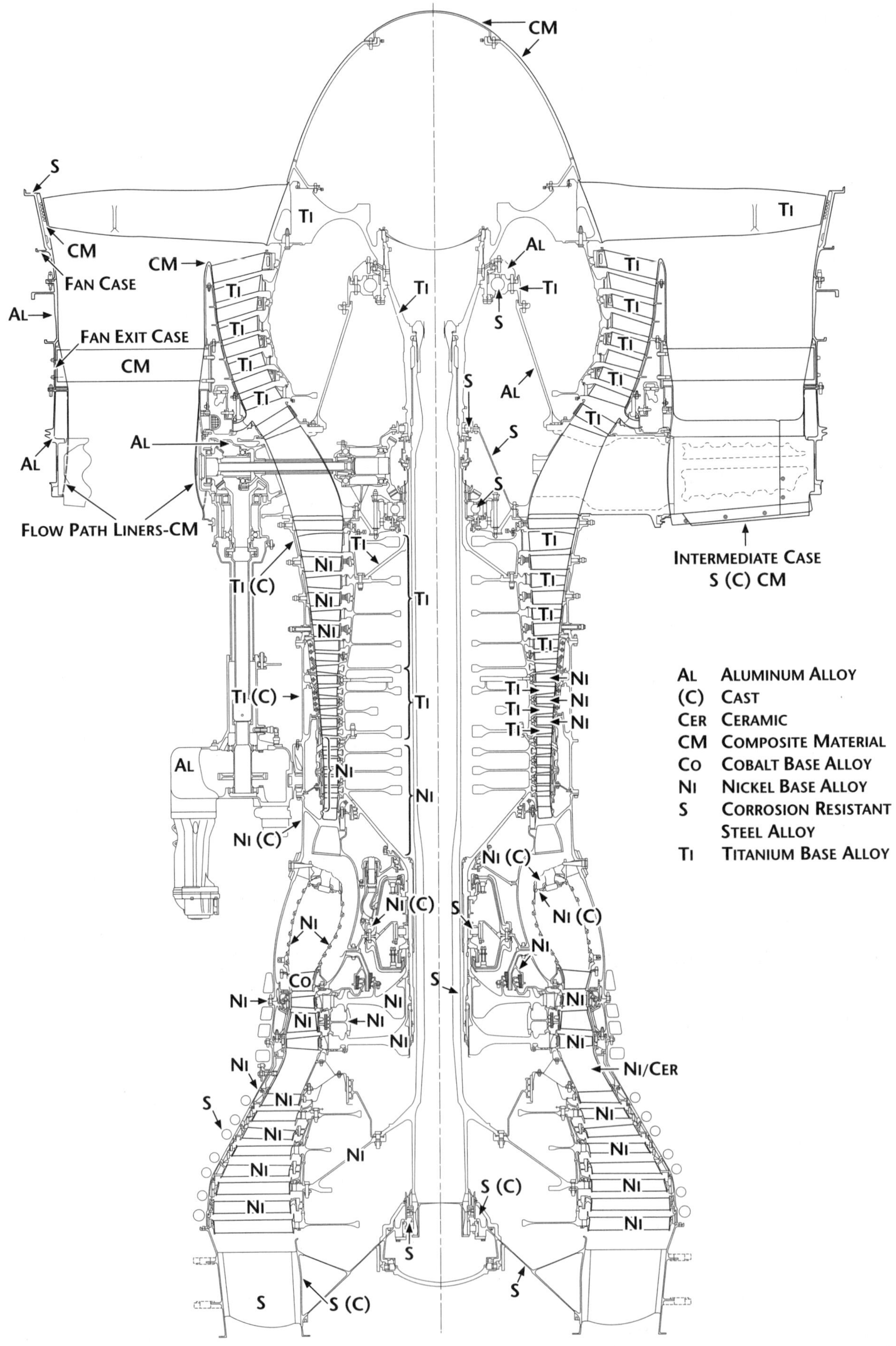

Figure 4-1-1. Engines are made from a variety of metals

num, composite materials (graphite-Kevlar), abradable plastics and—in the rear parts of the compressor—titanium. Toward the rear of the compressor, air temperatures and loads increase, requiring alloy steel. In the highest temperature areas of the compressor system, titanium and nickel-based alloys are used.

Compressor vanes are stationary and are placed after a rotor section in the compressor. These are constructed of nickel-steel-based alloys that have high fatigue strength against ingestion damage.

The mix of materials used for aircraft gas turbine construction has seen a significant increase in the amounts of titanium and nickel alloys used. It took some time for adequate development of titanium alloys to allow their substantial use in aircraft engines. This is shown in Figure 4-1-1. The use of nickel-based alloys has also greatly increased; most are used for turbine airfoils. Titanium-alloy-based, metal-matrix composites (MMCs) offer very low densities combined with very high strength and stiffness. Components in which this technology may be applied include supercritical shafts, very high speed fan/compressor disks and high-flow/high-temperature impellers.

Abradable seals are used in both compressor and turbine sections to minimize blade tip clearances or parasitic leakages in rotating seals. Extensive evaluations have been performed to identify materials suitable for use: plasma-sprayed metal or blended metal/nonmetal powders for abradable seals. New materials with higher temperature capability and improved durability are always in development.

Early development of disk materials has been driven by the need for high temperature strength and cyclic stress capability. As alloy development progressed, alloy content increased, resulting in alloys that were less forgeable and prone to alloy segregation.

Segregation and forgeability problems led to the introduction of powder metallurgy and isothermal forging as opposed to conventional cast and wrought processing. The materials that show the most promise are silicon carbide and silicon nitride. Metal powder components are formed in dies which use heat and pressure to form the components. These engine components will require less machining after the forming process.

One of the most common methods for forming powdered metallurgy components is hot isostatic pressing (HIP). This process uses extreme heat and pressure to form engine components which are very close to the finished dimensions. The most common use for this process is in making turbine disks. Low-pressure turbine blades are nickel alloy. This alloy has significantly higher temperature capability than other alloys and has adequate corrosion resistance.

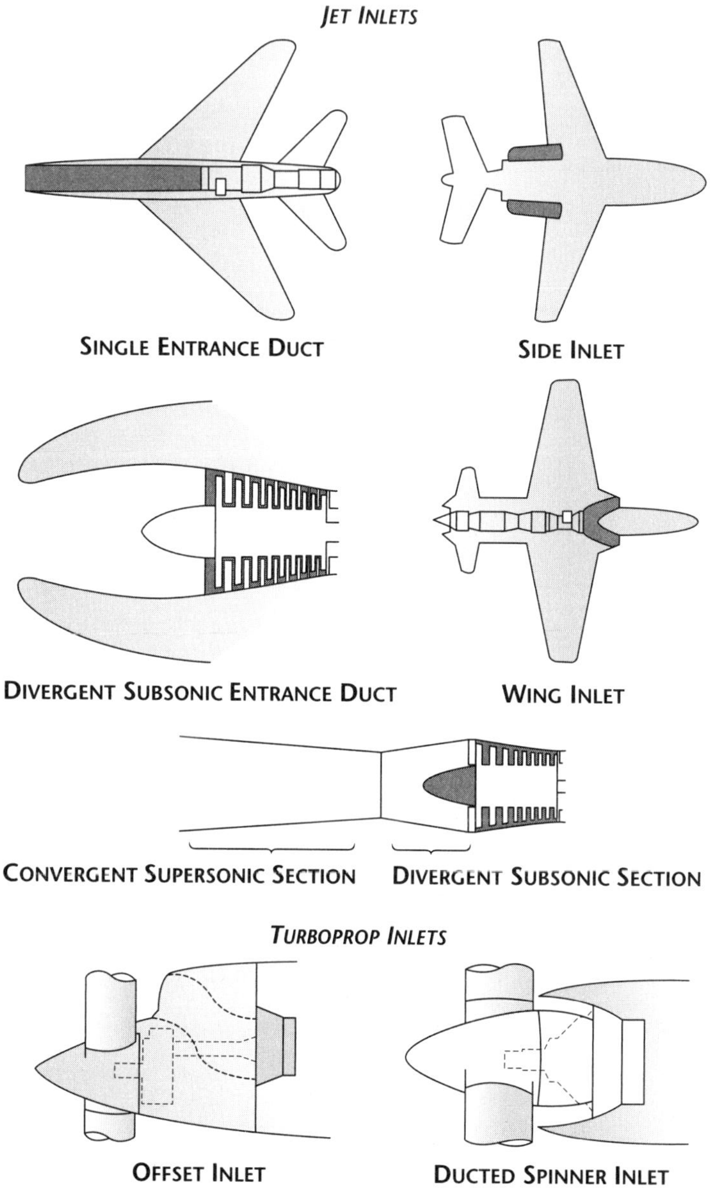

Figure 4-2-1. Engine inlets are optimized for the specific application.

Section 2

Engine Inlets

The air entrance is designed to conduct incoming air to the compressor with a minimum energy loss or distortion of the flow. The inlet flow should be free of turbulence to attain maximum efficiency during operation. Proper design of the inlet air duct is a major factor with regard to the ratio of compressor outlet pressure to duct inlet pressure. The quantity of air passing into the engine is dependent on

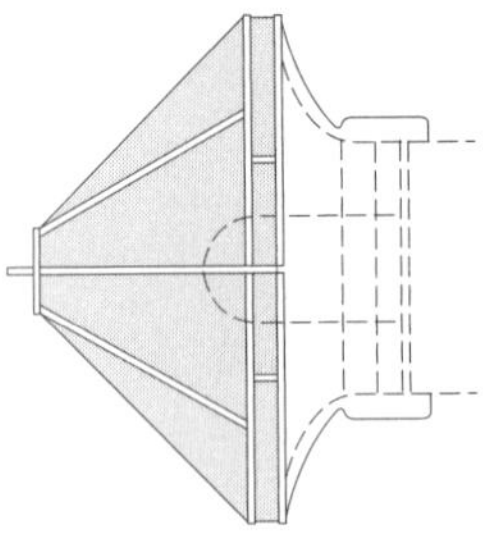

Figure 4-2-2. A bellmouth inlet cowl is used in a test cell to optimize airflow into the engine.

the compressor speed (r.p.m.), aircraft speed and the density of the ambient air. Generally, the modern inlet for turbofan engines is a short inlet cowl that is used to attain ram pressure by the air trapped in the air intake by aircraft speed. Several types of air intakes are explained below. Each is based on the requirements of the aircraft and the engine installation.

Subsonic inlets. Most aircraft, including large airliners, operate at less than the speed of sound. The inlet cowl forms the outside front of the nacelle. The inside of the inlet forms the airflow inlet duct into the engine. There are several different uses for gas turbine engines, but all use some type of inlet before the actual engine. This inlet directs airflow into the engine.

Figure 4-2-3. The inlet cowl for a large turbofan engine is a complex design.

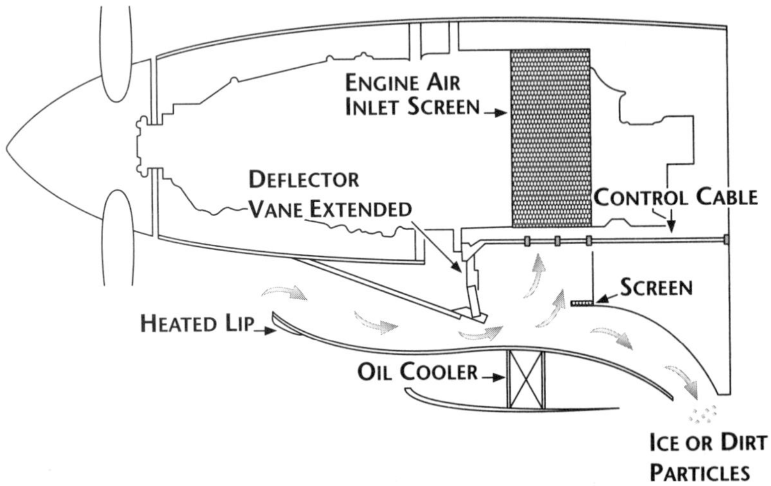

Figure 4-2-4. A PT6 engine inlet with a heated lip anti-icing boot.

The inlet is positioned upstream of the compressor and can have a strong influence on engine performance and net thrust. As shown in Figure 4-2-1, inlets come in a variety of shapes and sizes, with the specifics dictated by the speed of the aircraft.

An inlet commonly used in test cells is the bellmouth, which is shown in Figure 4-2-2. This type of inlet is used when the engine is tested in a static condition (in a test cell facility). The curved opening is used to promote smooth airflow into the engine and to make the diameter of the inside of the bellmouth 100% effective area. This allows for pressure measurements to be accurately taken in the inlet during testing. Without the curved opening on the front of the bellmouth, the inlet opening would have a square edge that would distort the airflow and inlet pressures would not be able to be taken accurately.

Each type of gas turbine engine has requirements that dictate the inlet's shape and component parts. The turbofan engine often uses an inlet cowling bolted to the front flange of the engine (A flange). This inlet cowl uses engine-bleed air to anti-ice the inlet. If ice is allowed to build up in the inlet, it distorts the airflow and could also break off (FOD) and damage the engine.

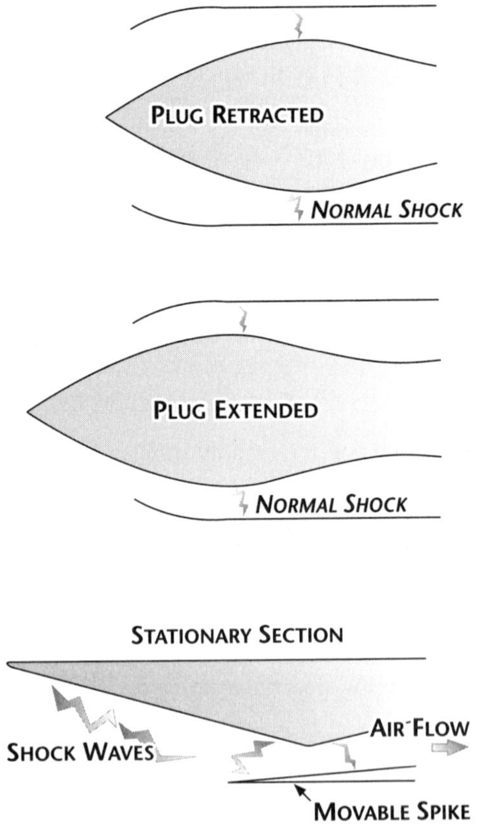

Figure 4-2-5. Supersonic inlets use a movable central cone or spike to control the speed of the air entering the engine.

The inlet cowl also helps reduce engine noise. The tips of the fan blades rotate close to an abradable strip that sets the tip clearances between the fan blades and the inlet cowl. A typical inlet cowl for a large turbofan engine can be seen in Figure 4-2-3. Another type of inlet used with turboprop aircraft incorporates a deflector door that can be extended on the ground to prevent dirt and debris from entering the engine. This type of inlet is generally anti-iced by an electric boot that attaches to the inlet lip and prevents ice build up, as shown in Figure 4-2-4.

Supersonic inlets. Inlets for supersonic aircraft have a relatively thin inlet lip. The inlet lip is sharpened to minimize the performance losses from shock waves that occur during supersonic flight. For a supersonic aircraft, the inlet must slow the flow down to subsonic speeds before the air reaches the compressor. Some supersonic inlets, like the ones shown in Figure 4-2-5, use a central cone or spike to reduce the flow down to subsonic speeds. Other inlets, like the one shown in Figure 4-2-6 use flat hinged plates to reduce the flow to subsonic speeds. This variable geometry inlet is typical of that used on many current fighter aircraft.

Hypersonic inlets. Inlets for hypersonic aircraft present the ultimate design challenge. For ramjet-powered aircraft, the inlet must bring the high speed external flow down to subsonic conditions in the combustion section. For scramjet-powered aircraft, the combustion environment is even worse because the flight Mach number is higher. Scramjet inlets are highly integrated with the fuselage of the aircraft.

Inlet characteristics. A gas turbine engine inlet should operate efficiently during all operational flight attitudes and aircraft speeds, even when the engine is static. At high speeds, the inlet must allow the aircraft to maneuver without disrupting airflow to the compressor. Because the inlet is so important to overall performance, it is usually designed and tested by the aircraft manufacturer.

The temperature in the inlet can vary slightly at different points on the air entry. This is why several inlet temperature probes are used on a bellmouth inlet during engine testing in a test cell. The total pressure (Pt) through the inlet changes because of flow effects.

The inlet's pressure performance ram recovery depends upon the aircraft speed. Inlet total pressure, which measures the ram and static pressure in the inlet, will recover as the aircraft speed is increased. As air molecules are packed into the inlet, the air becomes compressed and a certain amount of airflow is recovered. As aircraft speed increases, thrust will decrease some until enough air molecules are compressed into the inlet. The ram recovery depends on a wide variety of factors, including the shape of the inlet, the speed of the aircraft, the airflow demands of the engine and aircraft maneuvers.

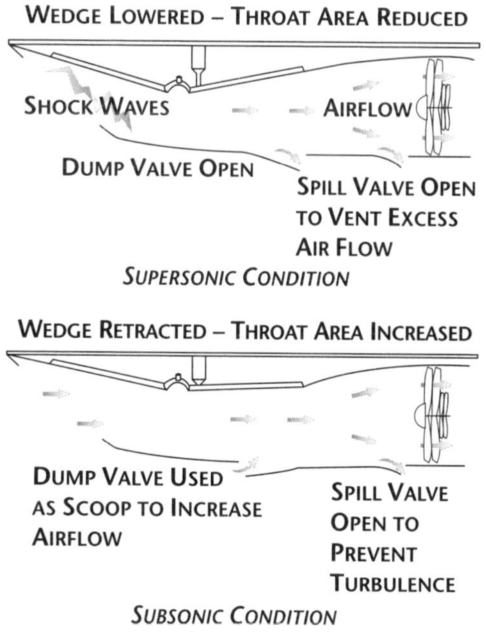

Figure 4-2-6. Some supersonic inlets use flat hinged panels to control the inlet air.

At supersonic flight speeds, there are additional losses created by the shock waves necessary to reduce the flow speed to subsonic conditions before entering the compressor. Another propulsion performance factor, which can decrease the inlet performance, is called spillage drag. Spillage drag occurs when an inlet allows air to flow around the outside of the inlet instead of flowing into the compressor. The quantity of airflow that bypasses the inlet is dependent upon aircraft attitude, altitude and throttle setting.

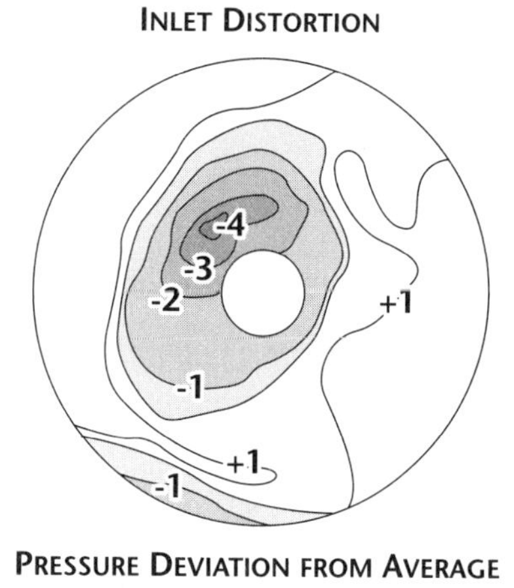

Figure 4-2-7. The pressure in the inlet is distorted by turbulence.

Figure 4-3-1. There are two types of compressors used in aircraft: (A) Axial and (B) Centrifugal

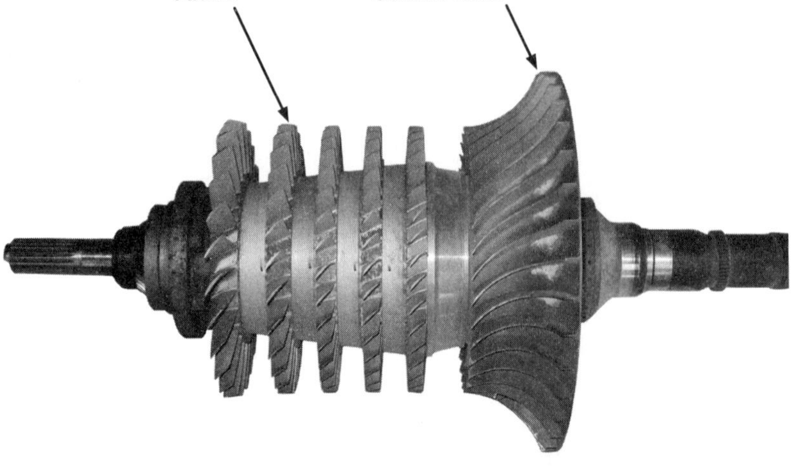

Figure 4-3-2. A combination compressor uses both axial and centrifugal elements.

The inlet is sized to allow the maximum airflow that the engine can absorb. The inlet bypasses (or allows the extra air to spill over the inlet lip) the actual engine airflow versus what the engine's maximum airflow would be at full power. As the airflows into the first stage of the compressor, the flow can be distorted due to turbulence from the inlet. At the first stage of the compressor, the flow may vary in velocity and pressure (inlet distortion) from one portion of the inlet area to another. This is shown in Figure 4-2-7.

As the distorted inlet flow encounters the compressor rotor blade, the flow conditions around the blade can change very quickly. The changing flow conditions can cause flow separation in the compressor which can cause other problems such as compressor stall. Compressor stall is described in Chapter 5. A high performance gas turbine engine inlet should produce high ram (pressure) recovery, low spillage drag and low inlet distortion.

Section 3

Compressor Section

Compressor performance has a substantial influence on total engine performance. The primary function of the compressor section of the turbine engine is to supply air in sufficient quantity to satisfy the requirements of the combustion section. Specifically, the compressor must increase the pressure of the mass of air received from the air inlet duct and then discharge it to the combustion section in the quantity and at the pressures required.

A secondary function of the compressor is to supply air for various purposes in the engine and aircraft. This is called user or customer air. Some of the current applications of user or customer bleed air are cabin pressurization, heating and cooling. It is also used for deicing and anti-icing systems and pneumatic engine starters.

The engine provides this bleed air for aircraft uses; it does not perform any engine function. The bleed-air is taken from any of the various pressure stages of the compressor. The exact locations of the bleed ports are dependent on the pressure or temperature required for a particular job. The bleed ports are openings in the compressor case adjacent to the particular stage from which the air is to be bled. Varying degrees of pressure or heat are available simply by tapping into the appropriate stage.

Air is often bled from the final or highest pressure stage since at this point pressure and air temperature are at a maximum. This is needed especially at engine idle speeds. At times it may be necessary to cool this high-pressure bleed air. This is done by an air to air heat exchanger, where fan air is passed through the exchanger to cool the hot bleed air. If bleed air is used for cabin pressurization, the air is sent through an air-conditioning package conditioning it for temperature before it flows into the passenger cabin.

The compressor section's location depends on the type of compressor or engine type. The two principal types of compressors are centrifugal and axial flow. Much use has been made of the terms centrifugal flow and axial flow to describe the engine and compressor. In fact, the terms are applicable to the flow of air through the compressor.

In some installations, as a part of the inlet nacelle, there are the auxiliary air-intake doors (blow-in doors). These blow-in doors admit air to the engine compartment during ground operation, when air requirements for the engine are in excess of the airflow through the inlet ducts. The doors are held closed by spring action when the engine is not operating. During operation the doors open automatically whenever engine compartment pressure drops below atmospheric pressure. During takeoff and flight, ram air pressure in the engine compartment aids the springs in holding the doors closed.

As shown in Figure 4-3-1, the two main types of compressors are axial and centrifugal. The axial compressor is so called because the flow travels through the compressor parallel to the axis of rotation. The centrifugal compressor is turned perpendicular to the axis of rotation.

Centrifugal compressors, which were used in the early gas turbine engines, are still used in smaller turbine applications. Many APUs, turboprops and turboshaft engines use centrifugal compressors because of the high per stage pressure ratio. Modern large turbofan engines use axial compressors and large fans as the first stage. Some gas turbine engines use a combination of axial and centrifugal, with multiple axial stages before the single stage centrifugal compressor. This type of compressor is termed a combination compressor and can be seen in Figure 4-3-2.

A compressor stage is an increase in pressure, which generally consists of an impeller and diffuser (centrifugal), or a rotor blade and stator vane (axial). A single-stage of a centrifugal compressor can increase the pressure by as much as an 8:1 ratio. This means that if the inlet pressure is 14.7 p.s.i.a., then the output pressure would be eight times this pressure or 117.6 p.s.i.a. per stage. It is much more difficult to produce an efficient multistage centrifugal compressor because the flow has to be ducted back to the axis at each stage.

Figure 4-3-3. A fan disk used in a turbofan is a complex piece of equipment.

Centrifugal compressors normally only use two stages due to decreased efficiencies. Because the flow is turned perpendicular to the axis multiple times, an engine with a centrifugal compressor tends to have high turbulence losses.

One advantage of the axial compressor is the ability to link together several stages and produce a multi-stage axial compressor. For these reasons, most high performance, high compression turbine engines use multi-staged axial compressors. At some point efficiency is decreased by the number of stages in the compressor all turning at the same speed. To overcome this problem, two axial compressors are used inline with each other (low and high-pressure compressors).

Each compressor is turned by its own set of turbines connected through a shaft so each rotates at a different speed. By allowing each compressor (spool) to rotate at its optimum speed range, the engine's efficiency is increased. A single-stage axial compressor usually increases the pressure from each stage by 1.25:1 to 1.3:1. In the multistage axial compressor, the pressure is multiplied from each rotor-stator combination (10 stages at 1.25 per stage would provide a 12.5:1 compression ratio). If the inlet pressure is 14.7 p.s.i.a. then the resulting outlet pressure would be 12.5 x 14.7 p.s.i.a. or 183.75 p.s.i.a.

Turbofan engine fans. The typical fan consists of a set of fan blades mounted to a fan disk. The fan disc supports the fan blades during operation. The fan and low-pressure compressor are housed in the fan case which is constructed of aluminum or composite material. The case is surrounded by several layers of Kevlar to prevent any uncontained fan blade failure.

The inlet cone is an aerodynamic fairing that helps to cause a smooth airflow into the engine. Some are made of composite material and others are metal.

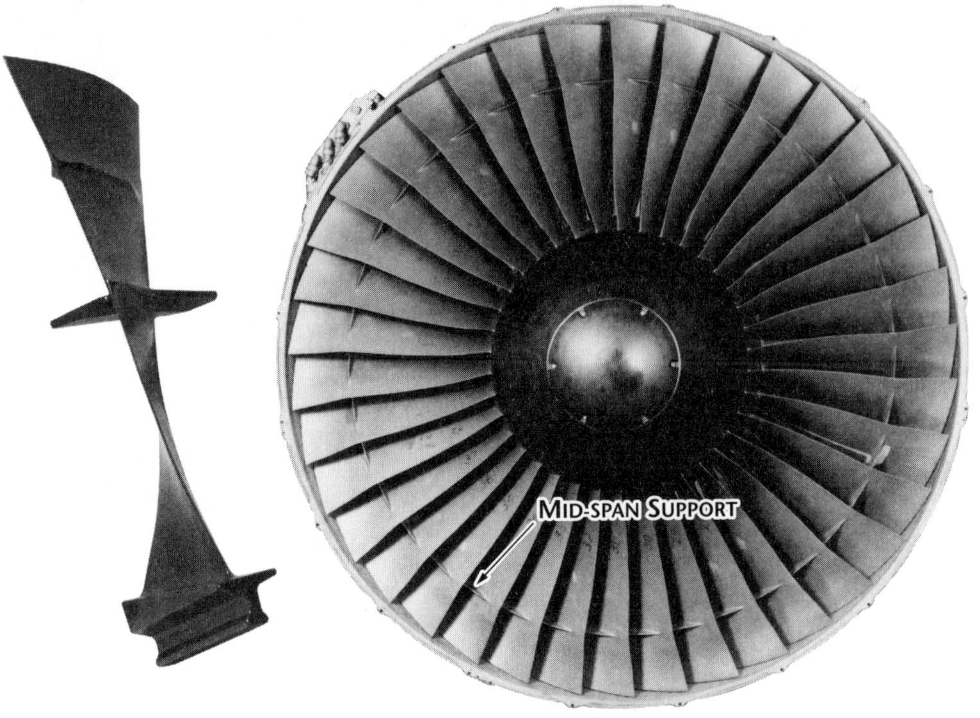

Figure 4-3-4. Using a mid-span support prevents aerodynamic instability in long blades.

Figure 4-3-5. Wide chord titanium blade construction features

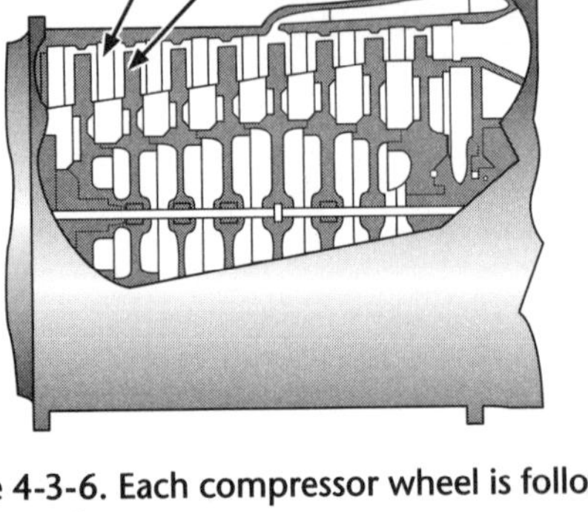

Figure 4-3-6. Each compressor wheel is followed by a row of stator vanes.

Fan disks are commonly made of titanium alloy and can be seen in Figure 4-3-3. The fan disk is connected to the fan shaft as well as the low-pressure turbines which make up the low-pressure spool.

Most modern high bypass ratio turbofan gas turbine engines use fan blades that are constructed from titanium or composite materials. A low weight fan blade is necessary because the front structure of the engine must be able to withstand the large out-of-balance forces that would result from a fan blade failure.

Titanium blades are machined from a solid titanium forging. In order to minimize the weight of each individual blade, long blades require a short chord (blade width). With this design, a mid-span support is needed to prevent aerodynamic instability. This is shown in Figure 4-3-4.

The diameter of many modern fans has increased to about 10 feet. Titanium blades are difficult to manufacture with both large surface area and light weight. This disadvantage has been overcome with the introduction of the wide chord fan blades; aerodynamic stability is provided by the increased chord of the blade, thus avoiding the need for mid-span supports.

Aerodynamically efficient hollow fan blades with advanced fan designs typically have much longer chords (wider blades) than older technology designs. Fabricating such advanced designs of solid titanium alloys would result in unacceptably heavy blades. Newer, wide cord titanium fan blade designs use rolled titanium panels assembled in dies with the aerodynamic shape formed in a furnace.

Chemical milling is used to remove material in the center of the panels where the honeycomb or expansion braces are placed. A diffusion bonding process is used in automated furnaces to join the panels together. The disk and blades must have a high defect tolerance and be able to accept the applied load. A wide cord fan blade construction is shown in Figure 4-3-5.

Composite technology is also used in low-temperature components such as fan ducts, nacelles and some fan blades. Some composite fan blades can be constructed from epoxy and graphite fibers with a metal leading edge.

The fan blades are installed in dovetail slots on the disk that hold the blades radially. A split ring blade lock and an anti-rotation pin on some engines hold the blades axially. Aft of the fan and its exit vanes, the low-pressure compressor usually has a few compressor stages before the airflow enters the high-pressure compressor. Airflow is separated into fan and core (gas generator) flow aft of the fan.

The blades are balanced by moment weighing during installation and by dynamic balancing after installation. A rubber seal below the blade platforms provides a seal between blades as shown in Figure 4-3-3. Fan blades are normally line replaceable. In a multi-spool engine, the spools turn independent of each other and consist of a high-pressure (N_2) and low-pressure spool (N_1). The fan is included in the low-pressure spool in most arrangements. The exception to this is the Rolls-Royce Trent series which has three spools.

Most large turbofan engines use a multiple spool design because it allows each spool to operate at a more efficient speed. An engine that has separate spools will have the engine speed set by the gas generator (N_2) through the fuel control system. This allows it to operate closer to its design point and its best inlet conditions. The low-pressure spool (N_1) will follow or lag behind the high-pressure spool. The low-pressure compressor will vary its speed according to changes in gas generator speed, the aircraft inlet, air density and flight maneuvers.

Axial compressors. An axial flow compressor uses a series of rotating blades and a series of stationary vanes that direct the airflow through the compressor gas path. The blades rotate around the axis of the compressor. In the axial compressor, cascades of small airfoils (compressor blades) are mounted on a disk (a drum-like structure) that is connected to a shaft that turns at a high rate of speed. Each compressor wheel (a disk with several blades attached), shown in Figure 4-3-6, is followed by a row of stator vanes.

Several rows, or stages, are usually used to produce a high compressor pressure ratio (CPR), with each stage producing a small pressure increase. Each stage consists of a rotor blade and a stator vane. The rotor blades accelerate the air and the stator increases pressure and directs the air into the next stage. By using multiple stages, the axial compressor can produce high CPR, which is one main advantage of the axial compressor.

Stages are numbered sequentially starting from the front of the engine or the fan. Sometimes a stage is added after the initial design. These stages are generally labeled by decimals. An example would be 1, 1.5, 2 and so on. These blades impel air rearward in the same manner as a propeller because of their angle and airfoil contour.

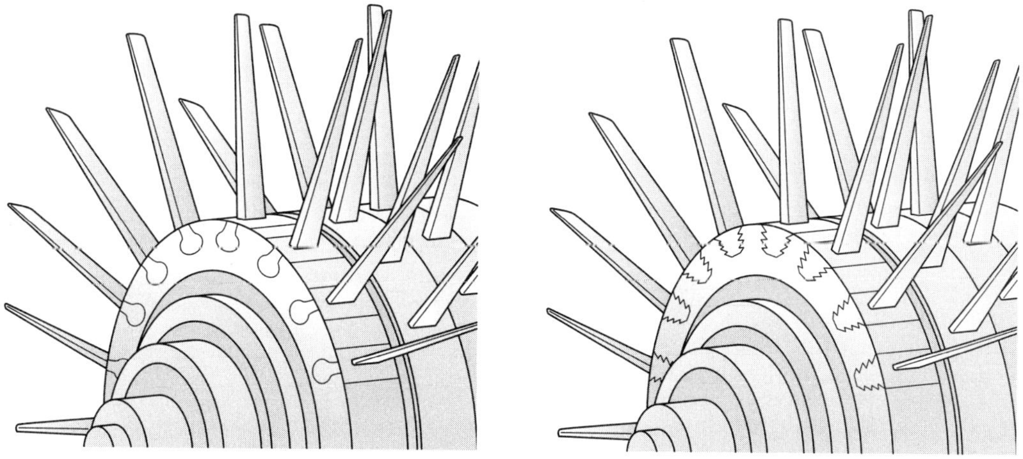

(A) (B)

Figure 4-3-7. Common retention methods used on compressor rotor blades: (A) Bulb root (B) Fir-tree

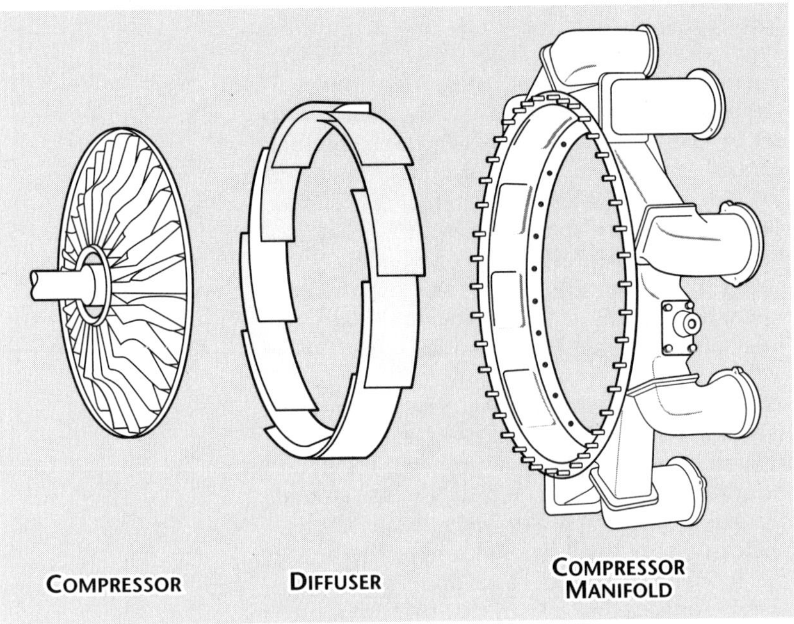

Figure 4-3-8. A centrifugal compressor

The rotor, turning at high speed, takes in air at the compressor inlet and impels it through a series of stages. The action of the rotor increases the compression of the air at each stage and accelerates it rearward through several stages. With this increased velocity, energy is transferred from the compressor to the air in the form of velocity energy. The stator blades act as diffusers at each stage, partially converting high velocity to pressure. Each consecutive pair of rotor and stator blades constitutes a pressure stage. The number of rows of blades and stator vanes (stages) is determined by the amount of air and total pressure rise required. The greater the number of compression stages, the higher the compression ratio.

Most present-day engines utilize from 10 to 16 stages. The stator has rows of vanes, dovetailed into split rings, which are in turn attached inside an enclosing case. The stator vanes project radially toward the rotor axis and fit closely on either side of each stage of the rotor.

A number of engines are designed with a compressor case that is split horizontally. Either the upper or lower half may be removed for inspection or maintenance of rotor and stator blades.

The vanes have two functions: they receive air from the air inlet duct or from each preceding stage of the compressor and deliver it to the next stage or to the burners at a workable velocity and pressure. They also control the direction of air to each rotor stage to obtain the maximum possible compressor blade efficiency. This arrangement is shown in Figure 4-3-6.

The rotor blades are usually preceded by an inlet guide vane assembly. The guide vanes direct the airflow into the first stage rotor blades at the proper angle. This improves the aerodynamic characteristics of the compressor by reducing the drag on the first-stage rotor blades. The inlet guide vanes are curved steel vanes usually welded to steel inner and outer shrouds.

At the discharge end of the compressor, the stator vanes are designed to straighten the airflow, eliminating turbulence. These vanes are called either straightening vanes or yhe outlet vane assembly and are part of the diffuser. The casings of axial-flow compressors not only support the stator vanes but also provide the outer wall for the axial path of the airflow. The stator vanes are made of steel with corrosion- and erosion-resistant qualities. Quite frequently they are shrouded (enclosed) by a band of suitable material to simplify installation. The vanes are welded into the shrouds.

Rotor blades are made of stainless steel. Methods of attaching the blades in the rotor disk rims vary in different designs, but they are commonly fitted into disks by either bulb-type of fir-tree-type roots (see Figure 4-3-7). The blades are then locked by means of screws, peening, locking wires, pins, or keys.

Compressor blade tips are reduced in thickness by cutouts, referred to as blade profiles. These profiles prevent serious damage to the blade or housing should the blades contact the compressor housing. This condition can occur if rotor blades become excessively loose or if rotor support is reduced by a malfunctioning bearing. Some times the tips are called squealer tip because of the noise they make when rubbing.

Even though blade profiles greatly reduce such possibilities, occasionally a blade may break under stress of rubbing and cause considerable damage to compressor blades and stator vane assemblies. The compressor blades vary in length from entry to discharge because

Figure 4-3-9. The vanes of a centrifugal compressor are carefully machined to achieve optimum efficiency.

the annular working space (blade length) is reduced progressively toward the rear of the compressor. This allows for even air velocity through the compressor.

Centrifugal compressors. The compressor, shown in Figure 4-3-8, is called a centrifugal compressor because the flow through the compressor is turned perpendicular to the axis of rotation and centrifugal force is used to accelerate the airflow. Centrifugal compressors perform work by increasing the pressure and temperature of the airflow.

Computational mathematical models are used to determine the design and performance of a centrifugal compressor. The CPR characterizes the performance across the compressor. Other performance factors include the rotational speed of the shaft necessary to produce the pressure increase and an efficiency factor that indicates how much additional work is required relative to an ideal compressor.

In the centrifugal compressor, the pressure increase results from accelerating the airflow radially from the center of the compressor. The air is accelerated by centrifugal force using the vanes of the centrifugal compressor, which can be seen in Figure 4-3-9. The air then flows into the diffuser, which is a divergent duct increasing pressure. This type of compressor has a high-pressure rise per stage, which is one of the advantages of using a centrifugal compressor.

The power to drive the compressor is from the compressor turbine or gas generator turbine(s), which is connected to the compressor by a shaft.

As the air passes through the compressor, it gains heat. This places temperature limits on the types of materials that are used in the compressor section. Engine performance has a direct relationship to the amount of pressure the compressor can deliver. The temperature at the exit of the compressor becomes a limiting design factor and affects the engine's overall performance.

Some centrifugal compressors are able to bring in airflow from both sides. This compressor is called a double or dual entry compressor, as shown in Figure 4-3-10. In the centrifugal-flow engine, the compressor achieves its purpose by picking up the entering air and accelerating it outwardly by centrifugal action. In the axial-flow engine, the air is compressed while continuing in its original direction of flow, thus avoiding the energy loss caused by turns. The centrifugal-flow compressor consists basically of an impeller (rotating), a diffuser (stationary) and a compressor manifold, (see Figure 4-3-8).

The two main functional elements are the impeller and the diffuser. Although the diffuser is a separate unit and is placed inside and bolted to the manifold, the entire assembly (diffuser and manifold) is often referred to as the diffuser. For clarification during compressor familiarization, these units are treated individually. The impeller is usually made from titanium or forged aluminum alloy, heat-treated, machined and smoothed for minimum flow restriction and turbulence.

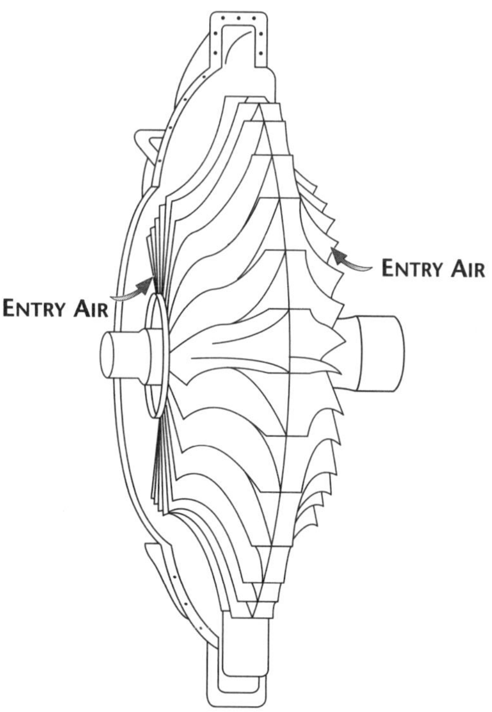

Figure 4-3-10. A double-entry compressor

The impeller, whose function is to pick up and accelerate the air outward to the diffuser, may be either single-entry or double-entry. Both are similar in construction to the reciprocating engine supercharger impeller, the double-entry type is similar to two impellers back to back. However, because of the much greater combustion air requirements in turbojet engines, the impellers are larger.

The principal differences between the two types of impellers are the size and the ducting arrangement. The double-entry type has a smaller diameter, but is usually operated at a higher rotational speed to assure sufficient airflow. The single-entry impeller permits the air to be ducted to the impeller eye (inducer vanes) as opposed to the more complicated ducting necessary to reach the rear side of the double-entry type.

Although slightly more efficient in receiving air, the single-entry impeller must have a large diameter to deliver the same quantity of air as the double-entry type. This increases the overall diameter of the engine. Double-entry centrifugal compressors are used with auxiliary power units.

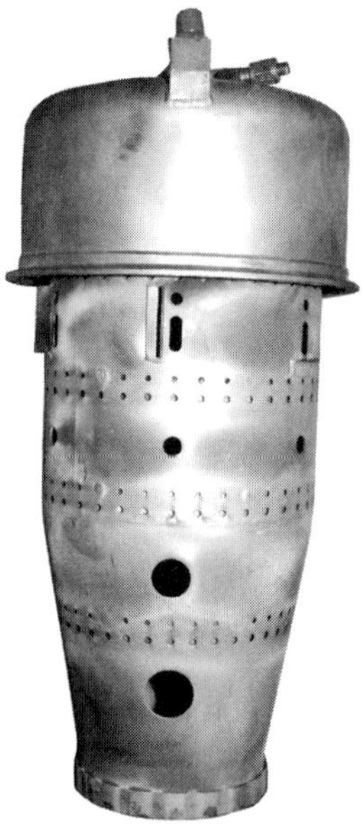

Figure 4-4-1. A can-type combustion chamber

The Diffuser

The diffuser for a typical gas-turbine engine is that portion of the air passage between the compressor and the combustion chamber or chambers. The purpose of the diffuser is to reduce the velocity of the air and prepare it for entry to the combustion area. As the diffuser forms a divergent duct, the air velocity decreases, its static pressure increases in accordance with Bernoulli's law. As the static pressure increases, the ram pressure decreases. The diffuser is the point of highest pressure within the engine.

The diffuser is an annular chamber provided with a number of vanes forming a series of divergent passages into the manifold. The diffuser vanes direct the flow of air from the impeller to the manifold at an angle designed to retain the maximum amount of energy imparted by the impeller. These vanes also deliver the air to the manifold at a velocity and pressure satisfactory for use in the combustion chambers.

The compressor manifold shown in Figure 4-3-8 diverts the flow of air from the diffuser, which is an integral part of the manifold, into the combustion chambers. The manifold will have one outlet port for each chamber so that the air is evenly divided. A compressor outlet elbow is bolted to each of the outlet ports. These air outlets are constructed in the form of ducts and are known by a variety of names, such as air outlet ducts, outlet elbows, or combustion chamber inlet ducts. Regardless of the terminology used, these ducts perform a very important part of the diffusion process; they change the radial direction of the airflow to an axial direction, where the diffusion process is completed after the turn. To help the elbows perform this function in an efficient manner, turning vanes are sometimes fitted inside the elbows. These vanes reduce air pressure losses by presenting a smooth turning surface. Many different types of diffusers are used depending upon the type of gas turbine engine.

Section 4

Combustion Section

Turbine engines have a combustion section, or burner, in which the fuel is combined with about 25% of the total airflow in the core or gas generator and then burned. The resulting high temperature and expanding exhaust gas are used to drive the turbine sections that produce mechanical power to turn the compressors. Depending upon the type of engine, the exhaust gases are used either to produce thrust when passed through a nozzle or to drive extra turbines that turn a shaft, propeller, or fan.

There are three types of combustors which are found in gas turbines:

- Can-type
- Can-annular type
- Annular type

Can-type combustion chamber. The can combustion section, seen in Figure 4-4-1, is an older style. It was the first type of combustion section on earlier engines. The basic design

Figure 4-4-2. A can-annular combustion chamber

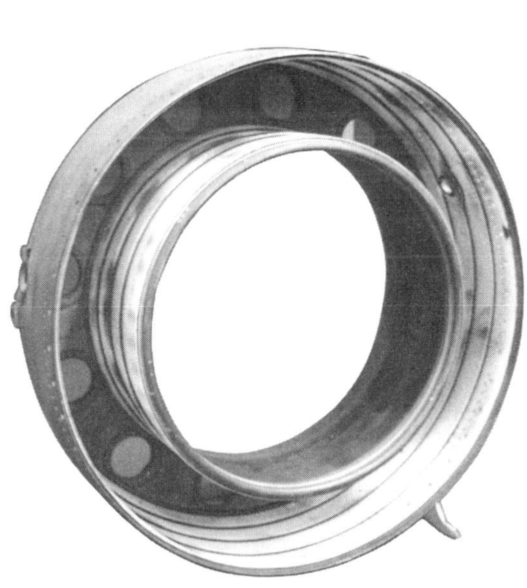

Figure 4-4-3. An annular combustion chamber

resembles a can, hence the name. This type did not offer the most efficient combustion for flight engines. The can combustion chamber is still used in APUs and in some turboshaft engines.

Can-annular combustion chamber. A compromise design is shown in Figure 4-4-2. This is a can-annular design, in which the casing is annular and the liner is can-shaped. The advantage of the can-annular design over the can design is that the individual cans are more easily serviced. Each burner section has both a liner and a casing and the cans are arranged around the shaft that connects the compressor and turbine.

Annular combustion chamber. Most modern engines use the annular type. The combustion section, shown in Figure 4-4-3, is an annular combustor with the two liners extended radially, one inside the other. One end is closed and generally holds the fuel nozzles. The other end is open to allow the hot expanding gases to enter the turbine section. The operation of a gas turbine engine combustion section is shown in Figure 4-4-4.

The combustion section is located between the compressor section and the turbine(s). The compressor-turbine central shaft that connects the turbine and compressor passes through the inside liner of the burner section.

Burner linings are made from materials that can withstand the high temperatures of combustion. A burner lining usually has holes at the closed end (fuel nozzle end). This allows the airflow to be slowed by swirl vanes, providing maximum mixing of the fuel and air to improve the combustion process. This mixing and burning of fuel is complex and requires extensive research to accomplish complete combustion and prevent overheating of the liner.

Combustion Process

The combustion process dramatically increases the temperature of the airflow, with only a slight decrease in pressure. The velocity of the airflow is decreased in the area of the flame where combustion is taking place. This allows the combustion process to take place and assists in more complete burning of the fuel. The pressure in the burner remains nearly constant during operation, decreasing by only a small percentage as the airflow passes through the combustion section.

Only about 25% of the airflow is used in combustion; the other 75% is used for cooling the sides of the liner and for dilution of combustion gases before they enter the turbine section. Swirl vanes and cooling holes are shown in Figure 4-4-5. The liner is often perforated to enhance cooling, with louvers directing the cooling airflow around the inside of the liner. This prevents the flame of combustion from making direct contact with the liner wall. (If the flame were allowed

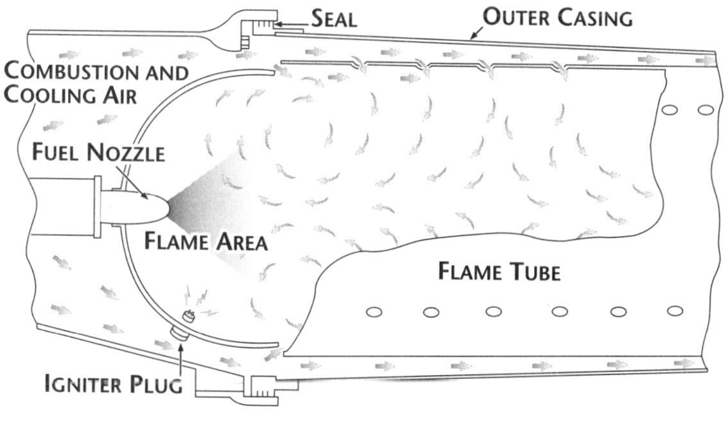

Figure 4-4-4. The operation of a gas turbine combustion section.

Figure 4-4-5. Swirl vanes and cooling holes

Figure 4-5-1. Typical turbine inlet guide vanes

to contact the liner wall, it would quickly burn holes and cause cracks in the liner).

In the burner, heat is released in the combustion process. The specific total enthalpy, or internal energy of the gas, is the fuel to air mass flow ratio. The heat release depends on the particular fuel that is being burned. An efficiency factor is also applied to account for losses during burning. The enthalpy is equal to the specific heat coefficient at constant pressure multiplied by the temperature.

The compressor and the external flow conditions determine the entrance temperature of the burner. In engine operation, we can set the fuel flow rate that determines the fuel/air ratio and sets the temperature ratio in the burner. The burner temperature ratio and pressure ratio determine a value for the engine temperature ratio. The engine pressure ratio can, in turn, determine the theoretical engine thrust.

It would seem that making the temperature ratio higher would result in as much thrust as possible, simply by increasing the fuel flow rate and the fuel/air ratio. The combustion process sets limits on the fuel/air ratio during engine operation. There is a maximum burner exit temperature, which is determined by the material limits of the turbine inlet guide vanes. If the engine is operated at a temperature higher than this maximum temperature, the burner and the turbine will be damaged. For this reason it is very important to monitor the temperature limits of the engine.

Most combustors are constructed of nickel-based or cobalt-based alloys. Thermal-barrier coatings (TBC) are used in many combustor designs. Typical TBCs are ceramic fiber reinforced materials applied to very high-temperature areas of the combustors. The higher the combustion temperature, the more efficient the burner and engine will be overall. Ceramic coated turbine components are used for combustors, turbine vanes and turbine blades. The most promising TBC materials are silicon carbide and silicon nitride.

Section 5

Turbine Section

The turbine section of a gas turbine engine is downstream of the combustion chamber and the gas flow path goes directly from the combustion chamber outlet into the turbine section. The turbine section transforms the kinetic (velocity) energy of the exhaust gases into mechanical energy to drive the compressor and engine accessories. The compressor turbine(s) (also called the high-pressure turbine) drives the compressor of the gas generator. This function absorbs approximately $^2/_3$ of the total energy from the exhaust gases.

Depending on the engine type, there may be multiple turbine stages used in the engine. The turbine assembly consists of two basic components—the turbine inlet guide vane and the turbine blade. As with the compressor, vanes are stationary and blades rotate. Turbine inlet guide vanes are known by a variety of names such as turbine nozzle vanes, turbine inlet guide vanes and turbine nozzle diaphragms. The turbine nozzle vanes are located directly aft of the combustion chambers and immediately forward of the first stage turbine wheel.

Inlet guide vanes. The function of the turbine inlet guide vanes is twofold. First, after the combustion chamber has introduced the heat energy into the mass airflow and delivered it evenly to the turbine nozzles, it becomes the function of the nozzles to prepare the mass airflow for driving the turbine rotor. Figure 4-5-1 illustrates typical turbine inlet guide vanes. The stationary vanes of the turbine inlet guide vanes (nozzles)

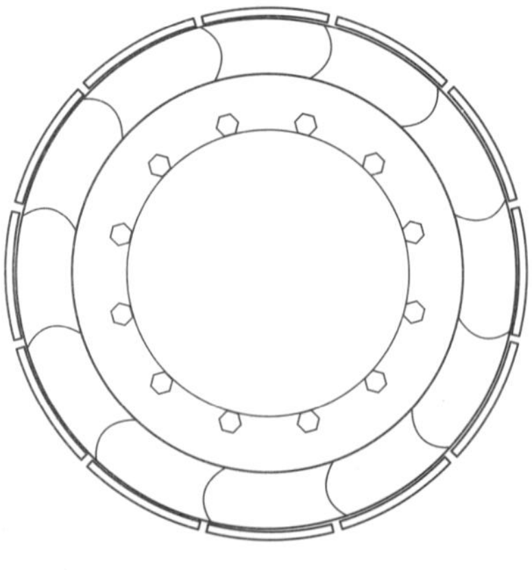

Figure 4-5-2. Single turbine vane of grouped turbine vanes

Figure 4-5-3. A turbine shaft and wheel

are contoured and set at such an angle that they form a number of small nozzles. Discharging the gas at extremely high speed, the nozzle converts a varying portion of the heat and pressure energy to velocity energy. This energy can be converted to mechanical energy through the turbine rotor blades and disk.

The second purpose of the turbine inlet guide vanes is to deflect the exhaust gases into the turbine wheel at a specific angle. Since the gas flow from the turbine inlet guide vanes creates force on the turbine blade, it is essential to aim the exhaust gases in the direction of the turbine blades in such a manner that the blades absorb the force from the flow of gases.

Nozzle assembly. The turbine nozzle assembly consists of an inner shroud and an outer shroud between which are fixed the turbine inlet guide vanes. The number of turbine inlet guide vanes varies with different types and sizes of engines. Although the actual turbine inlet guide vane will vary slightly in its configuration and con-

Figure 4-5-4. There must be clearances between the turbine blades and the shroud to allow for thermal expansion.

struction features, there is one characteristic common to all turbine section components.

This common characteristic is that the first stage of turbine inlet guide vanes is subjected to the highest (hottest) temperatures in the engine. This is where hot gases actually come into contact with the metal components of the engine. Turbine inlet guide vanes must be constructed from materials that are very heat resistant. High temperatures and temperature gradients can cause severe distortion, burning, cracking or warping of the metal components. To allow for thermal expansion, each vane fits into a contoured slot in the shrouds, which conforms to the airfoil shape of the vane. These supporting shrouds facilitate the removal of the inlet guide vanes. For example, turbine inlet guide vanes can be a single unit, or in groups of two as seen in Figure 4-5-2.

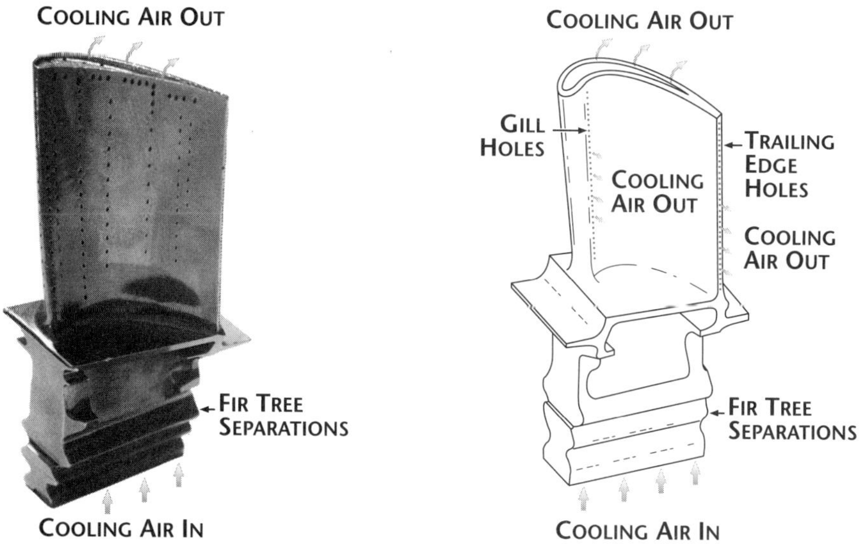

Figure 4-5-5. Turbine blade cooling holes providing a blanket of air along the metal surface of the blade.

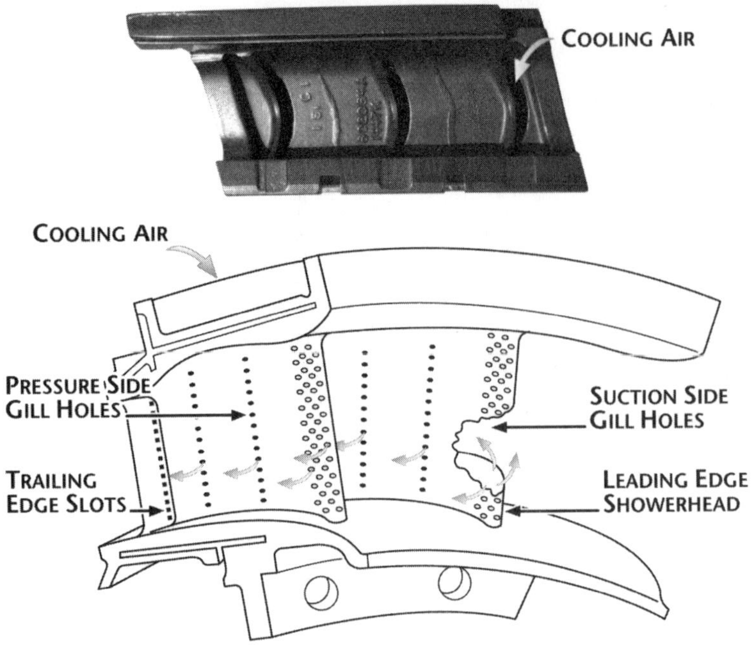

Figure 4-5-6. Air cooled turbine inlet guide vanes

Turbine rotor. The rotor element of the turbine section consists of a turbine disk and blades. When the turbine blades are installed, the disk then becomes the turbine wheel. The turbine wheel is a dynamically balanced unit consisting of blades that are attached to a rotating disk. The turbine shaft and wheel, illustrated in Figure 4-5-3, are usually fabricated from alloy steel. High work rates are imposed on the turbine disk: it must be capable of absorbing the high torque loads that are exerted on the turbine wheel which turns the compressor. The turbine wheel is mounted on the rotating shaft connected to the compressor.

The pressure drop across a single turbine stage can be much greater than the pressure increase across a compressor stage. A single turbine stage can be used to drive multiple compressor stages because of the high-pressure change across the turbine. The exhaust gases leaving the turbine inlet guide vanes impact the surface area of the turbine blades, causing the assembly to rotate at a very high rate of speed.

The high rotational speed imposes severe centrifugal loads on the turbine disk, along with high temperatures, resulting in high thermal and mechanical stresses. The disk is exposed to the hot exhaust gases passing through the blades and absorbs considerable heat from these gases.

Thermal Stress

Sufficient clearance must exist between the blade tip and the turbine shroud (the component that surrounds the turbine wheel), as shown in Figure 4-5-4. During high power engine operation, expansion of the disk and rotating blades must be accounted for to allow turbine blade tip clearances. The rim (outside of the disk) disk temperatures normally are high and well above the temperatures of the more remote inner portion of the disk. As a result of these temperature gradients, thermal stresses are added to the rotational stresses. Consequently, the turbine wheels and guide vanes must be made from materials that are extremely heat resistant.

Figure 4-5-7. Free power turbine

A method of relieving thermal stresses is internal cooling air, which is bled from the early stages of the compressor. This air flows through the inside of the engine to the blades, disk and inlet guide vanes. The blade or vane is hollow and cooling air flows through the blade and out through small holes on its surface.

These gill holes keep the surface cool by providing a blanket of air between blade surface and the hot gases as shown in Figure 4-5-5. The air also exerts a pressure against the area of the disk which is used to reduce axial loads on the bearings. Engine speed and temperature must be controlled to keep the turbine section within safe limits during operation. Air-cooled guide vanes are shown in Figure 4-5-6.

Figure 4-5-8. Fir tree method of attaching turbine blades to the disk

The engine must have a turbine(s) that drives its core or gas generator compressor. Turbofan, turboshaft and turboprop engines usually employ a separate turbine(s) and shaft to power the fan, propeller and turboshaft engine output shaft. The gear box and accessories are usually connected and driven by the gas generator or the high-pressure compressor through bevel gears and a tower shaft. Some engine models have accessories that are driven by ring gears directly from the main shaft.

All gas turbine engines use a gas generator that has a compressor burner and turbine. Hot exhaust gases then pass into the separate additional turbines that drive the fan or low pressure compressor. Such an arrangement is termed a two spool turbofan engine. For turboshaft and turboprop engines it is called a free turbine when there is no mechanical connection between the gas generator and the power turbines, as shown in Figure 4-5-7.

Some engines have the turbine stages mechanically connected to the compressor. This is termed a fixed turbine. The free turbine arrangement allows for the gas generator to start without the drag of the helicopter rotor or propeller. The load the turbine is driving determines the amount of energy absorption at the power turbine. As the gas generator picks up speed, the power turbine will also increase in speed until the load (propeller or helicopter rotor) is matched.

Blade attachment. There are various ways of attaching turbine blades to the turbine disks. The blades are retained in their respective grooves by a variety of methods including welding, locktabs and riveting. The most secure method is the fir-tree design shown in Figure 4-5-8. Figure 4-5-9 shows a typical turbine wheel using rivets for blade retention.

Another method of blade retention is to construct the root of the blade so that it will contain all the elements necessary for its retention. This method, illustrated in Figure 4-5-10, shows that the blade root has a stop made on one end of the root so that the blade can be inserted and removed in one direction only, while on the opposite end is a tang. The tang is bent to secure the blade in the disk. Turbine blades may be

Figure 4-5-9. Turbine wheel using rivets to secure the blades

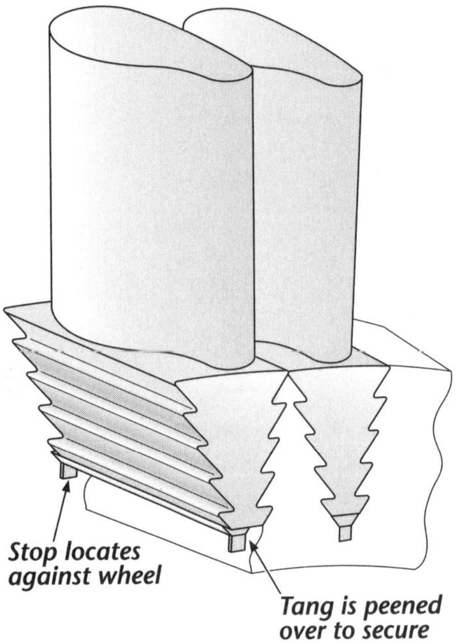

Figure 4-5-10. Turbine blades, featuring tang method of blade retention.

either forged or cast, depending on the composition of the alloys. Most blades are precision-cast and finish-ground to the desired shape.

Turbine Blade Considerations

As the flow passes through the turbine, the total pressure (P_t) and total temperature (T_t) decrease. This decrease in pressure is measured by the turbine pressure ratio (TPR). This is the ratio of the air pressure exiting the turbine to the air pressure entering the turbine. If the turbine entrance is station 4 and the turbine exit is station 5 then the TPR is equal to P_t 5 divided by P_t 4.

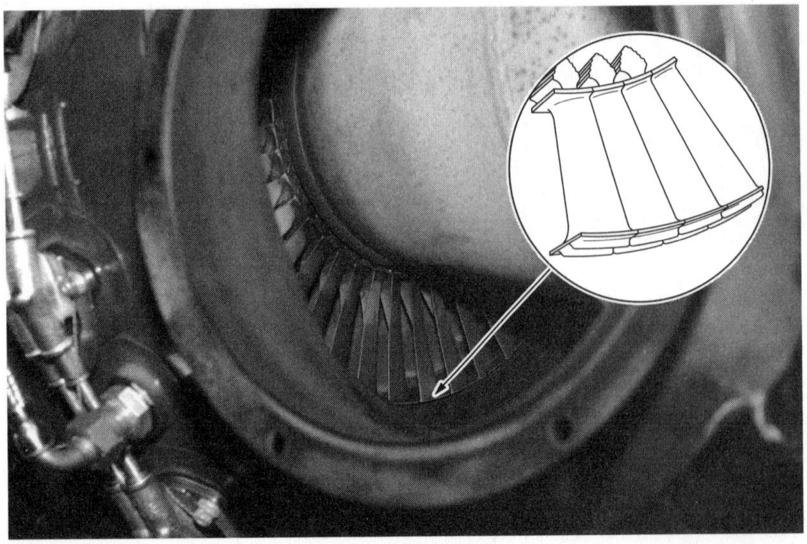

Figure 4-5-11. A shrouded type of turbine blade

$$TPR = \frac{P_t 5}{P_t 4}$$

Work is accomplished by the exhaust gas flow that turns the turbine and the shaft. The turbine work per mass of airflow (TW) is equal to the change in the specific (per mass of airflow) enthalpy (ht) of the flow from the entrance to the exit of the turbine.

$$TW = hT_4 - hT_5$$

Shrouded blades. Most types of high-pressure turbine blades are open at the outer perimeter (tip) of the blade; however, some low-pressure turbine blades are shrouded at the tip. The shrouded turbine blades, in effect, form a band around the outer perimeter of the turbine wheel connecting all the blade tips together. A shrouded type of turbine blade is shown in Figure 4-5-11. This improves blade efficiency by preventing air from spilling over the blade tips. Vibration characteristics are also improved by providing a lighter, longer blade. A disadvantage is that it limits turbine speed and requires more blades; hence its use in low-pressure turbines.

Turbine Stages

In turbine rotor construction, it occasionally becomes necessary to utilize turbines of more than one stage. A single turbine wheel often cannot absorb enough power from the exhaust gas flow to drive the components dependent on the turbine for rotational power; thus, it is necessary to add additional turbine stages. A turbine stage consists of a row of stationary inlet guide vanes, followed by a row of rotating turbine blades.

Some models of turboprop, turbofan and turboshaft engines utilize turbine stages after the compressor turbine stages; these stages are generally called the power turbines or low-pressure turbine stages. Some engines need several power turbine stages to claim enough energy from the exhaust gases to drive a fan, propeller, or shaft.

The use of more than one power turbine wheel or stage is warranted in cases of heavy rotational loads such as in turbofan engines. In the multiple-spool turbofan engine, where power is developed by two or more spools (compressor stages-shaft-turbine stages), it is possible for each spool to drive a separate compressor shaft turbine combination, which then divides the engine into separate spools. For example, a triple-spool turbine engine can be so arranged that the first turbine stages drive the high-pressure compressor and the accessories, the second spool turbine drives the intermediate compressor and the third spool furnishes power to turn

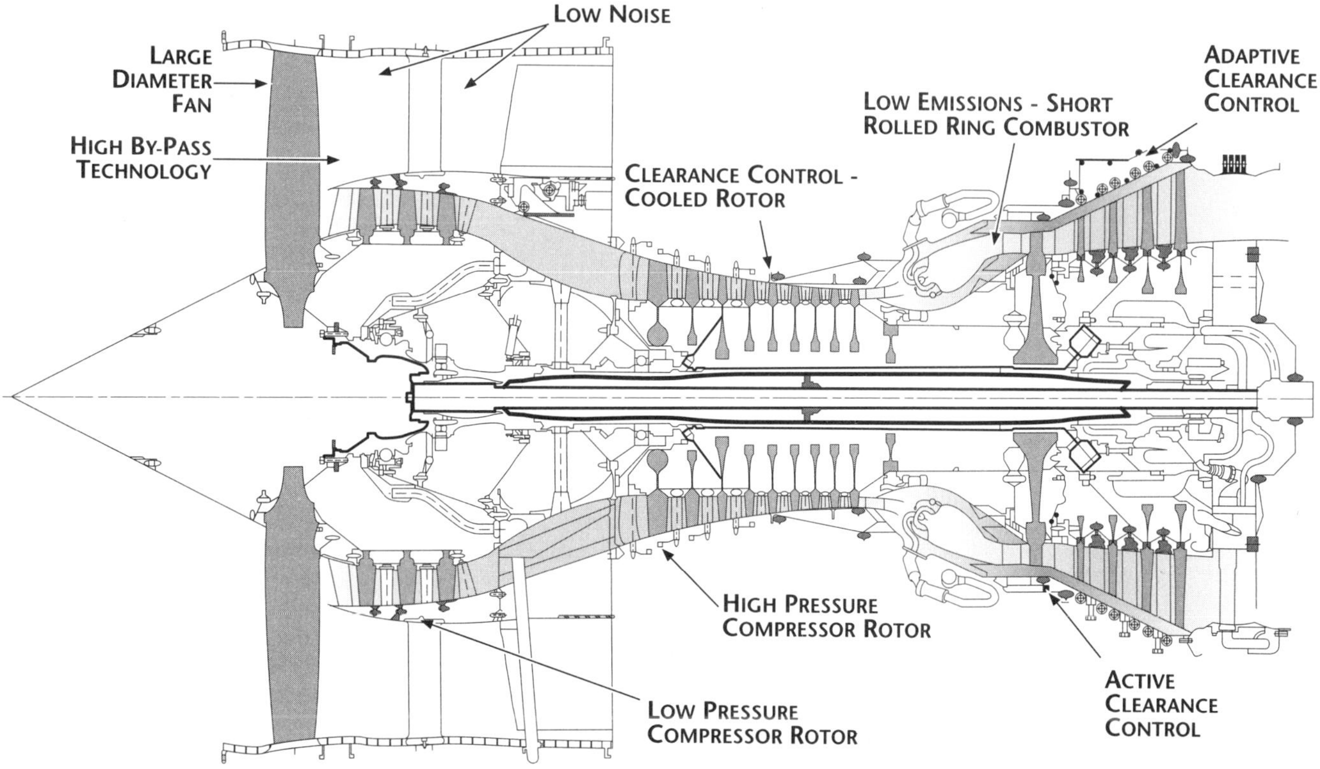

Figure 4-5-12. A multi-spool turbofan engine

the fan or low-pressure compressor. A diagram of a multi-spool turbofan engine is shown in Figure 4-5-12.

The spool arrangement for a dual-spool engine or split spool is shown in Figure 4-5-13. The difference here is that there is a gas generator spool (high-pressure compressor and turbine) and a low-pressure spool, which consist of the fan and some low-pressure compressor stages. In a two-spool turbine engine, the gas path flows through the fan which divides the airflow between fan bypass flow and gas generator flow or core flow.

Figure 4-5-13. A dual-spool, or split spool, arrangement

The turbine casing or housing encloses the turbine wheel and the nozzle vane assembly and at the same time gives either direct or indirect support to the stator elements of the turbine section. It has flanges provided, front and rear, for bolting the assembly to the combustion chamber housing and the exhaust exit guide vane assembly. A complete turbine section is illustrated in Figure 4-5-14.

Turbine Blade Manufacturing Technology

Most aircraft gas turbines employ investment-cast turbine blades and vanes of equi-axed grain—a multitude of randomly oriented grains in each casting. Equi-axed orientation is the natural order of grain orientation that occurs when the alloy solidifies without any manipulation.

The development of directional solidification (DS) technology allowed castings to be made with multiple directional grains, with the grain boundaries all essentially parallel to the principle stress axis. Since grain boundary cracking is the principle mode of high temperature stress-rupture failure, this development alone added about 50°F to the maximum use temperature of super-alloys.

Crystal technology. An improvement in directional solidification technology is the single grain (or single crystal) turbine blade shown in Figure 4-5-15. When such blades are produced, it is possible to alter the alloy chemistry by removing elements from the alloy whose primary role is for grain boundary strengthening. Some high-pressure turbine blades are cast as single crystals. That use an alloy that has high stress-rupture strength and permits metal temperatures higher than are possible with directionally solidified blades. Single crystal castings are made by a directional solidification casting technique, with a special construction in the mold permitting only a single grain to grow into the blade cavity.

The development of the specialized nickel- and cobalt-based heat-resistant alloys allowed for creep-resistant turbine blade alloys. Creep is the permanent elongation of the turbine blades due to extreme rotational forces and heat. In the worst case scenario, prolonged creep can cause part of the blade to rupture.

Blade coatings. Turbine blades are susceptible to corrosion and must be protected by applying a metal coating. Turbine blade coating consists of a platinum electroplate coating or a chrome/aluminum diffusion coating applied to the turbine blade, followed by an aluminide coating. The aluminide coatings are specified because of their improved corrosion resistance.

The use of powder metallurgy in producing a high-pressure turbine disk permits uniform mechanical properties that forgings sometimes do not have. This allows the manufacturer

Figure 4-5-14. A complete turbine assembly

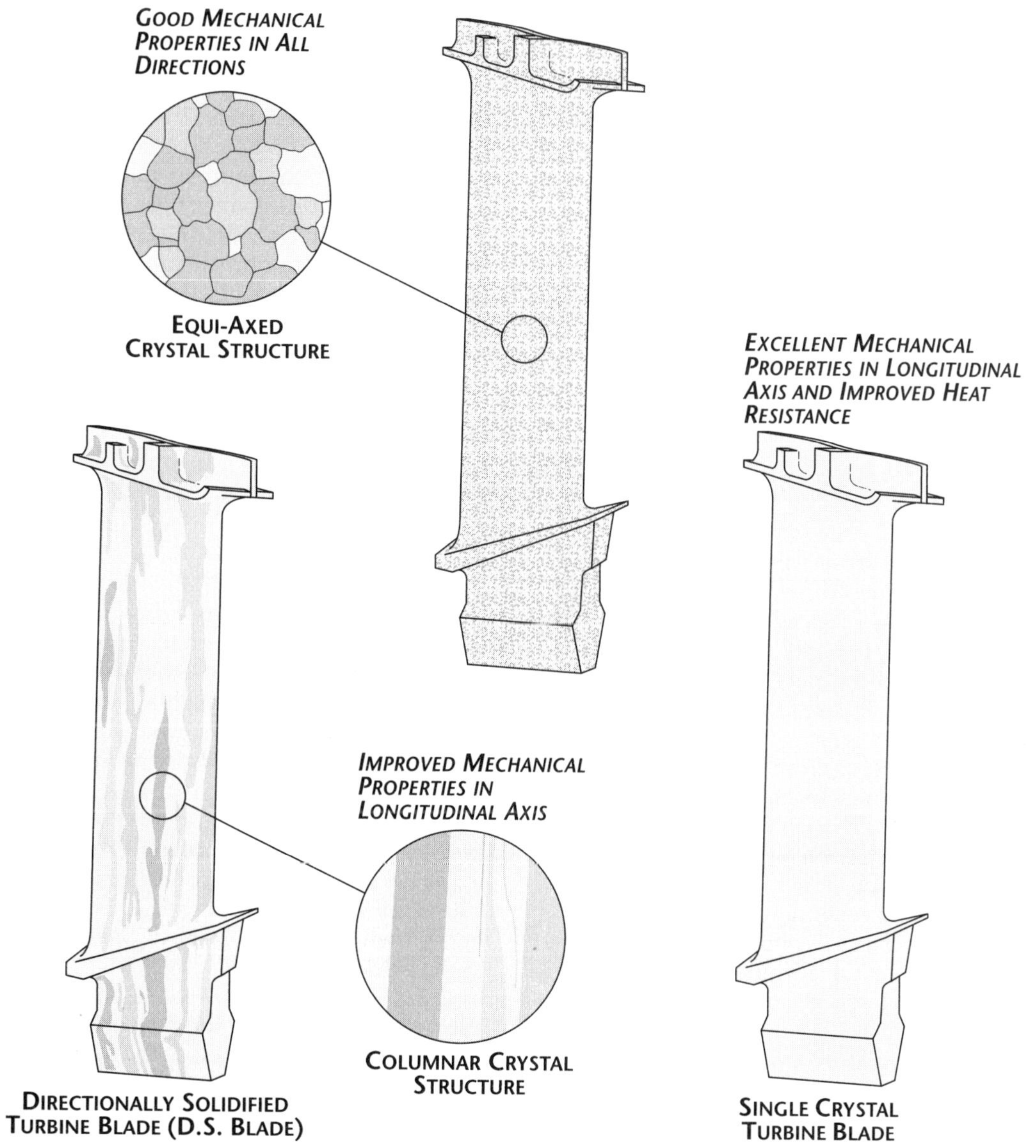

Figure 4-5-15. Equi-axed grain, directional and single crystal turbine blade

of the disk to require a minimum amount of machining. Improved defect tolerance is always an important design characteristic when producing turbine disks.

The effects of fatigue cracking limit the useful life of a turbine disk. Nickel based alloys and powder metallurgy technology have improved the resistance to fatigue cracking of turbine disks. Fatigue occurs when a stress is applied repeatedly until the component fractures. Stress that is less than the ultimate strength of the disk material can cause failures when the stress is applied to the disk many times.

The turbine disk is subjected to low cycle fatigue (LCF) that limits its useful life as well. What constitutes a cycle varies somewhat, but for turbine engines, a cycle is usually considered an engine start and shut-down. Most turbine disks are life-limited components.

Classification of Turbines

Turbines are classified into three basic types:

- Impulse
- Reaction
- Impulse-reaction

Impulse. By the use of convergent and divergent turbine inlet guide vanes, pressure and velocity can be manipulated to increase velocity by reducing the pressure. In the impulse type, the total pressure drop across each stage occurs in the turbine inlet guide vanes which, because of their convergent shape, increase the exhaust gas velocity flow while reducing the pressure. The impulse turbine is more efficient when the guide vanes increase the velocity at the expense of the pressure. The exhaust gas flow is then directed onto the turbine blades.

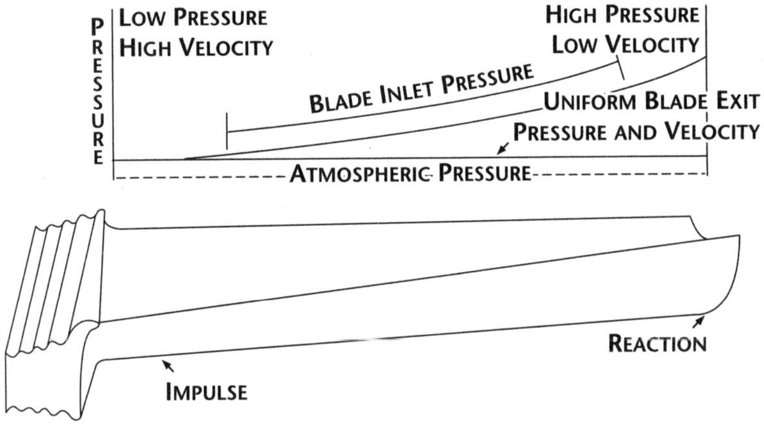

Figure 4-5-16. Impulse reaction turbine blade

The turbine blades experience an impulse (direct push), caused by the airflow impacting on the surface area of the blades. In a true impulse turbine, the only push on the blades is the exhaust gas flow (mass flow) directed on to the surface area of the blades.

Reaction. In the reaction turbine, inlet guide vanes are designed to change flow direction with a minimum change in pressure. The turbine blades form a converging passage which creates a reaction force resulting from the expansion and acceleration of the gas flow. This increase in acceleration out of the converging duct made from the turbine blades increases the force applied to the turbine wheel.

Impulse-reaction. Normally gas turbine engines do not use pure impulse or pure reaction turbine blades, but rather the impulse-reaction combination shown in Figure 4-5-16. The proportion of each blade that is impulse and reaction is incorporated into the design of a turbine blade. The overall percentage of impulse or reaction of a turbine blade is largely dependent on the type of engine. Generally, it is divided about 50% impulse and 50% reaction. The amount of reaction force varies from the blade root to tip, being least at the root and highest at the tip. The combination turbine (impulse-reaction) is used most widely on flight (propulsion) turbine engines. Straight impulse-type turbines are used mostly for auxiliary power units (radial inflow-turbine) and air turbine starters.

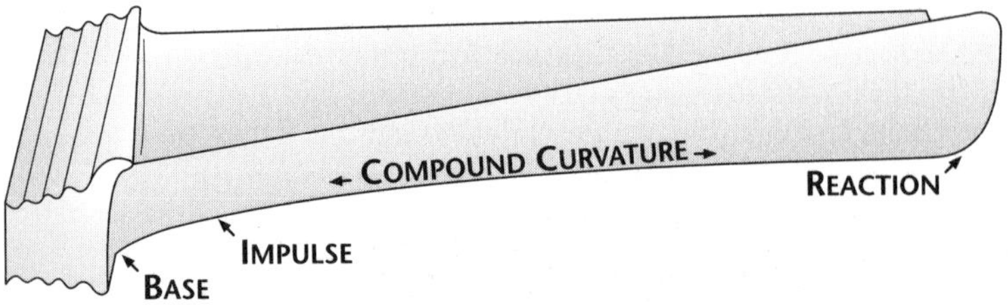

Figure 4-5-17. Turbine blade stagger angle, greater at the tip than at the root

The turbine inlet guide vanes and blades of the turbine incorporate a twist, the blades having a stagger angle that is greater at the tip than at the root as is seen in Figure 4-5-17. The reason for the twist is to make the exhaust gas flow accomplish equal work along the entire length of the blade. This ensures that the exhaust gas flow exits the blade with a uniform axial velocity and sets up changes in velocity, pressure and temperature, which occur throughout the blade length.

Section 6

Exhaust Section and Nozzle

All gas turbine engines have an exhaust nozzle that produces thrust. The nozzle is used to conduct the exhaust gases back to the ambient air. The exhaust nozzle area opening sets the mass airflow rate through the engine and is located after the last turbine stages in the gas path.

The type or shape of the nozzle is generally dictated by the function it provides. A relatively simple device, the nozzle consists of a heat resistant metal that is specially shaped into a tube through which the hot exhaust gases flow. In a simple exhaust nozzle the outlet is smaller than the inlet, forming a convergent duct, seen in Figure 4-6-1. The normal function of the exhaust nozzle, or cone, is to control the velocity and temperature of the exhaust gases. Although a certain amount of thrust would be produced even if there were no exhaust nozzle, the thrust would be comparatively low and the direction of flow would not be properly controlled.

Convergent nozzle. When a convergent nozzle is used, the velocity of the gases is increased and the flow is directed so the thrust is in line with the engine. This shape will increase the velocity of the exhaust gases exiting the nozzle and

Figure 4-6-1. Fixed geometry convergent nozzle

produce maximum thrust at full power. The nozzle opening area is very important to engine operation. The area of the nozzle opening must be large enough to allow maximum airflow at full power. If the nozzle opening is too small, the airflow through the engine will be choked; temperatures and pressures inside the engine will become too high, causing compressor stall.

Exhaust nozzles come in a variety of shapes and sizes depending on the type of aircraft where they are used. Some turbofan, turboprops and turbo shaft engines often have a fixed geometry convergent nozzle as shown in Figure 4-6-1.

Ducted turbofan engines can use a common (single) nozzle as shown in Figure 4-6-2 (single/mixed). The core and fan flows combine inside this common nozzle and exit the same nozzle opening. In the separate nozzle configuration, the core flow (gas generator) exits the center nozzle while the fan flow exits the fan nozzle. This is widespread with high bypass turbofan engines where the two flow paths are exhausted separately, as shown in Figure 4-6-3.

In the common (integrated/mixed) nozzle, the mixing of the two flows in the common nozzle is normally quieter than a simple convergent nozzle. In low bypass ducted turbofan engines, the gas paths are combined within the nozzle; this ensures the mixing of the two gas streams before flowing out of the common or mixed nozzle. The bypass engine ejects two gas streams into the atmosphere: the cool bypass fan airflow and the hot turbine discharge gases.

In a low-bypass-ratio engine, the two flows are combined by a mixer unit noise suppressor. This allows the bypass air to flow into the turbine exhaust gas flow in a manner that ensures complete mixing of the two streams. In high-bypass-ratio-engines, the two streams are usually exhausted separately; however, combining the two gas flows within a common, or integrated, nozzle assembly can make a reduction in noise. This partially mixes the gas flows prior to ejection into the atmosphere.

Figure 4-6-2. Turbofan using a common (single/mixed) exhaust nozzle

Augmented Thrust

Gas from the engine turbine enters the exhaust nozzle at velocities of 750 to 1,200 ft/sec.

Figure 4-6-3. A separate nozzle on a turbofan engine

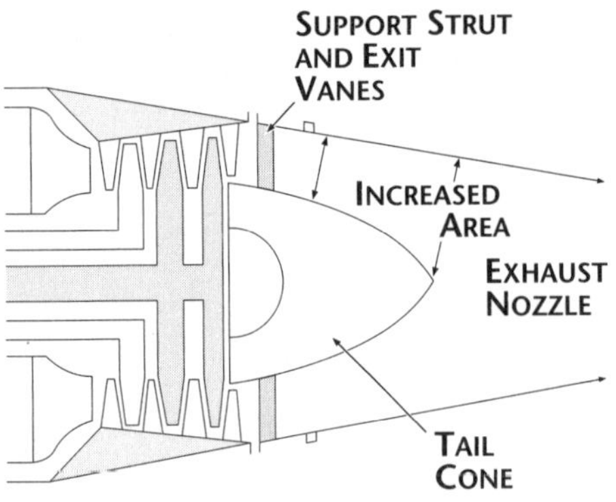

Figure 4-6-4. Diffusion of the flow between the exhaust cone and the outer wall

Because velocities of this order produce high friction losses, the speed of flow is decreased by diffusion. This is accomplished by having an increasing passage area between the exhaust cone and the outer wall, as shown in Figure 4-6-4. The cone also prevents the exhaust gases from flowing across the rear face of the turbine disk. It is usual to hold the velocity at the exhaust unit outlet to a Mach number of about 0.5, or approximately 950 ft/sec. Additional losses occur due to the residual whirl velocity in the gas stream from the turbine. To reduce these losses, the turbine rear struts (straightening vanes) in the exhaust unit are designed to straighten out the flow before the gases pass through the exhaust nozzle.

The exhaust gases pass into the atmosphere through the propelling nozzle. As the upstream total pressure is increased above the value at which the propelling nozzle becomes choked (reaches Mach 1), the static pressure of the gases at the exit increases above atmospheric pressure. This pressure difference across the nozzle provides what is known as pressure thrust. Pressure thrust is additional to the thrust obtained from the momentum change of the gas stream. It occurs mainly in low bypass turbofan engines and turbojet engines at high power settings.

Afterburning (augmented) turbojets and low bypass turbofans require a variable area nozzle that can open and close. The variable area nozzle is in the minimum area opening position during non-afterburning operation (gas turbine operation only) as shown in Figure 4-6-5. The variable nozzle opens when the afterburner or augmenter is selected by the pilot. This permits the resultant increase in volume (extra mass flow) to exit the nozzle without creating an excessive increase in pressure within the nozzle.

The pressure in the nozzle cannot be allowed to increase beyond limits, because this would negatively affect other engine sections. If the area of the nozzle stayed fixed, the pressure in the nozzle would cause too much back pressure and slow down the flow in the compressor, which would in turn cause compressor stall and engine damage. By allowing the variable nozzle to open when the afterburner is selected, the nozzle pressure is controlled.

The nozzle is controlled by the pressure ratio control unit that generally uses hydraulic pressure through actuating cylinders to open and close the nozzle opening. Low bypass afterburning turbofan engines mix the core flow (turbine exit gas path) and the fan path flow before the after-

Figure 4-6-5. Afterburning exhaust nozzle in the minimum open position

burner. This increases the flow and provides fresh air (more oxygen) for the combustion process in the afterburner. Fuel is then injected into the gas path stream and a flame holder (flame stabilizer) improves combustion as the gases are accelerated out the nozzle opening. The flame stabilizer provides an area of local turbulence that slows the velocity of the gas path to improve the combustion process. An igniter can be used to assure ignition during afterburner operation.

Whenever the engine pressure ratio (power setting) is high enough to produce exhaust velocities which might exceed Mach 1 at the engine exhaust nozzle, more thrust can be gained by using a convergent-divergent (CD) type of nozzle. The advantage of a convergent-divergent nozzle is greatest at high Mach numbers because of the resulting higher-pressure ratio across the engine exhaust nozzle. A convergent-divergent nozzle is shown in Figure 4-6-6.

The flow in this type of nozzle first converges (reduces) down to the minimum area opening, or throat, then is expanded through the divergent section to the exit. Rocket engines use CD nozzles to accelerate the exhaust path for maximum thrust. This type of engine usually has a fixed geometry CD nozzle with a much larger divergent section than is required for gas turbine engines.

With regard to supersonic velocity flows, the airflow principles will reverse. Once the exhaust gases reach Mach 1 in the throat of the nozzle, they are accelerated as they pass out the divergent part of the nozzle. To ensure that a constant weight or volume of a gas will flow past any given point after sonic velocity is reached, the rear part of a supersonic exhaust duct is enlarged to accommodate the additional weight or volume of gas that will be flowing at supersonic rates. If this is not done, the nozzle will not operate efficiently.

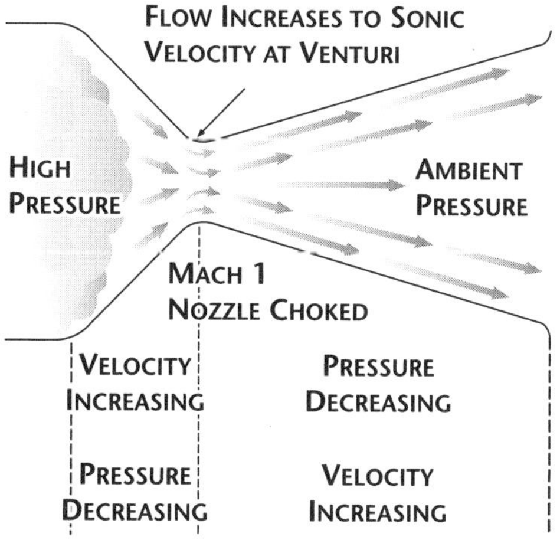

Figure 4-6-6. A variable geometry convergent divergent nozzle

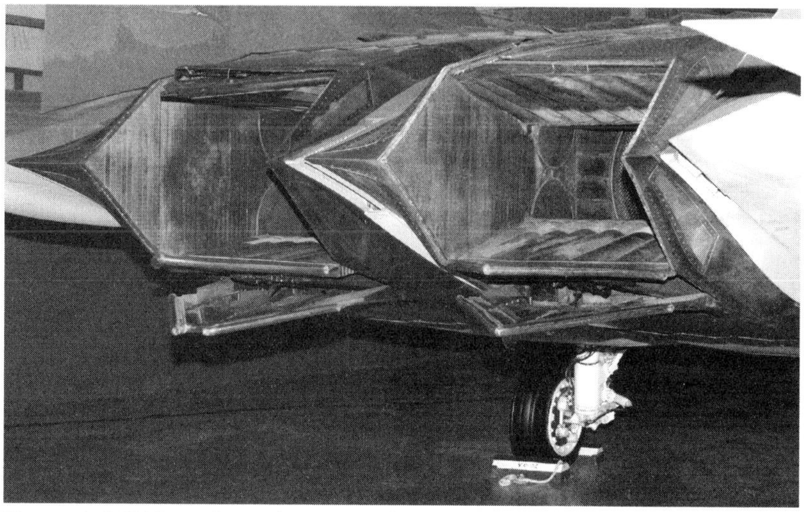

Figure 4-6-7. Vectoring exhaust nozzles

In the CD nozzle, the convergent section is designed to handle the gases while they remain subsonic and to deliver the gases to the throat of the nozzle just as they attain sonic velocity. The divergent section handles the gases, further increasing their velocity, after they emerge from the throat. After a velocity of Mach 1 is reached in the throat, the flow then accelerates to supersonic or multiple Mach numbers in the divergent section of the nozzle as mentioned earlier.

Vectoring Thrust

Some exhaust nozzles allow the exhaust gases to be easily deflected, or vectored, as shown in Figure 4-6-7. Changing the direction of the thrust slightly by moving the nozzle makes the aircraft much more maneuverable. Many modern fighter aircraft that use vectored thrust incorporate a rectangular type of nozzle.

Vectored thrust aircraft do not have to be vertical takeoff aircraft. The thrust can be used for maneuvering. Another type of vectored thrust is used for vertical take off. This can take several different forms such as swiveling engines, a lift fan, or swiveling exhaust nozzles which direct the exhaust gases straight down as shown in Figure 4-6-8. Once the aircraft starts to rise it must be controlled. This control can come in the form of bleed air from the engine ducted through jets in the four extremities of the aircraft. By controlling the flow of air through these ducts, aircraft control is achieved.

Exhaust Heat Isolation

It is necessary to prevent any heat from being transferred to the surrounding aircraft structure. This is achieved by passing ventilating air around the jet pipe, or by covering the section of the exhaust system with an insulating

Figure 4-6-8. Swiveling exhaust nozzles

blanket, as shown in Figure 4-6-9. Each blanket has an inner layer of fibrous insulating material contained by an outer skin of thin stainless steel, which is dimpled to increase its strength. Acoustically absorbent materials are sometimes applied to the exhaust system to reduce engine noise.

Due to the wide variations of temperature to which the exhaust system is subjected, it must be mounted and have its sections joined in such a manner as to allow for expansion and contraction without distortion or damage.

Section 7

Engine Noise

Gas-turbine engines create high decibel noise. This noise can be both a nuisance and a physical danger. High noise levels can be a nuisance to persons on the ground. They can also cause physical injury, primarily hearing loss. These issues have motivated engine and aircraft manufacturers together with government agencies to actively engage in efforts to reduce noise to an acceptable level.

Sound. Sound may be defined as that which can be heard. The reason sound can be heard is because it consists of a series of pressure waves in the air. A sound can consist of a combination of many waves in a wide range of frequencies, or it can consist of a pure tone which is a single-frequency wave that follows the sine wave pattern.

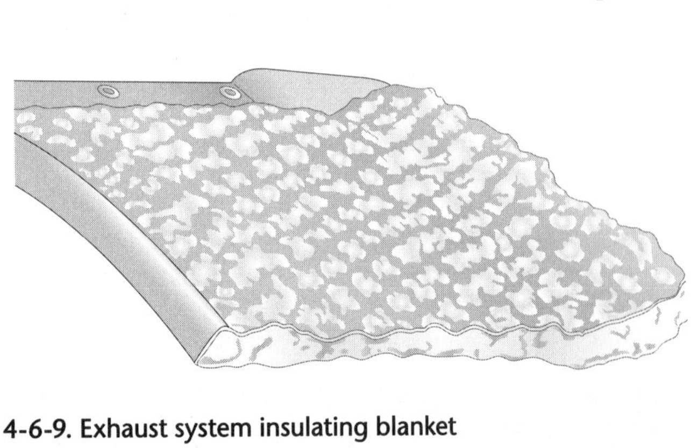

Figure 4-6-9. Exhaust system insulating blanket

Noise. Noise may be defined as unwanted and irritating sound. The noise produced by a turbine engine consists of all frequencies audible to the human ear with intensities reaching levels which can be physically destructive. The intensity of sound is measured in decibels (dB). One decibel is one-tenth of a bel (B), the basic unit. A barely audible sound has an intensity of 1 B, whereas the intensity of the sound produced by a turbine engine may attain a value of 155 dB (15.5 B) near the engine at takeoff power.

On the decibel scale, the intensity of sound increases on what is described mathematically as a logarithmic progression. This means that if the sound level in decibels is doubled, the intensity of the sound will be equal to the square of the original sound. If the sound level in decibels is tripled, the intensity of the sound will be equal to the cube of the original sound.

A scale indicating the decibel value of certain sounds is given in Figure 4-7-1. Any sound over 100 dB is very intense. The maximum level of sound that can be heard by the human ear is approximately 120 dB. Above this level, the ear can feel increasing intensity but cannot hear the difference. Also, above this level, loss of hearing can occur.

Sources of Noise

Noise from a turbojet engine is caused by a number of forces, but it basically stems from the 'torturing' of the air passing through the engine. Initially, the air is violently broken up and chopped into segments as it enters the inlet duct, passes through the inlet guide vanes and encounters the compressor blades. Much of the sound thus created is in a wide range of frequencies, but a single frequency is also heard. This is the familiar whine, caused by the compressor blades chopping the incoming air. A sound of this type is called discrete because it has an identifiable frequency and can be recognized in relation to other sounds.

The most intense sound at high-power engine settings comes from the exhaust nozzle. This sound is caused by the shear turbulence between the relatively calm air outside the engine and the high-velocity jet of hot gases emanating from the nozzle. The noise caused by the jet exhaust is termed broadband noise because it includes many frequencies.

The turbulence within the high-speed exhaust jet stream has very small eddies which produce relatively high-frequency noise. Farther downstream, as the velocity of the exhaust jet stream slows down, the exhaust jet stream mixes with the atmosphere and the turbulence from larger eddies causes low frequency noise. Compared with noise from other portions of the exhaust jet stream, noise from this portion has a much lower frequency.

As the energy of the jet stream finally is dissipated in large turbulent swirls, a greater portion of the energy is converted into noise. The noise generated as the exhaust gases dissipate is at a frequency near the low end of the audible range. The lower the frequency of the noise, the greater the distance it will travel. This means that the low-frequency noises will be greater in volume than the high-frequency noises and are more objectionable. High-frequency noise is weakened more rapidly than low frequency noise both by distance and with interference of atmospheric ambient air.

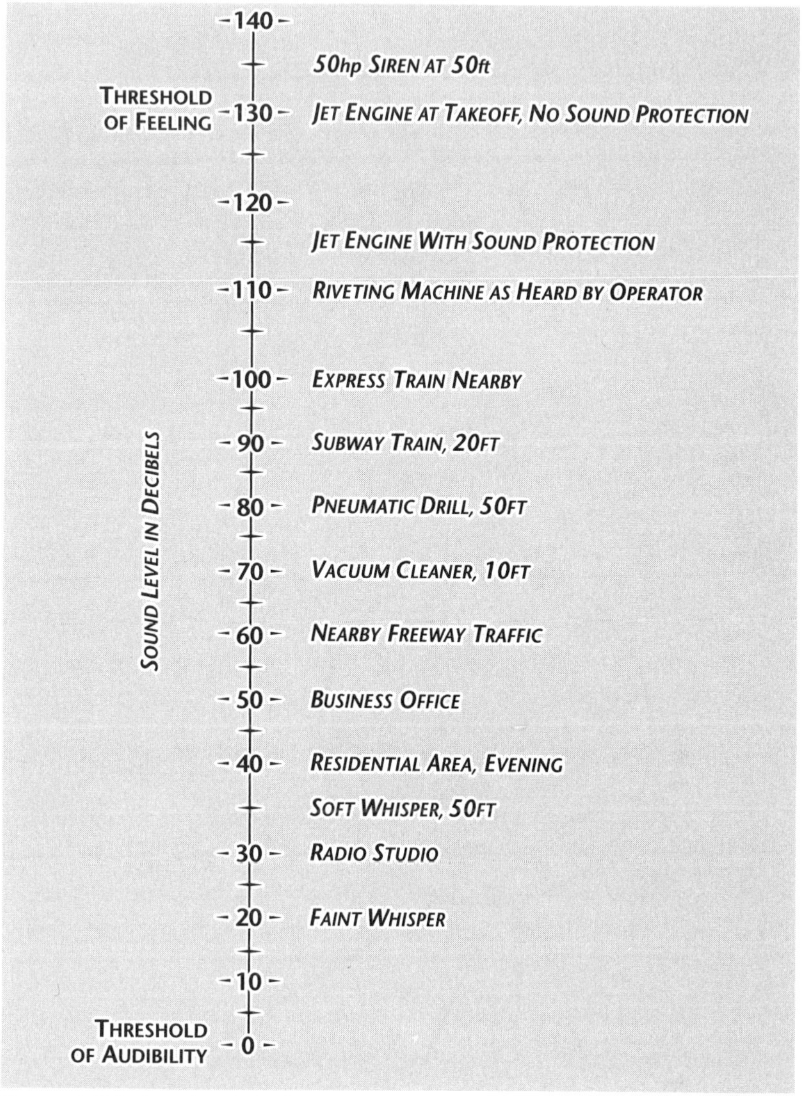

Figure 4-7-1. A scale of decibel levels

Turbofans and Noise

In a turbofan engine, noise is caused by the secondary airflow from the fan section of the engine. This air has a lower velocity than the primary jet exhaust; therefore, the noise is not as intense. An additional factor affecting the jet exhaust of the turbofan engine is that energy is extracted from the primary exhaust stream to drive the fan, resulting in decreased velocity for the exhaust jet. Thus, the noise produced is lower in intensity.

A high bypass turbofan engine is generally quieter during takeoff than a low bypass turbofan. The noise level produced by a fan-type engine is less, principally because the exhaust gas velocities ejected at the engine's core nozzle are slower than those for a pure turbojet or low bypass turbofan engine of comparative size.

Turbofan engines require more turbine stages to provide additional power to drive the fan. The low-pressure turbine stages reduce the velocity and energy present in the exhaust gases; and therefore they reduce the exhaust gas velocity and thus the noise produced. The noise produced by the exhaust gases is proportional to exhaust gas velocity. The exhaust from the fan itself is at a relatively low velocity and therefore does not create a major noise problem. A single stage fan (low-pressure compressor) significantly reduces compressor noise by reducing the air turbulence in the compressor.

Turbofan engines with a high bypass ratio will reduce the exhaust gas noise by absorbing most of the energy in the core's low-pressure turbines that drive the fan. Also the fan air stream will cause mixing and will surround the exhaust core airflow. Because it is characteristic of low-frequency noise to linger at a relatively high volume, effective noise reduction for a low bypass turbofan engine must be achieved either by revising the noise pattern or by changing the frequency of the noise emitted by the exhaust gases from the nozzle.

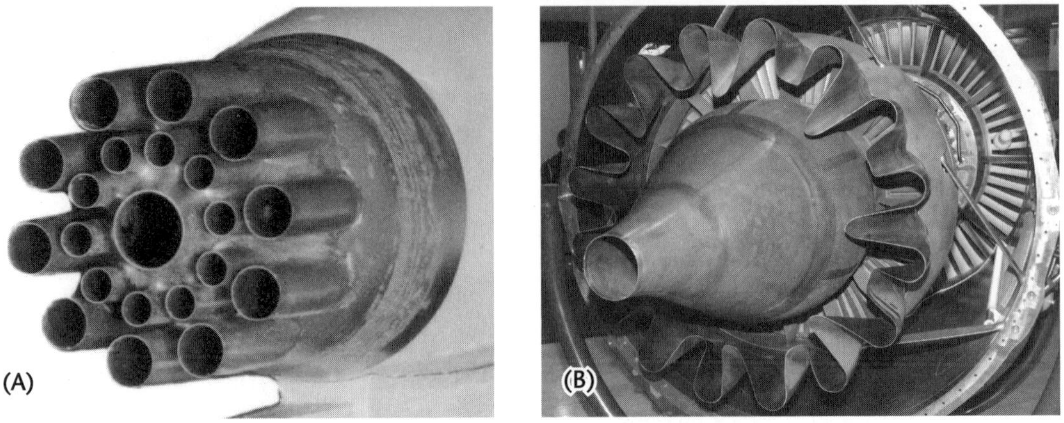

Figure 4-7-2. Two types of noise suppressors. (A) shows the multitube type and (B) shows the corrugated perimeter type.

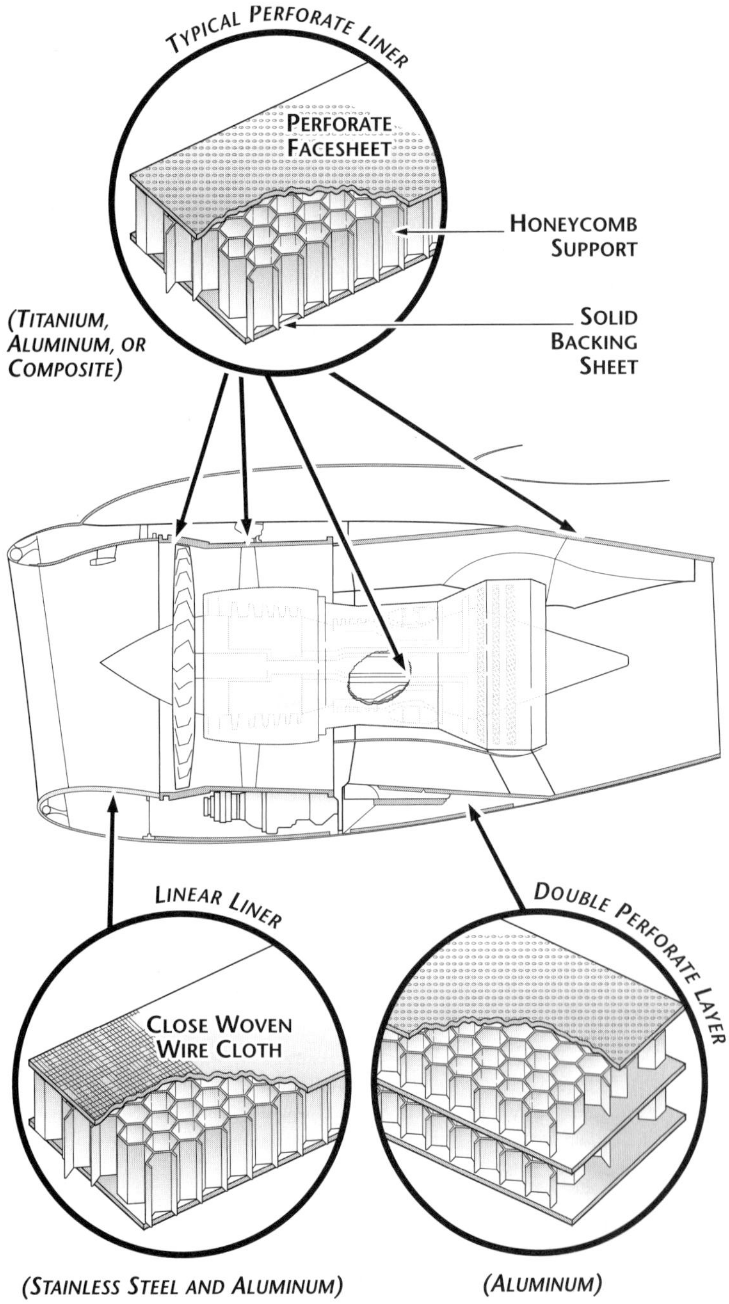

Figure 4-7-3. Acoustical absorbent lining used in the engine nacelle

Engine Noise Suppressors

Because the nozzle conducts the exhaust gas stream back to the ambient air, there can be serious interactions between the engine exhaust flow and the surrounding airflow. Aircraft powered by large, low bypass turbofan engines using a mixed nozzle, in which the core and fan air mix before exiting the engine from a single nozzle, generally require some sort of silencing device or noise suppressor.

Airport regulations require noise certification requirements, which govern the maximum noise levels aircraft are permitted to produce. The engine's exhaust gases (jet of airflow from the nozzle), the fan or compressor and the turbine section are the main areas that need noise suppression. Aircraft operating from airports located in or near densely populated areas must conform to certain noise controls. The most widely used noise suppressor is an integral, airborne part of the aircraft engine installation. Noise suppressors primarily suppress engine noise during takeoff, climb, approach and landing.

Types of suppressors. The two types of noise suppressors in current use are either of the corrugated-perimeter (internal mixing) type or the lobe (multi-tube) type nozzle; both are shown in Figure 4-7-2. These break up the single, main (core) exhaust gas stream into a number of smaller gas streams. This increases the total perimeter of the nozzle area and reduces the size of eddies created as the gases are discharged into the ambient air, promoting a rapid mixing of the gas streams.

Although the total noise-energy remains unchanged, the frequency is raised considerably. The size of eddies scales down, at a linear rate, with the size of the exhaust stream. This has two effects. First, the change in frequency can raise the noise above the audibility range of the human ear. Secondly, high frequencies within the audible range—which are more annoying—are reduced more by atmospheric absorption

Figure 4-7-4. Hearing protection and communication are combined in a good headset.

U.S. Navy photo

than are the low frequencies. Thus, the fall-off in intensity is greater and the noise level is less at any given distance from the aircraft.

Acoustically absorbent linings are used to convert acoustic energy into heat. These linings are used to line and surround the engine from the nacelle. The linings generally consist of porous skin supported by a honeycomb backing, shown in Figure 4-7-3. They provide a very high suppression level and are used to reduce the fan noise level.

The development of turbofan engines has made possible additional reduction of engine noise. In the turbofan engine, both the primary airflow and the secondary airflow are reduced in velocity compared with those in the turbojet. As explained previously, the reduced air velocity results in a decrease in noise intensity.

Protection against noise. It is essential that crew members working around turbine engines be provided with approved ear protectors. The most common types of protectors are over-the-ear devices in which earphones are installed for communication purposes. These protectors are muffs which completely enclose the ears, thus protecting them from noise while permitting voice communication. The ground crew in Figure 4-7-4 is wearing hearing protection that can be used for communicating with the air crew by using an integral microphone. All persons working in the areas where turbine engines are operated should have approved ear protectors for use when engines are operating.

Gas Turbine Emissions

Aircraft emissions affect the environment and may have global implications. Emissions from the engine include gaseous and particulate emissions that are a result of combustion. The emissions produced by gas turbine engines comprise 2% or less of the global sources of emissions.

The types of emissions can include a wide variety of items. Some of the emissions which are natural products are water vapor (H_2O) and carbon dioxide (CO_2). Other more harmful emissions that are regulated by the International Civil Aviation Organization (ICAO) include, unburned hydrocarbons (HC), carbon monoxides (CO) and nitrogen oxides (NOx).

Cleaner combustion requires technology that can deliver higher efficiency and lower uniform flame temperatures. One way this can be accomplished is by the premixing concept. Improved combustors burn fuel in the engine's combustor more efficiently and cleanly reduce hydrocarbons and other emissions.

The development of the twin-annular, premixing swirler (TAPS) combustor has greatly contributed to lower levels of emissions. By directing most of the fuel/air mixture through unique swirlers around the fuel nozzles, an ideal fuel/air environment of premixed fuel is present in the combustor. The production of NOx is dependant on combustion temperature. Low combustion temperatures provide for reduced NOx emissions. The lower and uniform combustion temperature contributes to lower emis-

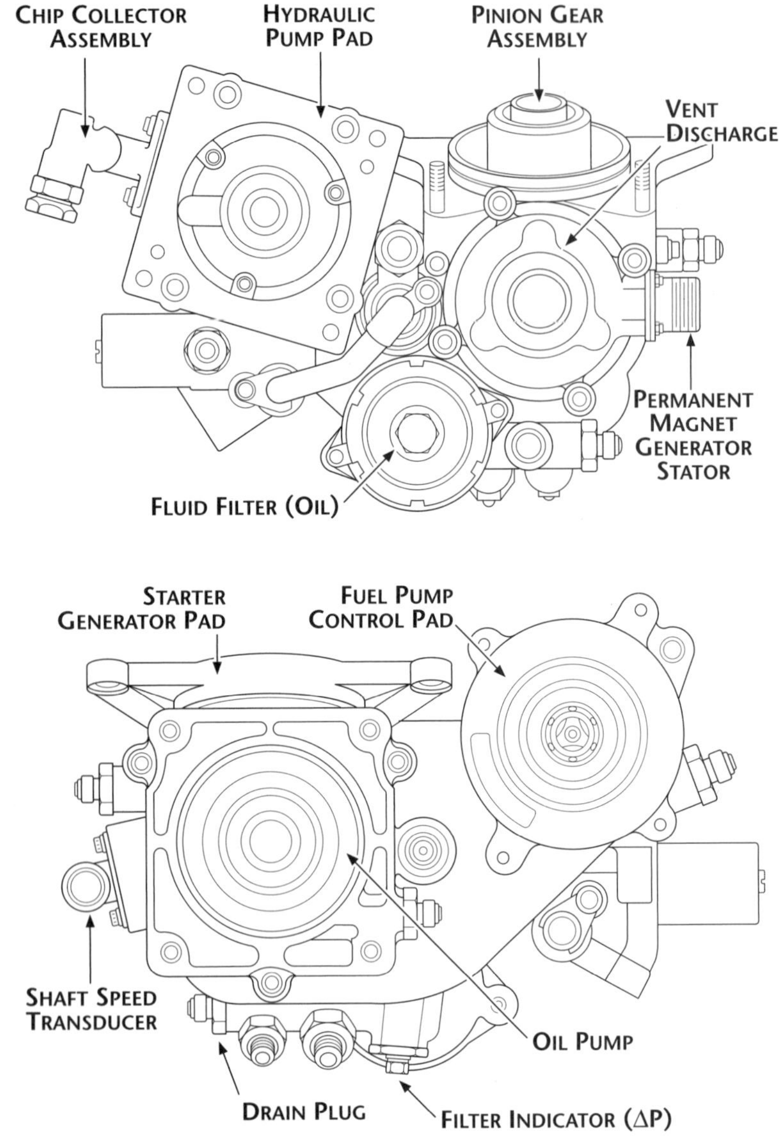

Figure 4-8-1. Accessory gear cases or boxes provide locations for mounting pumps, generators and starters.

sions and improved life of the down-stream components. Future advanced technologies will develop combustor and exhaust nozzle designs that will further lower the emissions from gas turbine engines.

Section 8

Accessory Section and Gearboxes

The arrangement and driving of accessories has always been a problem on gas-turbine engines. The components of the accessory section of all turbine engines have essentially the same purpose, even though they often differ in construction details and nomenclature. The accessory gearbox, shown in Figure 4-8-1, has the same functions as the accessory case or section and the terms are often used interchangeably. Also, engine installation in a particular aircraft may dictate the location or rearrangement of the accessory gearbox.

The accessory section of the gas-turbine engine has several functions. The primary function is to provide a mounting pad to drive the engine accessories that are needed for engine control, operation and aircraft electrical and hydraulic power. The gearbox (accessory section) is generally mounted on the bottom front of turbofan engines and is attached to the compressor section. Turboprop engines generally have the accessory section mounted at the rear of the engine.

Some of the engine accessories mounted on the gear box can include engine-driven fuel pump, fuel control, aircraft hydraulic pump, aircraft generators, speed governing device, permanent magnet generator (PMG), starter, starter/generator and sometimes oil pumps, speed reducing gears and a provision for the oil tank. The gearbox may be designed to act as an oil reservoir.

The accessory case is provided with adequate tubing or cored passages for spraying lubricating oil on the gear train and supporting bearings. The gear train is driven by the engine rotor through an accessory drive shaft gear coupling. The reduction gearing within the case provides suitable drive speeds for each engine accessory or component. Because the rotor operating r.p.m. is so high, the accessory reduction gear ratios are relatively high.

The accessory drives are supported by ball or roller bearings assembled in the mounting pad bores of the accessory case. Some large turbofan engines use two gearboxes connected by a horizontal shaft (lay or transfer shaft). This makes mounting pads (machined pads with studs to support the engine accessories) available while making the engine's diameter as small as possible. The gearbox is driven by the high-pressure compressor on most turbofan engines. The gearbox is connected by a tower shaft that operates perpendicular to the plain of rotation of the high-pressure compressor as shown in Figure 4-8-2. Some turboprop engines have two gear trains that are driven by the gas generator and a free power turbine.

The gear speeds can exceed 6,000 r.p.m. with a centrifugal breather turning 20,000 r.p.m. The centrifugal breather separates the air in the gear box (accessory section) from the oil used to lubricate the gears in the gearbox and other parts of the engine. Some engines that use a power tur-

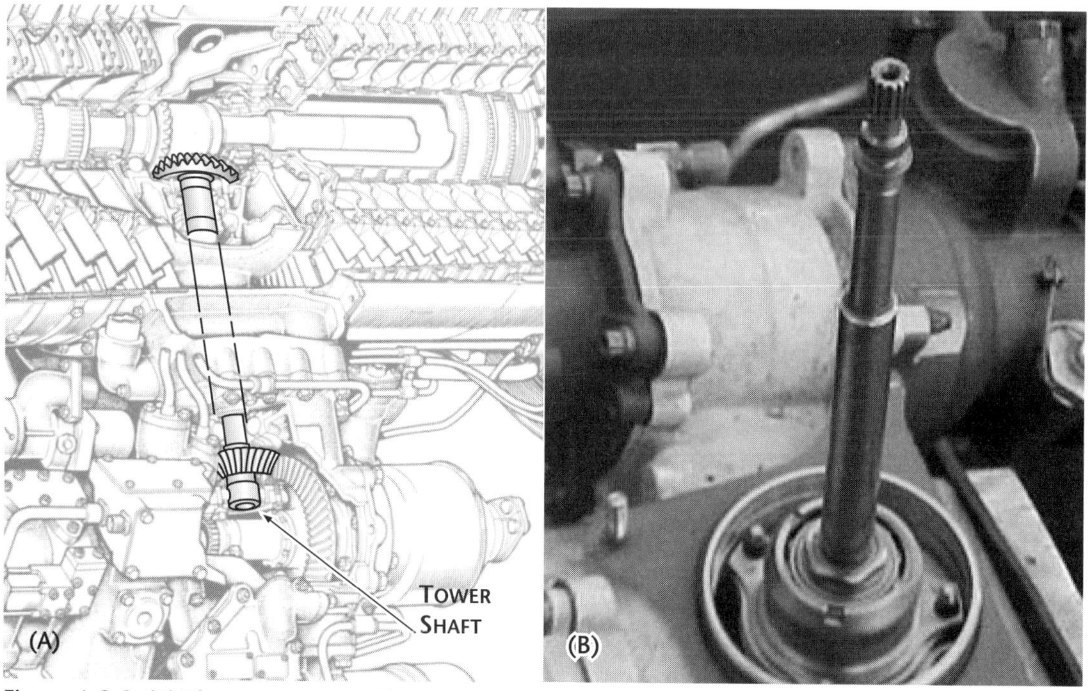

Figure 4-8-2. (A) The accessory gearbox is driven by a tower shaft from the high pressure compressor. (B) A tower shaft operates 90° to the engine rotation.

bine will have two separate gear systems that drive engine accessories according to the drive train involved. On some turboshaft engines, one gear train will be driven by the gas generator and the other by the power turbine.

Reduction Gear Systems

Reduction-gear systems for gas-turbine engines have a much higher reduction ratio than those for reciprocating engines. For example, the Pratt & Whitney of Canada PT6A engine employs a two-stage 15:1 reduction-gear system. This is necessary because the power-turbine speed is 33,000 r.p.m. Reduction-gear systems are also described in the sections covering turboprop and turboshaft engines. The gears utilized in engine reduction-gear systems, for turboprops and turboshafts, are subjected to very high stresses and are therefore machined from high-quality alloy-steel forgings. The larger shafts are supported by ball bearings designed to absorb and transmit to the engine all case loads imposed upon them.

Since reduction-gear systems are of critical importance in the reliability of engines, the overhaul of engines having reduction-gear systems—with the exception of spur-gear systems—is classified as a major repair. The overhaul and return to service of such engines must be under the direction of persons or repair stations suitably certificated by the FAA.

아시아나항공
F-WWKL
708

Chapter 5

SYSTEMS & maintenance

Left: **Aircraft systems are an extensive and complex part of modern transport aircraft.**
Photo courtesy of Airbus

To fully understand how a gas turbine functions, it is important to study the systems that support the engine's operation. These systems schedule fuel flow in response to power requirements, distribute the oil to the rotating parts of the engine and provide the ignition sequence during the engine start. The information discussed in this chapter is general in nature and should not be used for maintaining a specific engine. Always use the manufacturer's information for any maintenance functions.

Learning Objectives

- *Fuel Systems*
- *Fuel Controls*
- *FADEC*
- *Lubrication Systems*
- *Ignition Systems*
- *Starting*
- *Stall Surge Control*
- *Overheat and Extinguishing*

Section 1

Fuel System Controls

An important property of jet fuel is its high heat value. The heating value depends primarily on the type of hydrocarbons present in the fuel. Although the highest available heating value would be desirable, some compromise is necessary to maintain volatility and other qualities within required ranges.

The sulfur content of jet fuels is held to low values since sulfur compounds cause corrosive deterioration of engine and fuel system components. The fuel freezing point is also an important factor. When the fuel approaches the freezing point, waxy particles begin to form, clogging the filters and causing the fuel control system components to malfunction.

Combustion characteristics of fuel are carefully considered so that optimum benefit may be derived from the heat value. Important fuel characteristics are combustion efficiency, carbon formation, fuel smoking, flameout and the ability to relight (burn) at high altitudes. The type of hydrocarbon fuel used influences the

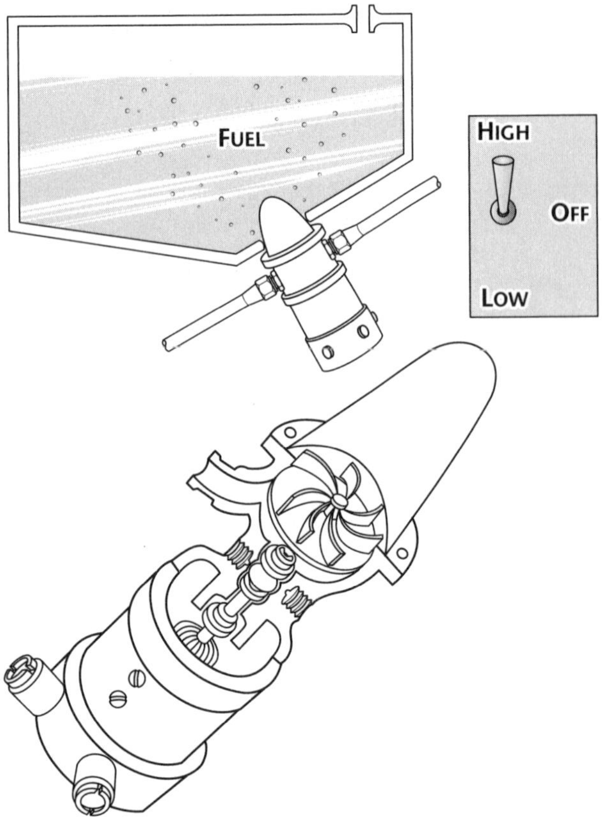

Figure 5-1-1. A tank-mounted centrifugal boost pump assures fuel under pressure to the engine driven pump

life of high temperature engine components. Clean and efficient combustion is more difficult with fuels having either greater molecular weight or a high carbon-hydrogen ratio.

Aside from its influence on engine performance, volatility of a fuel is important in its relation to the vapor-air mixtures that develop in the space above the fuel under various temperature and pressure conditions. Fuels with a low volatility are desirable because of low boiling (evaporation) losses and the narrower range of temperatures in which burner fuel air (F/A) mixtures are produced. Volatility is controlled by setting limits on specifications such as flash point, vapor pressure, distillation and boiling point.

Because jet fuels are not dyed, there is no on-sight identification for them. They range from a colorless liquid to a straw-colored (amber) liquid, depending on age or the crude petroleum source. Jet fuel numbers are type numbers and their performance in the engine has no relation to the number. The military uses JP numbers, such as JP-4 and JP-5, to designate types of jet fuel to be used in their engines.

Kerosene-type jet fuel (Jet A). Kerosene-type fuels consist essentially of the heavier hydrocarbon fractions and are denser than wide-cut gasoline fuels. Due to the greater density, kerosene has a higher heating value per gallon than gasoline.

The freezing point of kerosene-type fuels varies somewhat with the type of hydrocarbon fraction present. Solid, waxy particles capable of clogging fuel filters begin to form at a temperature slightly above the pour point. For some kerosene this occurs at approximately -40°C and for others as low as -50°C. For turbine fuels, the freezing points range from -40° to -60° C.

The vapor pressure of kerosene-type fuels is extremely low, averaging about 0.125 p.s.i. As a result, fuel boiling and evaporation losses are negligible under normal flight conditions. Also, the tendency to develop ignitable fuel/air mixtures in the space above the fuel is less than the gasoline-type fuels.

Fuel System Contamination

Several forms of contamination can occur in aviation fuel. Jet A can hold contaminants in suspension because of its higher viscosity. For this reason jet fuels are more susceptible to contamination than other aviation fuels. Contaminants that reduce the quality of turbine fuels can be other petroleum products, water, rust or scale with water being the worst problem.

Water. Although precautions are constantly taken to ensure that fuel being pumped into an aircraft contains as small a quantity of water as possible, it is not possible to have aircraft fuel which contains no water. The affinity that fuel has for water varies with its composition and temperature.

The saturation level for a jet fuel in parts per million (ppm) by volume is approximately equivalent to the temperature in degrees Fahrenheit. For example, a jet fuel at 50° F (10°C) may contain approximately 50 ppm of dissolved water. When the fuel is cooled, the water that is above the saturation level is rejected as discrete water in minute particles. Until this water can collect and settle to the bottom of the tank, it will be carried in the fuel.

At temperatures below the freezing point, these minute particles may be super-cooled and will be deposited out only when they strike a solid obstruction and freeze. At low temperatures, water droplets combine with the fuel to form a frozen substance referred to as gel. The mass of gel that may be generated from moisture held in suspension in jet fuel can be very high.

After a long flight at high altitudes, an aircraft will have fuel tank surfaces and fuel that are colder than the air being drawn into the tank during descent. When moisture-laden air enters the tank space, condensation may occur in the tank. Due to the higher viscosity of cold fuel, this water will not settle out readily and will be carried as dispersed water. Under these conditions, the dispersed water in the fuel may reach 100 ppm. Water can be present in the fuel as either dissolved or suspended water. Entrained or suspended water can be detected with the naked eye. The finely divided droplets reflect light and (in high concentrations) give the fuel a dull, hazy, or cloudy appearance. Particles of entrained water may unite to form droplets of free water.

Fuel can be cloudy for a number of reasons. If the fuel is cloudy and the cloud disappears at the bottom, air is present. If the cloud disappears at the top, water is present. A cloud usually indicates a water-in-fuel suspension. Free water can cause icing of the aircraft fuel system, usually in the aircraft boost pump screens and the low-pressure filters. Large amounts of water can cause engine stoppage.

Many turbine engine fuel systems incorporate a method for heating the fuel using an air to fuel heat exchanger that melts any ice before the fuel enters the engine. Either hot bleed air or hot engine oil is used to heat the fuel for this purpose.

Microbial Growth

Microorganisms of various types can grow in an aircraft fuel tank and in storage tanks if water is present. Such microorganisms grow best in fuel that has not been agitated for extended periods. If an airplane is stored with fuel and water in the fuel tank for an extended time, chances are that microorganisms will grow and appear as a slimy deposit in the water. The color will vary from brown to black, with all shades in between, including red. The organisms feed on the hydrocarbons that are found in fuels, but they need free water in order to multiply.

When fuel has been stored for a lengthy period, either in an aircraft or in a fuel storage tank, the fuel and tank should be examined for signs of microbial contamination. If the fuel is discolored or has an abnormal smell, the tank should be drained and cleaned. Contaminated fuel should be discarded.

Technicians who have the responsibility for fueling and defueling turbine-powered aircraft must be alert to detect microorganism contamination and take the required measures to eliminate it. Fueling procedures established by airlines provide for protection against microorganism contamination and should be followed carefully.

The effects of microorganisms in fuel are serious, regardless of whether the organisms are bacteria or fungi. The buildup of microorganisms not only can interfere with fuel flow and quantity indication, but, more importantly, can allow electrolytic corrosion to start in the aircraft's structure. Corrosive chemicals are formed which attack the metal walls and bottoms of fuel tanks. Many aircraft have suffered structural weakening of the wings because fuel tanks in large aircraft are usually integral with the wings. It has been common practice to coat the interior surfaces of wing tanks with corrosion-resistant materials. In some cases the microorganisms have penetrated the coating and created corrosion cells under the coatings.

New coatings have been developed which resist not only corrosion but also attacks by microorganisms. It is important that fuel tanks of aircraft which have been in service for a long time be thoroughly inspected. If evidence of microorganisms or corrosion exists, the interior of the tank should be cleaned, stripped and recoated. If appreciable corrosion exists, replacing or repairing sections of the tank walls and bottoms may be necessary.

Fuel additives. Additives have been developed to combat problems with fuel icing and/or microbial growth. One such additive is Prist, which is designed to prevent ice and bacterial contamination in aviation fuel. It is sometimes referred to as PFA 55MB and is covered by specification MIL-I-27686D. Pure ethylene glycol mono-methyl ether (EGME), the primary ingredient of Prist additive, is generally compatible with the components of turbine aircraft fuel systems. It is effective in preventing fuel ice because as the fuel temperature decreases the additive combines with the water in greater concentrations. This combination will keep the freezing point of the water lower than the temperature of the fuel. Prist should be protected from contact with oxidizing agents, including long-term contact with air.

The recommended concentration of Prist in fuel is from 0.06 to 0.15% by volume. It must be incrementally blended into the fuel because its solubility in fuel is limited. It is completely soluble in the water that is suspended in the fuel. Fuel-additive proportioners are engineered to blend the additive into fuel during refueling, so that the turbulence of the flowing fuel stream

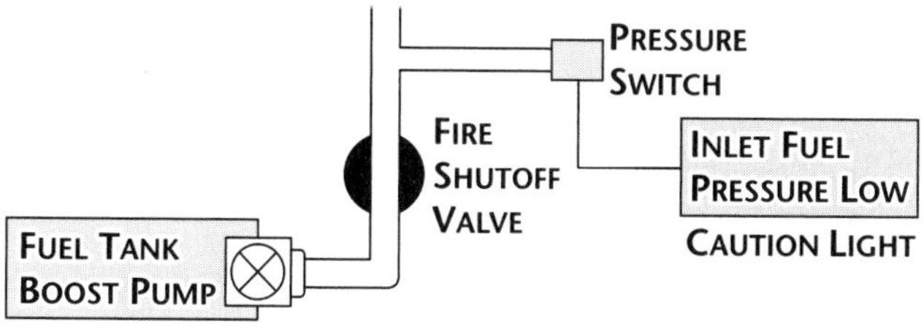

Figure 5-1-2. The low-pressure light illuminates when pressure drops at the inlet to the engine driven pump.

will provide a mixing action. In all cases, additive must be used as directed by the manufacturer. No fuel additive should be used in a particular system unless the system has been approved for it.

Contamination detection. Coarse fuel contamination can be detected visually. The major criteria for contamination detection are that the fuel be clean, bright and contain no perceptible free water. Clean means the absence of any readily visible sediment or entrained water. Bright refers to the shiny appearance of clean, dry fuels. A cloud, haze, or a water slug indicates free water. A cloud may or may not be present when the fuel is saturated with water. Perfectly clear fuel can contain as much as three times the volume of water as is considered tolerable.

Since fuel drained from tank sumps may have been cold-soaked, it is important to realize that no method of water detection is accurate while the fuel-entrained water is frozen into ice crystals. There is a good chance that water will not be drained or detected if the sumps are drained while the fuel is below 32° F. Draining will be more effective if it is done after the fuel has been undisturbed for a period of time, during which the free water can precipitate and settle to the drain point. However, the benefits of a settling period will be lost unless the accumulated water is removed from the drains before internal pumps disturb the fuel.

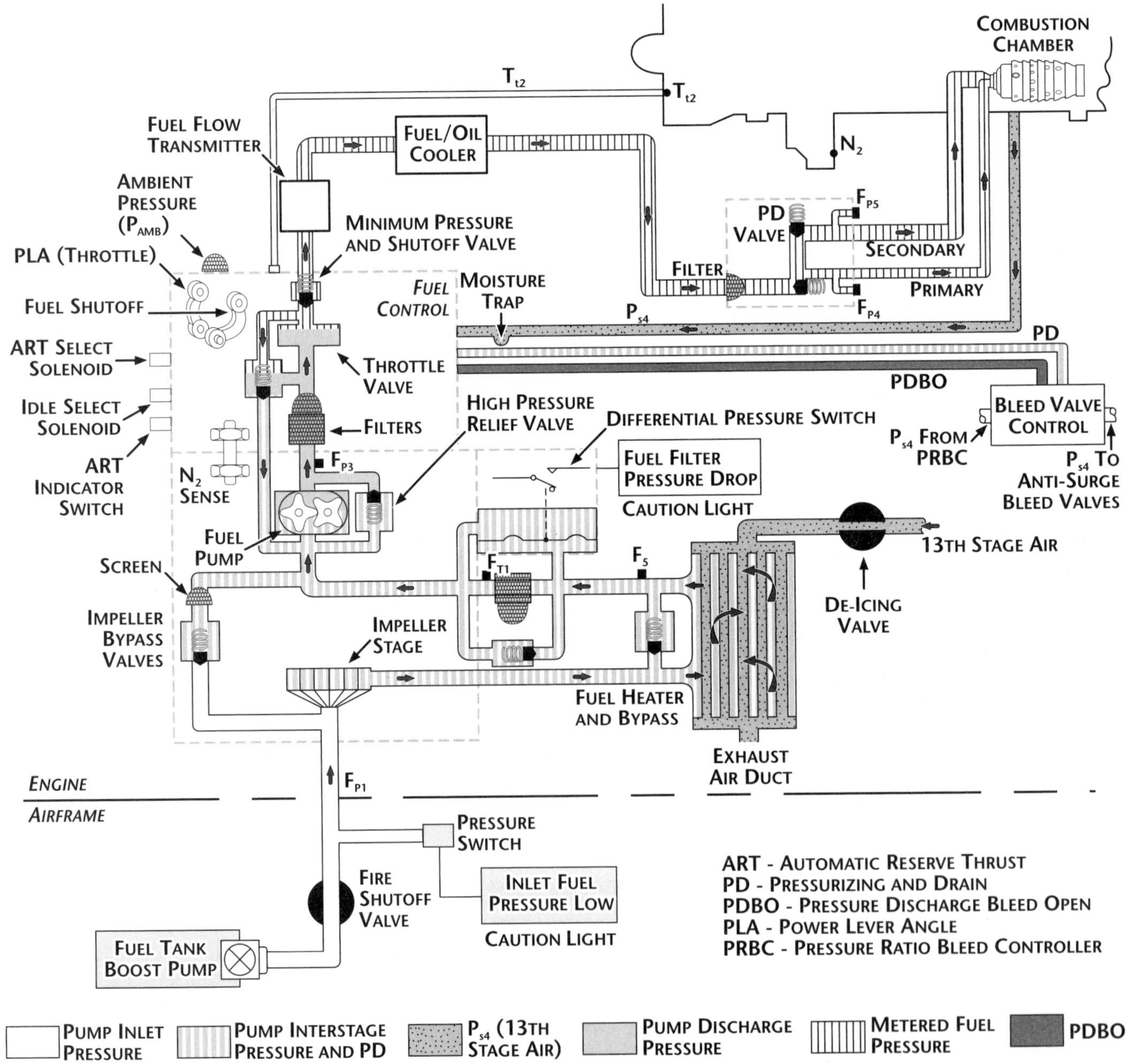

Figure 5-1-3. A typical high-pressure engine driven fuel system

Aircraft Fuel Systems

The aircraft fuel system (low-pressure system) both stores fuel and delivers the proper amount of clean fuel at the right pressure to meet the demands of the engine or engines. A well-designed aircraft fuel system ensures positive and reliable fuel flow throughout all phases of flight, including changes in altitude, violent maneuvers and sudden acceleration and deceleration.

Shown in Figure 5-1-1, the electrically driven aircraft centrifugal booster pump, mounted in the fuel tank, supplies fuel under pressure to the inlet of the engine-driven fuel pump. This type of pump is an essential part of the aircraft fuel system, particularly at high altitudes, to keep pressure on the suction side of the engine-driven pump from becoming too low. If the engine-driven pump is forced to draw the fuel from the aircraft fuel system, the pump is said to be in suction lift.

Suction lift often causes cavitation. Cavitation is the rapid formation and collapse of air bubbles. This action, over time, can cause erosion damage to the pump. Suction lift operation has a specific time limit and can require pump maintenance before further use.

The engine driven pump must be supplied with pressurized fuel that has the correct amount of flow at all times during operation. Each boost pump generally has an associated low-pressure light that illuminates when the pump is switched off. This is illustrated in Figure 5-1-2. Fuel pressure, fuel flow, warning signals and tank quantity are shown to give continuous indications of how the system is functioning. After the fuel is delivered to the engine fuel system, it generally passes through an engine-driven fuel pump.

The aircraft system is capable of providing fuel to any engine from any tank. This is known as a cross-feed system. The aircraft system can also balance the fuel load from wing to wing to trim out lateral imbalance. Each engine is provided with fuel shutoff valves in the nacelle to stop the flow of fuel in an emergency. Another part of the aircraft fuel system is the jettison or dump feature. This allows the pilot to jettison fuel clear of the aircraft or to reduce landing weights in emergencies.

Engine Fuel System

The purpose of a main fuel system is to provide a measured flow of fuel to the engine for a given set of engine operating conditions. The engine fuel system of a gas turbine engine senses a number of current engine and atmospheric conditions, compares these conditions to the desired conditions and then meters the required fuel flow to the engine's combustor. Some of the conditions or parameters sensed are engine speed, throttle position, compressor inlet temperature, compressor discharge pressure and exhaust gas temperature. Within certain operating limits, fuel must be metered for starting, acceleration, deceleration, as well as for constant speed operations.

Turbine engine fuel systems vary according to the method and components used to deliver fuel to the combustion section of the engine. The diagram in Figure 5-1-3 represents a typical high-pressure engine fuel system. Because turbine engines can have a wide range of operating characteristics that perform several types of missions, their fuel system arrangement and components can vary widely. The components and order of the components (flow) in the system can be different depending on the type of turbine engine and the aircraft installation. Some of the components that turbine engine fuel systems include are:

- Single or dual stage engine-driven fuel pumps
- High- and low-pressure filters and bypass valves
- Fuel controls
- Hydromechanical
- Supervisory electronic control (hybrid hydromechanical and electronic)
- Full authority digital electronic control (FADEC)
- Fuel flow transmitters
- Pressurization dump valves
- Fuel/oil coolers and bypass valve
- Fuel nozzles

The engine-mounted fuel system components on a typical gas turbine engine are the main fuel pump, fuel filter, engine fuel control, oil cooler, flow divider and fuel nozzles.

A fuel heater is used to prevent ice crystals from forming in the engine fuel system. A fuel filter is used in the system that passes the flow through the oil cooler. On many engines, a fuel-cooled oil cooler is located between the fuel pump and the inlet to the fuel filter. The oil cooler is placed here to transfer the heat from the oil to the fuel, thus preventing blockage of the filter element by ice particles. When heat transfer by this means is insufficient, the fuel is passed through a fuel heater. There is usually some method to warn the pilot or flight engineer of this icing danger. One method uses a differential-pressure switch that obtains signals from the entrance and exit of the fuel filter. When there is a specified pressure drop across the filter, the switch will turn on a warning light in the cockpit. The fuel anti-icing system can then be actuated. On newer aircraft this is an automatic function performed by the fuel oil cooler.

The high-pressure system includes the high-pressure fuel pump, fuel/oil cooler, filter, fuel control unit, fuel pressurizing/dump valve, fuel manifolds, fuel spray nozzles and various other components. Fuel enters the system from the fuel supply and passes through a low-pressure pump. It then passes through the high-pressure pump where it is pressurized up to several hundred p.s.i. From the high-pressure pump the fuel enters the fuel/oil heat exchanger that is used to cool the oil.

The fuel filter is next in the flow path. This filter has a bypass valve that will open if the filter becomes clogged. As mentioned earlier, the filter's inlet and outlet pressure are monitored to determine if the filter has become clogged. The fuel then passes into the main engine fuel control which meters the amount of fuel the engine requires for a given engine condition or r.p.m. Fuel on its way to the engine, either enters the pressurizing/dump valve, which directs fuel to the engine, such as in the engine running mode, or dumps fuel from the engine when the engine is stopped. The fuel continues through the fuel flow transmitter and on to the fuel manifold, which distributes the fuel to each fuel nozzle in the combustion section.

Illustrated in Figure 5-1-4 is another gas turbine engine fuel system. This system has many of the same components as described earlier, but it uses a flow divider just before the fuel manifold, which separates the fuel into primary and secondary fuel flow. The primary fuel flow is used during starting of the engine. As the engine requires more fuel at high engine speeds the secondary flow is added to the primary, allowing both flows into the combustion section.

Fuel System Components

Fuel lines and fittings. In a turbine engine fuel system, the various components are usually joined together by fuel lines made of metal tubing. Where flexibility is necessary, lengths of flexible hose can be used. The metal tubing is usually made of stainless steel if used forward of the firewall and the flexible hose is made of synthetic rubber or Teflon. The diameter of the tubing or hose is governed by the fuel flow requirements of the engine.

Fuel filters. Strainers or filters trap water and other contaminants. There are low- and high-pressure filters depending upon their location in the system. Many filters incorporate a bypass in the event that the filter becomes partially or completely clogged. If ice crystals are mixed with the fuel, they can collect in the filter until it begins to stop the flow of fuel. If this happens, a differential pressure switch illuminates a warning light. This warning light will alert the flight crew to the situation. See Figure 5-1-5. By using fuel heat (a process of heating the fuel with engine bleed air or hot engine oil), the ice crystals can be melted and the water will pass

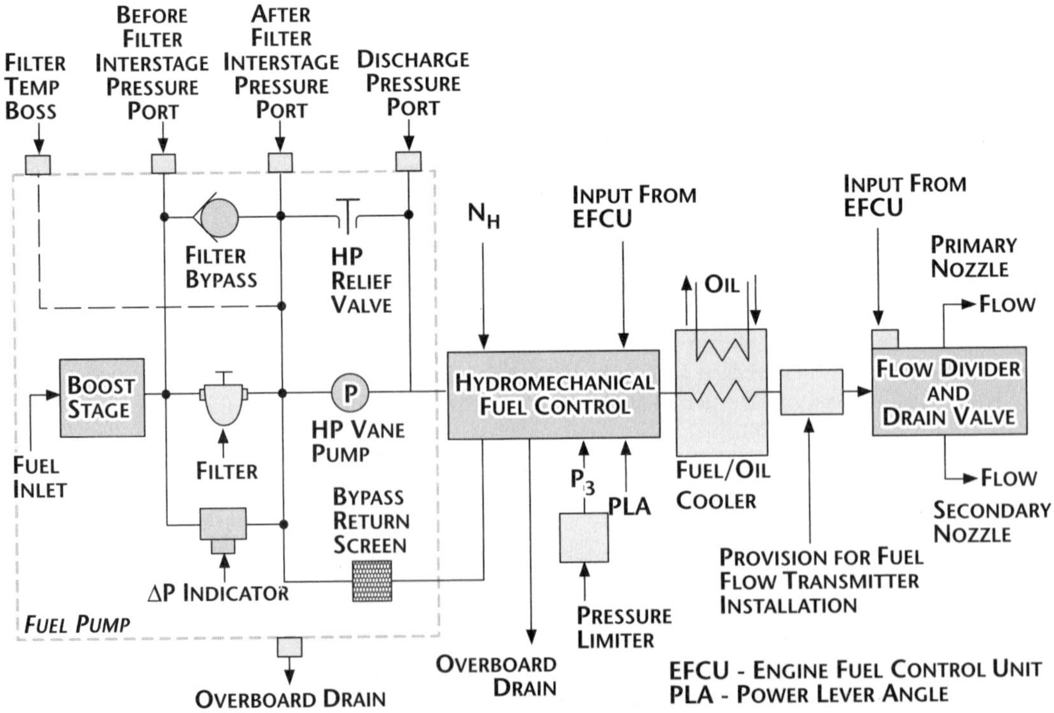

Figure 5-1-4. This fuel system uses a flow divider to separate the fuel into primary and secondary flow.

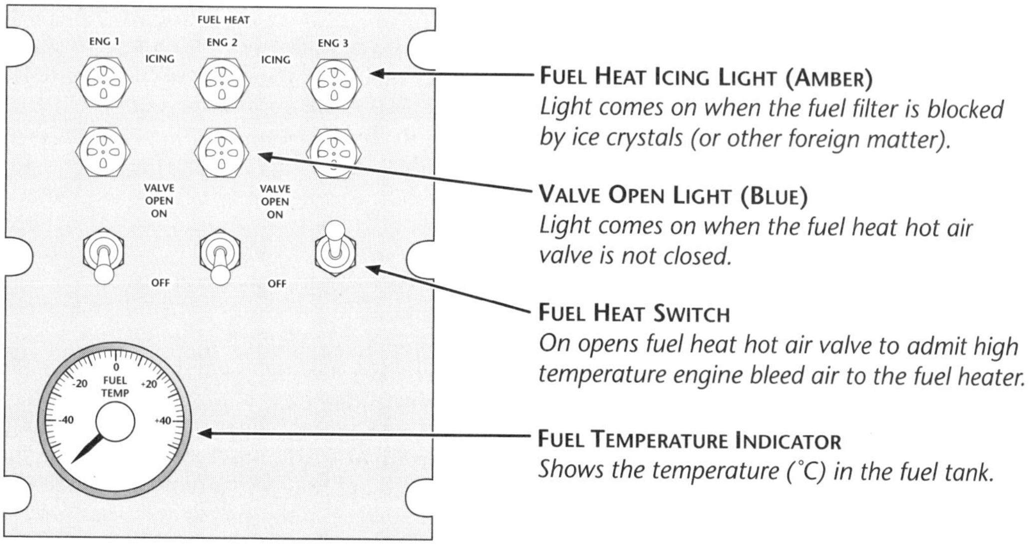

Figure 5-1-5. A typical cockpit fuel system control panel

through the engine. If ice crystals do not cause the blockage in the filter, then the filter blockage is from fuel contamination and the use of fuel heat will not correct the problem.

A low-pressure filter is installed between the supply tanks and the engine fuel system to protect the engine-driven fuel pump and various control devices. An additional high-pressure fuel filter is installed between the fuel pump and fuel control to protect the fuel control from contaminants.

The three most common types of filters are:

- Micron
- Wafer screen
- Plain screen mesh

The micron filter, seen in Figure 5-1-6, has the greatest filtering action of any filter type and is rated in microns (one thousandth of a millimeter). The porous cellulose material, frequently used in construction of filter cartridges, is capable of removing foreign matter measuring from 10 to 25 microns. These minute openings make micron filters susceptible to clogging; making a bypass valve a necessary safety element.

Engine-driven fuel pump. The engine-driven fuel pump delivers a continuous supply of fuel at the proper pressure and volume during engine operation. Many engine-driven pumps have two stages: a centrifugal (non-positive) displacement for the low-pressure side and a positive displacement, rotary vane type or gear-type pump for the high-pressure side. A positive displacement pump requires a regulating valve to relieve outlet pressure. Without a regulating valve, the pressure would be a function of the resistance to flow on the outlet side of the pump. In other words, if the outlet is blocked, either the pump must stop turning

Figure 5-1-6. The micron filter can remove extremely fine material from a fluid.

Figure 5-1-7. Engine-driven fuel pump

or the pressure line would burst. A picture of a typical engine-driven fuel pump is shown in Figure 5-1-7.

Pressurization dump valves and fuel flow dividers. The fuel pressurizing valve is usually required on engines incorporating duplex fuel nozzles to divide the flow into primary and secondary manifolds. At the fuel flows required for starting and idling, all the fuel passes through the primary line. As the fuel requirement increases, the valve begins to open the secondary line until at maximum flow the primary and secondary are both flowing fuel.

Fuel pressurizing valves will usually trap fuel forward of the manifold, giving a positive cutoff. This cutoff prevents fuel from dribbling into the manifold and through the fuel nozzles, eliminating after-fires and carbonization of fuel nozzles to a major degree. Carbonization occurs when combustion chamber temperatures are lowered and the fuel is not completely burned.

A flow divider, shown in Figure 5-1-8, performs essentially the same function as a pressurizing valve. It is used, as the name implies, to divide flow to the duplex fuel nozzles. Since units performing identical functions can be from different manufacturers, it is not unusual for them to use different nomenclature.

Fuel flowmeter and pressure transmitter. Although fuel flow transmitters use different operating principles, many turbine engine fuel systems use the mass flow type. The flowmeter transmitter should have a range suitable for the engine and measure in pounds per hour. It consists of a cylinder placed in the fuel stream so that the direction of fuel flow is parallel to the axis of the cylinder seen in Figure 5-1-9. The interior has a wheel with small vanes in the outer periphery. The wheel, called the impeller, is driven in proportion to the amount of fuel flow. This impeller velocity imparts a radio frequency or a magnetic pulse to the output of the transmitter. The output frequency is proportional to the fuel flow and is read out on the flight deck.

Figure 5-1-8. The flow divider separates fuel to duplex nozzle.

On aircraft where the fuel pressure gauge or low-pressure light sensor is located some distance from the engine, a transmitter is usually installed. The pressure transmitter may be a simple cast metal cell that is divided into two chambers by a flexible diaphragm or by electrical transmitters that send the fuel pressure to the gauge readout. The pressure warning lights are installed in the aircraft to alert the flight crew. Normal fuel pressure pushes against the power surface of the diaphragm that holds the electrical contacts apart. When the fuel pressure drops below specified limits, the contacts close and the warning light illuminates. This alerts the flight crew to take whatever action is necessary to provide boost fuel pressure to the engine.

Section 2

Mechanical Engine Fuel Controls

Turbine engines use a fuel control unit (FCU) to meter fuel flow to the engine. While significantly more complex, the FCU performs for the turbine engine a similar function to the carburetor or fuel injection system on a piston engine. There are three types of FCUs used on turbine engines: the hydromechanical, the supervisory and the full authority digital type. The older hydromechanical models were replaced by the supervisory control that combined electronics over mechanical control. The newest generation of control is the Full Authority Digital Engine Control (FADEC).

All fuel controls feature a computing section. Hydromechanical FCUs are mechanical computers that use flyweights, cams and gears to determine the proper fuel flow. FADEC units use modern digital computers. Supervisory electronic controls use some combination of mechanical, analog and digital electronic computing devices.

The hydromechanical fuel control is mounted on the accessory drive housing. It is mechanically linked and turned by the gas generator through the accessory drive. The supervisory electronic control systems combine a hydromechanical or hydropneumatic fuel control plus electronic systems that adjust fuel flow by inputs from the electronic control. The FADEC is an electronic fuel control computer. It is not driven by the gas generator; it receives its speed and other information needed to schedule the fuel from sensors mounted on the engine.

The fuel control function is very important and is designed to perform the following functions:

- Provide a means of varying fuel flow for different power settings
- Regulate fuel metering during starting and acceleration to prevent excessive turbine inlet temperature
- Control the rate of decrease of fuel metering during deceleration to prevent flameout
- Control engine speed outside of the operational limits
- Provide a measure of engine protection during an over-speed or high turbine inlet temperature event by reducing fuel flow
- Provide a starting fuel flow schedule which prevents over-temperature and compressor surge
- Compensate for changes in air density caused by variations in compressor inlet air temperature and pressure
- Provide a means of stopping the fuel flow for engine shutdown

The basic fuel control system senses the compressor inlet pressure, compressor inlet temperature and engine speed. Using these three factors and the setting of the power lever, the fuel control meters the proper amount of fuel throughout the range of engine operation. The fuel controls normally are set up to bypass extra fuel that is not needed as a means of scheduling the correct fuel flow. This excess flow always assures that sufficient fuel is available. The control includes a fuel cutoff valve for stopping fuel flow to the engine at shutdown. Mechanical linkage or an electrical actuator actuates the cutoff valve. It may be manually or electrically controlled. This valve must be in the open position to permit fuel flow. During an engine start, the valve remains closed until the engine reaches a predetermined speed when the valve is opened, permitting fuel flow to the engine.

Basic FCU Operation

Many types and models of fuel control units have been designed and used for gas-turbine engines. The simplest type of control can be a manually controlled valve; however, this is not practical, because the pilot would have to watch several gauges and make frequent adjustments to keep the engine operating and to prevent

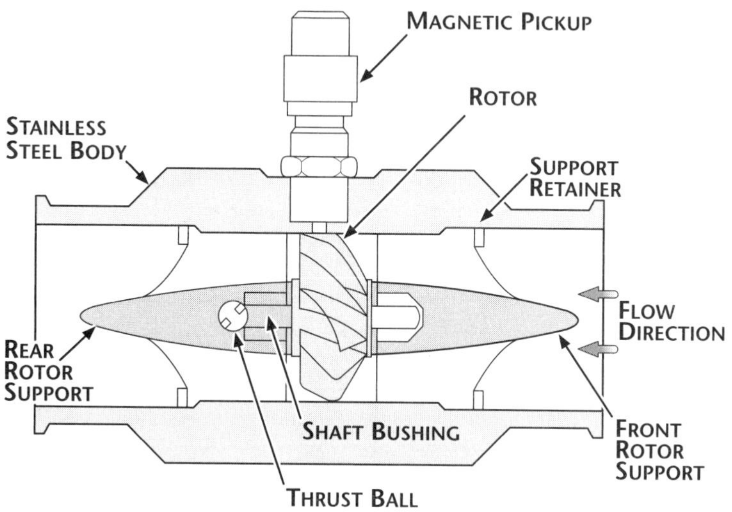

Figure 5-1-9. The fuel flow transmitter sends a signal to the cockpit indicator.

damage. If the quantity of fuel is not correct for the velocity and pressure of the air flowing through the engine, the engine cannot function. If too much fuel enters the combustion chamber or chambers, the turbine section may be damaged by excessive heat, the compressor may stall or surge because of back pressure from the combustion chambers, or a rich flameout may occur. A rich flameout takes place when the mixture is too rich to burn. If too little fuel enters the combustion chambers, a lean die-out or flameout occurs.

Among the various factors which must be considered in the regulation of fuel flow for a gas-turbine engine are:

- Ambient air pressure (P_{amb})
- Compressor inlet temperature
- Engine r.p.m.
- Velocity of air through the compressor
- Compressor inlet air pressure
- Compressor discharge pressure (same as burner pressure)
- Turbine inlet temperature (or exhaust temperature)
- Throttle or power lever setting

Since some of the factors listed above are interrelated, the parameters applied to the fuel control unit can be reduced to ambient pressure, compressor inlet temperature (CIT), burner pressure, high-pressure compressor rotor speed (N_2) and power-lever (throttle) position as a normal minimum.

A number of methods of operation are used in fuel control units; these are described in part by classification. The early fuel control units have

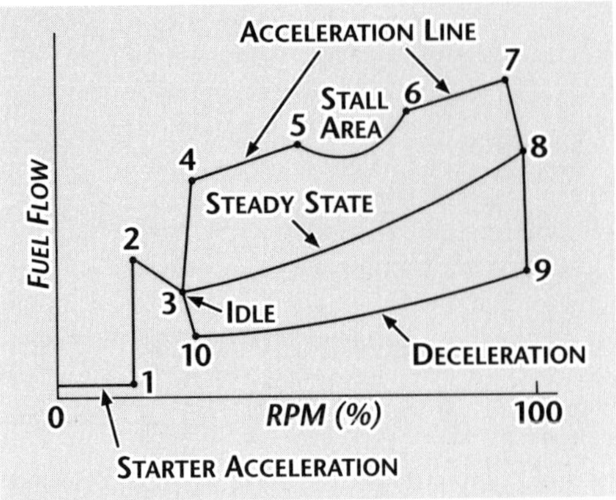

Figure 5-2-1. A typical fuel control response to engine conditions

been hydromechanical in their operation and are called hydromechanical fuel control units. This means that the operation is hydraulic and mechanical. A number of late-type engines are now controlled by means of electronic fuel control systems. These systems include computers that precisely measure all parameters and provide signals that result in maximum efficiency, reliability and fuel economy.

The principal sections of a fuel control unit are the fuel metering section and the computing section. The fuel metering section consists of a fuel metering valve across which a constant fuel pressure differential is established. The size of the opening in the valve is controlled by the power lever position and the information from the computing section of the fuel control. In order to prevent damage from excessive heat, stalling, surge or flameout, the compensating section of the control unit accepts signals from the engine and the pilot to determine how much fuel should be delivered to the fuel nozzles.

When the power lever is moved forward to demand more power from the engine, the computing section regulates the metering valve opening. The fuel requirements are matched to the airflow in order to accelerate the engine in a smooth, continuous increase. This reduces the possibility of over temperature by delivering an optimum F/A mixture to the burners.

Proper fuel flow permits maximum acceleration without engine damage. If the burner pressure approaches a level that could cause surge or stall, the computer will limit the fuel flow until the airflow is increased sufficiently. In some fuel control units, an air-bleed control system is included. This system regulates the bleed valve function, reducing excessive compressor backpressure and avoiding stall or surge.

The chart in Figure 5-2-1 shows how one type of fuel control unit responds to engine conditions, air pressure and temperature and power lever (throttle) position. In general, the following sequence takes place:

1. The engine is accelerated by the starter until the correct starting r.p.m. is attained.
2. The power lever is advanced to the IDLE position to provide fuel (positions 1 to 2 on the curve).
3. As the engine r.p.m. increases, fuel flow decreases from the acceleration level to the point where it is correct to sustain idle speed (position 3).
4. The power lever is advanced to the full-power position and fuel flow is increased as indicated by position 4.
5. As the engine r.p.m. increases, fuel flow increases to position 5 and then it is decreased to avoid the stall and surge area. In the range of speeds between position 5 and position 6, the fuel must be reduced to prevent back pressure from the combustion chamber, which could cause compressor stall or surge.
6. At position 6, fuel flow is restored to the normal maximum acceleration level until the engine approaches maximum speed (position 7).
7. Shortly before maximum speed is reached, the governor reduces fuel flow to prevent over-speeding. The fuel flow is stabilized, as shown at position 8, at a quantity which will maintain 100% engine r.p.m.
8. When it is desired to reduce engine r.p.m. to idle speed, the power lever is moved to the IDLE position. Fuel flow is immediately reduced to the value indicated by position 9 on the curve. This is a value that will permit maximum deceleration but will not let the F/A mixture drop to a ratio where a lean die-out may occur.
9. The engine r.p.m. decreases, as indicated by the curve between positions 9 and 10 and the fuel flow decreases slowly.
10. When the engine r.p.m. approaches idle speed, the fuel flow increases to the point where idle speed can be maintained. This is indicated by the curve between positions 10 and 3 in the diagram.

The curves of Figure 5-2-1 will vary considerably as air pressure and temperature change. These values are applied to the computing section of the fuel control to modify fuel flow as conditions dictate.

Speed-sensitive control and compressor discharge pressure. One of the simplest fuel controls is associated with auxiliary power units (APU). A typical APU fuel system schematic is shown in Figure 5-2-2. The speed-sensitive control is used with mechanical systems to control the engine speed. An APU operating at 100% r.p.m. with no load is operating at idle.

On flight engines, the fuel control is much more complicated and has to control the engine at all r.p.m. settings from idle to 100% r.p.m. Most flight engines idle at about 40% r.p.m. to 60% r.p.m. The engine must operate at any point of r.p.m. in this range which has been selected by the thrust lever input. The fuel control must function during all r.p.m. operating ranges of the engine. APU fuel controls maintain the speed at a constant r.p.m. Fuel flow is varied to accept loads placed on the APU.

The speed-sensing section of the APU fuel control normally sets the maximum allowable speed and provides overspeed protection controlled by the speed governor in the fuel control. The fuel is varied according to gas generator speed by a flyweight system. A flyweight type of speed control is shown in Figure 5-2-2 (governor). This is normally a part of the computing section of the fuel control and is driven by the gas generator. When the engine speed decreases, as when a load is applied, the governor flyweights move inward to close the amount of fuel bypassed. This permits greater fuel flow to the combustion section and allows the engine to regain any loss of r.p.m.

When the engine is starting, other fuel control components compute and meter the fuel flow. The compressor discharge pressure (CDP) is a good indicator of the speed and pressure being generated during the start sequence. This speed and compressor pressure (air flow through the engine) is generated and increased by the starter turning the gas generator of the engine, which causes air flow through the engine. The air is compressed by the compressor and is sensed by the fuel control as CDP.

Fuel flow should not start until a certain CDP is detected by the fuel control. By sensing the CDP, the fuel control can begin to schedule fuel to flow at the correct rates that will accelerate the engine to a self-sustaining speed. The CDP has a direct relationship with the quantity of fuel required to accelerate the engine. As the CDP increases, this tells the fuel control that the airflow and pressure have increased and the engine is ready for more fuel. The CDP is generally taken from the compressor outlet

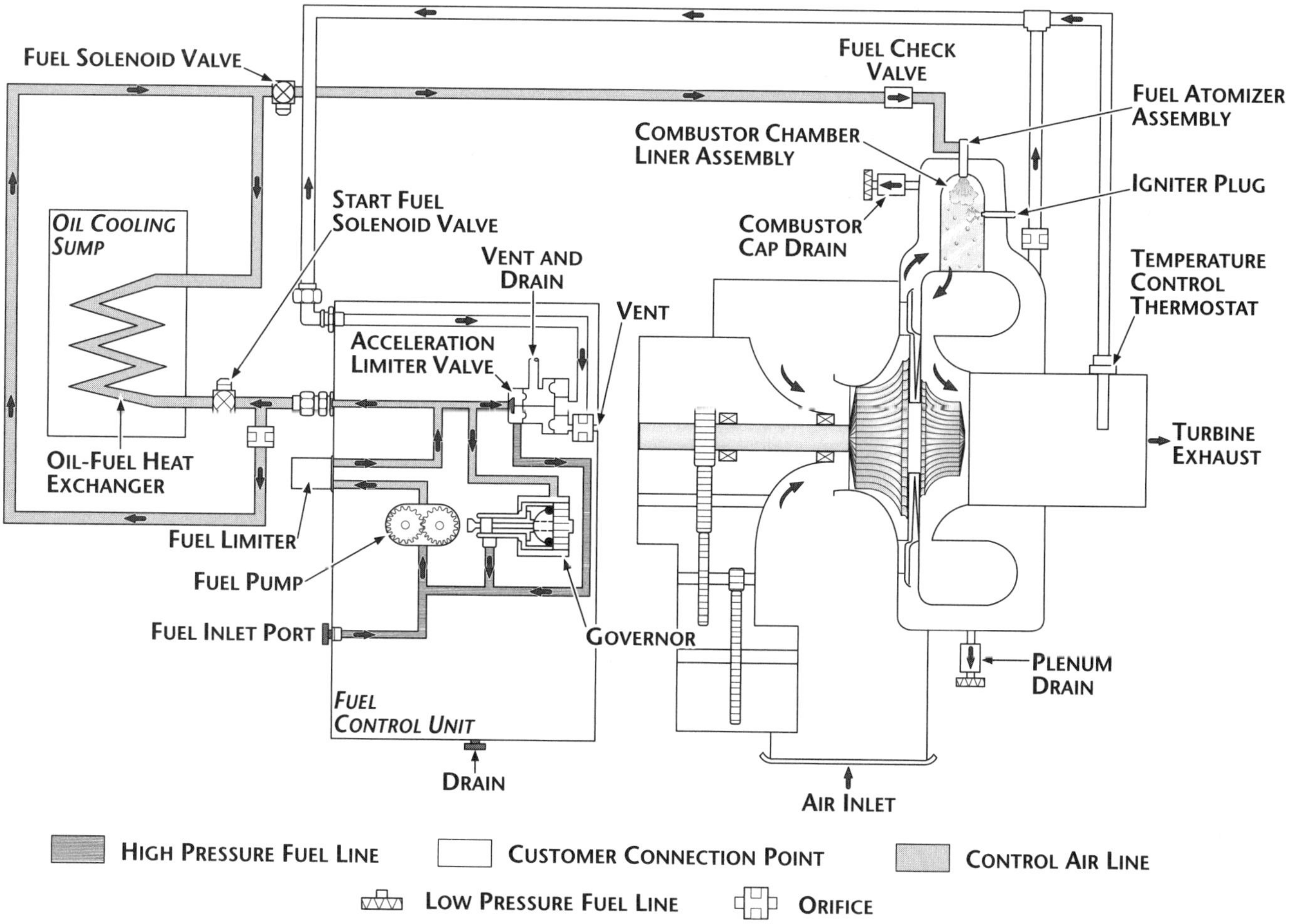

Figure 5-2-2. Schematic of a typical APU

and connected to the fuel control by tubing. This section of the fuel control is sometimes referred to as the acceleration limiter control.

Acceleration exhaust temperature and speed are controlled within established limits by the metering of the fuel flow through the fuel control's acceleration limiter valve. This valve references compressor air discharge pressure. A diaphragm-actuated poppet valve in the fuel control unit bypasses more or less fuel to maintain the required ratio of fuel flow to compressor air pressure.

During the early stages of engine starting and acceleration, the compressor air pressure is low. The acceleration poppet valve is restrained from bypassing fuel by an adjustable spring pressure against the actuating diaphragm. When the spring pressure on the diaphragm is overcome by CDP, the fuel is bypassed, providing the correct fuel flow as the engine starts. This action is shown in Figure 5-2-2. At the point that the fuel is bypassed, the limiter valve's cracking pressure has been reached.

The cracking pressure can be set by removing the fuel line at the nozzle and placing a pressure gauge in the line. Then disconnect the CDP line from the fuel control and while motoring the engine with the starter, adjust the cracking pressure.

General Turboprop Fuel Control

Turboprop fuel controls operate slightly differently. For reference purposes, a typical fuel control, shown in Figure 5-2-3, is described in the following section. The FCU is supplied with fuel at pump pressure P_1. Fuel flow is established by the minimum flow orifice, fuel flow valve and bypass valve system. The fuel pressure immediately after the minimum flow orifice and the fuel valve is called metered fuel (P_2). The bypass valve maintains an essentially constant fuel pressure differential (P_1 - P_2) across the fuel valve. The orifice area of the fuel flow valve is changed by valve movement to meet specific engine fuel requirements: with fuel pump output pressure in excess of these requirements, returned via internal passages in the FCU and pump to the pump inlet.

Bypassed fuel is referred to as P_0 fuel. The bypass valve consists of a piston operating in a ported sleeve and is actuated by a spring. In operation, the spring force is balanced by the P_1 - P_2 differential operating on the piston. The valve is always in a position to maintain the P_1 - P_2 difference; excess P_1 pressure is bypassed to P_0. By turning the adjuster, the force on the spring is varied. The adjuster is a manual compensation for fuels with specific-gravity values. An ultimate relief valve is incorporated in parallel

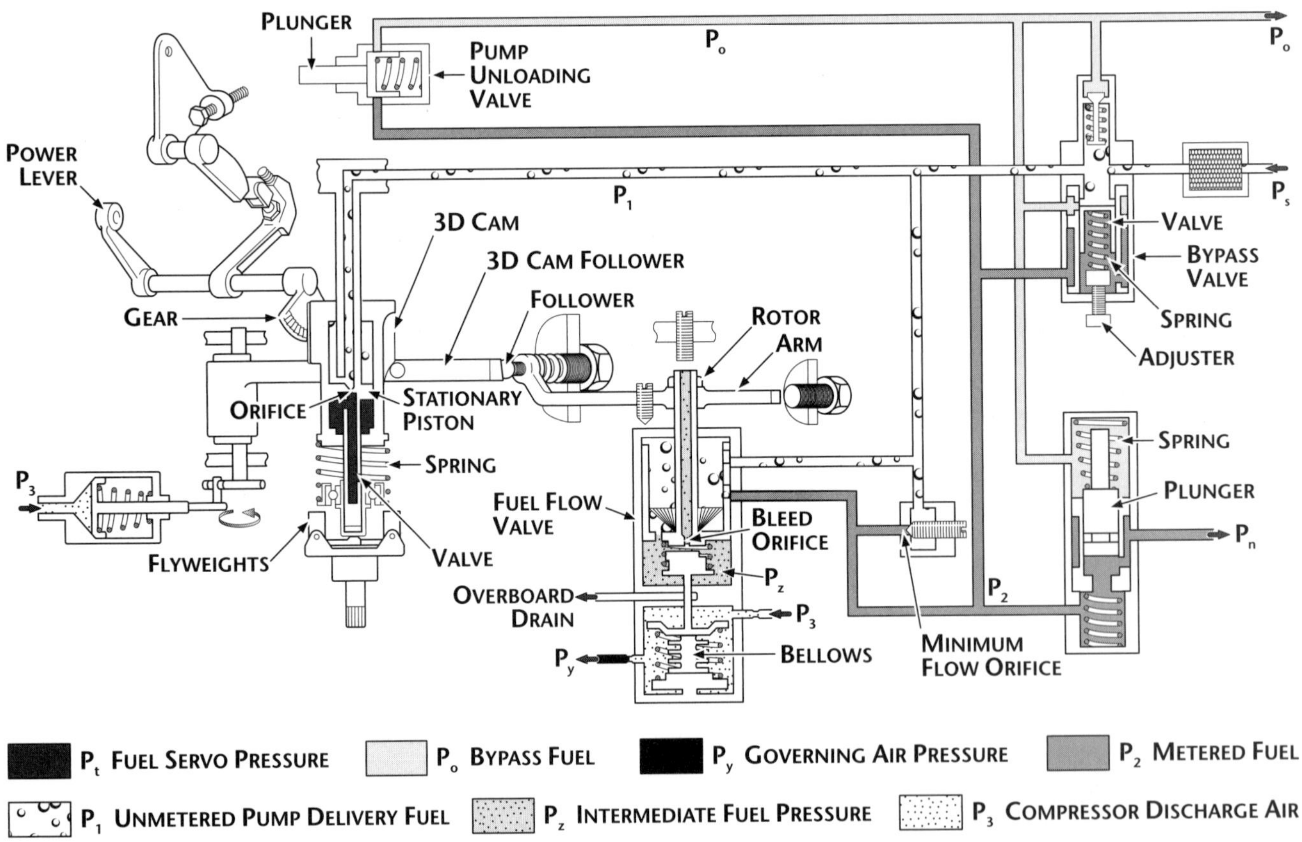

Figure 5-2-3. While a FCU has many interrelated components which control fuel flow, the basic fuel flow schematic is not complicated.

with the bypass valve to prevent excessive P_1 pressure in the FCU. The valve is spring-loaded closed and it remains closed until P_1 overcomes the spring force and opens the valve to P_0. As soon as the pressure is reduced again to an acceptable level, the valve closes.

A minimum pressurizing valve is incorporated in the output line to the flow divider. Its function is to ensure sufficient fuel pressure within the FCU to maintain correct fuel metering. A fuel shutoff valve in the same line provides a positive means of stopping fuel flow to the engine. During normal operation the valve is fully open and offers no restriction to flow of fuel to the flow divider. Engine shutdown is accomplished when the condition lever is moved to the shutdown position, the depressing plunger on the pump unloading valve, porting pressure P_2 to P_0. Decreasing pressure P_2 allows the pressurizing spring to expand, moving the valve plunger to the closed position and blocking the fuel flow.

Speed control. Engine speed is controlled by the N_g speed sensor (tachometer). The tachometer contains two flyweights mounted on a ball head driven by the engine. The centrifugal force generated by the flyweights is directly proportional to speed N_g and is transmitted to a valve by the toes of the flyweights. The spring, controlled by the three-dimensional cam, opposes this force. The valve is positioned by the three-dimensional cam.

Fuel at pressure P_1 is supplied through an orifice to the tachometer pilot-valve ports. Above the orifice, pressure P_1 is diverted to the area above the stationary piston and exerts an upward force on the end of the three-dimensional cam. The valve opening controls the pressure below the orifice. The three-dimensional cam is positioned at a point where the combination of the flyweight force and the spring sets the opening of the valve. By regulating the port area, an exact amount of pressure is bled off to maintain servo pressure (P_t) equal to $\frac{1}{2}P_1$. The three-dimensional cam is held stationary at this particular speed.

Overspeed. When an overspeed condition occurs, increasing speed N_g increases the force of the flyweights, which forces the valve upward. The area of the metering port is decreased and servo pressure (P_t) increases. Increased servo pressure (P_t) forces the three-dimensional cam downward. Force exerted by the spring opposes the movement of the cam. A balance point is reached when the cam is held stationary at the new speed position.

Underspeed. When an underspeed condition occurs, decreasing speed N_g reduces the force of the flyweights. The compressed spring moves the valve downward. The motoring port area increases and servo pressure P_t decreases. Pressure P_1 above the piston moves the three-dimensional cam upward and decreases the spring force until the system is in equilibrium again. The action of the N_g sensor (tachometer) keeps these forces continually in balance so that the axial position of the three-dimensional cam always represents engine speed N_g.

The follower on the arm is connected to the three-dimensional cam follower assembly. As the three-dimensional cam moves upward, the fuel valve port opens; fuel flow to the engine is increased and N_g increases. Downward movement of the three-dimensional cam decreases fuel flow and speed N_g. Engine speed is thus maintained by the N_g speed sensor (tachometer). Desired speed changes are set by the power lever, which determines the rotational position of the three-dimensional cam by means of a gear. When the power lever setting is changed, the positions of the cam followers are moved. The area of the port in the fuel valve is varied and the amount of fuel supplied to the engine is increased or decreased accordingly. Engine speed N_g is directly proportional to fuel flow.

Limiting the compressor discharge pressure. The compressor discharge pressure (CDP) (P_3) is a second input affecting the position of the fuel valve. The CDP P_3 sensor is a sealed, evacuated bellows assembly (11). Varying P_3 causes the bellows to expand or contract. This movement is transmitted by a hydraulic amplifier to move a rotor axially.

Fuel at pressure P_1 is applied to the upper side of the rotor, imparting a downward force. Fuel is metered through an orifice in the rotor to the area immediately beneath it. Intermediate pressure P_2 in this area exerts an upward force on the rotor, which is regulated by a bleed orifice.

Section 3

Electronic Engine Controls

Because of the need to precisely control the many factors involved in the operation of modern high-bypass turbofan engines, airlines and manufacturers have worked together to develop electronic engine control (EEC) systems. These systems prolong engine life, save fuel, improve reliability, reduce flight crew workload and reduce maintenance costs. The cooperative efforts have resulted in two types of EECs; one being the supervisory engine control system and the other, the full-authority engine control system (FADEC).

Essentially, the supervisory EEC includes a computer that receives information regarding vari-

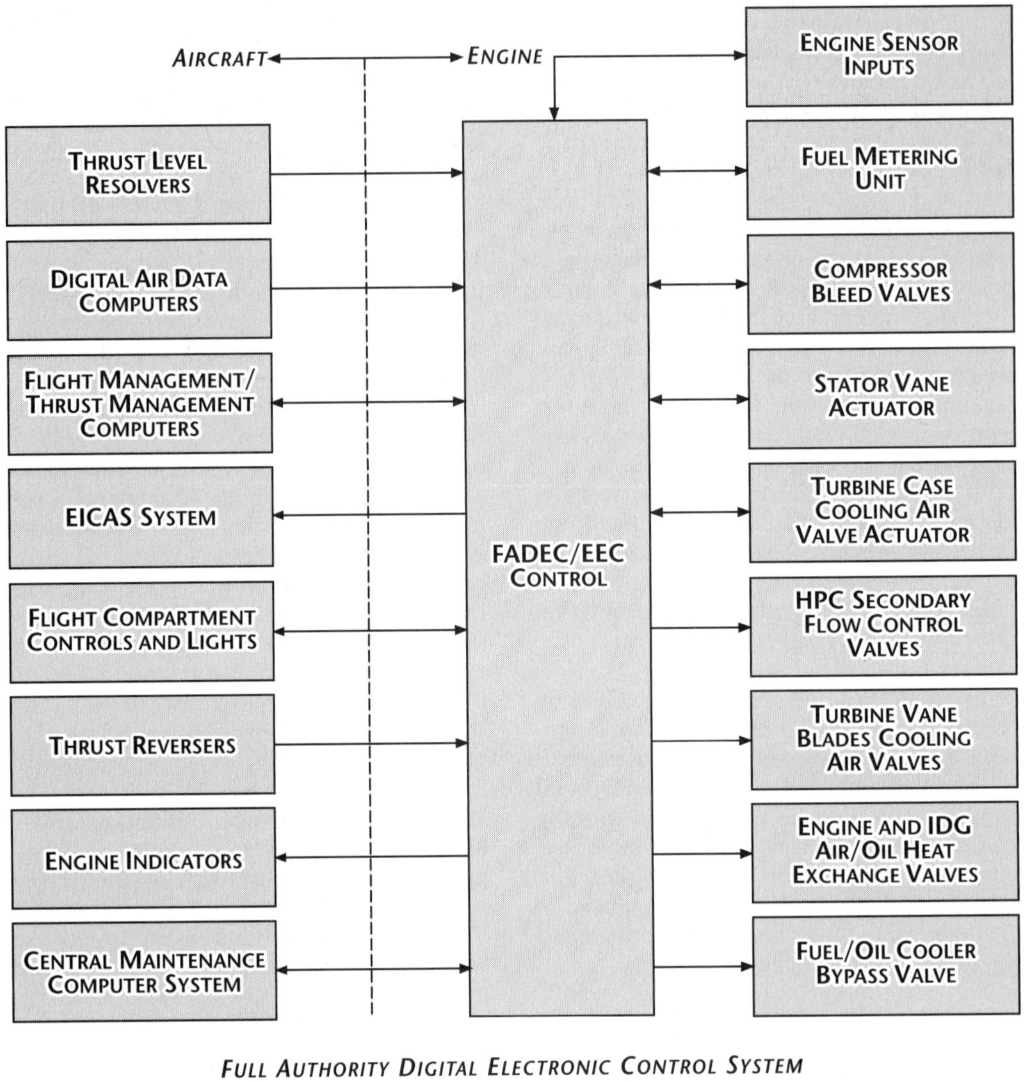

Figure 5-3-1. The FADEC/EEC has inputs from the airplane as well as the engine

ous engine operating parameters and adjusts a standard hydro-mechanical FCU to obtain the most effective engine operation. The hydromechanical unit responds to the EEC commands and actually performs the functions necessary for engine operation and protection.

The full-authority digital electronic control receives all the necessary data for engine operation, then develops the commands to various actuators to control the engine parameters within limits required for the most efficient and safe engine operation. This type of system is used with technologically advanced engines.

Supervisory EEC system. The digital supervisory EEC system is a hydromechanical FCU which is controlled by a supervisory EEC. A permanent-magnet alternator (PMA) is used to provide electric power for the EEC which is separate from the aircraft electric system. An engine inlet pressure and temperature probe is used to sense P_{t2} and T_{t2}. The hydromechanical units of the system control such basic engine functions as:

- Automatic starting
- Acceleration
- Deceleration
- High-pressure rotor
- Speed (N_2) governing
- Variable stator vanes (VSV) compressor position
- Modulated and starting air-bleed control
- Burner pressure (P_b) limiting

The EEC provides precision thrust management, N_2 and EGT limiting and cockpit display information of engine pressure ratio (EPR) limit, EPR command and actual EPR. It also provides control of modulated turbine-case cooling and turbine-cooling air valves and transmits information regarding parametric and control system condition for possible recording. Maintenance technicians utilize such recorded data when eliminating faults in the system.

The supervisory EEC, by measuring EPR and integrating thrust lever (throttle) angle, altitude data, Mach number, inlet air pressure P_{t2}, inlet air temperature T_{t2} and total air temperature in the computation, is able to maintain constant thrust from the engine regardless of changes in air pressure, air temperature and flight environment. Thrust changes occur only when the thrust lever angle is changed and the thrust remains consistent for any particular position of the thrust lever. Takeoff thrust is produced by the positioning of the thrust lever. The pilot makes thrust settings for climb and cruise as the thrust lever is moved to a position to obtain the correct EPR for the thrust desired. The EEC is designed so that the engine will quickly and precisely adjust to a new thrust setting without the danger of overshoot in N_2 or temperature. It adjusts the hydromechanical FCU through a torque motor electrohydraulic servo system.

In a supervisory EEC system, any fault in the EEC that adversely affects engine operation causes an immediate reversion to control by the hydromechanical FCU. At the same time, the system provides an annunciator light signal to the cockpit to inform the crew of the change in operating mode. A switch in the cockpit enables the crew to change from EEC control to hydromechanical control if it is deemed advisable. The supervisory EEC/FADEC is integrated with the aircraft systems as indicated in Figure 5-3-1. The input and output signals are shown by the directional arrows. The output signals of the supervisory EEC/FADEC that affect engine operation commands solenoid-actuated valves for control of modulated turbine-case cooling (TCC) and turbine blade and vane cooling air (TVBCA).

Full-authority Digital Electronic Control

A full-authority digital electronic control performs all functions necessary to operate a turbine engine efficiently and safely in all modes such as starting, accelerating, decelerating, takeoff, climb, cruise and idle. It receives data from the aircraft and engine systems, provides data for the aircraft systems and issues commands to engine control actuators.

The typical dual-channel unit shown in Figure 5-3-2 has a crosstalk capability so that either channel can utilize data from the other channel. This provision greatly increases reliability so that the system continues to operate effectively even though a number of faults may exist. Channel A and channel B are alternated on each flight leg. Input signals from the aircraft to the FADEC, shown in Figure 5-3-3, include throttle resolver angle (which tells the FADEC the position of the throttle), service air-bleed status, aircraft altitude, total air pressure and total air temperature. Information regarding altitude, pressure and temperature is obtained from the air data computer as well as the P_{t2}/T_{t2} probe in the engine inlet.

Outputs from the engine to the example FADEC include: overspeed warning, fuel flow rate, electric power for the FADEC, high-pressure rotor speed N_2, stator vane angle feedback, position of the 2.5 air-bleed proximity switch, air/oil cooler feedback, fuel temperature and oil temperature. There are also outputs for: automatic clearance control (ACC) feedback, power level angle (PLA) position, engine tailpipe pressure $P_{4.9}$, burner pressure P_b, engine inlet total pressure P_{t2}, low-pressure rotor speed N_1, engine inlet total temperature T_{t2} and exhaust gas temperature (EGT or $T_{4.9}$). Some FADECs reference pressures and temperatures at other locations or may use different nomenclature.

Sensors installed on the engine provide the FADEC unit with measurements of temperatures, pressures and speeds. These data are used to provide automatic thrust rating control, engine limit

Figure 5-3-2. The FADEC computer is mounted on the engine

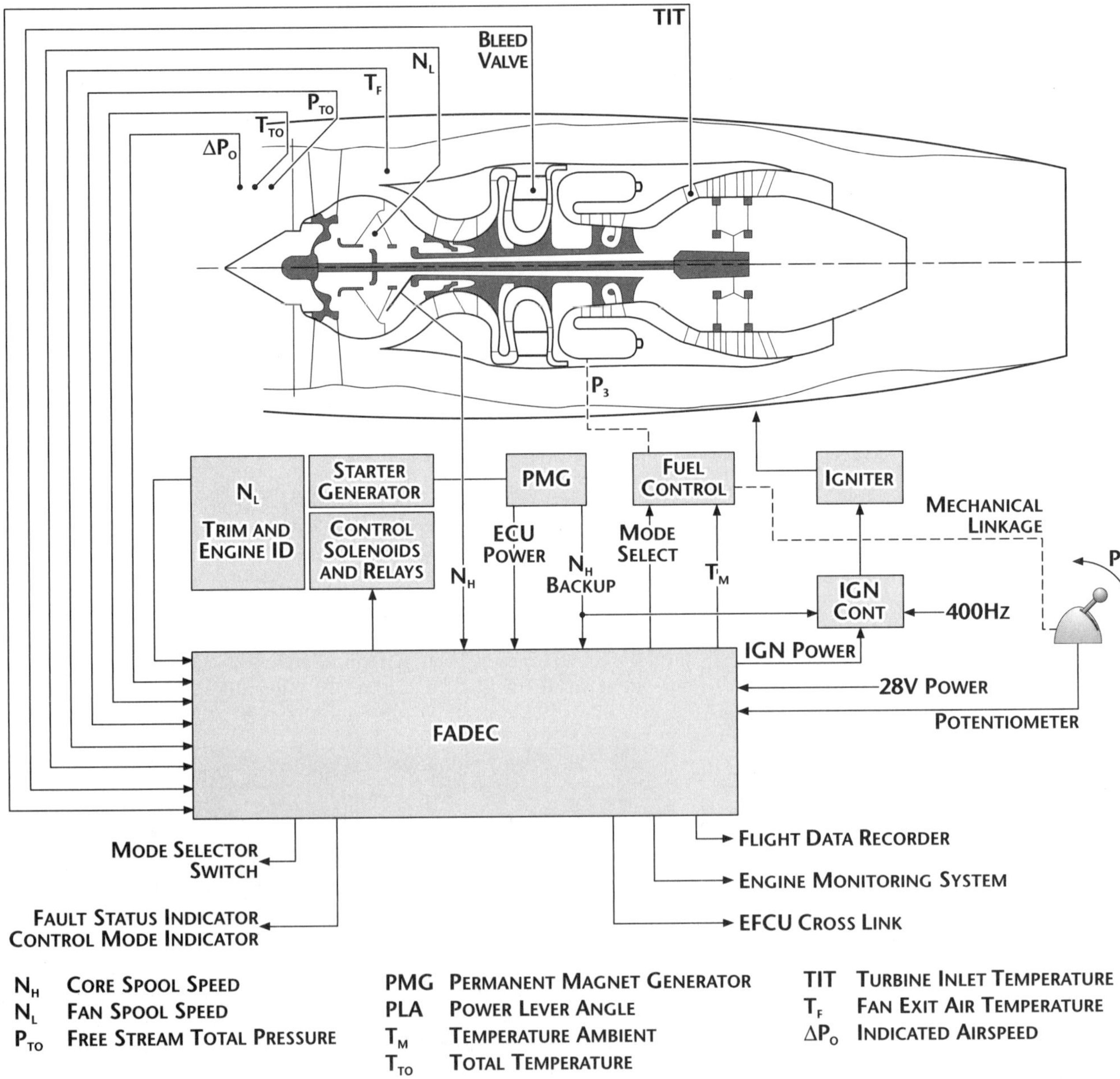

Figure 5-3-3 The FADEC controls all the engine operations.

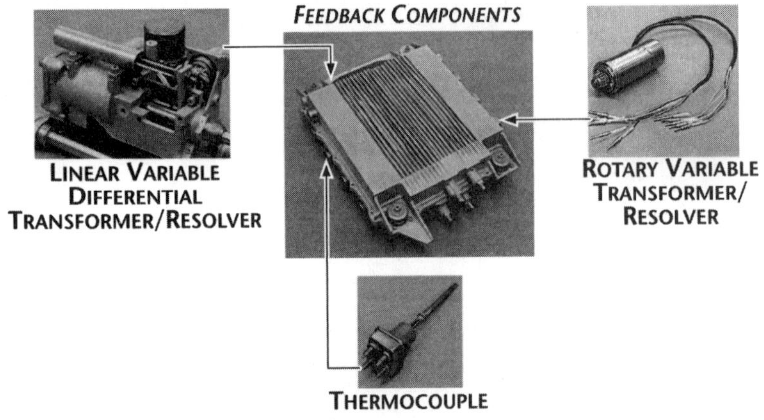

Figure 5-3-4. Mechanical inputs to the FADEC are converted to usable signals by the LVDTs or RVTs.

protection (overspeed, overheat and overpressure), transient control and engine starting.

Outputs from the FADEC to the engine include fuel flow torque motor command, stator vane angle torque motor command, air/oil cooler valve command, 2.5 air-bleed torque motor command, ACC torque motor command, oil bypass solenoid command, breather compartment ejector solenoid command and PLA command. The actuators, shown in Figure 5-3-4, that must provide feedback to the FADEC are equipped with linear variable differential transformers (LVDTs), rotary variable transformers (RVTs) and thermocouples to produce the required signals.

During operation of the engine control system, fuel flows from the aircraft fuel tank to the centrifugal stage of the dual-stage fuel pump seen

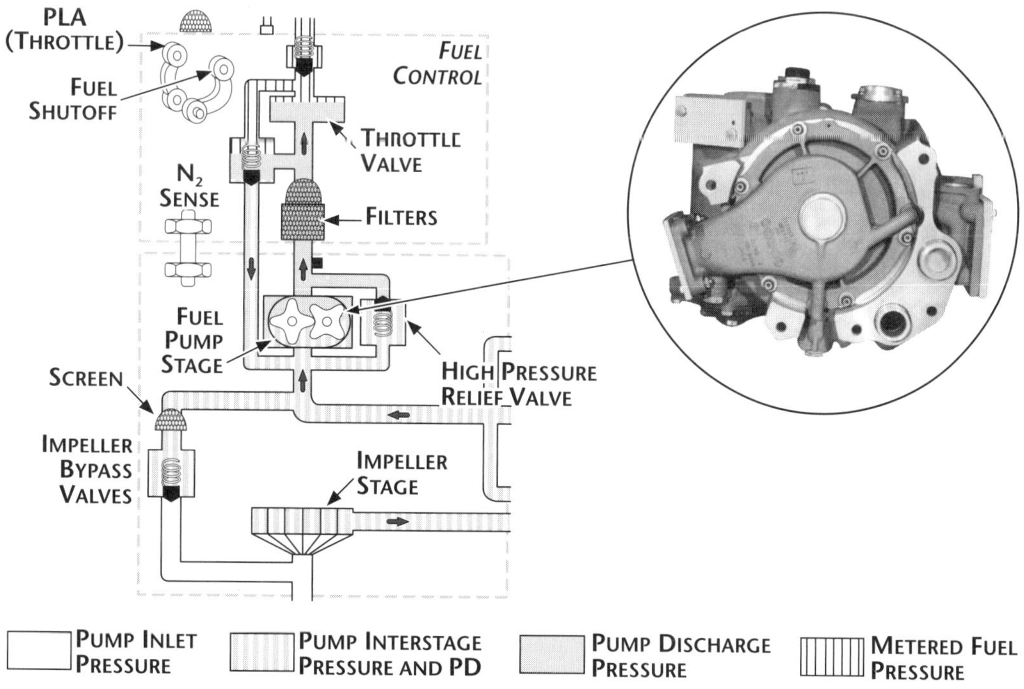

Figure 5-3-5. A dual stage fuel pump

in Figure 5-3-5. The fuel is then directed from the pump through a dual-core oil/fuel heat exchanger which provides deicing for the fuel filter as the fuel is warmed and the oil is cooled. The filter protects the pump main-gear stage and the fuel system from fuel-borne contaminants. High-pressure fuel from the main-gear stage of the fuel pump is supplied to the fuel metering unit (FMU) in Figure 5-3-6, which—through servo valves—responds to commands from the FADEC to position the fuel metering valve, stator vane actuator and air/oil cooler actuator.

Compressor air-bleed and turbine case cooling (TCC) actuators are positioned by and controlled directly by the FADEC, using redundant torque motor drivers and feedback elements. The word redundant means that units or mechanisms are designed with backup features so that a failure in one part will not disable the unit and operation will continue normally. Actuator position feedback is provided to the FADEC by redundant LVDTs for the actuators and redundant resolvers for the fuel metering unit. Fuel-pump discharge pressure is used as hydraulic power for the stator vane, 2.5 air-bleed, air/oil cooler and TCC actuators.

The FADEC and its interconnected components are shown in Figure 5-3-7. The FADEC is mounted on the left side of the engine fan case. The mounting is accomplished with vibration isolators (shock mountings) to protect the unit.

The benefits of employing full-authority digital electronic control include substantial savings for the aircraft operator. These benefits are:

- Reduced crew workload
- Reduced fuel consumption
- Increased reliability
- Improved maintainability

To set the thrust, the throttle lever angle is set to a position that results in lining up the EPR command from the FADEC with the reference indicator that is positioned by the thrust management computer. The FADEC will automatically accelerate or decelerate the engine to that EPR level, without the pilot having to monitor the EPR gauge. Fuel consumption is reduced because the FADEC controls the engine operating parameters so that maximum thrust is obtained for the amount of fuel consumed. In addition, the TCC system ensures that compressor and turbine blade clearances are kept to a

Figure 5-3-6. Fuel from the pump is supplied to the fuel metering unit (FMU)

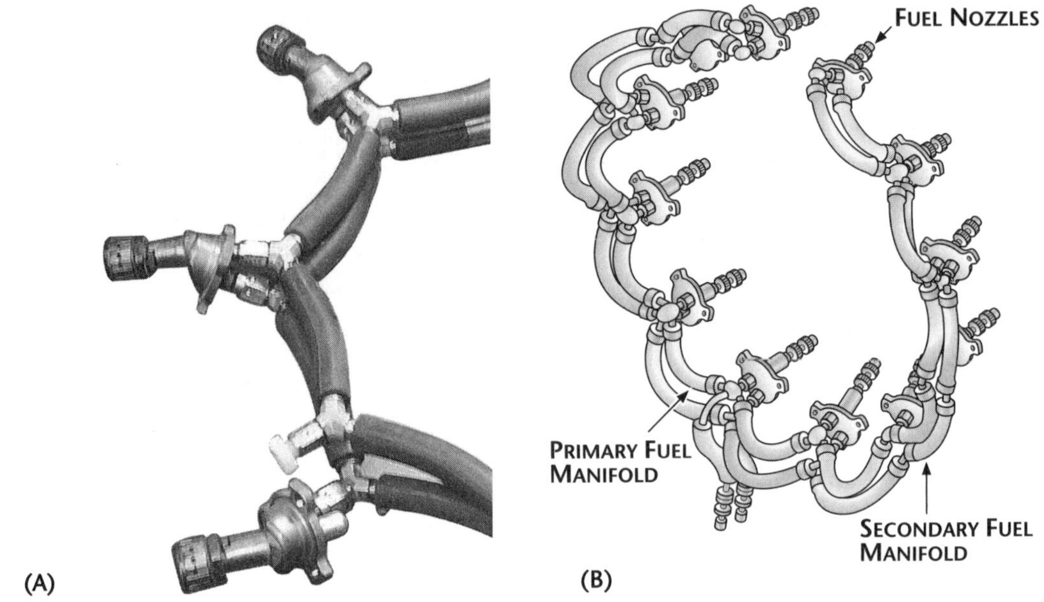

Figure 5-4-1. Hoses or tubing in a manifold allow for easy maintenance.

minimum, thus reducing pressure losses due to leakage at the blade tips. This is accomplished by the TCC system as it directs cooling air through passages and manifold that surround the turbine case controlling engine case temperature. This controls the diameter of the turbine case which sets turbine tip clearances. The FADEC controls the cooling airflow by sending commands to the TCC system actuator.

Engine trimming is eliminated or is accomplished with software changes by the use of the FADEC unit. When an engine is operated with a hydromechanical FCU, it is necessary periodically to make adjustments on the FCU in order to maintain optimum engine performance. The fault-sensing, self-testing and correcting features designed into the FADEC greatly increase the reliability and maintainability of the system. These features enable the system to continue functioning in flight and they provide fault information that is used by maintenance technicians when the aircraft is on the ground. The modular design of the electronic circuitry saves maintenance time because circuit boards with defective components are quickly and easily removed and replaced.

Figure 5-3-7. A FADEC with all its connections, mounted on the engine

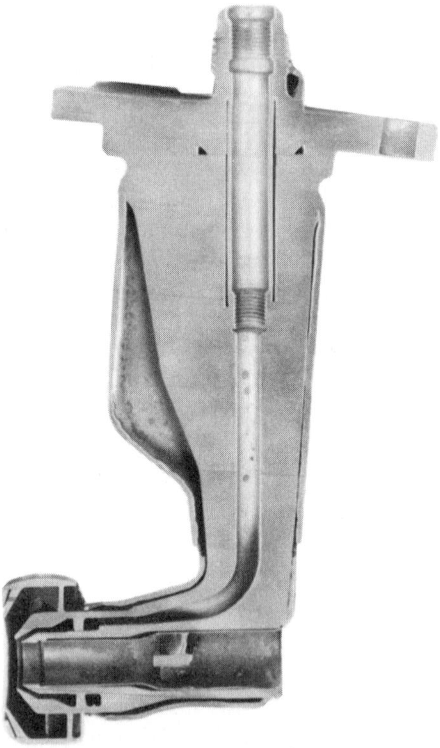

Figure 5-4-2. The simplex nozzle was one of the first effective nozzles.

Section 4

Fuel Spray Nozzles and Fuel Manifolds

The final components of the fuel system are the fuel spray nozzles and fuel manifolds. Theirs is the task of distributing and atomizing or vaporizing the fuel to ensure its rapid burning. The difficulties involved in this process include the high velocity of the air-stream from the compressor and the short length of the combustion system in which burning must be completed. Although fuel spray nozzles are an integral part of the fuel system, their design is closely related to the type of combustion chamber in which they are installed. It is important to match fuel nozzles in order to make each nozzle flow fuel at the same rate in a given engine. The fuel manifolds connect the fuel nozzles by using fuel manifolds that are generally made of tubing or hoses as pictured in Figure 5-4-1.

Fuel nozzles inject fuel into the combustion area in a highly atomized, precisely patterned spray so that burning is completed evenly and in the shortest possible time and in the smallest possible space. It is very important that the fuel be evenly distributed and well centered in the flame area within the liners. This is to prevent the formation of hot spots in the combustion chambers and to prevent the flame burning through the liner.

Fuel nozzle types vary considerably between engines, although for the most part fuel is sprayed into the combustion area under pressure through the small orifices in the nozzles. The two types of fuel nozzles most used in modern engines are the simplex and the duplex configurations, with the air-blast type used with both. The variable port and spill type of nozzles have very limited use on modern engines. The duplex nozzle requires a dual manifold and a pressurizing valve or flow divider for dividing primary and secondary (main) fuel flow, but the simplex nozzle requires only a single manifold to properly deliver the fuel. Five types of spray nozzles have been developed for turbine engines:

- Simplex
- Variable-port (Lubbock)
- Spill-type
- Duplex
- Air spray nozzle

Simplex spray nozzle. The simplex spray nozzle, shown in Figure 5-4-2, was first used on jet engines. It consisted of a chamber which induced a swirl into the fuel and a fixed-area atomizing orifice.

An early method of atomizing the fuel was to pass it through a swirl chamber where holes or slots caused the fuel to swirl, converting its pressure energy to kinetic energy. In this state, the fuel was passed through the discharge orifice that removes the swirl motion as the fuel was atomized to form a cone-shaped spray. This is called pressure jet atomization. The rate of swirl and the pressure of the fuel at the fuel spray nozzle are important factors in good atomization. The shape of the spray is an indication of the degree of atomization, as shown in Figure 5-4-3.

This fuel spray nozzle provides good atomization at the higher fuel pressures, but was problematic at the low pressures required at low engine speeds, particularly at high altitudes. The reason is that the simplex nozzle was by nature a square-law spray nozzle. The flow through the nozzle was proportional to the square root of the pressure drop across it. This meant that if the minimum pressure for effective atomization was 30 p.s.i., the pressure needed to give maximum flow would be about 3000 p.s.i. The fuel pumps available at that time made it difficult to cope with such high-pressures so the variable-port spray nozzle was developed in an effort to overcome the square-law effect.

The simplex fuel nozzle was replaced in most installations by the duplex nozzle which gave better atomization at starting and idling speeds. The air-blast simplex nozzle in Figure 5-4-4, is still being used in turbine engines. A simplex nozzle normally consists of a nozzle tip, an insert and a strainer made up of fine-mesh screen and a support.

Variable-port nozzle. The variable-port or Lubbock nozzle made use of a spring-loaded piston that controlled the area of the inlet ports to the swirl chamber and varied the area of the nozzle opening. At low fuel flows, the ports

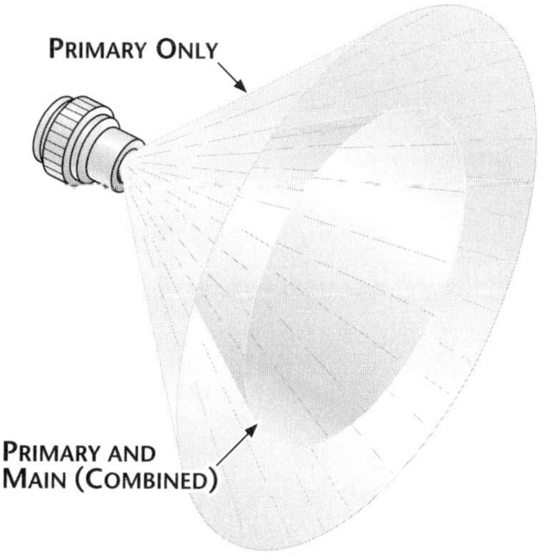

Figure 5-4-3. A correct spray pattern from the nozzle is important for complete combustion.

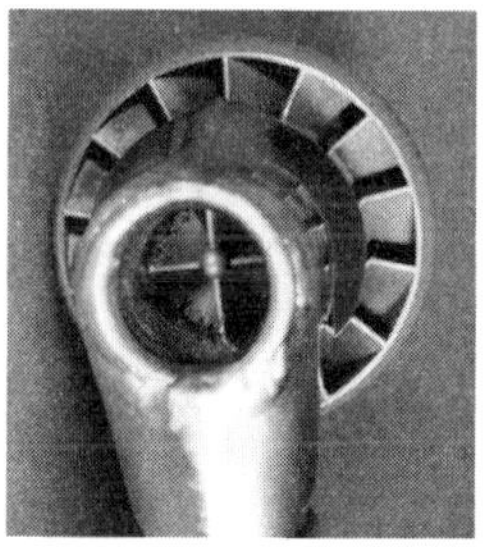
Figure 5-4-4. The simplex fuel nozzle was the next development in nozzle technology.

were partly uncovered by the movement of the piston; at high flows, they were fully open. By this method, the square-law pressure relationship was mainly overcome and good atomization was maintained over a wide range of fuel flows. Matching sets of spray nozzles and the sticking of the sliding piston due to dirt particles were inherent problems with this type of design. They were eventually replaced by newer designs of fuel nozzles.

Spill-type nozzle. The spill-type nozzle can be described as a simplex spray nozzle with a passage from the swirl chamber for spilling (bypassing) fuel away. As the fuel demand decreases with altitude or reduction in engine speed, more fuel is spilled away from the swirl chamber, leaving less to pass through the atomizing orifice.

The spill spray nozzle system involves a somewhat modified type of fuel supply and control system. A disadvantage of this system is that excess heat may be generated when a large volume of fuel is being re-circulated to the inlet, which may eventually lead to deterioration of the fuel and decreased fuel efficiency.

Duplex fuel nozzle. The duplex fuel nozzle is widely used in present-day gas turbine engines. As mentioned previously, its use requires a flow divider, but at the same time it offers a desirable spray pattern for combustion over a wide range of operating pressures. The duplex nozzle shown in Figure 5-4-5, requires a primary and a secondary fuel manifold and has two independent orifices, one smaller than the other. The smaller orifice handles the lower flows and the larger orifice deals with the higher flows as the fuel pressure increases.

A pressurizing valve (flow divider) may be employed with this type of spray nozzle to apportion the fuel to the manifolds. As the fuel flow and pressure increase, the pressurizing valve moves to progressively admit fuel to the secondary manifold and the secondary orifices of the fuel nozzle. This gives a combined flow down both manifolds. In this way, the duplex nozzle is able to give effective atomization over a wider flow range than the simplex spray nozzle, for the same maximum fuel pressure. In addition, efficient atomization is obtained at the low flows that may be required at high altitude.

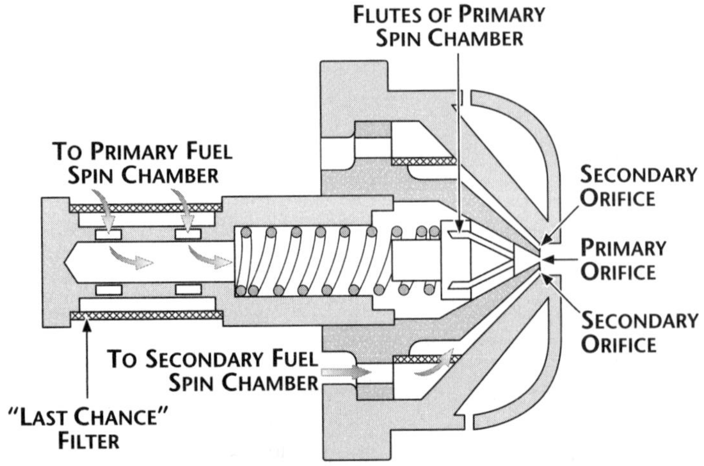

Figure 5-4-5. The duplex nozzle is widely used

Air spray nozzle. The air spray nozzle, illustrated in Figure 5-4-6, carries a portion of the primary combustion air with the injected fuel. An advantage of the air spray nozzle is that the low-pressures required for atomization of the fuel permits the use of lower pressures that can use the comparatively lighter gear-type pump. These modern fuel spray nozzles utilize the air spray principle that employs high-velocity air instead of high-velocity fuel to cause atomization.

This method allows atomization at low fuel flow rates (provided sufficient air velocity exists), thereby providing an advantage over the pressure jet atomizer by producing improved and more complete combustion. By aerating the spray, the local fuel-rich concentrations produced by other types of spray nozzles are avoided, thus reducing both carbon formation and exhaust smoke. By allowing the combustion process to take place under the most favorable conditions, less emissions are released in the exhaust. Developments in improved combustor design have greatly reduced emissions from gas turbine engines.

Section 5

Lubrication

Lubricating oils for gas-turbine engines are usually of the synthetic type. This means that the oils are not manufactured in the conventional manner from petroleum crude oils. Petroleum lubricants are not suitable for modern gas-turbine engines because of the high temperatures encountered during operation. These temperatures often exceed 500°F and at those temperatures petroleum oils tend to break down. The lighter fractions of the oil evaporate, leaving carbon and gum deposits (coking). This causes the lubricating characteristics of the oil to deteriorate rapidly.

Synthetic Oils

Synthetic oils are designed to withstand high temperatures and still provide good lubrication. Lubricants for gas-turbine engines must pass a variety of exacting tests to ensure that they have the characteristics required for satisfactory performance. Among the characteristics tested are specific gravity, acid-forming tendencies, metal corrosion, oxidation stability, vapor-phase coking, gear scuffing, effect on elastomers and bearing performance.

These tests are designed to provide indications that the oil will supply the needed lubrication under all conditions of operation. As gas turbines were developed to operate at higher speeds and temperatures, better low-viscosity synthetic oils were developed.

Because the density of oil is an important factor, it is common practice to employ the unit for kinematic viscosity in establishing the characteristics of gas-turbine lubricants. Kinematic viscosity is expressed in stokes (St) or centistokes (cSt) - one cSt being equal to 0.01 St.

The Saybolt Universal viscosity of an oil having a kinematic viscosity of 5 cSt is approximately 42.6. This is roughly equivalent to what is known as 20-weight lubricating oil. Type II synthetic lubricant is also described as a 5-centistoke (cSt) oil. This means that the oil must have a minimum kinematic viscosity of 5 cSt at a temperature of 210°F. This specification is necessary, because the oil must maintain sufficient body to carry all applied loads at operating temperatures.

The engine manufacturers and oil companies developed a military specification (Mil Spec) for the oil's properties. The Mil Spec was then published and the oil companies produced oil that would fit the specification. The first approval by the military was granted for a synthetic lubricant under MIL-L-7808. This oil, referred to as Type I, was a three-centistokes oil, which meant that it flowed easily at extremely cold temperatures.

This oil was a significant improvement over mineral oils, but didn't meet the needs of newer, more powerful engines. Higher pressure and temperatures, along with tighter clearances, called for oil that could withstand these stringent requirements.

A second generation of synthetic lubricants is known as Type II MIL-L-23699 was developed. These new oils were capable of service to temperatures that were 100°F higher than Type I oils. The new specification (MIL-L-23699) became the standard for the industry. This oil excels in the ability to withstand high temperatures without breaking down.

Type II continues to be the most widely used oil in the industry. Because Type I oils are three centistokes and the Type II are five centistokes oils, Type I is still used in the colder regions of the country. Some aircraft use it in their APUs. The APU is not operated at altitude and becomes cold-soaked. The three centistokes oil has better cold performance. The APU can be used in flight below certain altitudes for pneumatic and electrical power, which occurs during an in-flight main engine shutdown. The lower centistokes oil could aid in the starting process.

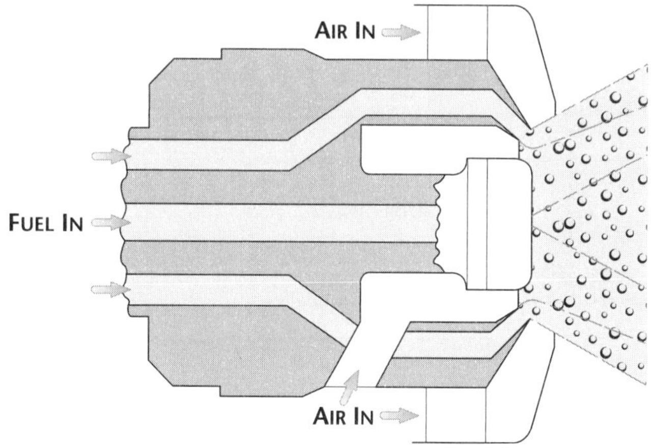

Figure 5-4-6. The air spray nozzle has significantly reduced carbon emissions.

Most gas turbines use low-viscosity oil for starting, particularly at low temperatures. Normal starts can be made in temperatures as low as -40°C. without having to pre-heat the oil. Turbo-propeller engines can use slightly higher viscosity oil due to the additional requirements of the reduction gear and propeller pitch change mechanism.

Material handling. The handling of synthetic lubricants requires precautions not needed for petroleum lubricants. Synthetic lubricants have a high solvent characteristic that causes them to penetrate and dissolve paints, enamels and other materials.

> **CAUTION:** *When synthetic oils are permitted to touch or remain on the skin, physical injury can result.*

It is essential that a technician handling synthetic lubricants uses every care to ensure that the lubricants do not make contact with the skin. If a synthetic lubricant is spilled it should be cleaned up immediately by wiping up or washing with a suitable cleaning agent. Safety precautions established by the aircraft operator should be observed carefully.

Mixing oils. The technician must be certain when changing or adding oil to a gas-turbine engine that the correct type and grade of lubricant is used. Although some oil manufacturers allow mixing their turbine engine oils with other synthetic turbine oils, some engine manufacturers do not recommend mixing oils. Some engine and oil manufacturers require draining, flushing and refilling when changing from one brand to another. Oil that passes MIL-L-23699 has undergone extensive compatibility testing. When changing to a different oil type or newer oil, a chemical shock the engine can occur, causing carbon to break loose. This

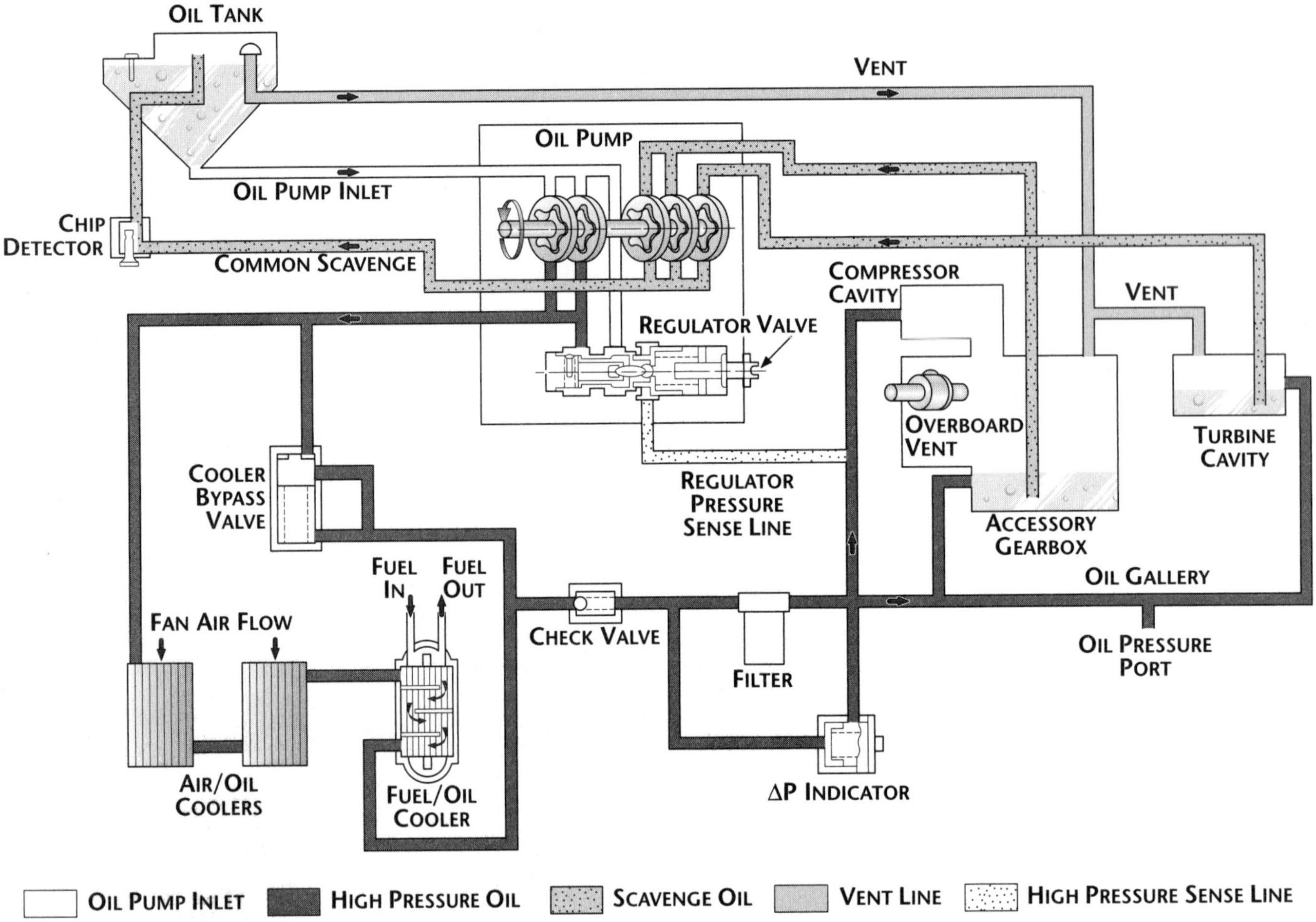

Figure 5-5-1. A pressure regulating valve oil system

carbon could subsequently become lodged in oil passages and cause problems.

> **NOTE:** *Always refer to the engine manufacturer's information on oil mixing or changing oil manufacturers during engine servicing.*

Engines that are not subject to higher temperatures and/or are not experiencing any problems with coking or oil deposits probably would not benefit from the types of new oils. Some engines have hot spots that cause frequent coking and carbon deposits. In this case, the newer oils could be of help. The third-generation oils essentially are Type II oils with an improved additive package that improves the cleaning capabilities of the oil. Third generation oils are not yet approved for all aircraft. Note also that the color of the new third-generation oils is darker than the Type II oil because of a darker colored additive.

Lubricant Service for Gas-Turbine Engines

Regardless of the type of oil being used, it is important to monitor the engine oil continuously through an oil analysis program to determine if a different type of oil is needed and to establish oil change intervals if necessary. If the viscosity of the oil is coming out significantly higher than the specifications, choose better oil, or do more frequent oil changes. In addition to oil analysis, observing carbon buildup and deposits during scheduled and unscheduled engine inspections can provide clues to the effectiveness of the oil.

In the past it has been the practice to drain and replace the lubricating oil in gas-turbine engines at specified intervals. At these times, the oil filters or screens were examined for residues of metal to detect incipient failures in the engine. But experience and extensive investigations, in some cases, have shown that the periodic changes of oil may not be necessary for some gas-turbine engines using synthetic lubricants.

To ensure continued effectiveness of the engine lubricant, two procedures are employed:

- Oil filtering
- Oil analysis

A typical procedure is to filter the oil every 250 hours of operation. This is accomplished by removing the main oil screen (or filter) and installing a filter adapter.

The filter adapter provides inlet and outlet connections by which a 15-micron filter is connected externally to the engine. When the filter has been connected, the engine is operated at medium speed for about 5 minutes. This causes all the engine oil to be passed through the filter, thereby removing even the smallest particles of suspended material. This filtering method provides for thorough internal engine cleaning because the hot circulating oil flushes the inside of the engine while the engine is running. If the oil were drained and filtered, pockets or pools of unfiltered oil would remain in the engine, along with residues that would normally settle in such pockets or pools.

After the filtering operation is completed, the 40-micron engine filter, having been examined for residues and cleaned, is reinstalled in the engine. Residues from the special 15-micron filter and from the engine oil filter are examined for metal particles. The metals are identified by means of a magnet (ferrous materials only) and by various chemicals to determine their base material (which identifies the component), in order to detect the possibility of imminent bearing failure.

Storage of turbine oil. Turbine oil must be used immediately upon opening the container. Turbine oil is hygroscopic, meaning that it absorbs moisture from the air. If you open a can of turbine oil, within five days it will absorb enough moisture from the air to be beyond the moisture limits.

Lubricating Systems

The engine oil distribution system consists of a pressure system that supplies lubrication to the engine bearings, accessory drives and other engine components.

Both wet and dry lubrication systems are used in gas turbine engines. Wet sump engines store the oil in the engine proper. Dry sump engines utilize an external tank generally mounted on the engine. The dry sump engine uses scavenge pumps to return the oil back to the oil tank.

The lubrication system is required to provide lubrication and cooling for all gears, bearings, splines. It must also be capable of collecting foreign matter. Additionally, the oil must protect the lubricated components that are manufactured from non-corrosion resistant materials. The oil must accomplish these tasks without significant deterioration to the engine.

Most gas turbine engines use a self-contained recirculatory lubrication system in which the oil is distributed around the engine and returned to the oil tank by pumps. There are two basic recirculatory systems:

- Pressure regulating valve system
- Full flow system

The major difference between them is in the control of the oil flow to the bearings. In both systems the temperature and pressure of the oil are critical to the correct and safe running of the engine. These parameters are indicated in the flight deck.

Pressure-regulating valve system. Oil pressure is a function of volume flow, restriction to flow and viscosity. Volume flow from the pressure element is determined by gas generator speed. Oil volume flow increases as the gas generator speed increases. Restriction to flow is determined by the size of the passages, lines and nozzles. Viscosity is a function of oil temperature. Thus, if the oil temperature and restriction to flow remain constant, oil pressure will increase with increases in gas generator speed until the regulated oil pressure is reached. Further increases in gas generator speed do not result in further increases in pressure, because the pressure regulating valve bypasses oil to the inlet of the pump.

In the pressure-regulating valve system, shown in Figure 5-5-1, the oil flow to the bearing chambers is controlled by limiting the pressure to a given design value. This is accomplished by the use of a spring-loaded valve, which allows oil to be directly returned from the pressure pump outlet to the oil tank, or pressure pump inlet, when the design pressure value is exceeded. The valve opens at a preset pressure, thus giving a constant oil pressure over normal engine operating speeds. However, increasing engine speed can cause the bearing chamber pressure to rise. This reduces the pressure difference between the bearing chamber and oil pressure jet, thus decreasing the oil flow rate to the bearings as engine speed increases.

To alleviate this problem, some pressure regulating systems use the increasing bearing chamber pressure to augment the regulating valve spring load. This maintains a constant flow rate at the higher engine speeds by increasing the oil pressure as the bearing chamber pressure increases.

Full flow system. The pressure regulating valve system operates satisfactorily for engines that have a low bearing chamber pressure, which does not unduly increase with engine speed. For engines that have higher bearing chamber pressures, it is less than satisfactory. For example, if a bearing chamber has a maximum pressure of 60 p.s.i., it would require a

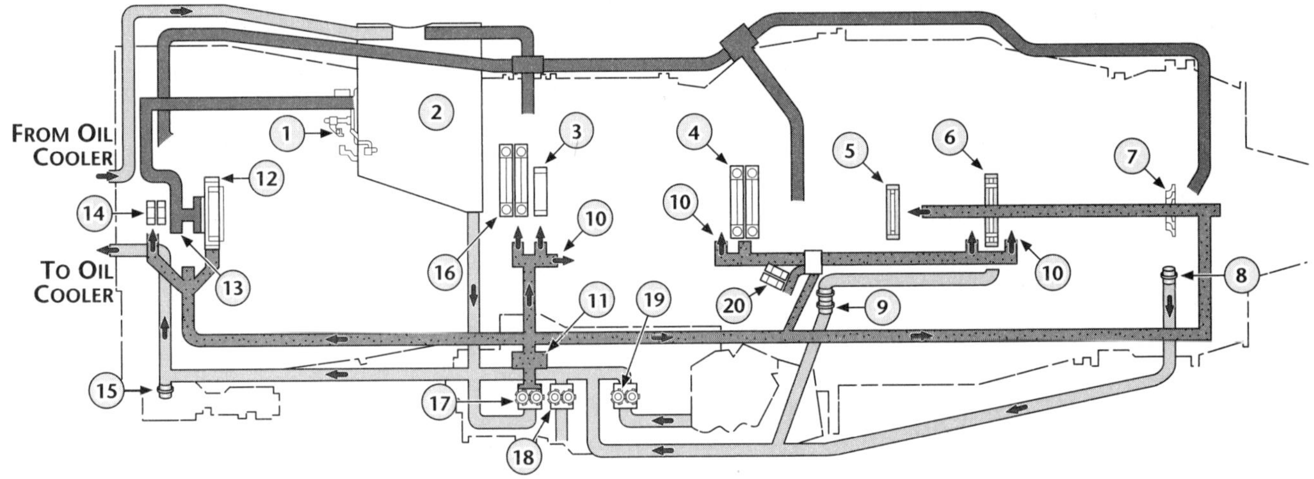

1. BREATHER PRESSURIZING VALVE
2. TANK PRESSURE RELIEF VALVE
3. REAR COMPRESSOR FRONT BEARING NO. 3
4. REAR COMPRESSOR REAR BEARING NO. 4
5. TURBINE INTERSHAFT BEARING NO. 4 $^1/_2$
6. TURBINE FRONT BEARING NO. 5
7. TURBINE REAR BEARING NO. 6
8. TURBINE REAR BEARING OIL SUCTION PUMP
9. COMPRESSOR REAR AND TURBINE FRONT BEARING OIL SUCTION PUMP
10. SEAL JET
11. MAIN PRESSURE OIL SCREEN
12. NO. 1 FRONT COMPRESSOR FRONT BEARING
13. BREATHER CENTRIFUGE
14. FRONT ACCESSORY DRIVE MAIN SHAFT REAR BEARING
15. COMPRESSOR FRONT BEARING OIL SUCTION PUMP
16. NO. 2 FRONT COMPRESSOR REAR BEARING
17. PRESSURE OIL PUMP
18. OIL PUMP AND ACCESSORY DRIVE HOUSING OIL SUCTION PUMP
19. ACCESSORY ELBOW OIL SUCTION PUMP
20. ANGLED ACCESSORY DRIVE SHAFT GEAR BEARING

PRESSURE OIL | RETURN OIL | BREATHER PRESSURE

Figure 5-5-2. A full flow oil system used on a turbofan engine

pressure regulating valve setting of 90 p.s.i. to produce a pressure drop of 30 p.s.i. at the oil spray jet orifice. This means that larger pumps are needed and that the oil flow at slower speeds must be matched to the bearing requirements.

The full flow system achieves the desired oil flow rates throughout the complete engine speed range by dispensing with the pressure regulating valve and allowing the pressure pump delivery pressure to supply the oil jet orifice directly. Figure 5-5-2 shows an example of this system on a turbofan engine. The pressure pump size is determined by the flow required at maximum engine speed.

Total loss regulating system. For engines that run for short periods such as booster or missile engines, the total loss oil system is generally used. The system is simple and incurs low weight penalties because it requires no oil cooler, scavenge pump or filters. Once the oil is used, it is disposed of and no oil re-circulates through the system.

Figure 5-5-3. Oil tanks can be separate units or part of the gearbox.

Oil System Components

Oil tank. The oil tank, Figure 5-5-3, is usually mounted on the engine as a separate unit, although it may also be an integral part of the external gearbox. It must have a provision to allow the lubrication system to be drained and replenished. A sight glass or a dipstick must be incorporated to allow the oil system contents to be checked. The filler is marked with the word OIL. Provision is also made for a continuous supply of oil to be available in aircraft that are designed to operate during inverted flight conditions.

As the pressure oil is distributed to all the lubricated parts of the engine, a substantial amount of sealing air mixes with it and increases its volume. Since air is mixed with the oil in the bearing chambers, a deaerating device is incor-

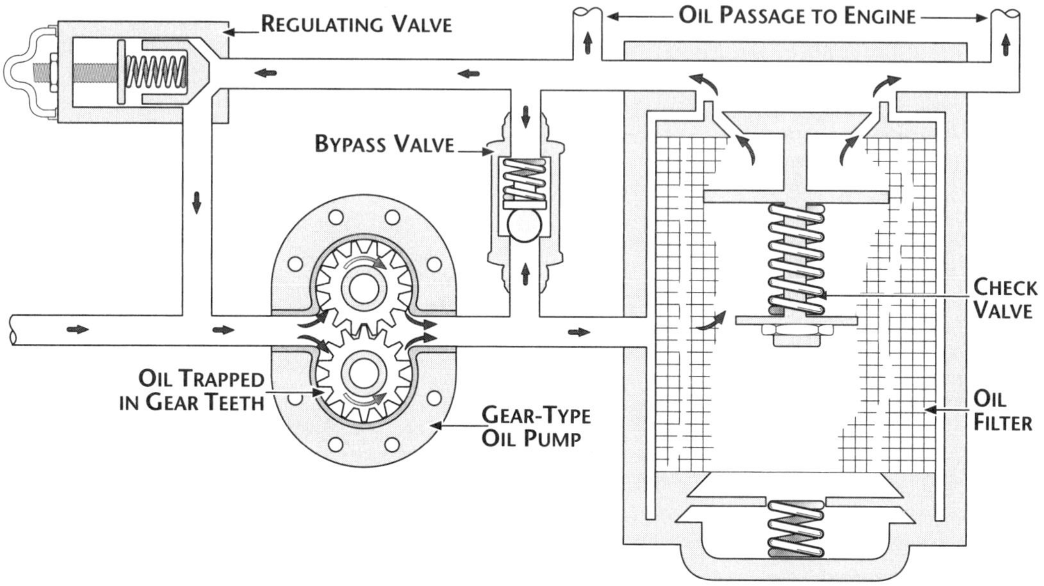

Figure 5-5-4. Gear-type pumps are positive displacement and have pressure-regulating valves.

porated within the oil tank or gearbox, which removes the air from the returning oil. The oil tank must also contain expansion space, due to the foaming action of the air and oil. The tank holds enough oil to lubricate the engine with some reserve for cooling and safety. Baffles minimize sloshing of the oil in the tank.

Oil pumps. Oil pumps (pressure and scavenge) are vital to the efficient operation of the engine. Failure of the pumps will necessitate a rapid shutdown of the engine. The bearing chambers operate under differing pressures. Therefore, to prevent oil accumulation in the bearing cavity, it is usually necessary to have a scavenge pump for each bearing cavity.

Gear-type pumps are normally used in pressure oil systems. The pressure oil pump, which is a gear-type pump, develops oil pressure by trapping oil in the gear teeth as it is rotated by the engine. Since a small quantity of incompressible oil becomes trapped in the gear mesh, gear pumps are of the positive displacement type. This action can be seen in Figure 5-5-4. Most turbine engines use this positive pressure (generally between 40 to 100 p.s.i.) to spray oil on the engine's bearings.

Gear pumps are used both as pressure (feed) pumps and scavenge (return) pumps and can be incorporated within a common casing. The oil pumps are driven by the accessory drive system.

Gas-turbine lubrication systems are usually of the dry-sump type: oil is scavenged from the engine and stored in an oil tank. Scavenge pumps return oil from the engine's bearing cavities to a sump in an accessory drive gearbox and then directly to the oil tank.

The scavenge system may consist of several stages; that is, individual pumps that draw oil from the different engine bearing cavities. Scavenge oil pumps normally have a higher capacity than engine-driven pumps because of the air that mixes with the oil (foaming) in the bearing cavities. Scavenge pumps operate in much the same manner as the pressure pump.

The most common type of oil distribution device at the bearing is a simple orifice (oil jet), shown in Figure 5-5-5, which directs a metered amount of oil onto the bearings. These oil jet orifices are positioned as close to the bearings as possible to keep the spray of oil from being deflected away from the bearing. The smallest diameter of an oil

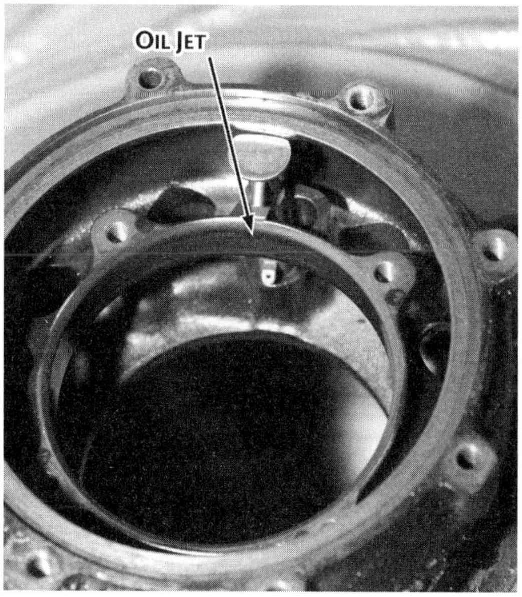

Figure 5-5-5. The oil jet sprays oil directly on the bearing.

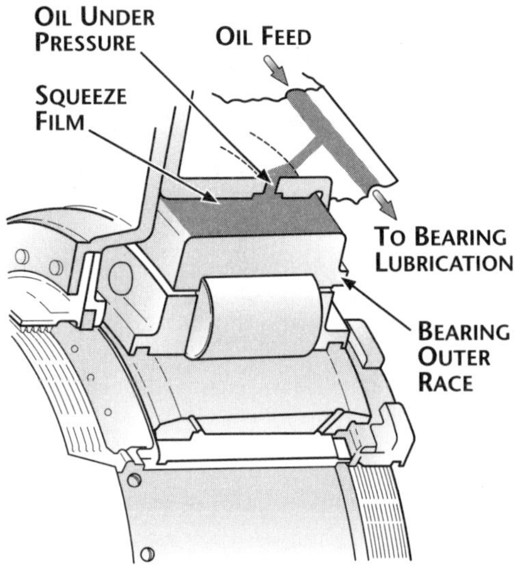

Figure 5-5-6. A bearing that is mounted in an oil film is vibration isolated.

jet orifice is 0.04 inch, which allows a flow of 12 gallons per hour when operating at a pressure of 40 p.s.i. The use of restrictors upstream can reduce the flow rate as required.

In order to minimize the effect of dynamic loads (vibrations) transmitted from the rotating assemblies to the bearing housings, a 'squeeze film' or hydraulic type of bearing can be used. This is shown in Figure 5-5-6. They have a small clearance between the outer race of the bearing and housing with the clearance being filled with oil. The oil film dampens the radial motion of the rotating assembly and the dynamic loads transmitted to the bearing housing, thus reducing the vibration level of the engine to the airframe and the possibility of damage by fatigue.

Oil filter. To prevent foreign matter from continuously circulating around the lubricating system, a number of filters and strainers are positioned within the system. The pressure section of the main oil pump forces oil through the main oil filter located immediately downstream of the pump discharge. A typical pressure oil filter for a gas turbine engine is illustrated in Figure 5-5-7. The oil enters the inlet port of the pressure filter, surrounds the filter cartridge and flows through the cartridge to the inner oil chamber and out to the engine.

If the filter becomes clogged, the oil is bypassed through the filter bypass valve to the discharge port. A differential pressure is required to unseat the filter bypass valve. Coarse strainers are usually fitted at the outlet of the oil tank or immediately prior to the inlet of the oil pumps to prevent debris from damaging the pumps. A fine pressure filter retains any small particles that could block the oil spray jets.

Thread-type filters, shown in Figure 5-5-8, are often fitted as 'last chance' filters immediately upstream of the oil jets. Sometimes perforated plates or gauze filters are used for this application. Scavenge filters are fitted in each oil return line to collect any debris from the lubricated components. They are of tubular construction with a pleated woven wire cloth or a resin impregnated with fibers as the filtering medium. Some filters contain one or more wire-wound elements, but these tend to be insufficient for fine filtration. A 'pop-up indicator' may be fitted to the filter housing to give visual warning of a partially blocked filter.

The size of the filter mesh is measured in microns. A red blood cell is about 8 microns in

Figure 5-5-7. A typical oil filter and relief valve.

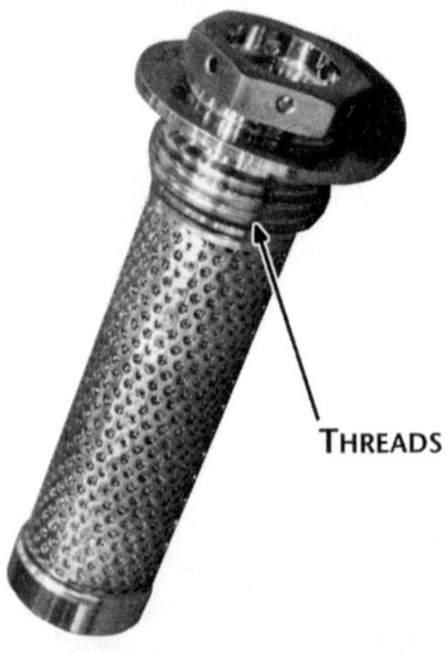

Figure 5-5-8. Last chance filters are the final filtration stage before the oil jets.

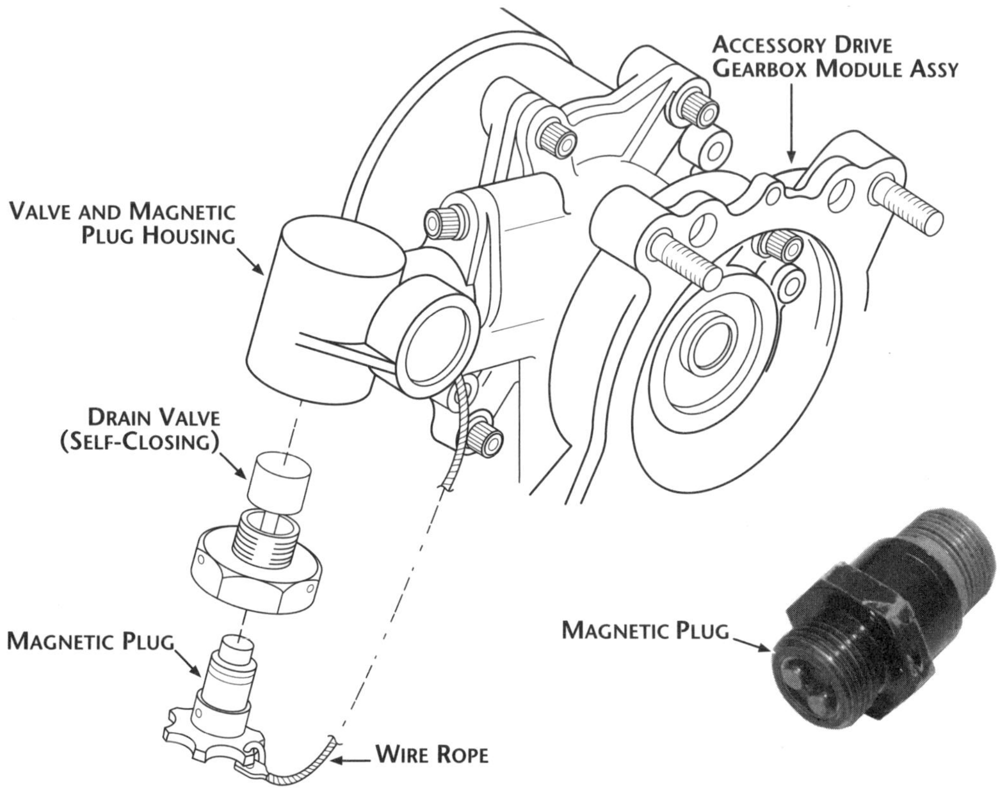

Figure 5-5-9. The magnetic chip detector will attract and hold ferrous metal in the oil system.

size. Many oil contaminants are small enough to require this type of filter.

Magnetic chip detector. Magnetic chip detectors can be installed in the scavenge lines, oil tank and accessory gearbox. A magnetic chip detector, illustrated in Figure 5-5-9, is installed in the side of the filter case. This detector indicates the presence of metal contamination without opening the filter. When the detector picks up ferrous-metal particles, the center plug will become grounded to the case. If a warning light is connected between the center terminal of the detector and ground, the light will illuminate and indicate metal particles on the detector.

Non-warning light chip detectors can also be used to detect metal contamination in the oil. These are removed from the engine and inspected for metal particles by the maintenance technician. These detectors are permanent magnets inserted in the oil flow and are retained in self-sealing valve housings. Safety features incorporated in the design ensure correct retention within the housing. Upon examination, chip detectors can provide a visual warning of impending failure without having to remove and inspect the filters. Chip detectors are designed to be removed during maintenance inspection for condition or monitoring purposes without loss of oil.

Oil coolers. All engines transfer heat to the oil within a bearing chamber or gearbox. It is therefore common practice to fit an oil cooler in recirculatory oil systems. The cooling medium may be fuel or air and in some instances both fuel-cooled and air-cooled coolers are used.

Some systems employ a fuel-cooled oil cooler, such as the one illustrated in Figure 5-5-10; others utilize ram air for cooling the oil.

The engine fuel oil cooler consists of an outer case that houses the cooler core. Fuel and oil

Figure 5-5-10. This oil cooler uses fuel to cool the oil.

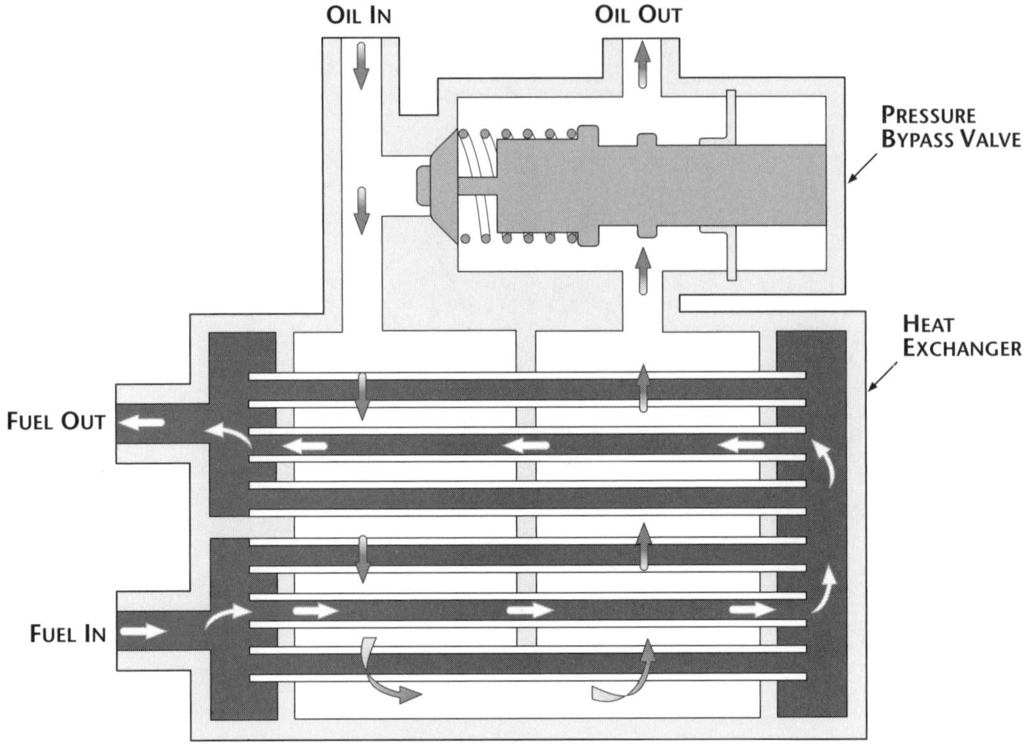

Figure 5-5-11. The fuel oil cooler has internal passages that resemble a radiator.

Figure 5-5-12. The bypass valve allows oil to flow around the cooler if it becomes blocked.

enters and leaves the cooler through passages in the cooler, shown in Figure 5-5-11. Metered fuel from the fuel control passes through the core tubes to absorb the heat from the oil. The hot oil passes around the tubes and is baffled to pass back and forth across the tubes to give maximum exchange of heat.

Although the fuel is cooling the oil by means of a heat exchanger, the oil and fuel are separate and do not come in contact with each other. If the cooler should become blocked, a bypass valve such as is shown in Figure 5-5-12 would unseat and allow oil to flow around the cooler.

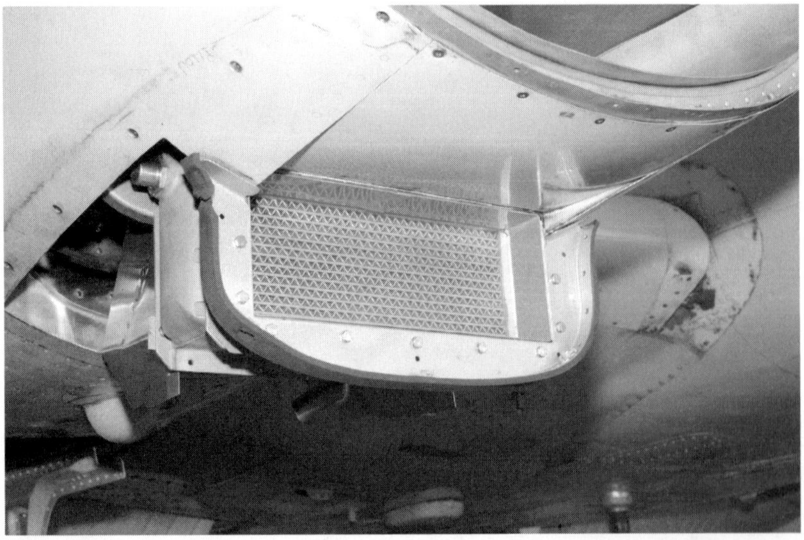

Figure 5-5-13. For this King Air 90 the passage of air across the fins cools the oil.

With an air-cooled oil cooler, oil passes through tubes that have radiating fins attached. Cooling air flows over these fins, absorbing heat from the oil. The cooled oil is then transferred back to the engine. A typical air oil cooler is shown in Figure 5-5-13.

Oil breather system. An oil breather system connects the engine bearing cavities, accessory drive gearbox and oil tank. Oil droplets and vapor are removed from the breather airstream by a centrifugal separator (breather centrifuge) located in the accessory gearbox. After passing through the separator unit, the clean oil-free breather air is exhausted overboard through a vent pipe. This action is illustrated in Figure 5-5-14. To prevent excessive air pressure within the oil tank, gearboxes and bearing chambers are vented to atmosphere through the engine breather outlet.

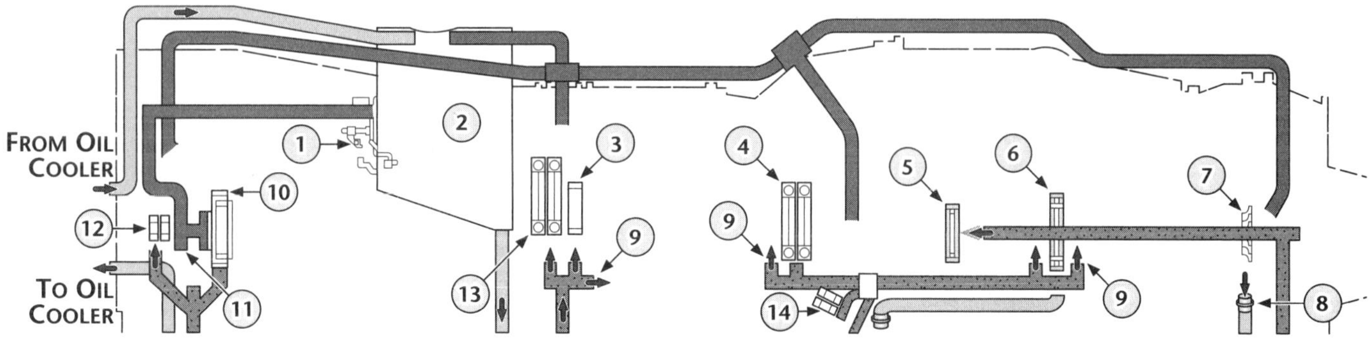

Figure 5-5-14. Oil is removed from the air by a centrifugal separator in the gearbox.

Oil Indicating and Warning Systems

The temperature and pressure of the oil are critical to the correct and safe running of the engine. Provision is therefore made for these parameters to be indicated in the cockpit.

On a typical oil indicating and warning system such as the one shown in Figure 5-5-15, the oil quantity indicating system consists of a capacitance tank unit probe electrically connected to an indicator on the instrument panel which forms a capacitance bridge circuit. A change in oil level alters the tank unit capacitance. The resulting flow of current is used to actuate a motor that positions a potentiometer wiper in the indicator to rebalance the circuit. The indicator dial pointer is connected to the potentiometer wiper and moves with the wiper to provide the oil quantity indication. An electronic ICAS indication is shown in Figure 5-5-15.

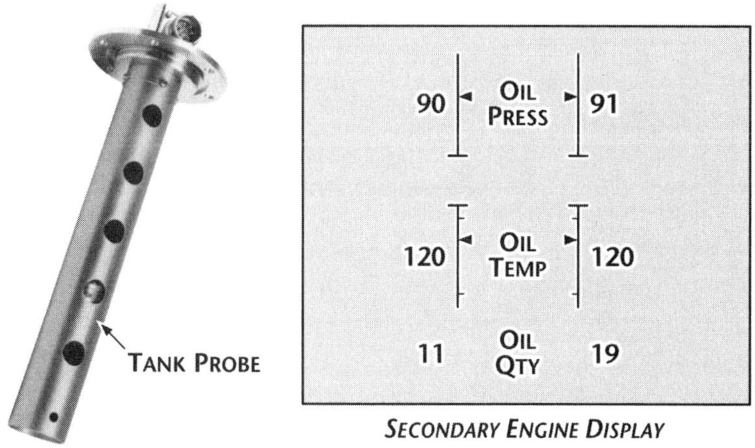

Figure 5-5-15. Oil temperature and pressure are indicated numerically and on a slider scale.

Oil pressure. The components of the oil pressure indicating system for each engine consist of an oil pressure transmitter and an indicator. The oil pressure transmitter senses oil pressure in the external pressure oil manifold and also senses ambient pressure. The difference between these two pressures is measured and converted into an electrical signal that actuates the oil pressure indicator.

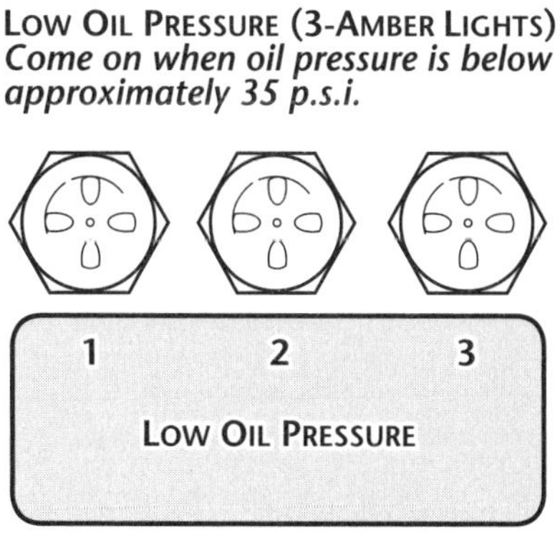

Figure 5-5-16. Low-pressure lights illuminate before the system reaches zero pressure.

Oil temperature. The oil temperature indicating system consists of an oil temperature indicator and a temperature sensing bulb. The oil temperature bulb contains a resistance element that varies its resistance with temperature. This resistance of the bulb controls the current flowing through the indicator deflection coil and therefore controls the angular position of the pointer. Thermocouples are used in electronic engine control systems that send a signal to the electronic engine control.

A warning light or ICAS message on the instrument panel is used to make the flight crew aware of a low oil pressure or oil filter bypass condition. This system can be seen in Figure 5-5-16.

Rolls-Royce 250 Turboshaft Engine Oil System

A typical pressure feed oil system is used on the Rolls-Royce 250 series engine. An immediate difference between this and other engines is the use of an airframe mounted oil tank. Many turbine engines have the oil tank attached to the engine. The Rolls-Royce 250 series engine is a typical small turboshaft engine. A schematic of the oil system is shown in Figure 5-5-17. It has all the components of most turbine engine oil systems. These components are:

- Scavenge pump
- Pressure pump
- Torquemeter system
- Bearing lubrication
- Air-oil separator
- Flow control and warning systems
- Oil filters

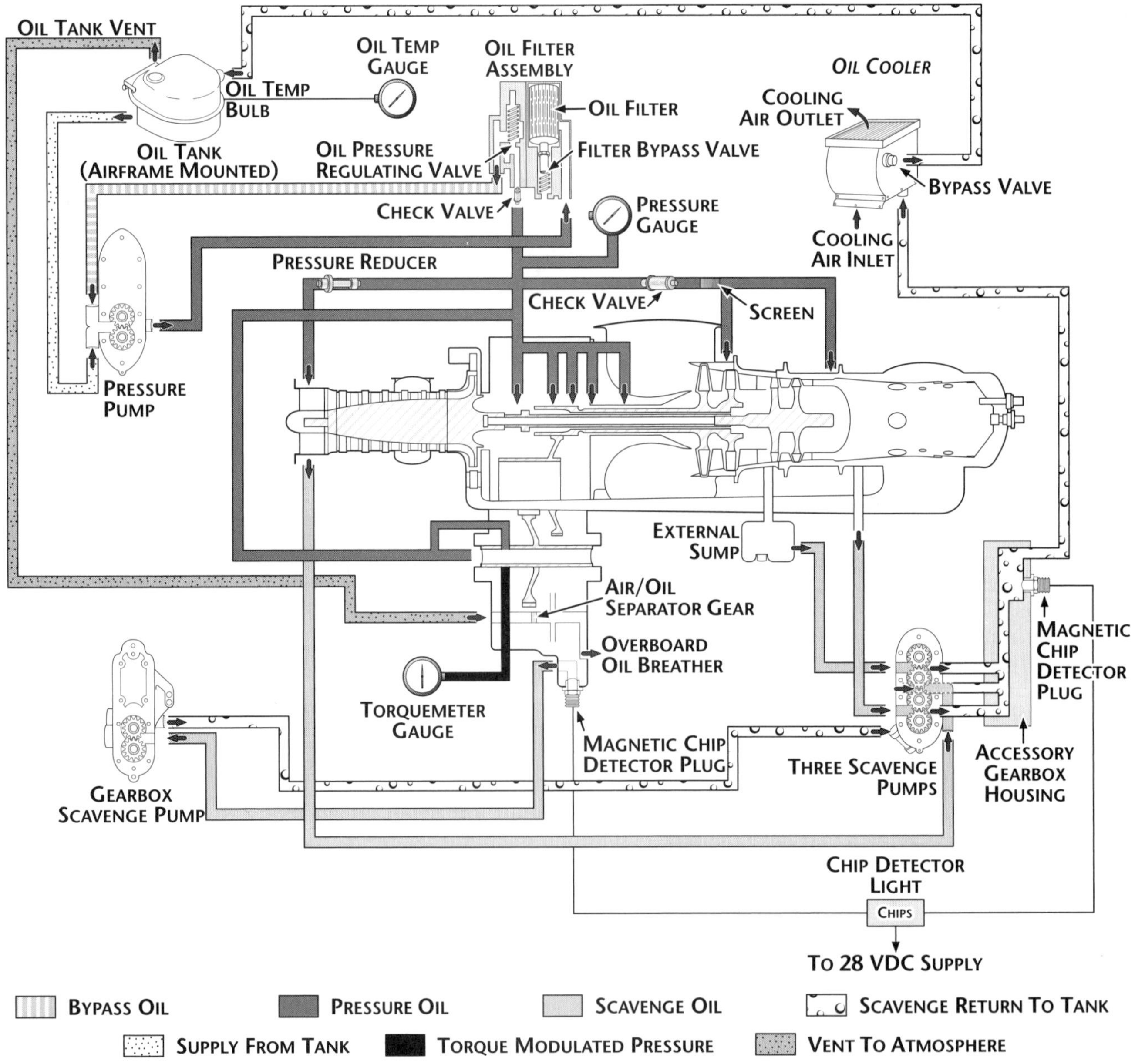

Figure 5-5-17. The RR250 oil system is representative of a small turboshaft engine

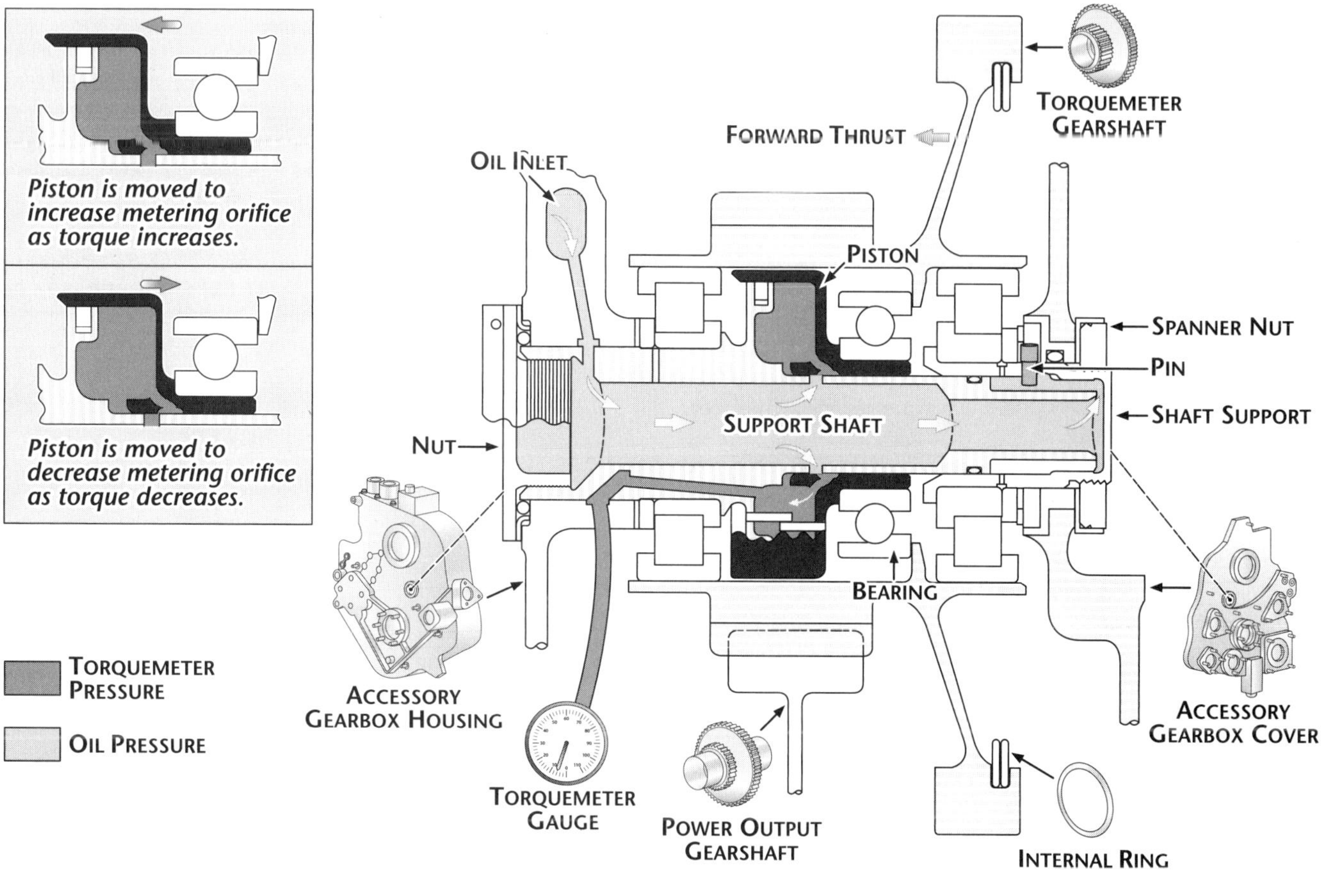

Figure 5-5-18. Oil pressure is used to indicate the torque of the engine.

Scavenge pump. This pump draws oil from the following sumps:

- Compressor front support sump
- Accessory gearbox sump
- Power turbine support external sump
- Gas producer turbine support sump

A gear-type pressure and scavenge pump assembly, consisting of one pressure element and four scavenge elements, is mounted within the accessory gearbox. An assembly containing an oil filter, filter bypass valve and a pressure regulating valve is located in the upper right-hand side of the gearbox housing. The gearbox housing and cover are magnesium alloy castings that have passages for pressure and scavenge oil. The accessory gearbox assembly incorporates a number of oil transfer tubes. External stainless steel tubes are used to transfer pressure and scavenge oil. Passages in the gearbox castings, the oil transfer tubes and the external tubes direct oil pressure and scavenge oil as required by the lubrication system.

Pressure pump. The pressure element in the oil pump assembly pumps oil from the gearbox oil inlet port to the oil filter. The filtered oil is delivered through a one-way check valve into the gearbox housing header passage, then to the oil pressure sensing port. Filtered oil is also directed to the pressure-regulating valve. Other than during starting and low gas generator operation, the outlet of the pressure element is in excess of engine requirements and the pressure-regulating valve controls system pressure to 115 to 130 p.s.i. by bypassing the excess oil to the inlet of the pressure pump. The oil pressure tube within the gearbox directs oil onto the gears of the 2nd stage N_2 (power turbine) gear reduction.

The scavenger oil pump assembly has three levels of gears, numbered from front to rear. The first level has four gears, which are housed in the scavenge oil pump body and covered by the pump cover. The second level has two gears which are housed in the scavenge oil pump body and covered by a separator. The third level has two gears that are housed in the pressure oil pump body and covered by a separator.

Torquemeter system. Oil delivered to the torquemeter, shown in Figure 5-5-18, enters a cavity formed by the torquemeter support shaft and support. Oil from this cavity is delivered to three small ports, which supply oil to the:

- Torquemeter front roller bearing

- Torquemeter rear roller bearing
- Torquemeter piston

The torquemeter piston delivers oil into the torquemeter oil chamber formed by the piston and the support shaft. The torquemeter piston has a small hole that delivers oil from the torquemeter oil chamber to the ball bearing. The pressure in the torquemeter oil chamber is a function of the torque output of the engine—the greater the torque, the higher the pressure. The torque indicating system, which is connected to the torquemeter pressure sensing port, senses pressure in the torquemeter oil chamber.

Bearing lubrication. Oil delivered to the No. 1 bearing drains into the compressor front support sump. Oil that lubricates the No. 6 and No. 7 bearings and the turbine to compressor coupling splines, drains into the power turbine support external sump. The No. 8 bearing oil drains into the gas producer turbine support sump and to a scavenge oil outlet fitting on the bottom strut of the gas producer turbine support. Oil delivered to the No. 2 bearing, No. 5 bearing bellows oil seal and all components within the gearbox, drains into the accessory gearbox sump.

Air-oil separator. Each sump has a scavenge element which pumps oil from the sump to the oil outlet port. Oil flows from the outlet port through the oil cooler back into the oil supply tank. The capacity of scavenge elements far exceeds the amount of oil to be scavenged because there will be some air trapped in the oil returned to the tank. Thus, it is necessary to vent the tank to prevent excessive tank pressurization.

The tank is vented to the interior of the gearbox by means of an interconnecting line from the tank to the vent port on the gearbox. The gearbox has an air-oil separator which vents the gearbox to the overboard vent port. The spur gas producer train idler gearshaft serves as the air-oil separator. It has radial holes in the web portion of the gear that port to the interior of the shaft and then to the overboard vent port.

This gearshaft rotates and any air vented from the gearbox must flow radially toward the center of the gearshaft. Since oil vapor weighs more than air, air and oil vapor are separated and oil is retained within the gearbox.

Flow Control

The engine lubrication system incorporates two screens, two magnetic chip detector plugs and two check valves. The check valve between the oil filter and gearbox header passage prevents the oil tank from draining into the engine when it is not in operation. Oil, delivered to the No. 6, No. 7 and No. 8 bearings, flows through a check valve and screen. This check valve prevents drainage of oil into the low volume turbine sumps. To further prevent internal oil leakage at engine shutdown, especially at nose-up engine attitudes, an external sump is connected to the scavenge oil line at the power turbine support.

One magnetic chip detector plug is in the accessory gearbox sump and the other one is in the scavenge oil passage which delivers oil to the oil outlet port on the gearbox.

Oil filtering. The oil filter assembly has three ports, or openings, which are:

- From the oil pump
- To the accessory gearbox header passage
- To the oil pump

Oil from the pump is directed to the filter and to the filter bypass valve. Normally, all the oil flows through the filter, to the oil pressure-regulating valve and to the check valve. The filter bypass valve is in parallel with the oil filter. As oil flows through the oil filter, there will be a slight drop in pressure and as the filter picks up contamination from the oil, the pressure drop across the filter increases. In the event of abnormal filter contamination, the filter bypass valve will open and bypass the filter as shown in Figure 5-5-17.

Filtered oil is delivered through the check valve into the accessory gearbox header passage that distributes the oil. The check valve is not a physical part of the oil filter assembly. When an engine is not in operation, the check valve is spring-loaded closed to prevent the oil supply tank from draining into the engine.

The oil pressure-regulating valve is spring-loaded closed and it remains closed until system pressure increases to 115 to 130 p.s.i. Whenever system pressure tries to increase beyond 115 to 130 p.s.i., the oil pressure regulating valve opens to deliver oil back to the inlet of the pressure element. If system pressure is out of limits at higher gas generator speeds, the oil pressure-regulating valve can be adjusted.

Oil Analysis

The analysis of the oil condition in the engine can be tested in two basic areas. The first test is to determine the amount of wear metals in the oil sample while the second test identifies the larger contaminants. These wear metals are very small amounts of metal that have been worn away as the engine operates. By identifying each wear metal and noting the quantity present in the oil, the laboratory processing the oil sample can generally determine whether this amount of metal is excessive and what part of

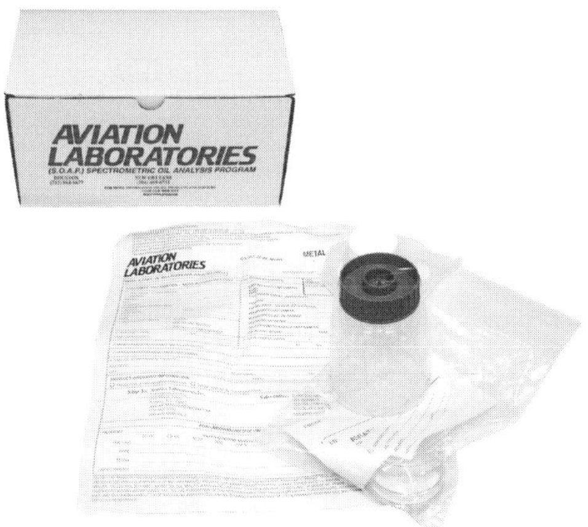

Figure 5-5-19. Oil analysis can give an early indication of elevated metals and contaminants.

the engine it came from. The quantity of wear metals in the oil is measured in parts per million (PPM). Wear metals are generally smaller than 1 micron. This microscopic metal is much smaller than the oil filter is capable of removing from the system, so the metals will remain suspended in the oil. The larger contaminants are trapped and retained by the filter. The analysis of these larger particles is another important part of the oil analysis process.

The two most common methods for analyzing wear metals involve atomic absorption and the optical emission spectrometer. In the atomic absorption method, a small quantity of the oil sample is burned (ionized) in a high-temperature flame. Special equipment detects how much energy was absorbed from a particular chemical element and its quantity in parts per million is read out. The equipment is calibrated for a specific element and must be readjusted to test for other metals. The atomic absorption method provides the greatest level of accuracy per metal analyzed, but the test is very time-consuming.

In the optical emission spectrometer procedure, a small quantity of the oil sample is also burned, but the detection device measures the levels of light emitted. This equipment simultaneously measures the emitted light for as many as 18 wear metals. The emission spectrometer offers somewhat lower accuracy than the atomic absorption method, but in little more than a minute it can complete its analysis of wear metals to within several parts per million.

The value of chemically analyzing the content of larger particles in the oil supply relies heavily on chemically identifying the material and its origin in the engine. As the engine operating hours increase, the amounts of some materials in the oil tend to increase. A reading can be affected by either the addition of clean oil or a complete oil change. If the analysis of an oil sample indicates a sudden departure from the normal trends that have been established over previous inspections, a problem may be developing. An analysis kit is shown in Figure 5-5-19. By comparing the past analyses of many engines, predictions can be made about the engine's condition. This information can also help the technician choose further tests or inspections to accurately determine engine condition.

Section 6

Gas Turbine Engine Ignition Systems

To ensure that a gas turbine engine will start satisfactorily, two systems are required. One system must rotate the compressor and turbine up to a speed at which adequate air passes through the combustion chamber to mix with fuel from the fuel spray nozzles. A second system must enable ignition of the fuel-air (F/A) mixture in the combustion chamber. During engine start-up these two systems must operate simultaneously. The functioning of both systems is coordinated during the starting cycle.

Ignition systems. Ignition systems for gas turbine engines consist of three main components:

- Exciter box
- Ignition lead
- Igniter

The exciter box provides a high voltage to the ignition lead that transfers the high voltage to the igniter. The igniter is mounted in the engine in such a way as to allow it to protrude into the combustion section of the engine. When the system is activated, the exciter creates a high voltage that is discharged across the igniter electrodes and ignites the fuel inside the engine's combustion section during starting.

Ignition systems for gas-turbine engines are required to operate normally for starting only. An important characteristic of a gas-turbine ignition system is the high-energy discharge at the igniter plug. This high-energy discharge is necessary because it is difficult to ignite the fuel-air (F/A) mixture at high altitudes or in cold conditions. The high-energy discharge is accomplished by means of a storage capacitor in what is called a high-energy capacitance discharge system. The effect of this system is to produce a very hot spark at the electrodes of the igniter plug. The technician must use great care when working on gas-turbine ignition systems because of the constant possibility of a lethal shock.

Ignition units are rated in joules and are designed to give outputs that can vary according to ignition requirements.

Turbine ignition systems and components. A typical ignition system includes two exciter units, two ignition leads and two high-tension igniters. The ignition system is actually a dual system designed to fire two igniter plugs for back up and safety reasons.

The spark ignition system has been developed to provide turbine engines with an ignition system capable of operating in a wide voltage range. Systems can be energized from the aircraft 28 vDC supply or from 115 vAC, 400 Hz, or both. The normal spark rate of a typical ignition system is between 60 and 100 sparks per minute. As input voltage decreases, so will the sparks per minute.

The typical gas turbine engine is equipped with a capacitance discharge type of ignition system consisting of two identical independent ignition units operating from a common low-voltage DC electrical power source, the aircraft battery, the AC electrical system, or an engine driven permanent magnet generator (PMG). Gas turbine engines can be ignited readily in ideal atmospheric conditions, but since they often operate in the low temperatures of high altitudes, it is imperative that the system be capable of supplying a high-heat-intensity spark. Thus, a high voltage is supplied to arc across a wide igniter spark gap, providing the ignition system with a high degree of reliability under widely varying conditions of altitude, atmospheric pressure, temperature, fuel vaporization and input voltage.

Exciter Units

As shown in Figure 5-6-1, the ignition exciter unit is a small box mounted and secured to the engine. Flexible absorption mounts are often used in mounting the ignition exciter in order to isolate the exciter from the effects of engine-induced vibration.

Most ignition exciters are sealed units containing electronic components encased in an epoxy resin. The exciter transforms the input voltage to a pulsed high-voltage output through solid-state circuitry, transformers and diodes.

Continuous or low intensity ignition. Under certain flight conditions such as takeoff, landing, heavy rain, snow, icing, compressor stall, or emergency descent, it may be necessary to have the ignition system operating continuously to give an automatic relight should a flameout occur. For this condition, a low-value output (from 3 to 6 joules) is preferable, because it results in a longer life for the igniter plug and the ignition unit. Consequently, to suit all engine operating conditions, a combined system giving both a high- and low-value output is needed. Such a system can consist of one ignition unit emitting a high output to one igniter plug and a second unit giving a low output to a second igniter plug, or it can consist of an ignition unit that is capable of supplying both high and low outputs, with the output value being pre-selected as required.

Figure 5-6-1. Igniter units are sealed and compact.

Glow plug ignition system. A glow plug system, which is used on some models of gas turbine engines, provides current to a hot coil element in each plug that makes the plug glow red-hot. This glow plug reaches an extremely high temperature very rapidly and it ignites the fuel spray in the combustion section of the engine during starting.

Auto-ignition system. An auto-ignition system is generally used on turboprop engines. The ignition is activated when the system is armed and the engine torque drops below a certain value. If this condition occurs the system will automatically activate the engine's ignition system in order to help prevent the engine from flaming out or stopping. If the system is armed and the engine torque remains above the torque activation value, the auto-ignition system will remain inactive.

PW4000 Ignition System

A widely used gas-turbine engine is the Pratt & Whitney PW4000 series high-bypass turbofan, which powers several Boeing aircraft as well as other aircraft. The ignition system for this engine is a good example of modern ignition systems for gas-turbine engines. A drawing of the system is shown in Figure 5-6-2.

The complete system includes two separate heat-shielded and shock-mounted exciters. Each exciter supplies ignition energy to a recessed gap igniter plug through a high-tension lead. A small amount of engine-fan air is directed to cool the high-tension leads, the exciter boxes and the igniter plugs.

Input power for operation of the ignition exciters is 115 vAC, 400 Hz, with an input current not in excess of 2.5 amp to each exciter. The power from the aircraft electrical system is applied through a filter circuit consisting of a reactor and a feed-through capacitor to prevent high-frequency feedback into the aircraft electric system. The reactor also serves as a power choke to limit spark rate variations over the input voltage frequency range. From the filter, the voltage is applied across the primary windings of the power transformer.

The high voltage generated in the secondary windings of the power transformer is rectified in the doubler circuit by action of the two solid-state rectifiers and the doubler capacitors so that with each change in polarity, a pulse of DC voltage is sent to the storage capacitor.

The resistors in the doubler circuit limit the current passing through the rectifiers during those intervals of discharge of the storage capacitor when the voltage has reversed. With successive pulses, the storage capacitor assumes a greater and greater charge at increasing voltage.

When the voltage of the storage capacitor reaches the predetermined level for which the spark gap in the discharger tube has been calibrated, the gap breaks down and a portion of the charge accumulated on the storage capacitor flows through the primary windings of the high-tension transformer and to the trigger capacitor. This flow of current induces in the transformer secondary voltage high enough to ionize the air gap in the igniter plug. With the gap thus made conductive, the remaining charge on the storage capacitor is delivered to the igniter plug as a high energy spark across the gap. This gives the high-energy spark necessary to produce ignition under adverse conditions.

The bleeder resistor is provided to dissipate the energy in the circuit if the igniter plug is absent or fails to fire. It also provides a path to ground for any residual charge on the trigger capacitor between cycles. When the storage capacitor has discharged all its accumulated energy, the cycle of operation repeats. Variations in input voltage or frequency affect the spark repetition rate but the stored energy remains virtually constant.

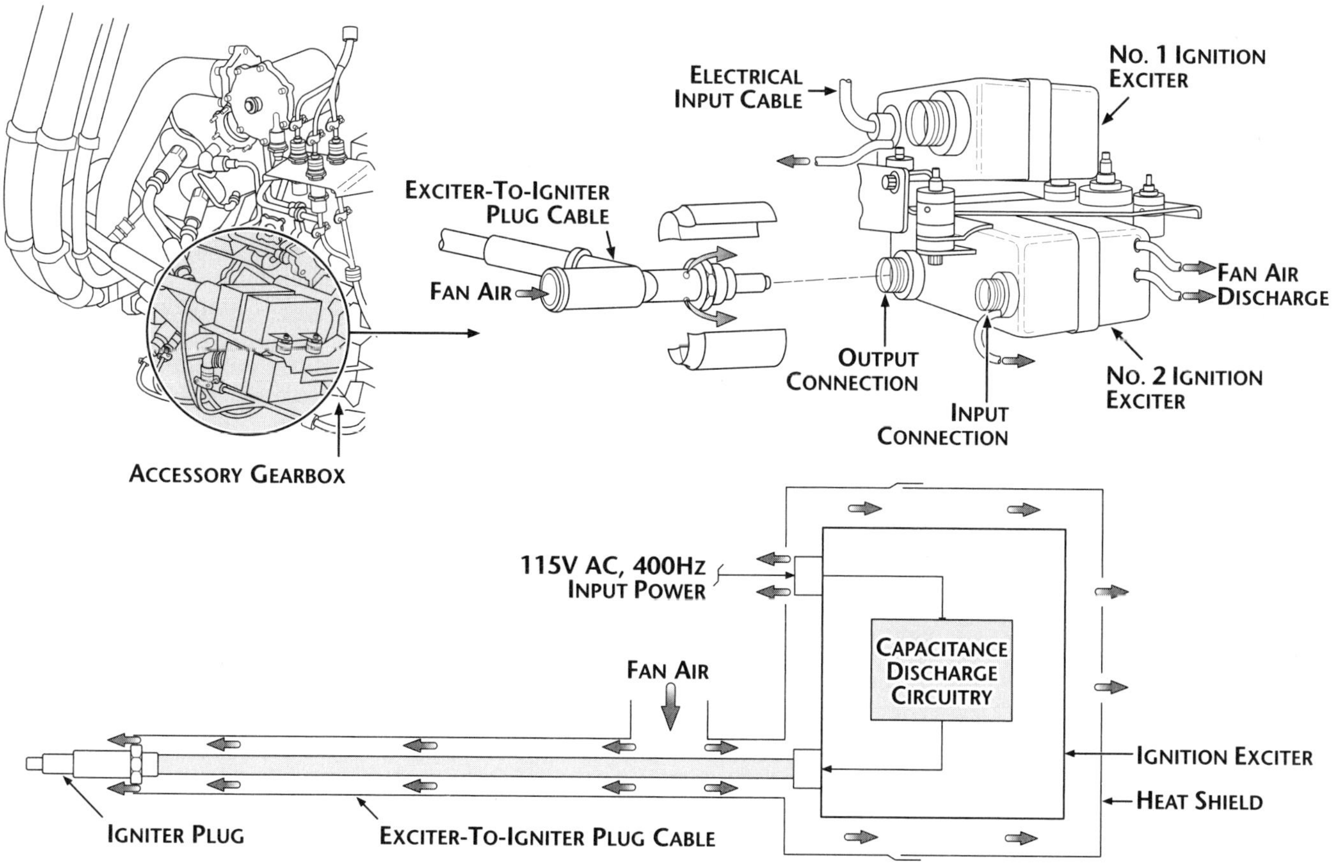

Figure 5-6-2. The PW4000 ignition system is typical of the type used on high bypass turbofan engines.

Figure 5-6-3. Fan air is used to cool the igniter leads.

Ignition cable assemblies. There are two individual ignition cable assemblies that carry the electrical energy output from the ignition exciter to the engine-mounted spark igniters. Each lead assembly consists of an electrical lead contained in a flexible metal braiding. Coupling nuts at each end of the assembly facilitate its connection to respective connectors on the ignition exciter and spark igniter. A fan cooled ignition cable assembly and ignition cables are illustrated in Figure 5-6-3.

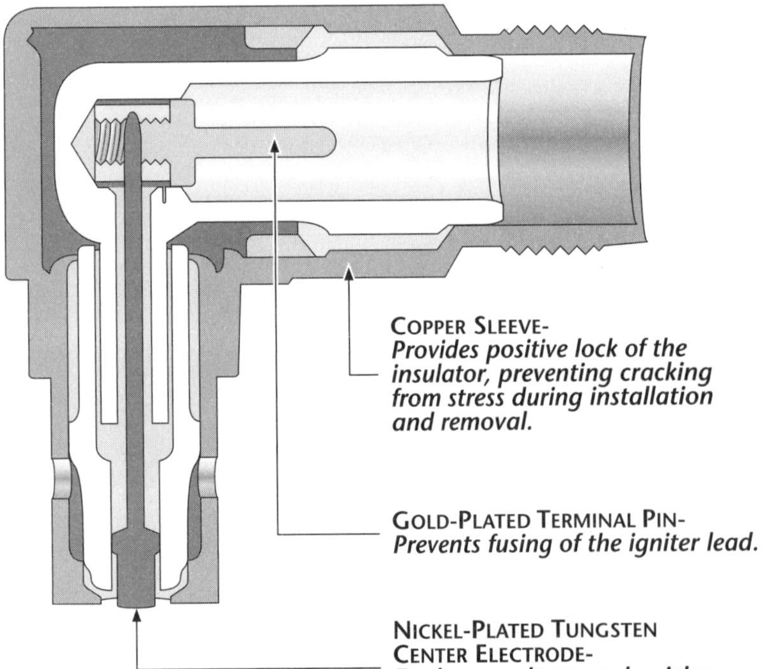

Figure 5-6-4. Turbine engine igniters are built to withstand high temperatures and voltages

Turbine Engine Igniters

A cross-sectional view of a typical igniter can be seen in Figure 5-6-4. The igniter is made up of four parts: insulators, electrodes, a shell body and internal seals. Insulators are made of an aluminum-oxide ceramic with a diamond-like hardness that provides mechanical strength, high-voltage insulation and rapid heat conductivity. Electrodes are made of Inconel, Chromel D, tungsten, or any of various nickel alloys, depending on specific service requirements. The shell body is made of extremely high-quality stainless steel or Inconel to resist burner-can combustion temperatures. The internal seals are made of ceramic materials.

The sizes and shapes of igniters are not standardized therefore there are no fixed rules for service and maintenance. In any case, it is important to follow the manufacturer's recommendations for cleaning and reconditioning. For example, it is desirable to clean the firing end of some types of igniters, while cleaning the firing end of certain other types will make them completely unusable.

Figure 5-6-5 illustrates the various types of igniter plugs and a glow plug. Since an igniter is designed to operate at a lower surrounding pressure than is a spark plug, the spark gaps in an igniter are greater. The power source for the igniter supplies a very high level of energy; therefore, the spark produced is of relatively high amperage and resembles a white-hot flame rather than a spark.

Service and inspection of igniters and glow plugs. Although the procedures and techniques given in this section provide a general guide to ignition system maintenance, they do not supersede instructions provided in approved maintenance manuals. Igniters will need to be serviced, cleaned and sometimes replaced because of erosion and carbon buildup. Specific operational, maintenance and inspection procedures concerning igniters are contained in the appropriate aircraft and service engine manuals. These manuals provide specific details that apply to the particular requirements of a given model engine or aircraft. There are several steps involved in servicing igniters. With the exception of the operational check, the instructions that follow are generally confined to the servicing of an igniter once it has been removed from the engine.

Operational check. All igniters, except the glow plug variety, emit a sharp snapping noise when firing. Spark noise is directly related to the degree of energy in the ignition system. Engine cowling suppresses the noise level considerably. In performing an operational check, one technician stands to one side of the engine while another technician in the cockpit turns on the ignition. Igniters are operating satisfactorily if a steady pulse firing is heard from both igniters.

Removal precautions. When it becomes necessary to remove igniters for visual inspection, servicing or replacement, extreme care should be exercised. The electric charge, which may be stored in the condenser of high-energy ignition units, is potentially lethal. It is essential that any safety precautions spelled out in the applicable engine manual be strictly followed. For example, some manuals call for disconnecting the low-voltage primary lead from the ignition exciter unit and waiting several minutes before disconnecting the high-voltage cable from the igniter, to permit the stored energy to dissipate.

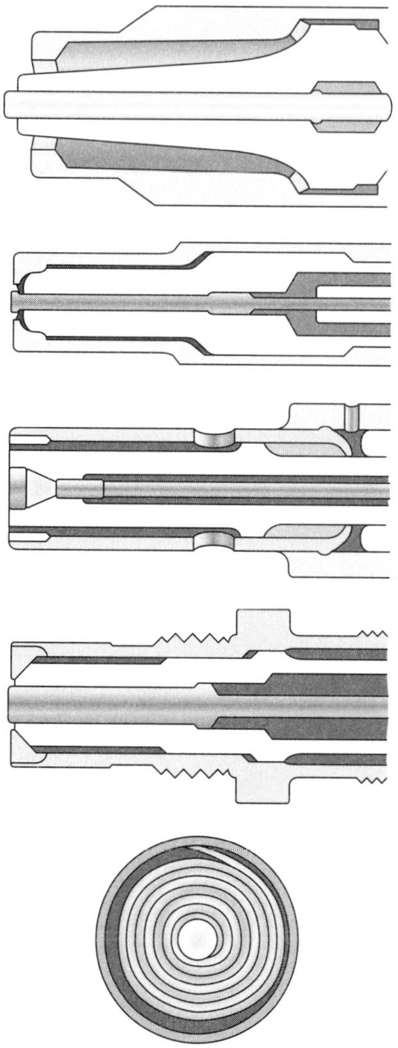

Figure 5-6-5. There are many types of igniter plugs in use.

Inspection. Prior to igniter inspection, residue should be removed from the shell exterior using a dry cloth or fiber bristle brush.

> **CAUTION:** *Do not, under any circumstances, remove any deposits or residue from the firing end of low-voltage igniters. Only on glow plugs and high-voltage igniters can the firing end be cleaned to aid inspection.*

Visually inspect the igniter for mechanical damage. An igniter should be rejected if it shows thread damage, cracked or loose ceramic in the terminal well, or chipped, cracked, or grooved ceramic in the firing-end insulator. Also discard an igniter if the wrench hexagon or the mount flange is physically damaged, or if the electrode or shell end is severely burned or eroded.

Consult the engine manual for specific limits concerning electrode erosion. Discard any igniter that exceeds wear limits or that will exceed wear limits before the aircraft can complete an addi-

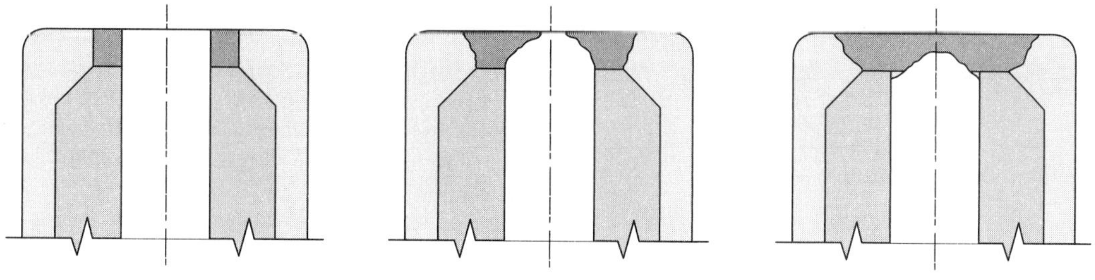

Figure 5-6-6. Eroded electrodes will create starting problems for the engine.

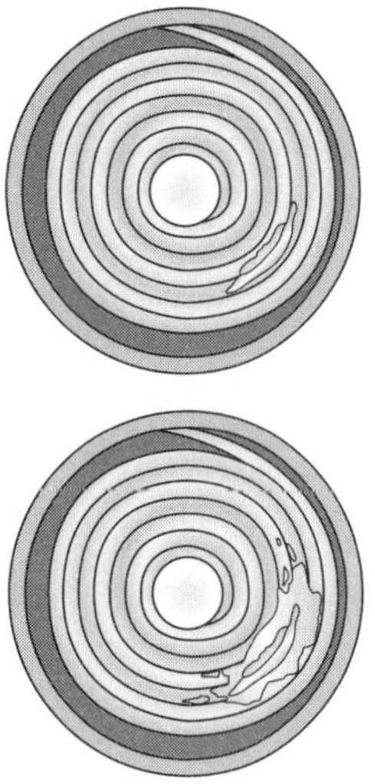

Figure 5-6-7. Inspect the glow plug coil for fusing of the element.

tional scheduled operating period. An example of electrode erosion can be seen in Figure 5-6-6.

Reconditioning. The terminal well insulator should be cleaned with a cotton or felt swab saturated with Stoddard solvent or methyl-ethyl-ketone (MEK). Do not use a metal brush for cleaning.

If stains on the terminal well insulator cannot be removed with solvent alone, abrasives such as Bon Ami or finely powdered pumice may be used. Dip a swab in the solvent and then in the abrasive. Scrub the well insulator thoroughly with a twisting motion and a stroke long enough to remove the stain. Wet a second clean swab with solvent only and clean out all residue. Then blow the terminal well dry with an air blast. The connector seat at the top of the shielding barrel should be cleaned to ensure a satisfactory seal and shield bond when the ignition lead is installed. If solvent alone does not remove dirt and corrosion from the chamfered surface, use fine-grained garnet paper or sandpaper. Do not use emery cloth or paper. Hold the igniter in a partially inverted position to prevent abrasive particles from entering the terminal well. After cleaning thoroughly, blow out the terminal well with air.

Examine the cleaned terminal well thoroughly for insulator cracks or terminal damage and reject those igniters with physical faults.

The firing end of the igniter should be cleaned only if a cleaning procedure is approved by the manufacturer. Some igniters have semiconductor materials at the firing end and will be damaged if usual cleaning procedures are followed.

If inspection of a glow plug element reveals that it has carbon deposit buildup, it may be serviced as follows:

1. Immerse element end of glow plug in cold carbon remover to loosen carbon deposit (as required).
2. Brush off loosened carbon with a soft nylon or fiber brush. Never use a metal brush, as it will damage the oxide insulation coating on the element coils.
3. Rinse element thoroughly in hot running water. Blow the element dry with air.
4. Inspect element for possible fused area, as illustrated in Figure 5-6-7. The fusing of element coils is a random condition caused by a combustion deposit bridging the coils or an over-wattage surge. Any plug that exceeds the manufacturer's acceptable fused limit should be replaced.

Electrical testing. Some igniters are tested using a high-voltage source, with the firing end pressurized with compressed air; others are tested in open air utilizing the engine ignition system. A steady firing across the gap indicates that the igniter is satisfactory. To test glow plugs, the technician should attach the plugs to the engine ignition system leads and turn the ignition switch on while adhering to all safety procedures. The glow plug element should heat up to a bright yellow color within 30 seconds.

Installation information. Igniter installation mountings vary extensively. Consult the appropriate instruction manuals for each particular engine model to get specific igniter installation instructions.

Installation gaskets come in many sizes and shapes and are generally available only from the engine manufacturer. An installation gasket is considered an engine part. In a few instances,

Figure 5-7-1. The starter is mounted to the accessory gear box.

gaskets are supplied by the igniter manufacturer and are packaged with the igniter.

Some igniters require a specific mounting-gasket thickness to position the igniter-firing end properly in the combustor-can. The gaskets are usually supplied in a set containing gaskets of several thicknesses. If an igniter is mounted too deep, the firing-end temperatures can increase considerably, resulting in both reduced life and reliability of the igniter.

Figure 5-7-2. A starter generator is a dual purpose unit that saves space and weight in the engine compartment.

Section 7

Gas Turbine Engine Starting Systems

Starters for gas-turbine engines may be classified as air-turbine (pneumatic) starters, electric starters, fuel-air (F/A) combustion starters and cartridge-type starters. Most modern aircraft use either electric or air-turbine starters.

Electric starter. Comparatively small gas-turbine engines (under 6,000 lb. of thrust) are often equipped with heavy-duty electric starters or starter generators. These are simply electric motors or motor-generator units that produce a very strong starting torque because of the large torque loads involved with turning the engine.

The electric starter is coupled to the engine through a reduction gear and ratchet mechanism, or clutch, which automatically disengages after the engine has reached a self-sustaining speed. An example of an electric starter can be seen in Figure 5-7-1.

The electric supply (generally a NiCad 24 volt battery) is passed through a system of relays to allow the full voltage to be recovered progressively as the starter gains speed. The electric supply is canceled when the starter load is reduced, after the engine has started and reached a self-sustaining speed (40% r.p.m. to 60% r.p.m.)

Some engines use a starter-generator. This unit combines the functions of both an electric starter and a generator in one housing. Equipped with two sets of field windings, it can be motored to rotate the engine. After engine start, the second set of fields is switched on, changing the function of the unit from a motor to a generator. Most modern light turbine engines use starter-generator systems. A typical starter generator is shown in Figure 5-7-2.

Air-turbine starter. The most commonly used starter on large engines is the air-turbine starter. This type of starter requires a high-volume air supply, which may be provided by a ground starter unit, a compressed-air bottle on the airplane, an auxiliary power unit (APU) on the aircraft or compressor bleed air from other engines on the aircraft. The most common is an on board auxiliary power unit.

Low-pressure air-turbine starter. The low-pressure air-turbine starter is designed to operate with a high-volume, low-pressure air supply, usually obtained from an air compressor unit mounted on a ground power unit (GPU), or from the airplane's low-pressure air supply, normally from an APU. The air supply must produce pressure of about 35 p.s.i.g and a flow of more than 100 lb./min.

An air-turbine starter is shown in Figure 5-7-3. This starter is a lightweight turbine air motor equipped with a rotating assembly, a reduction gear system, a splined output shaft, a cutout switch mechanism, an overspeed-switch assembly and gear housing. The air passes through nozzle vanes to the outer rim of the turbine wheel. Since this is an impulse turbine design, the air expands, increasing its velocity through

Figure 5-7-3. Air turbine starters need a source of high volume air to motor the engine for starting.

Figure 5-8-1. Variable stator vanes are adjusted to maintain the airflow in the engine.

inlet guide vanes and is then expelled through the screen and out into the atmosphere.

In the unit shown, the expansion of the air from a pressure of about 35 p.s.i.g to atmospheric pressure imparts energy to the turbine wheel, causing it to reach a speed of about 55,000 r.p.m. This low-torque high speed is converted to a high-torque low speed by means of the reduction gearing. Typical gear ratios are in excess of 20:1. Most air-turbine starters operate with similar pressures, speed ranges and reduction ratios.

High-pressure air-turbine starter. The high-pressure air-turbine starter is essentially the same as a low-pressure starter except that it is equipped with an axial-flow turbine in place of the radial, inward-flow turbine previously described. The high-pressure starter is fitted with both low-pressure and high-pressure air connections to provide for operation from either type of air supply.

Figure 5-8-2. Fixed inlet guide vanes prepare the air for entry into the engine.

The usual air supply for the high-pressure starter operation is a high-pressure air bottle mounted in the airplane. This air bottle is charged to a pressure of about 3,000 p.s.i. and is used for starting one of the engines when an internal low-pressure source is not available. This type of starter is not widely used today.

Combustion starter. The two principal types of combustion starter are the gas-turbine starter and the cartridge-type starter. The turbine-operating section of these starters is similar or identical to that of air-turbine starters.

A gas-turbine starter is used for some jet engines and is completely self-contained. It has its own fuel and ignition system, its own starting system (electric or hydraulic) and a self-contained oil system. This type of starter is economical to operate and provides high power output for comparatively low weight.

The starter consists of a small, compact gas-turbine engine, featuring a turbine-driven centrifugal compressor, a reverse-flow combustion system and a mechanically independent free-power turbine. The free-power turbine is connected to the main engine via a two-stage reduction gear, an automatic clutch and an output shaft. This type of starter has very limited use.

The cartridge-type starter may be considered an air-turbine starter operated by means of hot gases from a solid fuel cartridge instead of compressed air. Some air-turbine starters can be adapted to cartridge operation merely by installing a cartridge combustion chamber and a gas duct on the air-turbine starter. This starter has very limited use.

Air impingement starting. Some gas-turbine engines are not fitted with starter motors but instead use air forced onto the turbine blades as a means of rotating the engine. The air is obtained from an external source or from a running engine and it is directed through non-return valves and nozzles onto the turbine blades. This type of system also has very limited use.

Inspection and Maintenance of Turbine Engine Starters

Inspections of turbine starters are similar to inspections of other accessories. These inspections include checks for security of mounting; freedom from oil leaks; and security of air and gas ducts, fluid lines and electrical wiring. Special inspections required for particular units are listed in the manufacturer's operation and service instructions.

Maintenance and service include the changing of the lubricant in the gear housing. Since the starter is attached to the engine, it is likely to be exposed to very high temperatures. For this reason, the lubricant used is of the high-temperature type, such as MIL-L-7808C or MIL-L-23699. Even this type of lubricant will lose its lubricating qualities after a time; therefore, it must be tested or changed regularly. An overhaul of turbine starters should not be necessary at fewer than 2,000 hours of engine service; however, the life of a starter is largely dependent on the skill and knowledge of the personnel who operate it.

Section 8

Compressor Surge/Stall Control Systems

Compressor stall. Compressor ratios for gas turbines have increased. Some engines on large transport aircraft can have compressor pressure ratios of 30:1 and higher. These pressure ratio increases have improved engine performance and specific fuel consumption radically, but with this improvement in engine performance comes an increase in the likelihood of compressor stall. Compressor stall is the failure of the compressor blades to move the air at the designed flow rate. When this occurs, the air velocity in the first compressor stage is reduced to a level at which the angle of attack of the compressor blades reaches a stall value. This unstable condition is often caused from air piling up in the rear stages of the compressor.

Even though compressor rotor blades do not have variable angles, the effective angle of attack does not remain the same under all conditions. Compressor stall occurs most frequently whenever there is unusually high compressor r.p.m. and a low air inlet velocity. A decreasing inlet air velocity meeting an unchanged compressor r.p.m. changes the effective angle of attack. When the effective angle of attack increases because of the same high compressor speed meeting a lower inlet velocity, the angle of attack is increased to a stall condition. Gas turbine engine compressors are designed with adequate margin to prevent compressor stall from occurring under normal conditions.

Stall Control

Variable inlet guide vanes and variable stator vanes. Where high-pressure ratios on a single shaft are required, it becomes necessary to introduce airflow control into the compressor design. This may take the form of variable inlet guide vanes for the first stage, plus a number of stages incorporating variable stator vanes, as illustrated in Figure 5-8-1. As the compressor speed is reduced from its design value, these stator vanes are progressively closed in order to maintain an acceptable air angle value onto the following rotor blades.

The variable vanes are automatically regulated in pitch angle by means of the fuel controlled actuator unit. The regulating factors are the compressor inlet temperature and the engine speed. The effect of the variable stator vanes is to provide a means for controlling the direction of compressor inter-stage airflow and quantity of air, thus ensuring the correct angle of attack for the compressor blades and reducing the possibility of compressor stall. An inlet guide vane does not have a rotor in front of it that makes it a guide vane instead of stator vane.

Inlet guide vanes (IGV) can be fixed or variable and are generally used at the inlet of the com-

Figure 5-8-3 The unison ring moves all the stator vanes at the same time.

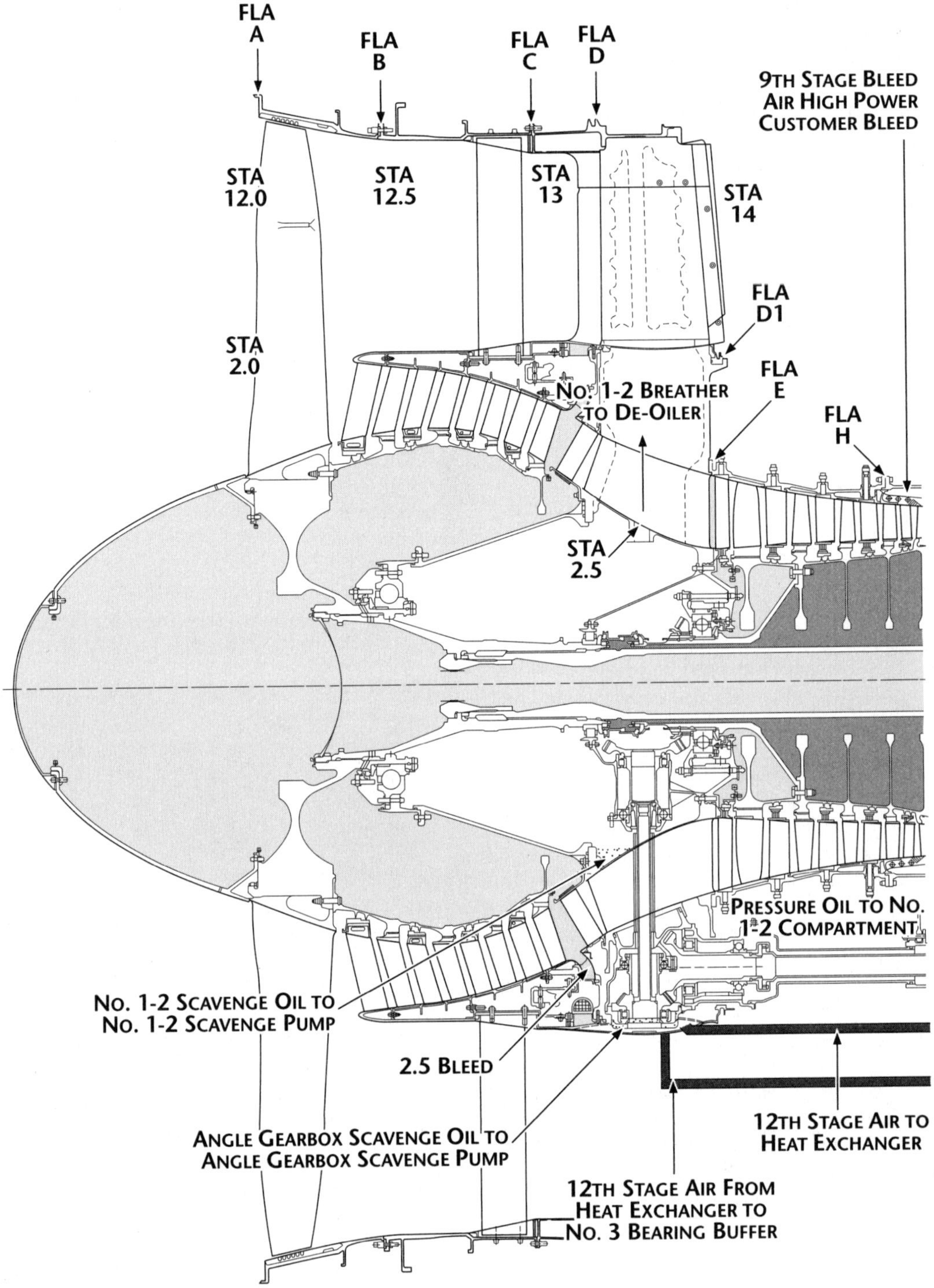

Figure 5-8-4. Compressor bleed air is used to cool the engine internally.

pressor. Inlet guide vanes are used to either straighten the inlet air flow or restrict air flow into the inlet of the engine's compressor. As shown in Figure 5-8-2, fixed inlet guide vanes are not movable and their main purpose is to provide a smooth flow of air into the engine.

The variable inlet guide vanes (VIGV) are used to adjust the flow into the compressor as needed to provide a smooth air flow into the compressor. Variable stator vanes (VSV) are stator vanes that are preceded by a compressor rotor and are movable. They are generally in the first few stages in the high-pressure compressor and are used to adjust air flow in the high-pressure compressor. VSVs also prevent compressor surge or stall. As seen in Figure 5-8-3, each one is attached to a unison ring which is moved by the variable stator vane actuator. When activated, the unison ring moves each stator vane the same amount. Each row of stators has its own unison ring. All of the unison rings are moved by the one actuator.

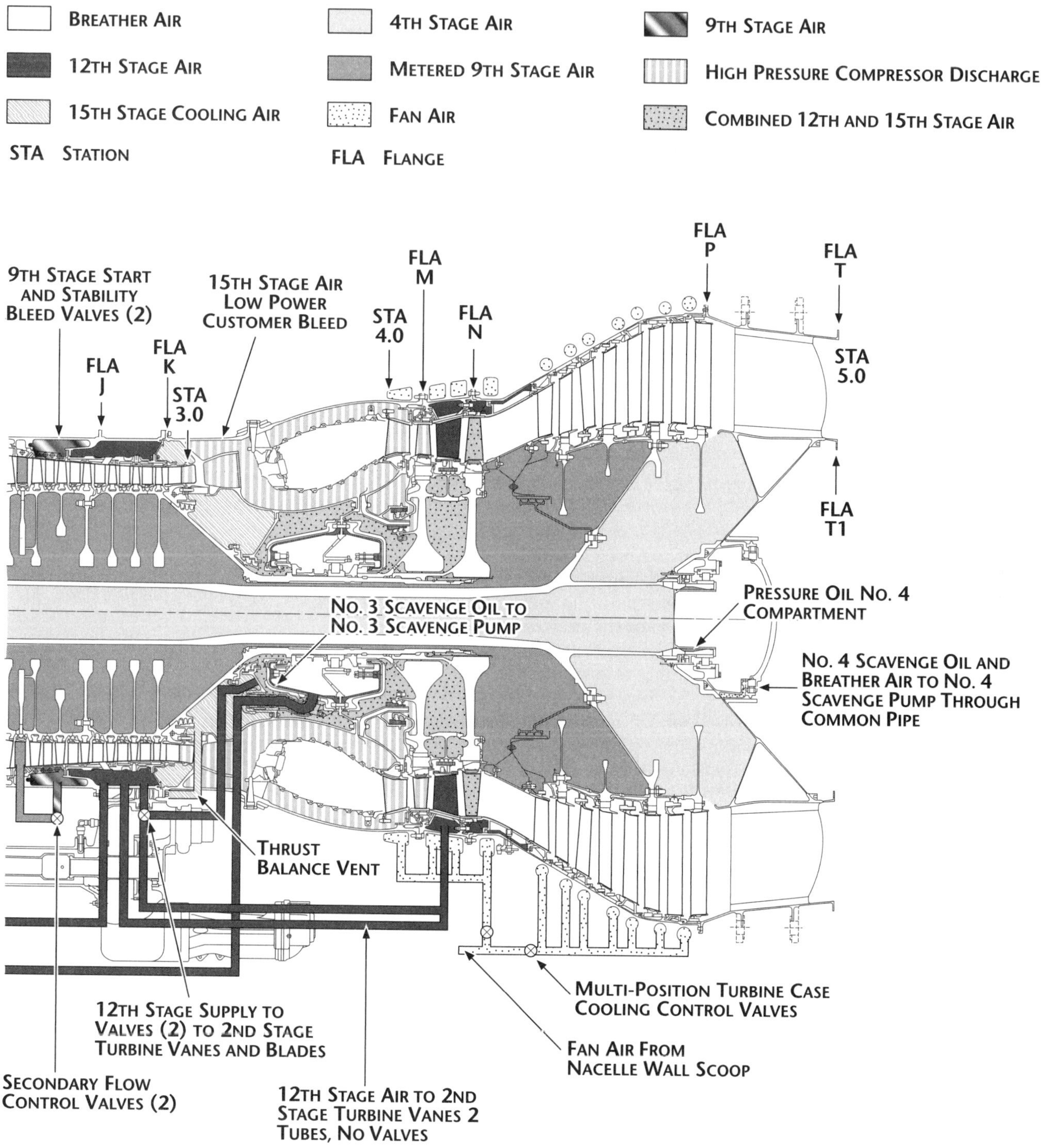

Air-bleed valves and internal air systems. Compression of air as it moves through the compressor causes a substantial rise in temperature. For example, air at the last stage of the compressor may reach a temperature of greater than 650°F as a result of compression.

Some engines are provided with automatic air bleed valves that operate during engine starting or low r.p.m. conditions to prevent air from piling up at the high-pressure end of the compressor and slowing the velocity of the compressor air flow resulting in a stall or surge. This bleed valve permits easier starting and accelerating while reducing the danger of compressor stall. A more detailed explanation of bleed systems and internal bleed air use appears in Chapter 7, PW-4000 engine.

Compressor air, illustrated in Figure 5-8-4, is also utilized within the engine to provide cooling for the engine's internal hot section components, turbine wheel and the turbine inlet guide vanes.

Bleed air from the compressor is used to cool the vanes and blades by allowing some of the relatively cool air in the compressor to flow through and out of the turbine vanes and blades. Although the air in the compressor is fairly hot, it is still cooler than the turbine gases flowing over the blades and vanes. Cooling systems are used to cool the turbine vanes and blades that allow the engines temperatures to be raised, making the engine more efficient. This system can also be controlled so the amount of the cooling air passing over the blades and vanes is at its minimum during cruise power settings. Maximum flow is used during high power settings. Internal air systems are also used to cool the turbine disk, to serve as buffers around bearing compartments, anti-icing and offset thrust loads on bearings and thermal stabilization.

Turbine Engine Inlet Anti-ice Systems

Most gas turbine engines are seriously affected by the formation of ice on compressor inlet guide vanes. All turbine engines are very susceptible to icing. Ice forms on the guide vanes or inlet screen and restricts the flow of inlet air. This is indicated by a loss of thrust and a rapid rise in exhaust gas temperature (EGT). As the airflow decreases, this raises the turbine inlet temperature. The fuel control attempts to correct any loss in engine r.p.m. by adding more fuel, which aggravates the condition. To correct this condition, the inlet guide vanes can be heated to prevent the formation of ice.

The inlet guide vanes and the inlet struts of axial compressor engines are usually hollow. Hot, high-pressure air is bled from the rear of the engine compressor and is ducted through an anti-icing system control valve to the hollow sections of the inlet struts and guide vanes, seen in Figure 5-8-5. The heat provided prevents the formation of ice. Because such a system may not melt ice once it has formed, icing conditions should be anticipated in advance. Once ice has formed on the inlet struts or vanes, anti-icing air could cause large chunks of ice to enter the compressor, damaging the blades.

Anti-icing systems cause a reduction in thrust and should be used only when necessary. The engine specifications usually define the maximum allowable extraction of compressor bleed air at any one time. With all the anti-icing systems in use at one time on certain aircraft, power loss could be as much as 30%.

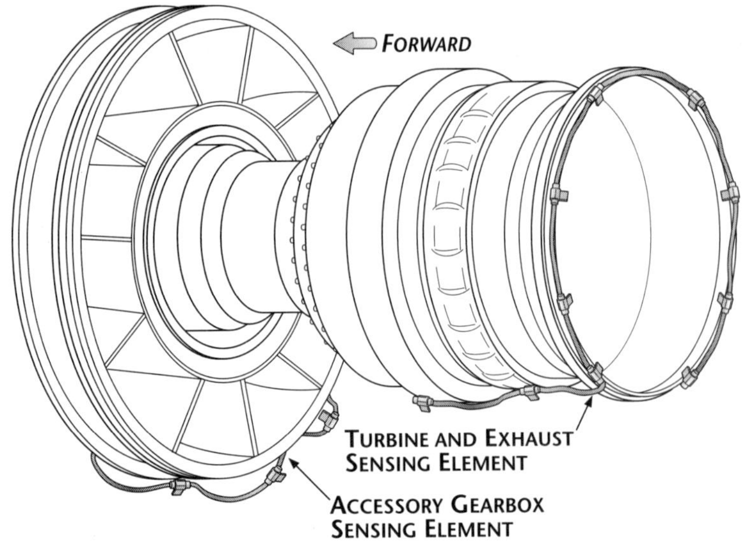

Figure 5-9-1. A continuous loop sensing element provides complete coverage of the engine

Section 9

Overheat Detection and Extinguishing Systems

Turbine engine fire zones. A possible fire zone in a turbine engine installation is any area in which an ignition source, together with combustibles, combustible fluid line leakage, or combustible mixtures may exist. The following engine compartments usually are protected:

- Engine power section, which includes the burner, turbine and exhaust nozzle
- Engine compressor and accessory section, which includes the compressor and all the engine accessories
- Complete powerplant compartments, in which no isolation exists between the engine power section and the accessory section

Turbine engine fire extinguishing agents. The effectiveness of the various agents is influenced by the type of turbine engine fire protection system used, whether it is a high-rate-of-discharge (HRD) system rather than a conventional system, or whether the method of distribution is nozzle, spray ring, or open-end outlet. The choice of agent is also influenced by the airflow conditions through the engine. Freon and CO_2 are the two most common engine extinguishing agents used in aircraft.

Types of fire or overheat detectors. The following list of detection methods includes those most commonly used in turbine engine fire protection systems. The complete aircraft fire protection system of most large turbine engine aircraft will incorporate several of these detection methods:

- Rate-of-temperature-rise detectors
- Radiation sensing detectors
- Smoke detectors
- Overheat detectors
- Carbon monoxide detectors
- Combustible mixture detectors
- Fiber-optic detectors
- Observation of crew or passengers

The three types of detectors most commonly used for fast detection of engine nacelle fires are the rate-of-rise, radiation sensing and overheat detectors.

Typical Gas Turbine Fire Protection System

On newer generation aircraft, the information from the warning systems is fed into the Engine Indicating and Crew Alerting System (EICAS), which provide messages or warnings to the flight crew on multifunction displays (MFDs). A turbine engine fire protection system for a large multi-engine turbine powered aircraft must provide warning and extinguishing as an integrated system.

The engine fire protection system used on large turbine engine aircraft consists of two subsystems: a fire detection system and a fire extinguishing system. These two subsystems provide fire protection to the engine and nacelle areas as well as the APU compartment. Each turbine engine has an automatic heat-sensing fire detection circuit. This circuit includes a warning light in the cockpit for each circuit and a common alarm bell.

The heat-sensing unit of each circuit is a continuous loop, which is routed around the areas to be protected. These areas tend to be around the hot section areas (combustion, turbine and exhaust) of the engine. A continuous-loop detector or sensing system permits a more complete coverage of a fire hazard area than any other spot-type temperature detector. Figure 5-9-1 illustrates the typical routing of a continuous-loop fire detection circuit in an engine nacelle.

Two widely used types of continuous-loops are the Kidde and the Fenwal systems. In the Kidde continuous-loop system, two wires are imbedded in a special ceramic core within an Inconel tube. One of the two wires in the Kidde sensor is welded to the case at each end and acts as an internal ground. The second wire is a hot lead that provides a current signal when the ceramic core material changes its resistance with a change in temperature.

Figure 5-9-2. High rate of discharge (HRD) fire extinguishing bottles in a B737

Another continuous-loop system, the Fenwal system, uses a single wire surrounded by a continuous string of ceramic beads in an Inconel tube. The beads in the Fenwal detector are wetted with a eutectic salt, which suddenly lowers its electrical resistance as the sensing element reaches its alarm temperature. In both the Kidde and Fenwal systems, the resistance of the ceramic or eutectic salt core material prevents electrical current from flowing at normal temperatures. In case of a fire or overheat condition, the core resistance drops and current flows between the signal wire and ground, energizing the alarm system.

A typical continuous loop is made up of sensing element sections that are joined to each other by moisture proof connectors. The entire loop is attached to the aircraft structure by attachments or clamps every 10 to 12 inches of its length. Too great a distance between supports may permit vibration or chafing of the unsupported section and become a source of false alarms.

In turn, each of the loops is connected to a control unit, which contains the circuitry for the warning and test features. Each system contains test modes which simulate a fire or overheat condition in the circuit. This tests the integrity of the detection loop. The output of the control unit is used to energize an appropriate fire-warning device.

The fires and overheat warning devices for each engine and nacelle are located in the cockpit. A fire warning light for each engine usually is located in a special fire switch handle on the instrument panel, glare shield, or fire control panel. These fire switches are sometimes referred

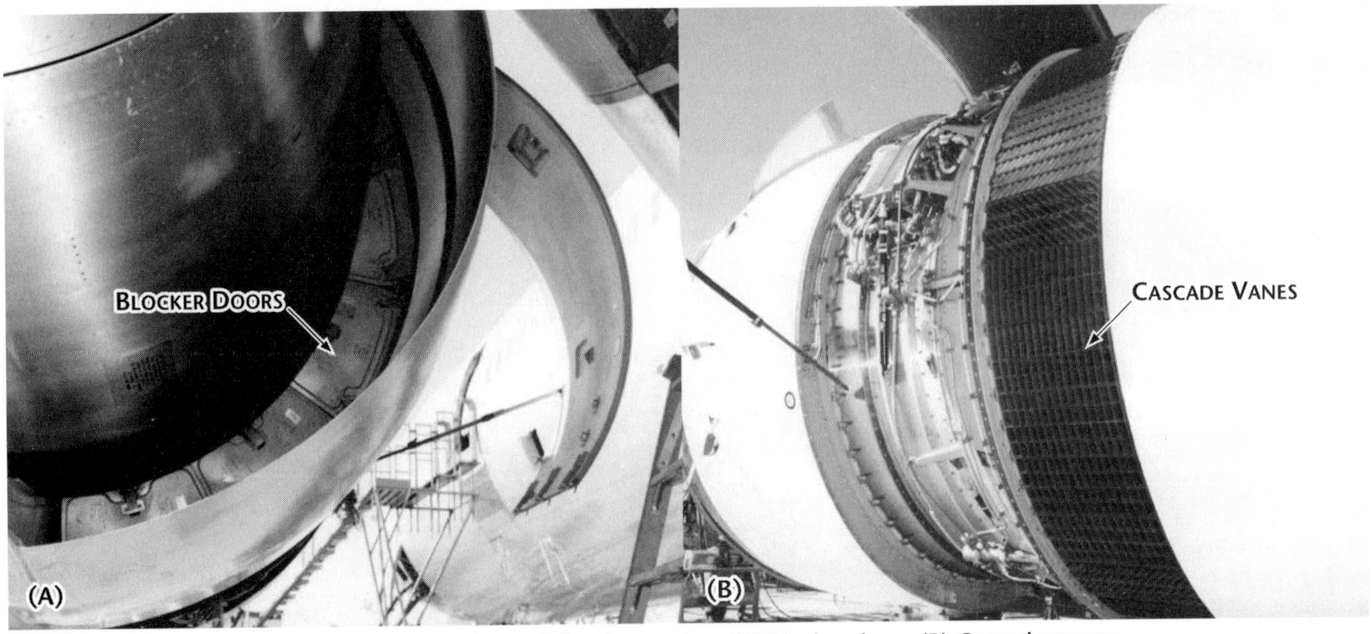

Figure 5-10-1. Aerodynamic blocking is one form of thrust reversing. (A) Blocker doors (B) Cascade vanes

to as fire-pull handles. The fire handle contains the fire detection warning light. In some installations, pulling the fire handle exposes an extinguishing agent switch and actuates the firewall fuel shutoff valves. At the same time the generator is taken offline and the hydraulic valves are closed. The pilots must activate the fire extinguishing agent switch. Generally, two containers of extinguishing agent are available.

The fire extinguishing portion of a fire protection system includes a cylinder or container of an extinguishing agent capable of reaching each engine and nacelle area. This system uses an extinguishing agent container similar to the type shown in Figure 5-9-2. This type of container is equipped with two discharge valves that are operated by a switch in the cockpit. The two valves are the main and the reserve controls that release and route the agent to the engine or nacelle. This type of configuration permits the release of a second charge of fire extinguishing agent to the same engine or another engine if another fire breaks out. The agent is released from the bottle by an electrically activated discharge cartridge or squib. The squib is discharged by the cockpit switch.

Turbine Engine Ground Fire Protection

The problem of ground fires has increased in seriousness with the increased size of turbine

Figure 5-10-2. Mechanical blocking of the exhaust stream is another way of reversing thrust.

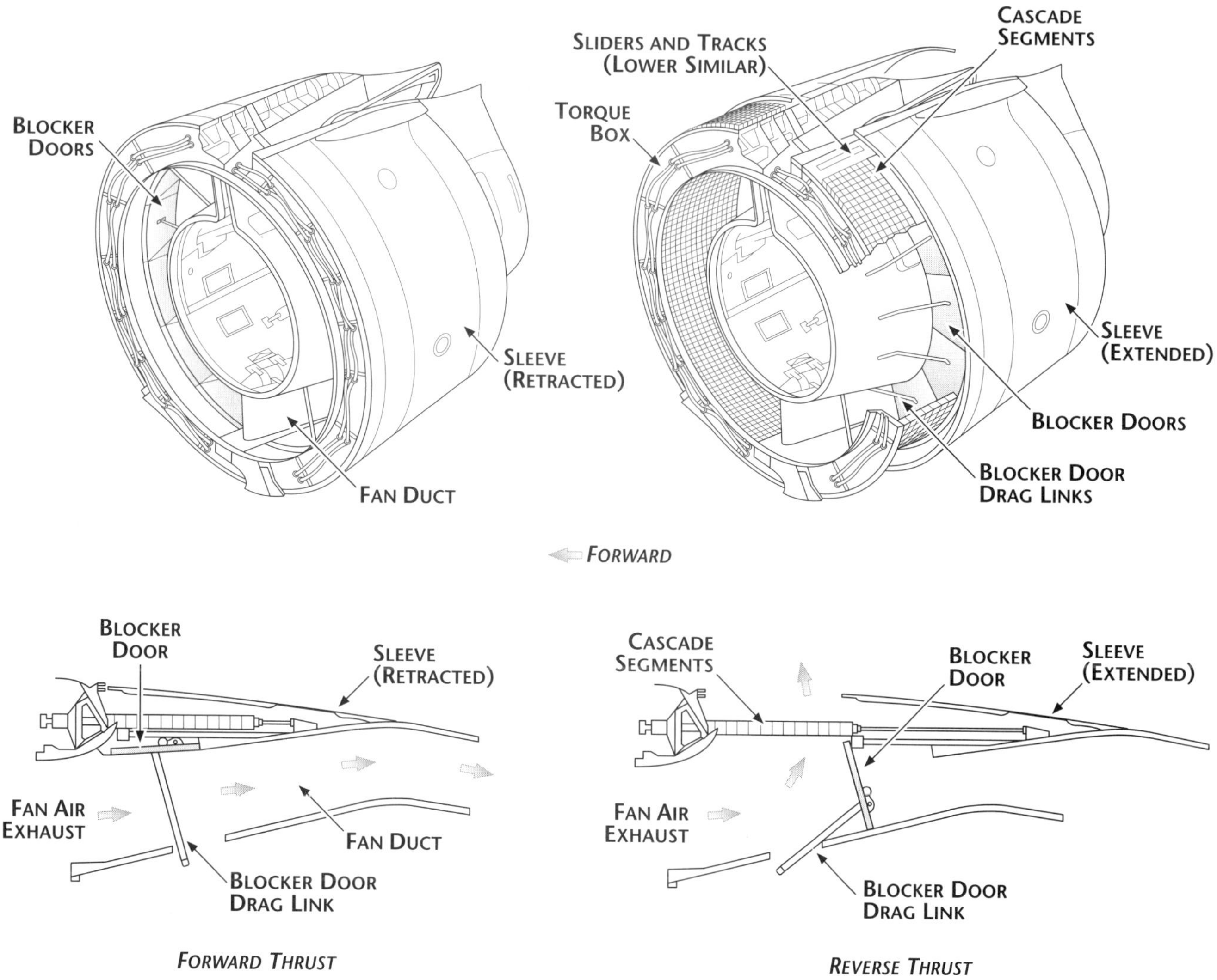

Figure 5-10-3. Cascade vanes are used to re-direct the cold stream air for added braking.

engine aircraft. For this reason, a central ground connection to the aircraft's fire extinguishing system has been provided on some aircraft. Such systems provide a more effective means of extinguishing ground fires and eliminate the necessity of removing and recharging the aircraft-installed fire extinguisher cylinders. These systems usually include means for operating the entire system from one place, such as the cockpit or at the location of the fire extinguishing agent supply on the ground.

On aircraft not equipped with a central fire extinguishing system, means are usually provided for rapid access to the compressor, exhaust, or burner compartments. Thus, many aircraft systems are equipped with spring-loaded or pop-out access doors in the various compartments.

Internal engine exhaust fires that take place during engine shutdown or false starts can be blown out by motoring the engine with the starter. If the engine is running, it can be accelerated to rated speed to achieve the same result. If such a fire persists, a fire-extinguishing agent can be directed into the engine nacelle. Remember that excessive use of CO_2 or other agents that have a cooling effect can shrink the turbine housing which can cause engine damage.

Section 10

Thrust Reverser Systems

Turbine aircraft include thrust reversers to assist the brake system in slowing the aircraft after landing. The two most commonly used types of thrust reversers are the aerodynamic blockage system, illustrated in Figure 5-10-1 and the mechanical blockage system, illustrated in Figure 5-10-2.

Both the aerodynamic system and the mechanical system are subjected to high temperatures and to high gas loads. The components of both systems, especially the doors, are therefore con-

Figure 5-10-4. Active clearance control maintains the dimensions of the engine case within acceptable limits.

structed from heat-resisting materials and are of particularly heavy construction.

Aerodynamic blockage. The thrust reverser shown in Figure 5-10-3 is equipped with vanes and deflectors by which the exhaust gases and cold fan stream air are deflected outward and forward and are controlled through the thrust lever in the cockpit.

The system consists of a number of cascade vanes and solenoids with a pneumatic or hydraulic motor operating through gears shafts and torque tubes. As the blocker doors in the fan air-stream close, the translating cowl opens. This allows the cascade vanes to direct fan air aft. As shown in Figure 5-10-3, the operating mechanism incorporates many components that are used to operate the blocker doors and translating cowl.

> **CAUTION:** *When working in the area of the thrust reversers, the lockout must be in place. If there is any one in the area of the blockers doors when the system is actuated they could be crushed. The lockout is generally a mechanical means of preventing the reversers from being deployed.*

As an example of operation, after the aircraft has landed, the pilot moves the power levers to the rear of the IDLE position. Then the pilot moves the thrust reverser levers aft. This action causes the deflecting vanes (blocker doors) to move into the mainstream of the fan-air flow through the engine and the air-stream to reverse the airflow in the opposite direction. The translating cowl also moves to the open position at the same time allowing fan air to pass through cascade vanes, directing the thrust forward. At the same time as the thrust levers are moved further rearward, the fuel flow to the engine is increased. When the thrust levers are in the FULL REVERSE position, the engine power output is approximately 75% of full-forward thrust capability. Advantages of the fan reverser system are that the fan air is not very hot, the amount of thrust provided is much greater than most mechanical blockage systems.

Mechanical blockage. The mechanical blockage reverser consists of two blocker doors, or clamshells, which, when stowed, form the rear part of the engine nacelle. When the doors are deployed as shown in Figure 5-10-2, they form a barrier to the exhaust gases and deflect them to produce a reverse thrust. This thrust reverser is hydraulically or pneumatically operated and electrically controlled. This reverser cannot be deployed unless the engine r.p.m. is less than 65%. Some aircraft utilize a reverse thrust lever that is separate from the thrust lever. This is to prevent the thrust reverser from being deployed above the IDLE position. On most turboprop aircraft, the throttle and thrust lever are the same levers. By moving the throttles aft, passed the idle position (over the gate), the propeller will go into a negative pitch and slow down the aircraft upon landing. Although this is not a thrust reverser system the results are very similar.

Active clearance control. Turbine case cooling system (TCCS) is a type of active clearance control used to adjust the clearance between the turbine blade tips and the surrounding shroud. It is used under certain engine power settings. The normal operation of the system is at cruise power and high altitudes. The clearance between the blade tips and surrounding shroud at high power takeoff power settings must be maintained for proper turbine efficiencies. This clearance can become excessive at lower power settings and at the colder air temperatures found at high altitudes. To maintain this clearance cooling air is directed on the turbine cases causing them to shrink and to take up the excess clearance between the shroud and the turbine blade tips at cruise power settings. This system uses fan air through control valves controlled by the FADEC engine control and manifolds that surround the turbine case (high and low pressure turbine) as shown in Figure 5-10-4. This system is explained in more detail in the chapter on turbofan engines.

Chapter 6

TESTING & operation

Safe, economical and reliable operation of turbine engines depends on accurately measuring engine temperature and pressure during operation. This is accomplished through the science of instrumentation. The flight crew has primary responsibility for monitoring the instruments and maintaining engine power settings within preset limits. Modern electronic control systems (primarily the FADEC and EEC) have expanded beyond the task of simply keeping the engine within safe operating parameters.

Computers have made long-term data storage possible. Engine information is recorded and kept in files that can be easily retrieved by maintenance personnel. Instrumentation is critical to monitoring condition of the gas path. Most problem-solving and performance evaluations are dependent on obtaining accurate data (parameter values) from the engine. Engine instruments must be calibrated on a regular basis in order to obtain worthwhile data. Evaluation of this data is the basis for determining engine condition. The proper operation of a gas turbine engine is critical to prolonging the engine's life. Performance evaluation, instrumentation, starting procedures and operational problems for different types of gas turbine engines will be studied in this chapter.

Learning Objectives

- *Engine Starting*
- *Instrumentation*
- *Turbofan Indicators*
- *Turboprop Instruments*
- *Operational Procedures*
- *Engine Performance Tests*
- *Standard Day Conversions*

Section 1

Starting and Instrumentation

General starting procedures. All turbine engines need three conditions to occur in the correct sequence for successful engine starting. The first is airflow at the correct volume and pressure provided by the compressor turned

Left. A turbofan engine being tested under actual operating conditions.

by the starter. Next, the spark igniters provide ignition, followed by fuel flow to the combustion section through the fuel nozzles. Starting the turbine engine requires that the compressor (high-pressure or gas generator) be rotated at a speed at which sufficient airflow is initiated. The power to accomplish this is significant and may be provided by different types of starters which are dictated by the size of the engine.

Turbine engines under 6,000 lbs. thrust may utilize electric motors which may be either DC electric or starter-generator type. In larger turbine engines—since the starting loads require so much starting energy—a large electric starter and high current flow make this option impractical.

On larger engines, air turbine starters are used because they operate at high power output. Air to operate this type of starter is generally supplied from a ground-based air source, aircraft auxiliary power unit (APU), or compressor bleed air from another on-board operating engine. In a two-spool engine, only the high-pressure compressor is turned by the starter in the process of starting.

The low-pressure compressor (fan), or in the case of a turboprop, the power turbine, reduction gear box and propeller will begin to rotate when airflow is adequate. Once the compressor begins to rotate and has reached a specified r.p.m., ignition is turned on, followed by fuel, which is accomplished by moving either the throttle/power lever or a condition lever to the appropriate position which is detailed in Figure 6-1-1. In some cases this actuates a switch that moves a solenoid valve to introduce ignition and fuel.

The rise in turbine gas temperature is the first indication that the fuel and air in the engine's combustion section has lit off (is burning) during an engine start. The starter continues to

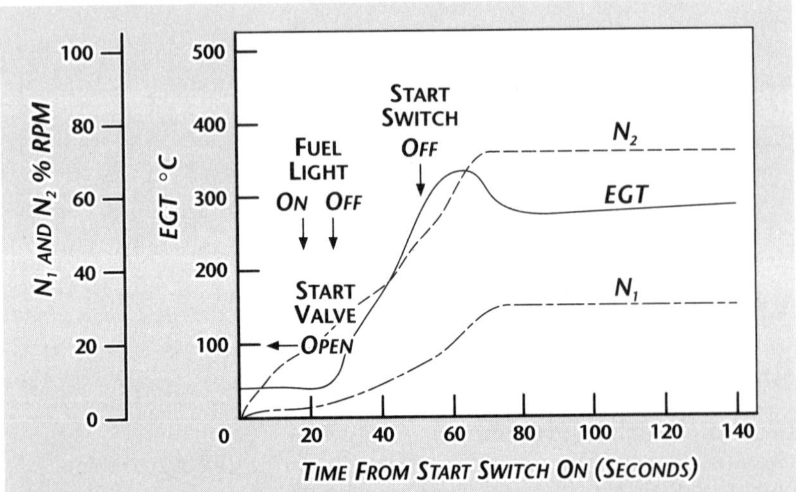

Figure 6-1-1. The engine starting cycle shows the relationship between compressor speeds and EGT.

Figure 6-1-2. Turbine engine tachometers indicate in percent of r.p.m.

assist in compressor rotation until the compressor r.p.m. reaches a speed at which the combustion process provides sufficient energy for the engine to accelerate on its own.

When self-sustaining speed is achieved, the ignition is turned off, followed by cutout of the starter. Throughout this process, fuel flow and EGT must be monitored closely for expected values. The specific r.p.m. values for the application of ignition, fuel and cut-out of the starter as well as the limiting values for turbine gas temperature differ widely depending upon the type of engine.

Basic Instrumentation

Tachometers. A turbine engine tachometer or tach, shown in Figure 6-1-2, is slightly different from those used in reciprocating engine systems. Firstly, it measures in percent (percent r.p.m.) of engine speed. Also, r.p.m. is not normally used to set engine power. Engine power for thrust engines (turbojet and turbofan) is set by referencing the engine pressure ratio (EPR). This is the inlet pressure divided into the outlet pressure. Turboshaft and turboprop engines set power by referencing torque.

The tachometer is used for engine start and to indicate an overspeed condition. Because turbine engine output can vary with changes in atmospheric conditions, it is possible to have variations in speeds from one day to another depending upon the density of the airflow. Percent speed or r.p.m. of the fan (N_1) can sometimes be used to set engine power.

Turbofan and Turboshaft Tachometers

The speed indications for turbofan and turboshaft engines display the percent r.p.m. of the

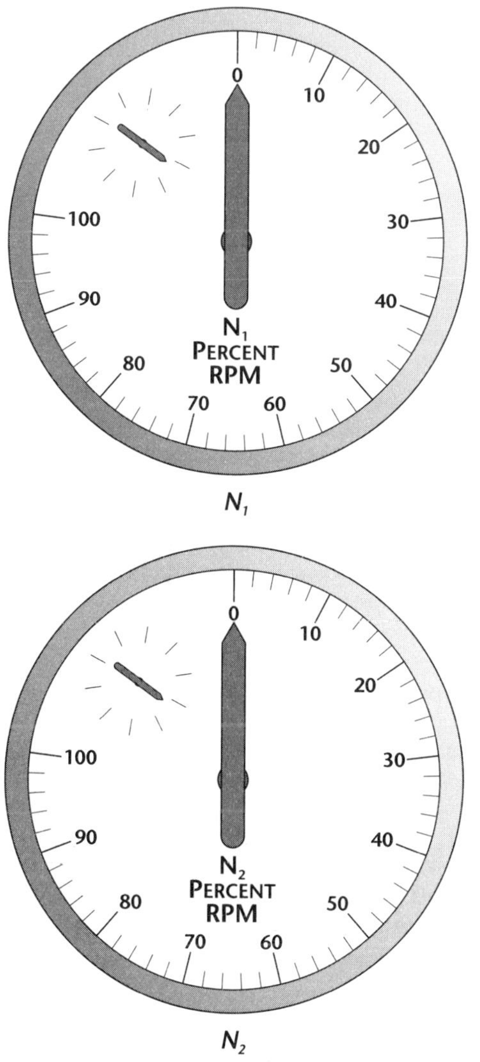

Figure 6-1-3. N_1 and N_2 percent r.p.m. indicators

different spools in the engine. These gauges can be marked differently for each installation. In some turboprop aircraft they are labeled for propeller r.p.m as N_p and the gas generator as N_g, instead of N_1 and N_2.

High-pressure spool percent r.p.m. (N_2) speed indicator. On a single-spool engine the high-pressure (HP) tachometer is the only one available. It provides the N_2 indication. On a split-spool engine the HP tachometer indicator, in Figure 6-1-3, measures the high-pressure compressor r.p.m. On the flight deck there is an N_2 tach for each engine. The indicators show HP compressor r.p.m. in percent. The units are self-powered by a tach generator or a speed pickup located on the engine. Newer engines use a magnetic pickup, which is triggered by a rotating gear in the gearbox. The pickup is connected to the instrumentation or computers in the flight deck displays.

Low-pressure spool percent r.p.m. (N_1) speed indicator. A low-pressure (LP) tachometer indicator for each engine is used on all multispool turbofan engines, whether high or low bypass. The indicators show LP compressor r.p.m. percentage. The operation of this system is similar to the N_2 r.p.m. indicators.

Intermediate pressure spool percent r.p.m. speed indicator. Some Rolls-Royce engines use a three spool design. These engines contain an intermediate pressure spool between the high- and low-pressure (fan) spools and is designated N_3.

The percent r.p.m. indicator can use either a tach generator or a magnetic pickup. The tach generator is turned by the accessory section and provides a current and frequency that is read by the indicator in the flight deck. Some systems use a magnetic pickup which is in close proximity to a turning gear which provides pluses to the system. As the teeth of the gear pass the pickup, a pulse is generated that is read by an indicator or Engine Indicating Crew Alerting System (EICAS) system.

Engine oil pressure. To guard against engine failure resulting from inadequate lubrication and cooling of the various engine parts, the oil supply to engine bearings and other critical areas must be monitored. An engine oil pressure indicator, shown in Figure 6-1-4, is necessary for each engine. A transmitter mounted in the pressure side of the oil system senses oil pressure. The oil pressure indicator reads the oil pressure pump discharge pressure.

A transducer sends an electrical signal to the instrument in the flight deck. This electrical signal is proportional to the pressure. When engine oil pressure is below normal operating range, warning indicators such as a low oil pressure light, master warning panel, or Engine Indicating Crew Alerting System (EICAS) alert the crew to the problem.

Figure 6-1-4. As with any combustion engine, oil pressure is critical. A loss of pressure will rapidly bring on a complete engine failure.

Figure 6-1-5. Excessively high oil temperature is a sign of an impending problem. With high temperatures bearings and gears do not get adequate lubrication.

Engine oil temperature. Engine oil temperature indicators, shown in Figure 6-1-5, are used for each system. The indicator is typically scaled from 0°C to 180°C or higher. Oil inlet temperature is sensed by a probe that sends a signal to the flight deck indicator. The temperature of the engine oil has a major effect on its lubricating qualities.

(A)

(B)

Figure 6-1-6. (A) EGT and (B) TIT are, for all intents and purposes, the same thing. EGT is the most critical temperature during engine operation.

Overheating of the engine oil can boil away solvents in the oil and cause coking. The solid material remaining after the solvents are gone can leave dark, gummy deposits on the bearings and oil seals. The build-up of coke on the bearings and seals can cause the bearings to fail and the seals to leak. For this reason, efficient performance of the oil cooling system is very important.

Turbine gas temperatures. Turbine gas temperature has several descriptions which are based on the location where the temperature is sensed. Exhaust gas temperature (EGT) probes are generally situated after all turbine stages. When the temperature probes are located between the turbine stages, it is commonly called inter-turbine temperature (ITT). When the probes are placed before the first turbine, it is usually called turbine inlet temperature (TIT). Other locations for taking the engine's turbine temperature can be turbine outlet (TOT) and turbine gas temperature (TGT).

These temperature probes are thermocouple probes that are connected to an instrument or a display unit on the flight deck, shown in Figure 6-1-6. As the temperature increases, a small voltage is generated due to the dissimilar metals used in the thermocouple. Generally, several temperature probes are placed at equal intervals around the turbine area gas flow. These probes give an average temperature over the area of gas flow through the turbine section.

The most critical temperature is the air temperature flowing over the first stage turbine inlet guide vanes. Gas turbine temperatures are one of the most important engine operating limits and are used to monitor the integrity of the turbine section during all engine operating conditions.

Turbine gas temperature, no matter where it is taken, is the most important consideration in engine instrumentation. Turbine gas temperatures determine the rate at which the fuel can be burned (added) in the combustion section before the critical temperature (melting of internal components) of the turbine sections is reached. Digital instrumentation has reduced the difficulty in reading gas temperature gauges. Temperature gauges must be calibrated at regular intervals to ensure their accuracy.

Fuel flow indicator. Fuel flow indicators measure fuel flow in pounds per hour for each engine as shown in Figure 6-1-7. Fuel flow should also be monitored during the starting cycle because an indication of excess fuel flow could be the first indication of a hot start. Most flow meters are of the turbine type. A small wheel is placed inline with the fuel flow. This turbine wheel rotates as fuel passes through it and as the flow increases, the turbine speed also

Figure 6-1-7. Fuel flow is normally indicated in pounds per hour. An abnormal fuel flow is always an indication that requires troubleshooting.

increases. This turbine sends a signal based on its speed to an indicator on the flight deck. This signal is proportional to changes in flow.

The flow meter is located in the fuel system after the fuel control and can help monitor fuel consumption. Fuel flow is a very important parameter when checking engine performance and troubleshooting. Fuel flow is tied to the exhaust gas temperature and as the fuel flow increases, the exhaust temperature also increases. If the fuel flow decreases, the exhaust temperature should also decrease. If this relationship is not as described above, it indicates a problem.

Engine Indicating and Crew Alerting Systems (EICAS)

Most new aircraft use digital electronic instrumentation that is presented on a cathode ray tube (CRT) or liquid crystal display (LCD). Glass cockpit technology has all but eliminated the traditional analog gauge. In this system, known as the engine indicating and crew alerting system (EICAS), all engine sensors transmit information to the EICAS computer. The EICAS display (seen in Figure 6-1-8) then sends digital data to the flight deck display units. In most cases, the information is presented on the computer monitor in a form that graphically resembles the face of an analog instrument.

All of the information presented on conventional gauges is displayed on the cockpit display. Typically there is only one cockpit display unit. This unit may replace as many as 36 conventional analog instruments. A significant benefit is reduced maintenance in the cockpit along with enhanced aircraft reliability. The presentation can easily be tailored to meet specific operational needs. In the event of a screen failure, the EICAS information can be displayed on a flight display screen or vice versa.

One benefit of the EICAS system is its ability to alert the flight crew of failures or abnormal conditions. The screen shows system status messages in addition to basic engine data during all phases of a flight. It can display color-coded alert messages communicating both the type and severity of a failure. The crew can set the display to show only the primary parameters at all times and allow the EICAS to monitor secondary systems, presenting information on those systems only when specified parameters are exceeded. This simplifies the amount of information the crew must absorb and reduces crew workload and fatigue.

A typical EICAS system will provide the following primary information to the flight crew:

Figure 6-1-8. Typical EICAS display in a modern corporate jet glass cockpit displays all of the engine operating information. *Photo courtesy of Hawker Beechcraft Aircraft*

Figure 6-2-1. An EPR indication shows the ratio between engine inlet pressure and engine outlet pressure. It indicates an engine's thrust.

- Actual and commanded N_1 speed
- Transient N_1 (the difference between actual and commanded N_1)
- Maximum potential and permissible N_1

Additional indications occur if N_1 limits are exceeded. These are:

- Current thrust lever position
- Thrust reverser system status
- Exhaust gas temperature (EGT)
- Max permissible EGT

Additional indications occur if EGT limits are exceeded. These are:

- N_2 rotor speed
- Fuel flow

Additional secondary data can be presented if needed, including amount of fuel used, oil quantity, oil pressure, oil temperature, vibration sensor data, oil filter status, fuel filter status, ignition system status, start valve position, engine bleed pressure and nacelle temperature.

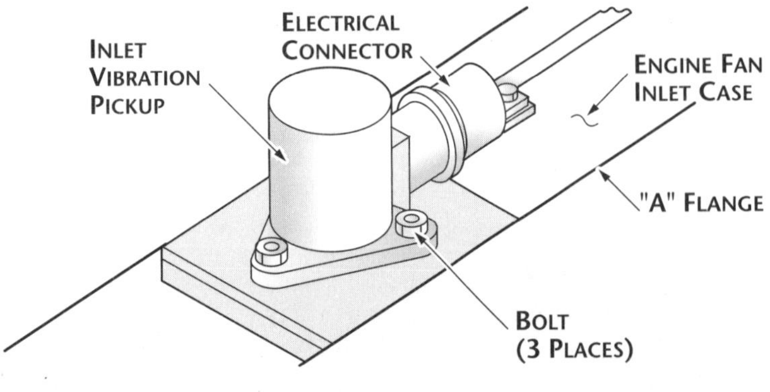

Figure 6-2-2. Fan vibration pickup

The EICAS system provides several advantages for the AMT. The system can automatically record trend monitoring information, eliminating hand recording (and the potential for mistakes). After an engine or system fault, all of the data listed previously can be called up and evaluated during the troubleshooting process. There is much more information available than with conventional systems. Maintenance personnel can use the EICAS on the ground to monitor many systems and access the computer's Built-In-Test-Equipment (BITE). Many systems on modern, digitally-controlled aircraft have the ability to perform extensive self-testing. The computer can analyze circuits and system status and relay the information back to the EICAS panel. BITE systems are covered in more detail in a later section of this chapter.

In addition to displaying engine-related information, the EICAS presents vital information regarding pressurization, aircraft configuration and other key systems. Information management system (IMS) is another term used by aircraft manufacturers to refer to these types of systems.

Section 2

Turbofan-specific Indicators

Engine pressure ratio (EPR). This type of indicator measures the engine pressure ratio to determine the amount of thrust being developed by the engine. It provides an indication of engine power in the form of the ratio of exhaust total pressure (P_7) to intake total pressure (P_1). EPR also requires the monitoring of several other parameters to be correct. Before the digital age, EPR required the use of charts to compute the correct reading for the particular conditions. With digital fuel controls, all the variations are compared and computed automatically. Thus EPR is an actual presentation of engine thrust. An EPR gauge is seen in Figure 6-2-1.

Vibration Indicators

The turbine vibration indicators (TVI), see Figure 6-2-2 provide a continuous monitoring of the balance of the rotating assemblies in the engine in order to detect a possible internal failure that could result in an engine failure. The indication is normally picked up from the low-pressure compressor or the low-pressure turbine.

Vibration indications for both engines are normally presented on a single indicator with a switch to allow either compressor or turbine vibration to be displayed. Although onboard vibration monitoring systems are not new, in the digital age they are more reliable and useful than before. Not only can vibrations be monitored, but a vibration can be cross referenced to a specific speed range, producing a better picture of what component or spool is producing the vibration.

Section 3

Turboprop- and Turboshaft-specific Indicators

Torquemeter

A torquemeter is used with turboprop and turboshaft aircraft and measures engine power output. The torquemeter system in a turboprop aircraft measures the pressure output from the torquemeter. This pressure can be converted to indicate the amount of horsepower, percentage of horsepower, or feet pounds of torque produced by the engine. Figure 6-3-1 is a torquemeter indication. Three basic methods are:

- Torsional deflection
- Hydromechanical
- Load cells

Each system consists of a transmitter (part of the engine extension shaft), a phase detector and an indicator.

Torsional deflection. The first measures torque at an extension shaft. It measures the torsional deflection (twist) of the extension shaft as it sends power from the engine to the propeller. The more power the engine produces, the greater the twist in the extension shaft. Magnetic pickups detect and measure this deflection electronically. The indicator registers the amount of deflection in shaft horsepower.

Figure 6-3-1. Torquemeter indicator shows the torque developed by the engine.

Hydromechanical. The second system in common use is a hydromechanical torquemeter. This system uses oil pressure to measure torque. Rotational forces within the engine gearbox are used to meter oil pressure in a torquemeter sensing chamber. The system then measures the difference in pressure between the oil in the sensing chamber and the internal oil pressure of the gearbox. This pressure differential is transmitted through a transducer to the cockpit torquemeter via an electrical signal. Since the torquemeter is generally used to sense takeoff power, its calibration is very critical and should be checked often. Calibration is done by applying a known pressure to the transducer and comparing it with the reading on the torquemeter in the flight deck.

Load cells. Some newer engines use a third method of measuring torque by using a load cell or a combination of load cells mounted to the gear box structure. These flex with power application and the signal is electronically varied in proportion to power transferred to the shaft or propeller. This signal is sent to the flight deck instruments.

Section 4

Engine Operations

Turbofan Operation

Since most turbofan engines are two spool type engines, the operation of a two spool turbofan engine will be used as an example. After accomplishing all of the normal pre-start checks: oil quantity, oil cap for security, inlet and exhaust ducts should be clear and area of operation should be checked for FOD. The fan spool should also turn freely without binding or dragging (N_1). Check that proper starter energy is available; if there is an electric starter, check the voltage available (24 vDC). When an air turbine starter is used, check for proper compressed air duct pressure; 30 p.s.i. or higher.

Once all pre-start checklist items are accomplished, the starter should be engaged. The N_2 compressor should start to turn and continue to gain speed. Although it varies from engine to engine, the oil pressure should be checked for proper pressure. At a predetermined r.p.m. of N_2, the ignition followed by fuel is turned on. A check for N_1 rotation should be made at this time. The engine has about 10 seconds to light off. Light-off is indicated by a rise in EGT, as shown in Figure 6-4-1. If the engine does not light off in 10 seconds, the start should be aborted.

Figure 6-4-1. EGT is closely monitored during starting and during flight.

If the start attempt was aborted and fuel is present in the engine, a drain time and a clearing motoring should be accomplished. If light off occurred normally, the starter is still engaged and is helping the engine increase N_2. As fuel flow is increased, the N_2 should continue to increase the r.p.m. After the engine reaches a self-sustaining speed (around 40%), the starter is disengaged. As the r.p.m. reaches the idle setting, the N_2 will stop accelerating and stay at a set idle r.p.m. The N_1 will continue to increase in r.p.m. until it reaches its idle speed. The N_1 will always follow or lag behind the N_2 r.p.m.

Because the N_2 is controlled by input from the pilot and the fuel control governor, it will lead the N_1, with the N_1 reacting to changes in N_2. During the acceleration of N_2 the EGT should be monitored to prevent a hot start. The start process will take about one minute under normal operating conditions. Cold starts can take longer and sometimes need extra fuel during the starting process.

Normal shutdown is accomplished by placing the cutoff lever or switch in the cutoff position and monitoring the engine for normal roll down. Always refer to the aircraft or engine manual for specific starting procedures.

Turboprop Operation

NOTE: *The details for starting the Pratt & Whitney PT6 turboprop engine series are listed here. Although the following procedures are typical for this engine, operators should make reference to the specific applicable instructions for starting details.*

Controls for this engine generally include a power lever, a propeller lever and a condition lever that controls fuel, seen in Figure 6-4-2. For starting, the power lever is placed in the idle position, the propeller lever is moved full forward to high r.p.m. and the condition lever remains in the fuel cut-off position until the starting sequence calls for its movement. The start procedure is as follows in Figure 6-4-3:

Figure 6-4-2. PT6 engine controls include power propellers and condition levers.

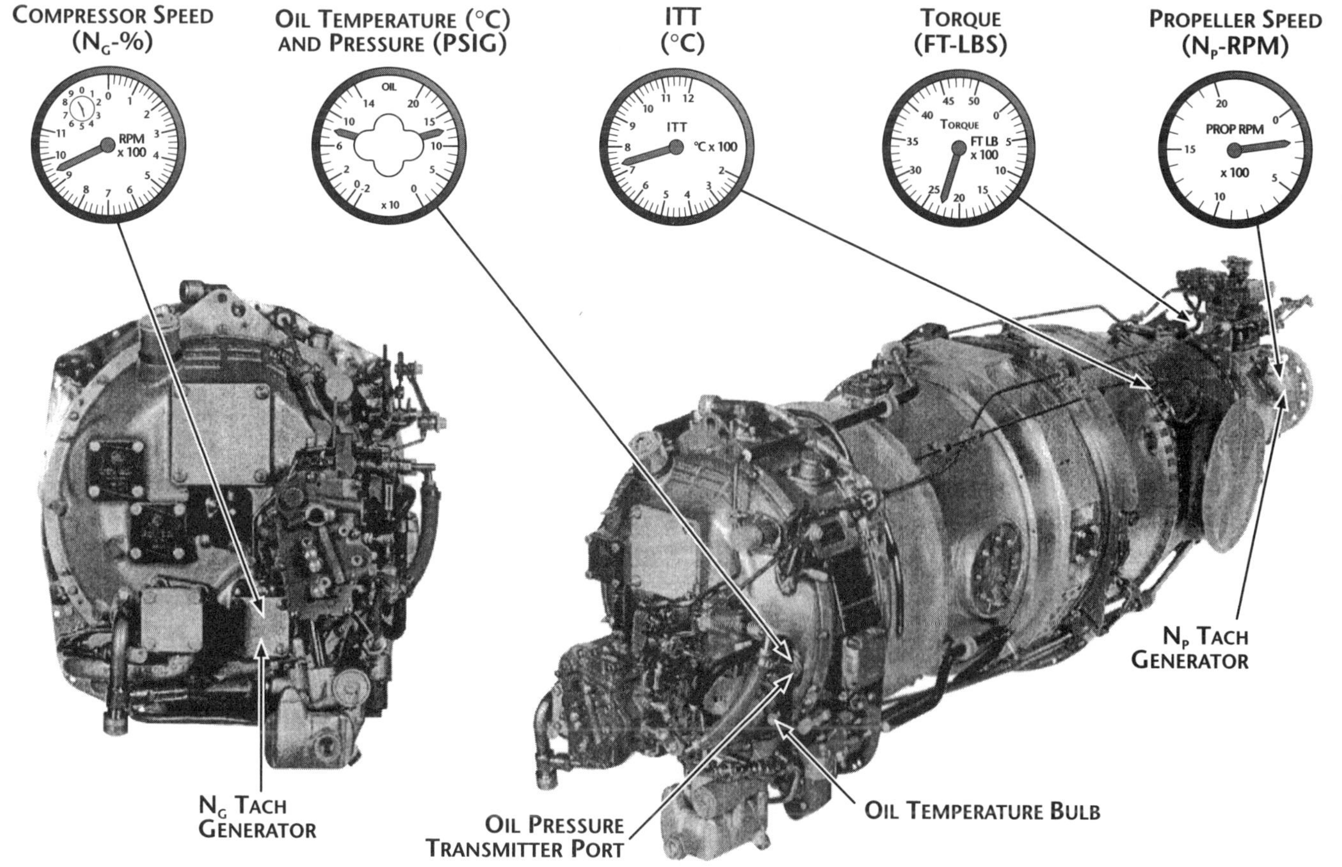

Figure 6-4-3. Turbine engine instruments and engine sensor locations

Photo courtesy of Pratt & Whitney

1. Starter switch on. Minimum gas generator speed for starting is 4,500 r.p.m. or 12% N_g.
2. Check that engine oil pressure is climbing to a normal value.
3. After N_g r.p.m. has stabilized at a satisfactory r.p.m. (12% minimum), move the condition lever to the low-idle position. This will provide ignition and fuel flow.
4. Observe that the engine accelerates to the specified low-idle r.p.m. and that maximum ITT (also known as the T_5 temperature on the PT6) is not exceeded.

If a light-off does not occur within 10 seconds after moving the condition lever to low-idle, abort the start by shutting off the fuel, starter and ignition. A drain period should then be observed. Then a 15-second dry motor run should be performed to remove fuel in the engine before subsequent start attempts. Caution should be taken to avoid exceeding the starter limits during all start procedures. Starter limits are specified in the aircraft or engine manuals.

With the free turbine engine, of which the PT6 is a representative example, the propeller shuts down in the feather position. During starting operations, it is driven out of feather by oil pressure supplied by the propeller governor. During shutdown, oil pressure drops to a point where the propeller feathers or is feathered by the prop control at shutdown, as shown in Figure 6-4-4.

Figure 6-4-4. King Air starting sequence showing the propeller unfeathering automatically on startup

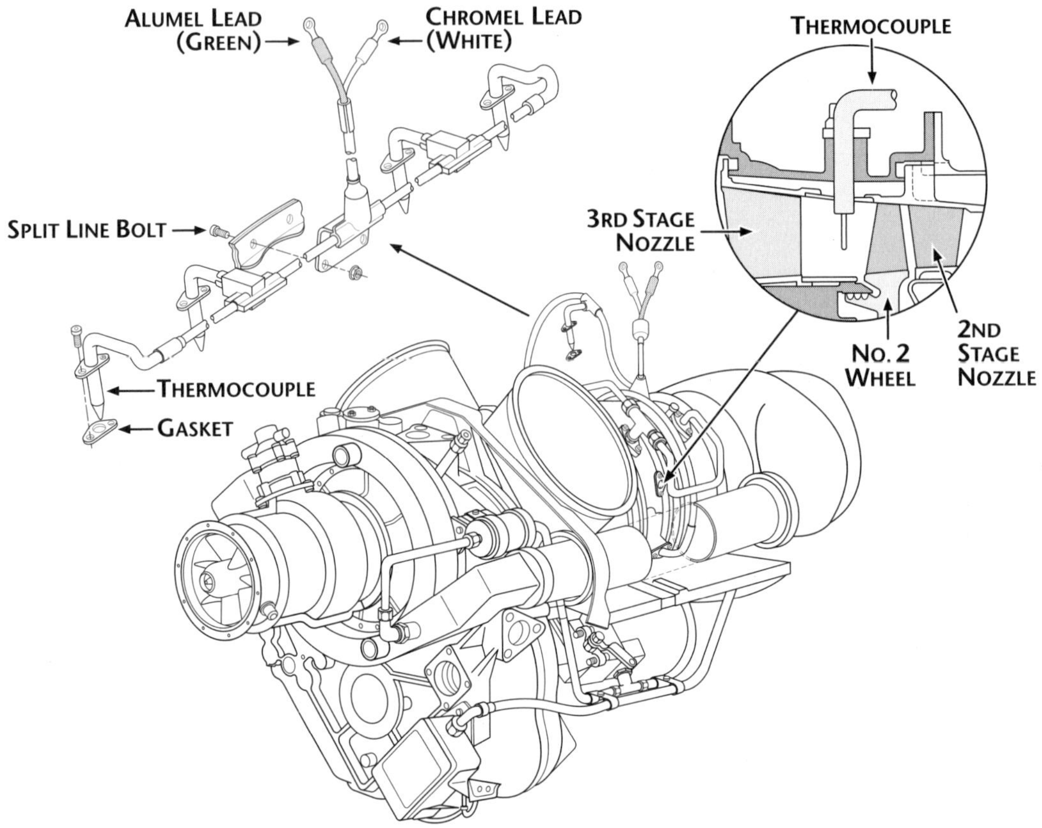

Figure 6-4-5. Turbine outlet temperature is closely monitored during engine startup. The themocouple harness provides an average temperature for the engine.

Turboshaft Operation

Many of the aspects of operation and indication for turboshaft engines are very similar to a turboprop. Turboshaft engines are rated and their output is measured in shaft horsepower (SHP). The example engine for the turboshaft will be the Rolls-Royce (RR) 250 series engine. During the starting of the RR-250 engine, the need for proper procedures is most important. The first parameter to take into consideration is the TOT limit for all operating conditions. TOT for this engine is the turbine outlet temperature. The exhaust temperature system is shown in Figure 6-4-5. Using the proper operational techniques will provide benefits such as engine reliability, durability, a decrease of maintenance proportionate to flight hours, less premature engine removals and—as a result—a marked decrease in the cost of operation per flight hour.

Operator attention to engine parameters will preclude hot starts and other operational problems. Damage to the engine, as a result of hot starts, is a starting problem that requires constant attention during this process. Sufficient time will normally be available to abort a start without incurring engine damage by using the proper starting procedures. The following is a general example of the starting procedure. Aircraft or engine information manuals should always be used for engine operation.

Example Starting Procedure

This example is based on a helicopter engine, which is where most turboshaft engines are used, shown in Figure 6-4-6.

1. If possible, the use of external power is always suggested. This helps increase the airflow during starting, which reduces starting temperatures and engine wear. A ground power unit (GPU) will help in the start of almost all turbine engines.
2. Always check throttle for complete closed or cut-off position before turning on boost pumps and engaging starter. If the throttle is not in cut-off, the fuel can flow and pool in the engine before the start.
3. Set minimum collective blade angle
4. Engine anti-ice air OFF and cabin heat OFF.
5. Residual TOT should be below 150°C before moving the throttle to idle position (ignition and fuel on).
6. The starter is actuated and must be kept ON until 58% gas generator speed

is reached unless the start is aborted. Always observe the starter limits.

7. Proper r.p.m. prior to opening the throttle is exceedingly important.
8. A positive indication of oil pressure should occur just prior to light-off r.p.m. This is accomplished by twisting the throttle to idle position.
9. Light-off should be within three seconds. If not, immediately move the throttle to cut-off, or closed position.
10. Motor the engine for thirty seconds whenever required to close the throttle due to a false start, or to abort start due to possible over-temperature.
11. Monitor TOT closely from light-off to stabilized idle r.p.m.
12. There should be an indication of power turbine or rotor r.p.m. by 25% gas generator speed, or abort start.
13. Peak temperature should be expected at approximately 30% gas generator speed.
14. Malfunction of the compressor bleed valve, particularly on a hot day, may cause compressor stall. Depending on severity of stall, it may be evidenced by a rise in TOT and a change in the engine sound. If TOT increases to starting limits, abort start immediately.
15. It is generally important to anticipate the possibility of over-temperature. The maximum temperature limit is 927°C and/or a maximum of 10 seconds between 810°C and 927°C. If the temperature rapidly approaches 900°C, the chance of exceeding 927°C is high and the throttle should be twisted off before reaching 927°C. This reduces the possibility of exceeding 927°C before being able to shutdown the engine. These temperatures and times are subject to change, so always consult the aircraft or manufacturer's manual.
16. Check oil pressure upon reaching idle r.p.m.
17. Idle speed should be somewhere between 59% to 65% gas generator speed.
18. Upon reaching idle speed, allow engine to warm up for at least a one-minute period.
19. Wait until completion of warm-up before turning on the generator switch. This keeps the generator load off the engine, particularly in hot weather, preventing possible decay of gas generator speed to less than the minimum stabilized idle speed of 59% N_1. This also allows battery to recover thus reducing the charging rate or load on generator.

The same example engine uses the following shutdown procedure:

1. Allow engine to run in the idle position for at least a two-minute period of time.
2. After two minutes, twist throttle to complete cutoff, or closed position.
3. Check for TOT decrease.
4. Turn off all engine switches and, as necessary, aircraft switches.

Turbine Engine Starting Problems

Problems starting turbine engines are less likely to occur for engines with automatic starting systems or electronic controls. This type of advanced control monitors and records equipment malfunctions automatically. This helps prevent starting problems that could lead to a hot, hung, or no start condition.

Operators of turbine engines must exercise vigilance during the start procedure to prevent the unlikely occurrence of a starting problem. Generally, this requires that EGT, fuel flow and speeds be carefully monitored for expected values during the start cycle.

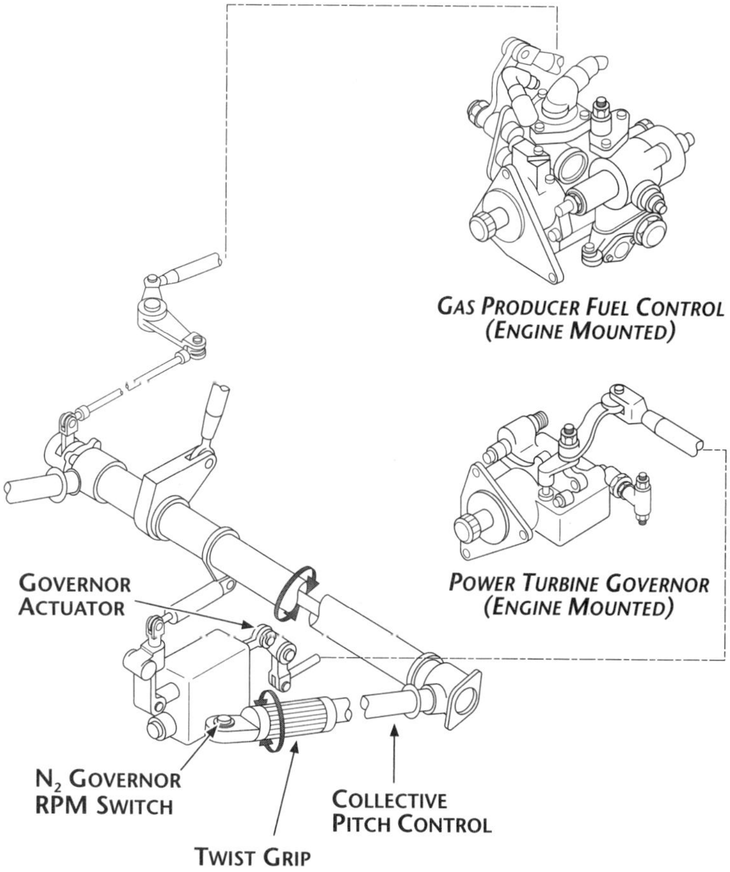

Figure 6-4-6. Helicopter turboshaft engine controls are mounted on the collective.

NOTE: *Failure to follow the procedures outlined in the airplane operating manual or an equipment malfunction may lead to a hot start, a hung start, or a false start.*

Hot Start

A hot start is indicated by EGT rising above the starting limit, generally resulting from an excessive amount of fuel to airflow through the engine. An early indication of this problem may be a rapid rise in fuel flow above that normally expected, particularly in the event that compressor r.p.m. does not continue to rise in a typical fashion. Excessive fuel, combined with inadequate airflow, leads to a ratio that ultimately results in a hot start. In the event of a hot start, prompt intervention is required to avoid or limit damage to the hot section of the engine. Fuel should be cut off while continuing to motor the engine for cooling purposes.

Following engine shutdown, inspection and further maintenance may be necessary if a hot start has occurred. Two factors dictate the required procedures: the temperatures observed and the duration of the event. Each engine has limits based on these factors that will direct the required inspection and subsequent maintenance procedures.

In the case of a short duration hot start at a minimal over-temperature value, only an inspection of certain hot section components may be necessary. In a worst case scenario, hot section maintenance, including removal and replacement of turbine stages and other components, may be the end result.

Hung Start

Hung starts occur when the engine lights off but fails to accelerate. A hung start will prevent the engine from reaching idle r.p.m. This type of start should be attended to promptly. When the compressor r.p.m. is observed to remain at a low value (below idle), the operator should shut off the fuel. Subsequent troubleshooting may focus on the EGT value during the start procedure if it remained low. The problem is generally fuel-related. Usually fuel flow to the fuel control is verified then the operation of the fuel control bypass valve and enrichment pressure switch is confirmed.

False (no) Start

A false start, or no start is present when light-off fails to take place. This scenario has its roots in either a fuel delivery or an ignition problem. It is important to determine which starting problem is the cause prior to subsequent starting attempts. If the problem is no fuel delivery, proceed with a normal engine start procedure after correction. However, when an ignition problem causes a false start, the presence of fuel in the combustion chamber could lead to a hot start in any follow-up attempt. Under these circumstances, it is important to motor the engine and allow the fuel to drain prior to starting. As always, compliance with operating instructions is critical.

Ground fire. Starting any turbine engine can produce a potential fire hazard and gas turbine engines are no exception. If a tailpipe fire starts from excess fuel, shut off the fuel flow and continue to motor the engine, trying to blow out the fire. If the fire is too large for that process, CO_2 extinguishers should be used. They will not contaminate the engine interior or damage any auxiliary systems. Remember that CO_2 is also a cooling agent. If a fire were to start during shutdown, it could cause the compressor or turbine case to shrink quickly, causing possible rotor drag.

Section 5

Performance Factors, Limits and Ratings

All turbine engines are limited in the amount of thrust produced by three factors: rotor speeds, turbine temperature and a thrust limit placed on the engine by the airframe manufacturers. Turbine engines are designed and certified based on a limit system, referred to as the flat-rate rating for the engine.

Flat-rating of engines. A flat-rated turbine engine is one where output power is less than the engine's physical capacity of producing power. A lower flat-rating means that under normal operating conditions the engine is subjected to less stress which will increase the overall life of the engine.

As the engine accumulates operating time, more of the rated power will remain available to the air-

TFE731 THRUST RATINGS		
Model	Thrust	OAT (S/L)
TFE731-2-1	3,230	30°C
TFE731-2-2	3,500	22°C
TFE731-3-1	3,700	24°C
TFE731-3-B	3,650	15°C
TFE731-5-1	4,300	22.5°C
TFE731-5A-1	4,500	23°C

Table 6-5-1. Turbine outlet temperature

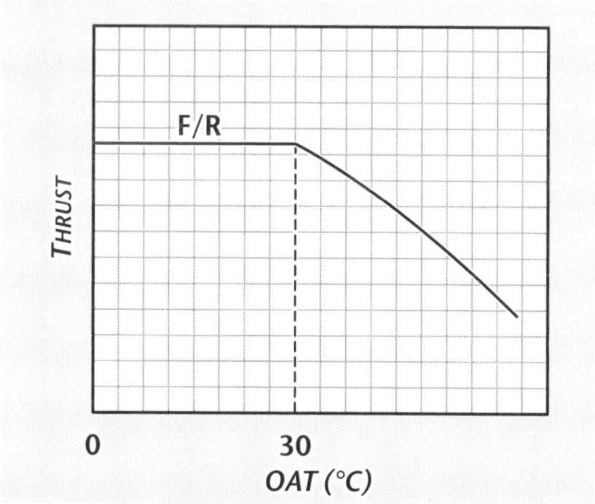

Figure 6-5-1. Flat rate thrust schedule

craft as the engine's components wear (seals and turbine components erode). The chart in Table 6-5-1 depicts thrust ratings of a typical turbofan engine. The ratings are for uninstalled engines at standard day conditions. The outside air temperature (OAT) column indicates the maximum temperature at which the engine will produce rated thrust. For example, the engine will produce rated power in pounds of thrust up to 30°C. When this temperature is exceeded, less thrust will be produced as can be seen in Figure 6-5-1.

Some twin-engine turbine aircraft have an automatic performance reserve (APR) system that will increase maximum thrust limits from one engine in the event of power loss in the other engine. This increased thrust mode is intended for short duration emergency use only, since use of APR power increases rotor stress. Additionally, some engine installations utilize a restricted performance reserve (RPR) system designed to enhance hot day-high altitude takeoff characteristics. The system provides an increase over normal takeoff thrust in some regions, determined by pressure altitude and OAT.

Engine flat-rating at temperatures up to a set number would allow the engine to produce rated thrust at sea level up to a flat-rated temperature. The fan speed required to produce rated thrust will be determined by OAT. At temperatures above the flat-rating temperature, rated thrust will not be developed because of lower air density.

Effect of air density. Air density is changed by differing altitude, temperature and airspeed. Since the main working medium is air in turbine engines, air density affects most of the engines' operating parameters. The thrust output improves rapidly with a reduction in OAT at constant altitude, r.p.m. and airspeed. This increase occurs partly because the energy required per pound of airflow to drive the compressor varies directly with the temperature, leaving more energy to develop thrust. In addition, the thrust output will increase since the air at reduced temperature has an increased density. The increase in density causes the mass flow through the engine to increase.

Effect of Temperature on Performance and Components

Materials used within the turbine section determine the temperature limit. As temperatures rise, more stress is placed on components and erosion of turbine rotors and nozzles occurs. Limits are therefore placed on turbine temperatures based on the type of materials used in the turbine. This is often referred to as the thermodynamic thrust rating. This rating identifies the maximum thrust capability of an engine when operating at a maximum turbine temperature at standard sea level conditions.

Effect of altitude on thrust. The altitude effect on thrust, as shown in Figure 6-5-2, is a function of density and temperature. An increase in altitude causes a decrease in pressure and temperature. Since the temperature lapse rate is less than the pressure lapse rate as altitude is increased, the density is decreased. Although the decreased temperature increases thrust, the effect of decreased density more than offsets the effect of the colder temperature. The net result of increased altitude is a reduction in the thrust output.

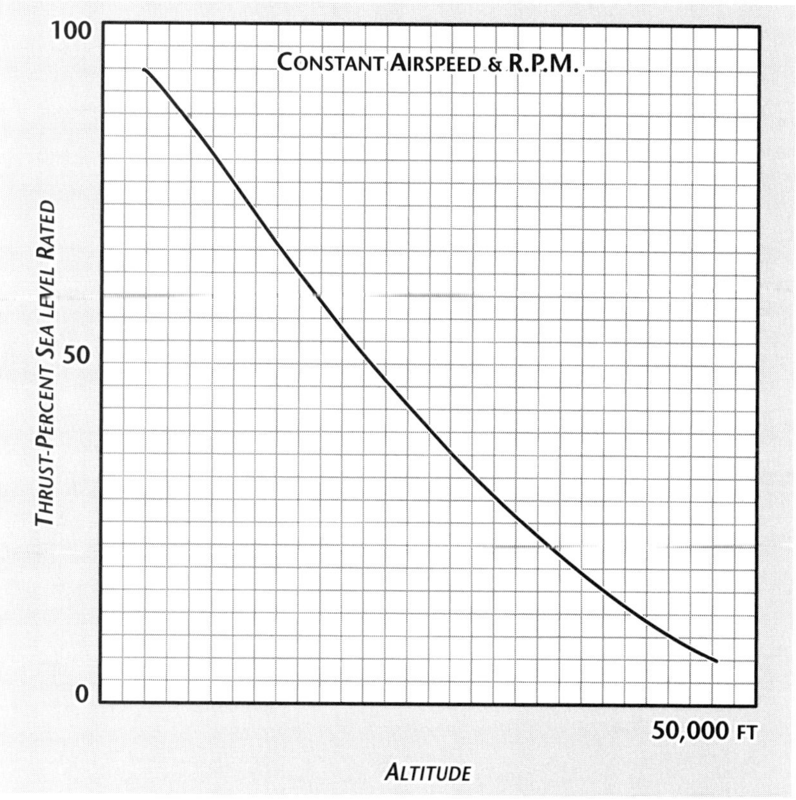

Figure 6-5-2. The effect of altitude on thrust output: as altitude increases the thrust tends to decrease.

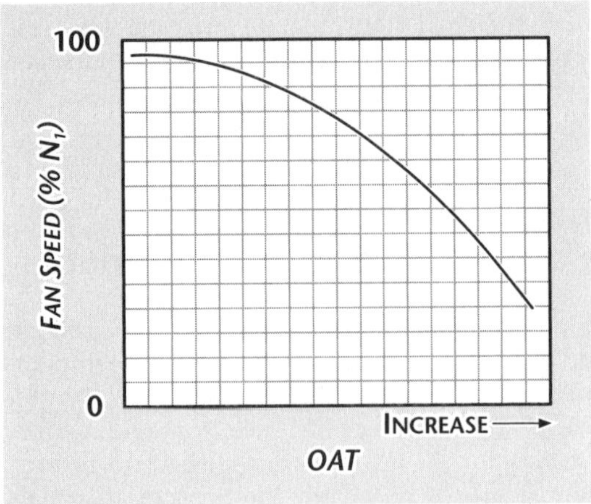

Figure 6-5-3. Maximum speed (MN) schedule as OAT increases

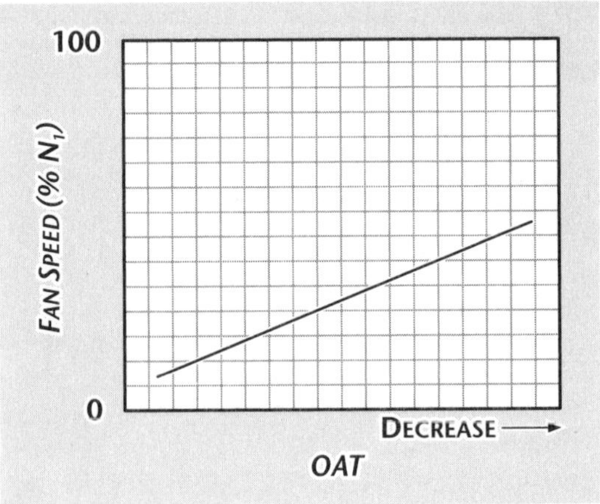

Figure 6-5-4. Flat rated schedule as OAT decreases

Effect of Engine Rotational Speed on Performance

All compressor and turbine rotors when subjected to extreme centrifugal forces at ultra-high speeds can fail due to structural limits of the material. The designed safe rotor speed is calculated and tested under actual operating conditions. The verified maximum r.p.m. with a considerable safety margin is then established as 100% r.p.m. While the actual r.p.m. will vary due to the size of the rotational components, 100% r.p.m. is considered maximum speed for most turbine engines. Some engines will exceed this r.p.m. under some conditions, but this over-limit is time limited on most aircraft.

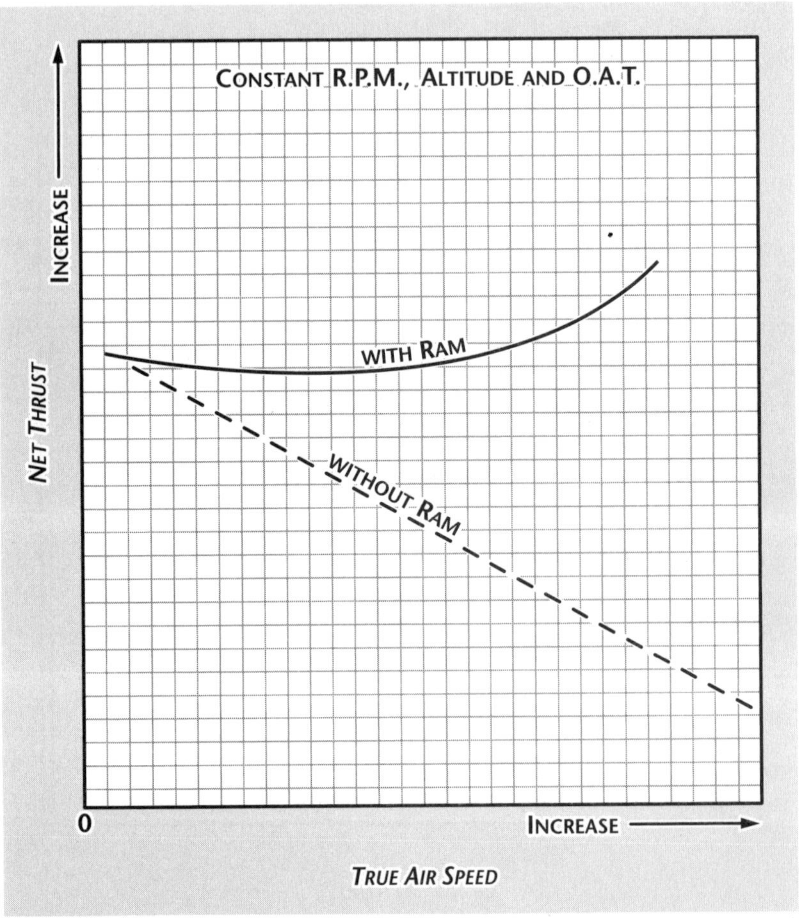

Figure 6-5-5. The effect of airspeed on net thrust will decrease without ram effect. Ram air will recover some thrust lost as the aircrafts' speed is increased.

As the outside air temperature increases, the fan speed may have to decrease in order to keep the engine within its thermodynamic limits, seen in Figure 6-5-3. Conversely, as the outside air temperature decreases, the fan speed (thrust) can increase. The increase in speed (thrust) under extremely cold conditions can continue until the fan-spool speed limit is reached. The fan speed limit decreases as OAT decreases. Since the air becomes denser at a colder OAT, the fan speed must decrease to maintain the same rated thrust.

As the air thins with higher temperatures, fan speed must increase to maintain the same rated thrust. Variations in fan speed within the limits of the flat-rating will provide rated thrust. If the fan speed increases to satisfy the thrust requirements as OAT increases, at some point the engine thermodynamic thrust limits will be reached, which can be seen in Figure 6-5-4.

The effects of altitude also effect fan speed. Therefore, moving from sea level to 2,000 feet pressure altitude would require an increase in fan speed in order to maintain the same thrust level. At higher altitudes, the engine will be limited by the thermodynamic thrust rating.

The flight manual determines takeoff power settings, using pressure altitude and OAT. The operator would determine the intersection between OAT and the flat-rated schedule as applicable. The intersect point would indicate the maximum N_1 that the engine could produce for takeoff. For a given air density, thrust is proportional to fan r.p.m.

Effect of Aircraft Airspeed on Engine Performance

Using fan speeds as an indication of thrust has generally the same accuracy as an engine pressure ratio gauge on some aircraft. Most turbofan engines are subjected to a test cell performance run where N_1 r.p.m. (fan) versus thrust is verified. This test results in setting the required thrust at lowest possible turbine temperatures. As fan r.p.m. increases, the mass airflow from the fan increases and more thrust will be produced. As fan speed or air density changes, the quantity of the thrust produced changes.

The effect of airspeed on the thrust of a gas turbine engine is shown in Figure 6-5-5. To explain the airspeed effect, it is first necessary to understand the effect of airspeed on the factors that combine to produce net thrust. These factors are specific thrust and engine airflow. Specific thrust is defined as the pounds of net thrust developed per pound of airflow per second. As airspeed is increased, the ram drag increases rapidly. The exhaust jet velocity remains relatively constant; therefore, the effect of the increase in airspeed results in decreased specific thrust, as shown in Figure 6-5-6. In the low-speed range the specific thrust decreases faster than the airflow increases and causes the net thrust to decrease.

A rise in pressure above existing outside atmospheric pressure at the engine inlet, as a result of the forward velocity of an aircraft, is referred to as ram pressure. Since any ram effect will cause an increase in compressor entrance pressure over atmospheric pressure, the resulting pressure rise will cause an increase in the mass airflow and jet velocity, both of which tend to increase thrust. Although ram effect increases the engine thrust, the thrust being produced by the engine decreases for a given throttle setting as the aircraft gains airspeed. Therefore, two opposing trends occur when an aircraft's speed is increased.

What takes place is the net result of these two effects. An engine's thrust output temporarily decreases as aircraft speed increases, but soon stops deceasing. Toward the higher speeds, thrust output begins to increase again. The ram pressure increases at the engine inlet as the aircraft accelerates. This has the effect of increasing density (see Figure 6-5-5). Differences in inlet plenum shapes will also affect the air density at the engine inlet.

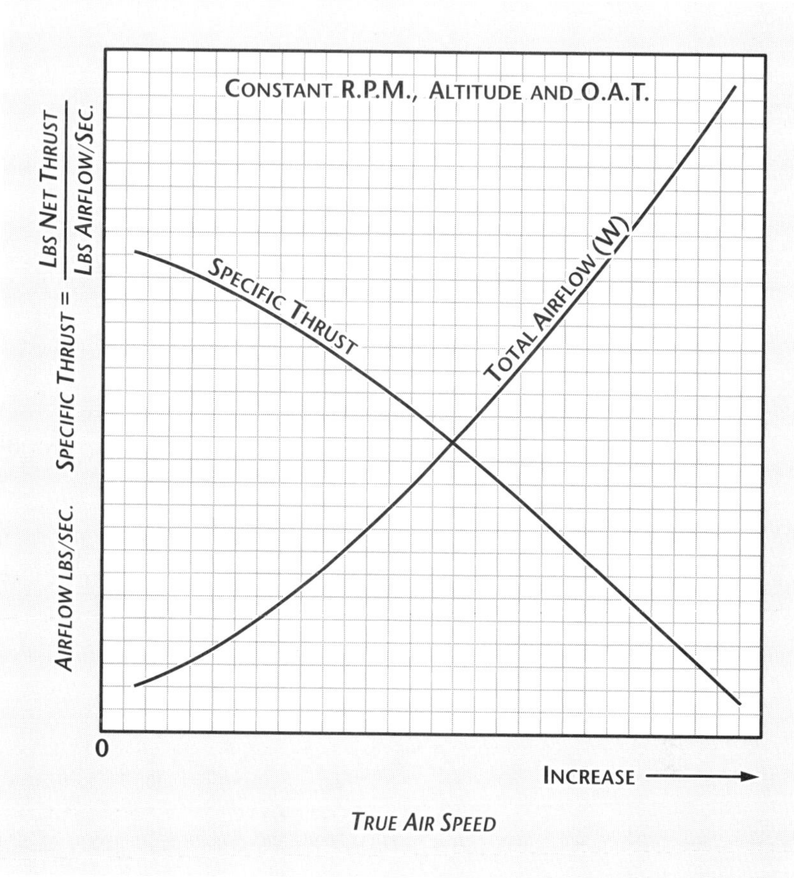

Figure 6-5-6. The effect of airspeed on specific thrust will decrease without ram effect. Ram air will recover some thrust lost as speed is increased.

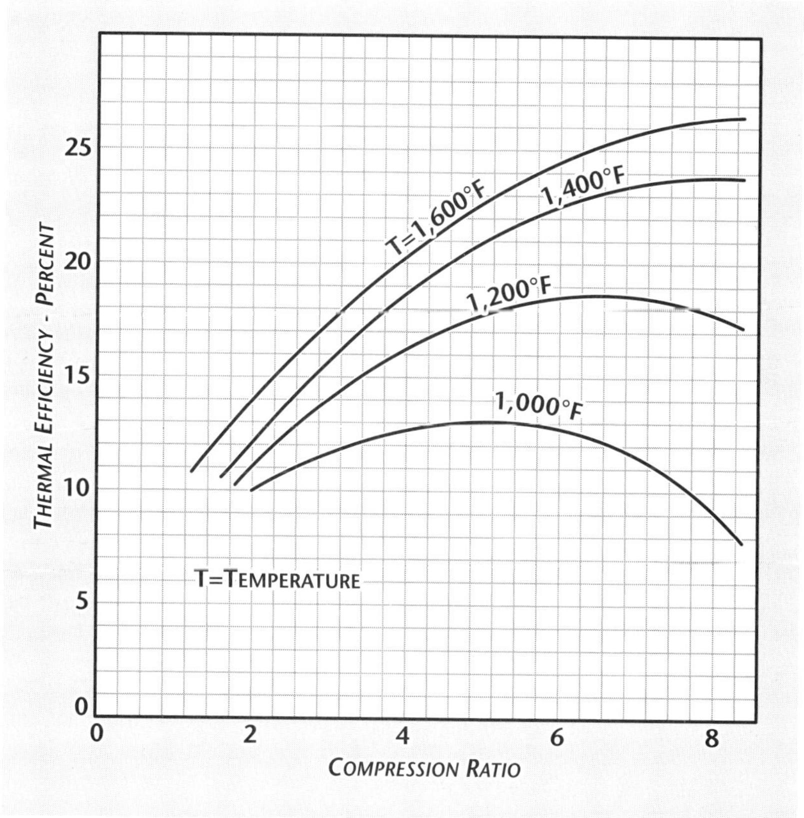

Figure 6-5-7. Thermal efficiency will increase with increases in CR and turbine temperature.

Effect of Thermal Efficiency

Thermal efficiency is a prime factor in gas turbine performance. It is the ratio of total work produced by the engine to the amount

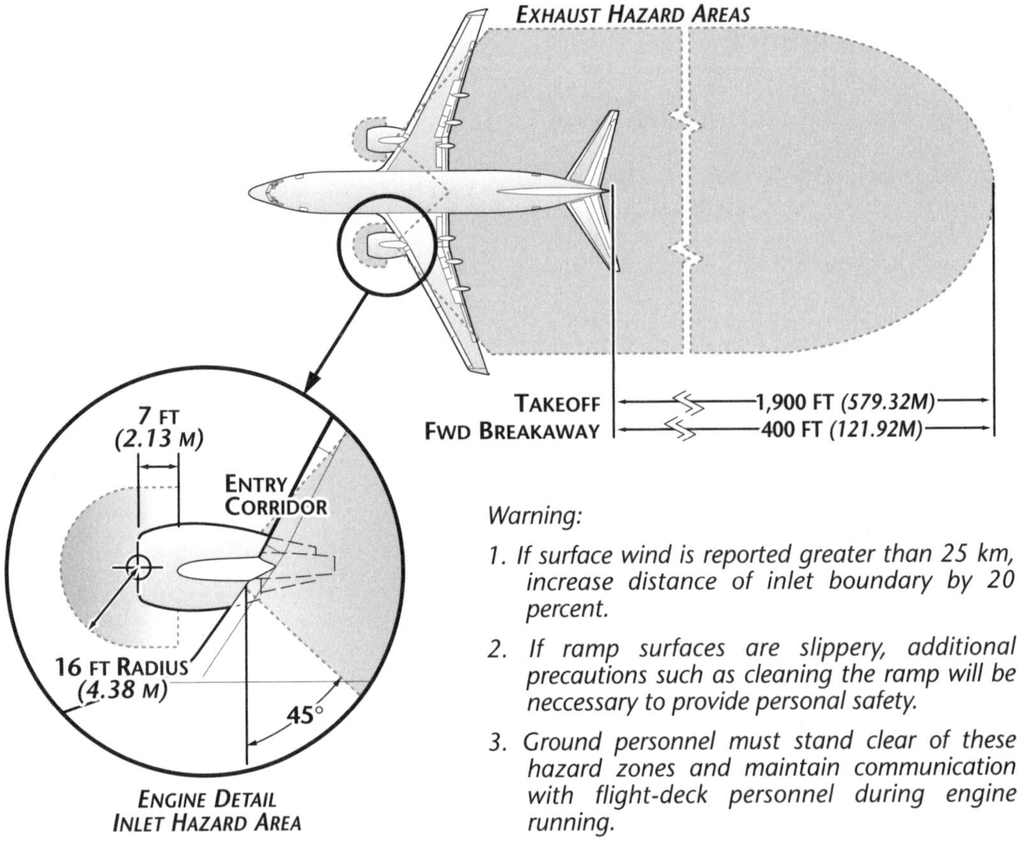

Figure 6-6-1. Takeoff thrust power hazard areas with regard to turbine engine operation

of chemical energy supplied in the form of fuel. The three most important factors affecting the thermal efficiency are turbine inlet temperature, compression ratio (CR) and the component efficiencies of the compressor and turbine. Other factors that affect thermal efficiency are compressor inlet temperature and burner efficiency.

Figure 6-5-7 shows the effect that changing compression ratio has on thermal efficiency when compressor inlet temperature and the component efficiencies of the compressor and turbine remain constant.

In actual operation, the turbine engine exhaust gas temperature varies directly with turbine inlet temperature at a constant compression ratio. Engine r.p.m. is a direct measure of compression ratio; therefore, maximum thermal efficiency can be obtained by maintaining the highest possible exhaust gas temperature at constant r.p.m.

Since the engine life (time between overhauls) is greatly reduced at a high turbine-inlet temperature, the engine should not be operated at an exhaust gas temperature that exceeds specified temperature limits for continuous operation or hot section damage will occur.

Section 6

Engine Performance Tests

High-bypass ratio turbine engines present a danger to personnel and objects in front of the engine. This is particularly the case with wing-mounted turbofan engines having minimal ground clearance. Specific clear-distance information is available for each aircraft powerplant installation.

During test operations or maintenance engine runs, personnel stationed around the aircraft engine's inlet should monitor the surrounding area and notify the flight deck personnel of any potential problem.

Personnel, intake, exhaust, safety practices and hearing protection. Prior to conducting test operations, attention should be given to the engine inlet area and the exhaust path for personnel and ramp equipment.

The ramp area immediately in front of the engine should be checked for the presence of foreign objects that could lead to foreign object damage (FOD) to the engine. Given the high velocity and temperatures of the gases pro-

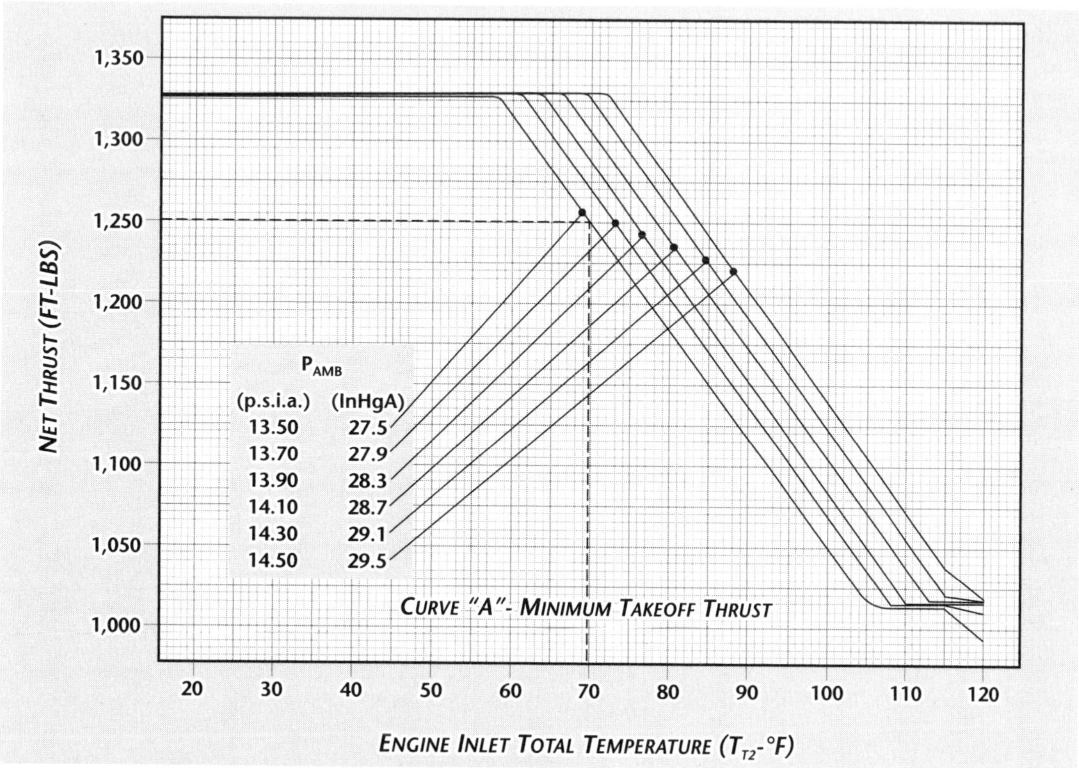

Figure 6-6-2. Thrust vs. temperature and pressure (P_{amb})

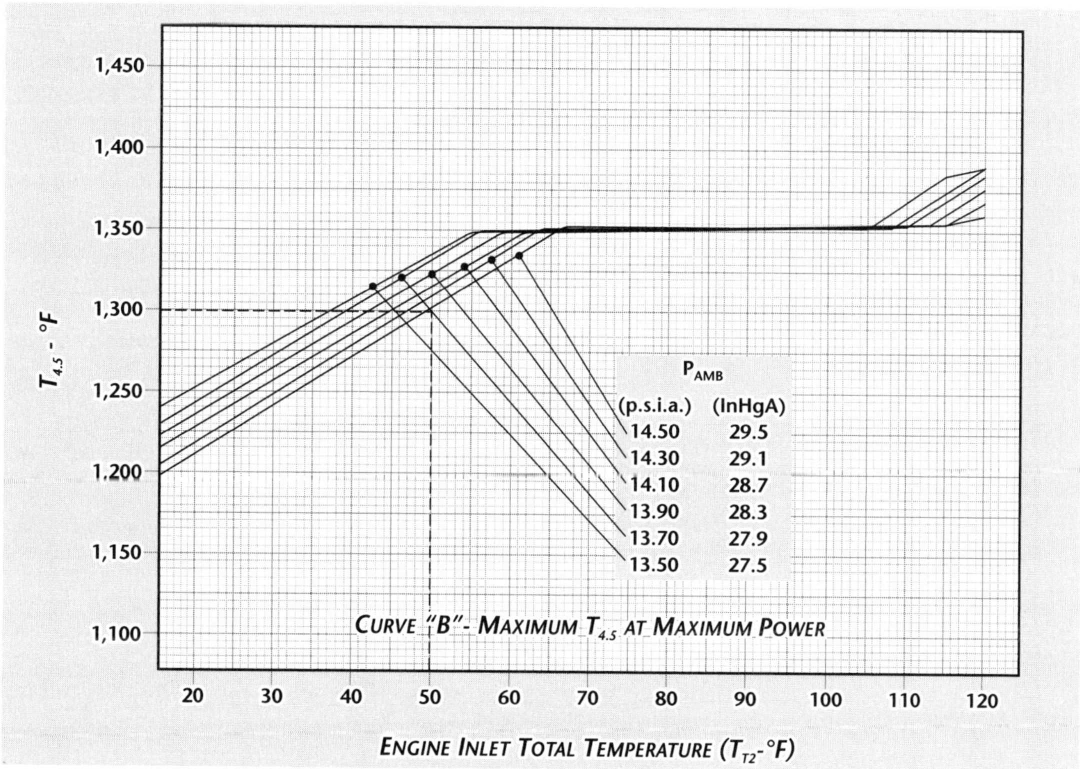

Figure 6-6-3. Maximum ITT vs. temperature and pressure (P_{amb})

duced by the exhaust, every effort must be made to assure a clear area for a distance dictated by the thrust of the engine shown in Figure 6-6-1. Personnel in and around the area of operating engines must also be provided with approved hearing protection.

Engine Test Cell Testing and Performance Evaluation

Test instructions are generally provided with detailed information concerning the test procedures, data requirements, test techniques and methods. For the performance test on most turbine engines to be valid and reproducible, there must also be specifications for the equipment, fixtures and instrumentation. The acceptance-rejection criteria are part of the documentation that accompanies the engine historical records.

Normally, all aircraft turbine engines are subject to final acceptance testing and must meet all requirements as specified. The acceptance

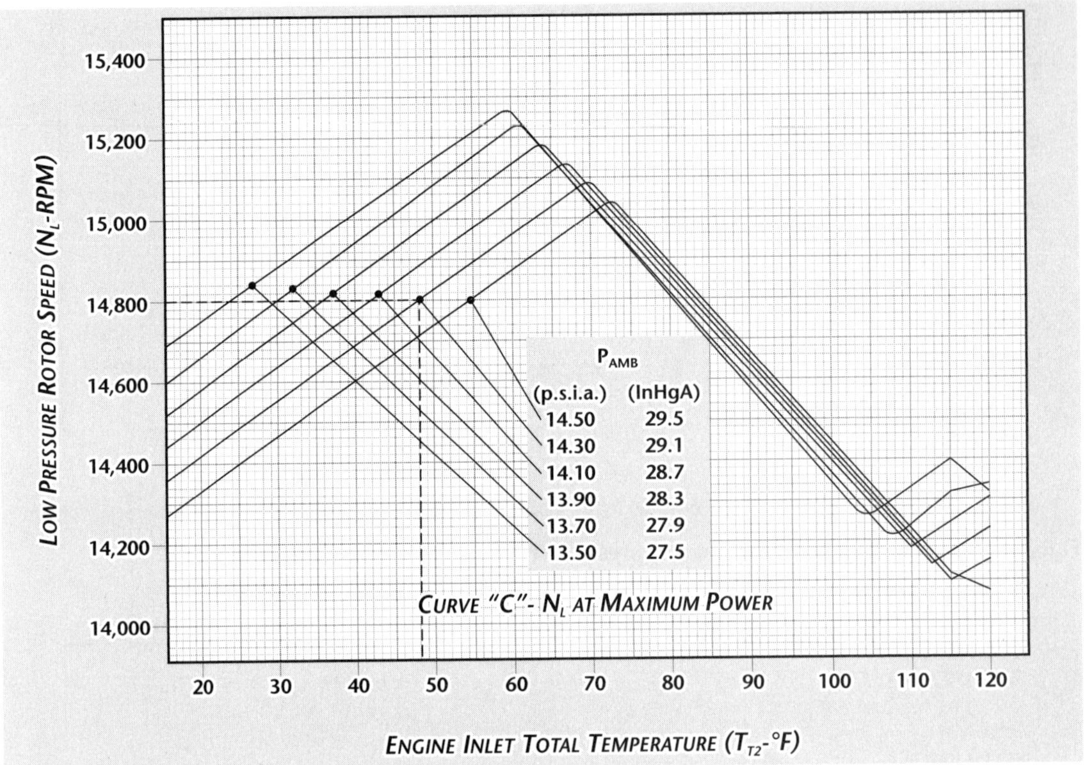

Figure 6-6-4. Max N_1 r.p.m. vs. temperature and pressure (P_{amb})

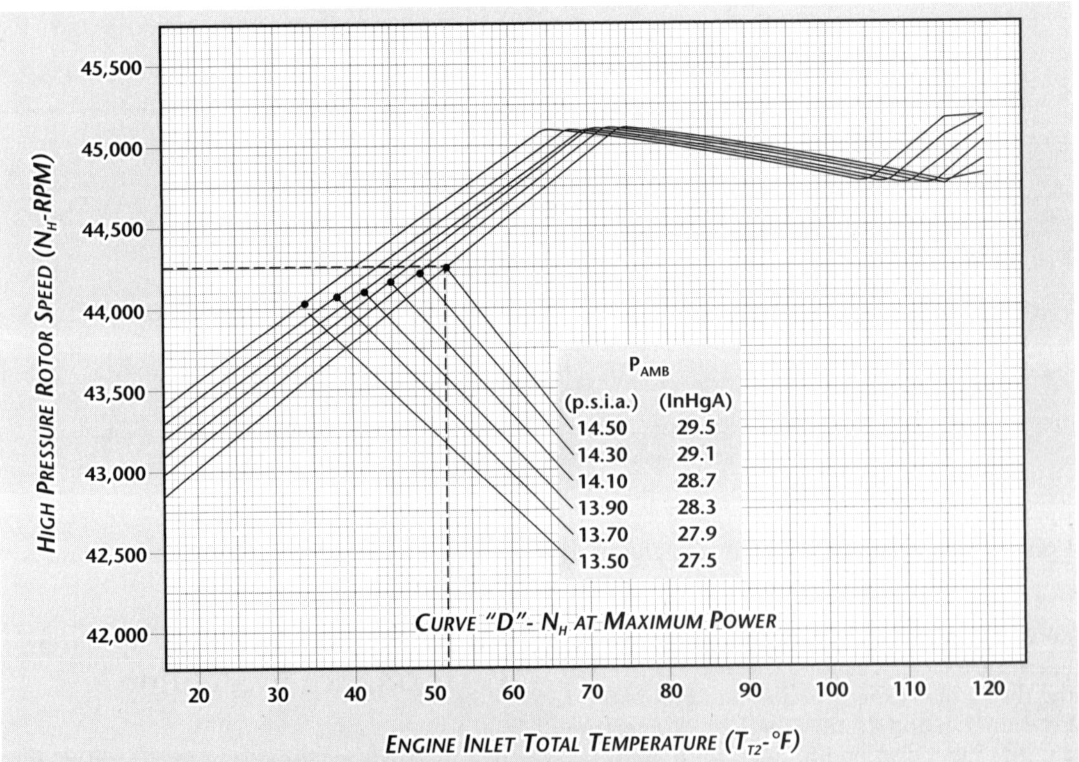

Figure 6-6-5. Max N2 r.p.m. vs. temperature and pressure (P_{amb})

test shall be considered satisfactorily completed when the engine, its components and related hardware have passed the final acceptance test runs in compliance with the engine specification requirements and operating limits.

One requirement is the minimum takeoff thrust for ambient engine inlet temperature and pressure. This test is done to evaluate the engine's thrust performance. An example of the thrust that the engine should produce is defined in Figure 6-6-2, curve A. At 70° F and a pressure of 13.6 p.s.i.a., the resulting thrust should be 1,250 lbs. Maximum $T_{4.5}$ (ITT) is shown in Figure 6-6-3, curve B . The maximum ITT for an inlet temperature of 50° F and an inlet pressure of 14.5 p.s.i.a. is 1,300° F. The N_1 speeds at maximum power are defined in Figure 6-6-4, curve C. At a temperature of 50° F and a pressure of 14.3 p.s.i.a., the N_1 should be 14,800 r.p.m. The N_2 maximum speed, for a temperature of 52° F and a pressure of 14.5 p.s.i.a., is 44,250 r.p.m. in Figure 6-6-5, curve D.

During testing, fuel and oil samples are taken to assure their systems are free of contamination and to check for unusual wear. A special laboratory fuel filter can be installed in the engine fuel system between the fuel/oil cooler and the fuel flow divider for evaluation after all initial runs. A laboratory oil filter is installed in the engine oil system between the fuel/oil cooler and the gearbox for lab evaluation of contaminates after testing. No leakage except at the drains provided for this purpose is acceptable.

PARAMETER	UNIT	ENGINE RANGE
HP Compressor Vertical Vibrations	ips*	0 to 1.5
HP Compressor Horizontal Vibrations	ips	0 to 1.5
HP Turbine Vertical Vibrations	ips	0 to 1.5
HP Turbine Horizontal Vibrations	ips	0 to 1.5
Gearbox Vertical Vibrations	ips	0 to 1.5
Gearbox Horizontal Vibrations	ips	0 to 1.5
Scavenge Pump Oil Exit Temperature	°F	0 to 350
Engine Oil Inlet Temperature	°F	0 to 350
Engine Oil Inlet Pressure	p.s.i.g.	0 to 50

ips= inches per second

Table 6-6-1. Mechanical instrumentation requirements

Drainage of combustible fluids from engine drains, fuel pump seal, starter generator pad and hydraulic pump pad, also must not exceed a set value after normal engine shutdown.

Engines are subjected to acceptance testing in a test cell with calibrated test equipment. Initial starts can be done using an air turbine starter. These starters may be used for engine testing with the exception of the start-time test that requires an electric starter. Instrumentation is provided is shown in Table 6-6-1 (mechanical instrumentation) and in Table 6-6-2 (performance parameters).

Vibration pickups (accelerometers) are mounted on the unused engine mount pad of the front engine frame. Vibration brackets are mounted on the mid-frame aft flange and the gearbox

PARAMETER	SYMBOL STATION	UNIT	RANGE
Cockpit Low Rotor Speed	N_L	r.p.m.	0 to 20,000
Cockpit High Rotor Speed	N_H	r.p.m.	0 to 55,000
HPC Exit Pressure	P_{S3}	p.s.i.g.	0 to 350
EPC Exit Temperature	T_3	F	0 to 1,000
HPT Discharge Temperature	$T_{4.5}$	F	0 to 2,000
Inlet Screen Temperature	1_A	F	0 to 125
Bellmouth Total Pressure	P_{1A}	p.s.i.g.	±1.5
Bellmouth Static Pressure	PS_{1A}	p.s.i.g.	±1.5
HPC Interstage Bleed Connect Flange	PB24E	p.s.i.g.	0 to 150
Core Discharge Temperature	$T_{7.5}$	F	0 to 1,200
Core Discharge Total Pressure	$P_{7.5}$	p.s.i.g.	0 to10
Nozzle Exit Static Pressure	P_{S8}	p.s.i.g.	±1.5
Fan Exit Temperature	T_{13}	F	0 to 300
Bypass Exit Temperature	P_{T7}	F	0 to 10
Bypass Exit Total Pressure	T_{17}	p.s.i.g.	0 to 10
Measured Thrust	F_N	lb	0 to 1,500
Barometric Pressure	P_{BAR}	p.s.i.a.	13 to 15
PLA Engine	PLA ENG	deg	0 to 130
Fuel Temperature	T_{Fuel}	F	0 to 125
Fuel Specific Gravity	SFG	(NA)	0.1 to 0.9
Fuel Flow	WF	gpm	0 to 2.5
Scanivalve Numbers 1 and 6 zero REF	V1 REF V2 REF	p.s.i.g.	±1

Table 6-6-2. Performance parameters instrumentation requirements

vibration brackets are mounted on the starter pad drain.

The instrumentation and equipment used in a test cell must be calibrated in accordance with standard procedures. Staging is where extra instrumentation is mounted on the engine such as extra temperature and pressure probes, vibration probes and a special exhaust nozzle.

The staging process is accomplished prior to installing the engine in the test cell. Staging technicians use a staging checklist and indicate compliance by signing in the appropriate space provided. Upon receiving the engine and prior to beginning the preparation for the test process (staging), inspect the engine for obvious abnormalities and/or damage to lines, external components and general engine appearance. To prevent FOD, use the following inspection procedure:

1. Inspect the fan rotor assembly, the fan inlet housing and the low-pressure turbine exit guide vanes prior to operating. Inspect the inlet housing and inlet bellmouth for loose hardware. Be meticulous when inspecting behind the fan at the bottom of the housing. Rotate the fan manually through at least one revolution and look for loose objects. Rotate the high-pressure rotor N_2 assembly through at least one revolution to ensure free movement and check for any unusual noises.
2. Visually inspect the unit for completeness, damage, significant defects and loose connections. Check for free action of moving parts and ensure that all laboratory and engine plumbing and electrical harnesses necessary to instrument the engine are installed and lock-wired where applicable.
3. If either the cold end or hot end of the engine is disassembled and reassembled, the inspections outlined above must be repeated.
4. Upon completion of engine testing and before removing the engine from the test stand, re-inspect the fan assembly and low-pressure turbine for any damage.
5. Note inspection results in the engine test log.

Turbofan Engine Test Cell Procedure

An air turbine starter is required for initial motoring and seal break-in. Engine motoring must be done with the power lever in the cut-off position. Ensure that the fuel supply is connected to the fuel pump and that the test cell boost pump and fuel solenoid are operating before motoring the engine. The test cell fuel boost pump must remain on during engine test motoring and operation.

As the engine starts to rotate, verify positive engine oil pressure. With the fuel power lever cutoff in the closed position and utilizing the air turbine starter motor, the following high-pressure spool speeds (N_2) are run: 4,000; 6,000; 8,000; 10,000; and 12,000 r.p.m. Accelerate to the specific speed and roll down. Listen for any unusual noises on each roll down. This procedure will accomplish the initial break-in of the engine seals and check for engine problems. Before each engine start, on the engine test log, record the maximum inter-stage turbine temperature ($T_{4.5}$), start number, time and any abnormalities noted during acceleration for all engine starts. Perform engine starts as follows:

1. Accelerate the engine with the starter to a high-pressure spool speed (N_2) of 4,500 r.p.m.
2. Advance the power lever to the IDLE position (ignition activates at this point and fuel flow starts).
3. Confirm LIGHT-OFF by a rise in $T_{4.5}$. (allow only 10 seconds)
4. Check for fan rotation
5. Make certain the starter deactivates at an N_2 of 20,388 ± 400 r.p.m. and continue accelerating to idle speed.

Under no circumstances may any of the operating limitations in the table of operating limits be exceeded during engine testing. If any of the limits are exceeded, the engine should be shutdown and the cause determined. Corrective action should be made before progressing with any further engine testing.

Always operate the engine at idle speed for a minimum of four minutes prior to shutdown. Place the power lever in cut-off and time the roll-down of N_1 and N_2 from the cut-off actuation to zero r.p.m. Record the engine's roll-down times on the engine test log after each shutdown. If N_1 or N_2 roll-down time is less than 50 seconds (specification for this example engine), or any unusual noise is detected during roll-down, record the results on the engine test log and investigate and make repairs before another starting attempt is made. The fan must stop after the N_2.

Some of the tests that the engine must undergo include the following:

- Maximum power
- Idle and maximum thrust transient
- Short transient
- Performance
- Vibration survey
- Oil consumption
- Laboratory fuel and oil filter element inspection
- Start time test
- Air purity

- Leak check
- Metal chip detector inspection
- Preservation procedure
- Engine weigh-in procedure

Following completion of the acceptance test, the dry engine weight including EFCU will be measured in the horizontal position by recording the actual weight less five pounds for residual fluids. Operational testing procedures are performed for new engines prior to delivery, in order to validate performance, security of the engine and to check for leaks.

Other operational checks performed in the field (after installation in the aircraft) include idle checks and power assurance tests, whereby hot day take-off thrust may be confirmed. A dry motor check may be required to assure that the starting system is operating normally, the engine is rotating freely and the instrumentation is indicating properly. During such checks, neither the ignition nor the fuel is activated and the starting system is energized only for that period of time necessary to observe r.p.m. and oil pressure instrumentation indications. Observe starter limitations while motoring.

Turbine engines have specific shutdown procedures. Many times the manufacturer will specify a short cool-off period before actual shutdown. This procedure requires the operator to monitor engine temperatures after operation at high power settings. When the engine has idled for a short period of time, the internal temperature will fall below a preset minimum. Once this minimum temperature has been met, the operator may shut-down the engine.

The purpose of this cool down is to allow the component temperature gradients to equalize as much as possible. This allows the turbine blades to cool by the same amount as the engine case, reducing the possibility of blade tip rub. Many turbine engines have a residual temperature maximum before a restart can be performed. If the engine has just been shut down and the turbine temperature is above this residual temperature, a restart is not advised until the engine has cooled.

Sea Level Standard Day Conversions

Since engines must be tested at different ambient pressures and temperatures, measured engine data must be corrected to sea-level standard day conditions to ensure consistent data. New engines are subject to performance validation runs performed in a fully instrumented test cell, using a bell-mouth air inlet to eliminate turbulence as the air enters the engine. These test operations require that engine parameters be corrected for non-standard conditions such that meaningful performance analysis can be conducted, regardless of the ambient temperature and pressure. Greek letters delta (δ) and theta (θ) symbolize the correction factors for pressure and temperature, respectively. Correction factors are listed below:

Standard sea level temperatures are:

- 59°F,
- 15°C
- 518.67°R
- 288°K

Standard sea level pressure

- 14.696 p.s.i.a
- 29.92 in. hg

The sea level standard temperature can be different for the temperature scale used. Rankine (R) and Kelvin (K) are absolute scales, with the relative scales being the Fahrenheit (F) and Celsius (C) scale. Although each has a different numeric value, they are all the standard temperature. By placing the ambient temperature (temperature of the actual engine testing) over the standard temperature, theta can be calculated. Theta is used to correct temperatures.

$$\theta = \frac{\text{Ambient temperature}}{\text{Standard temperature}}$$

Delta is calculated by:

$$\delta = \frac{\text{Ambient pressure } \delta = P_{amb}}{\text{Standard pressure}}$$

Square root of theta is also used as a correction factor along with θ and δ. By applying the correction factors to the engine's physical quantities, the sea level standard day values can be calculated. Some of the physical quantities or parameters are airflow, fuel flow, pressure, speed, thrust, torque, temperature and horsepower. These formulas, units and symbols are illustrated in Table 6-6-3. Temperatures are corrected by using θ. Speeds are corrected by using √ø. Pressures and flows use δ. Refer to Table 6-6-3 for the conversion of physical quantity corrected to sea level formulas.

PHYSICAL QUANTITY	SYMBOL	UNIT	CORRECTED GROUP
Airflow	W_a	LBM/SEC	$W_a\sqrt{\theta}/\partial$
Fuel Flow	W_F	LBM/HR	$W_F/\partial\sqrt{\theta}$
Horsepower	HP	Horsepower	$HP\sqrt{\partial}/\theta$
Pressure	P	LBF/IN^2	P/∂
Speed	N	REV/MIN	$N/\sqrt{\theta}$
Thrust	F	LBF	F/∂
Torque	T	FT-LBF	T/∂
Temperature	T	R	T/θ

Table 6-6-3. Standard day conversion formulas

Chapter 7

TURBOFAN engines

Manufacturers produce turbofan engines of various types and sizes. Although some turbofan engines had aft-mounted fans, the use of this engine configuration has been very limited. Common turbofan engines use forward fan configurations and start with thrust ratings as small as 500 lbs. of thrust to over 100,000 lbs. of thrust.

Small- and medium-sized business aircraft are usually equipped with turbofan engines in the range of 500 lb. to 5,000 lb. thrust. Larger business class aircraft are generally powered by the two-spool turbofan engine in the 1,000 lbs-8,000 lbs. thrust range. Large transport aircraft now use engines with 115,000 lbs of thrust per engine.

Learning Objectives

- *Types and Thrust Ratings*
- *PWJT8D*
- *PW2000 Series*
- *PW4000 Series*
- *RR Trent Series*

Section 1

Types and Thrust Ratings of Turbofan Engines

Many smaller turbofan engines use a fan driven by the N_1 spool that drives the fan through reduction gears. Examples of these engines include the Honeywell TFE-731 series, TFE-738 series, Rolls-Royce-3007, Pratt & Whitney JT15D series and the General Electric CF34. Airliners are commonly equipped with engines from Pratt & Whitney (PW), General Electric (GE), or Rolls-Royce (RR).

The most common PW engine models are the JT8D, JT9D, PW2000 series, PW4000 series, and PW6000 series engines. GE provides several series of engines, including the CF6 series and GE90 series engines. Rolls-Royce has several series of engines available over a wide range of thrust ratings, such as the RB211 series, the Trent series and the Tay series.

Left: Turbofan engines power the largest aircraft in commercial aviation.

Figure 7-2-1. Pratt & Whitney JT8D engine

The CFM56 engine series and the IAE 2500 engine series are also widely used engines on transport category aircraft. Several versions of low bypass augmenter (afterburning) turbofan engines are made by the same manufacturers and are used on military aircraft.

The construction and general configuration of commonly used engines for large and medium-sized transport aircraft will be discussed in this chapter. Engines for large aircraft are axial-flow, dual-spool (except Rolls-Royce, which uses three spools) turbofan engines with thrust ratings from 14,000 lbs. to over 115,000 lbs. of thrust. Turbofan engines of this type have proven to be the most efficient and economical for the operation of large airliners.

In recent years, makers of turbofan engines have improved their engines by changing the aerodynamic design of turbine and compressor blades and vanes, utilizing improved alloys for blades and vanes (which allow operation at higher temperatures), and modifying fan blade design. They have changed the internal engine-cooling systems, increased the bypass ratio and made other modifications. As a result, the engines are more fuel-efficient, develop more thrust for their weight and are quieter.

It is beyond the scope of this text to cover every engine in detail, so the Pratt & Whitney JT8D and the PW4000 series will be used as examples for detailed discussion. Basic descriptions of some other turbofan engines are also contained in this chapter. Most turbofan engines have the same general engine systems and construction, varying mainly in size, configuration and overall complexity.

The primary goals for improvement of gas-turbine engines have been to reduce fuel consumption, increase reliability and thrust and reduce noise and exhaust emissions. Through use of improved materials, improved aerodynamic compressor and turbine design, the engines are now more efficient than in the past. Improved blade design and vane cooling techniques as well as more effective gas seals and other refinements have contributed to the improvement in efficiency as well.

The use of graphite composite in areas of the engine and nacelle which are temperature appropriate has greatly reduced the weight both of the engine and the nacelle. By refining the design of the compressor and turbine blades geometry, the operational efficiency of these critical components has been increased.

By using turbine blade cooling techniques such as internal air cooling and heat resistant materials, the temperature of the turbine section can be raised, increasing the overall efficiency of the engine. Reducing the amount of air bleed from the gas path of the engine for gas seals and aircraft use can also reduce fuel consumption.

Improved fan design, better sound-absorbing materials and the use of a multiple-tube core exhaust discharge has improved noise reduction. The manufacturers and operators of all modern gas-turbine engines continually seek

Figure 7-2-2. General configuration of a JT8D engine

Pratt & Whitney photo

to improve the performance, dependability and cost-effectiveness of their engines.

Section 2

Pratt & Whitney JT8D Gas-turbine Engine

The Pratt & Whitney JT8D turbofan is one of the most widely used turbofan engines in existence. The original JT8D engine produced 14,000 lb. of thrust. This performance was gradually increased to 17,400 lb. The latest model, the JT8D-200, produces thrust from 19,250 lbs. to 20,850 lbs.

The Pratt & Whitney JT8D is a twin-spool axial-flow gas-turbine engine that is equipped with a secondary air duct that encases the full length of the engine. This type of configuration is referred to as a ducted fan turbofan engine. An example of a JT8D engine is shown in Figures 7-2-1 and 7-2-2. The specifications for a typical original JT8D engine given here are for information only. As explained previously, the various models of a particular type of engine may have differing specifications in some areas.

- Length 120.0 in.
- Diameter 43.0 in.
- Weight (approx.) 3,300 lb.
- Takeoff thrust 14,500 lbs.
- Power-weight ratio 4.50 lbs./lb.
- Fuel consumption 0.57 lb./lbs./hr.
- Oil consumption 3.0 lb./hr.
- Compressor ratio 16.9:1
- Bypass ratio 1.03:1
- Fan pressure ratio 1.91:1
- Air mass flow, fan 159 lb./sec.
- Air mass flow, core 163 lb./sec.

The general configuration of the JT8D engine may be understood by examining Figure 7-2-3. The bearing arrangement in the JT8D is similar to that of many turbofan engines. The No. 1 and No. 2 bearings support the low-pressure compressor (N_1) rotor. The No. 3 and No. 4 bearings support the high-pressure compressor (N_2) rotor. The No. 4.5 bearing is the intershaft bearing, supporting the inner drive shaft within the hollow outer drive shaft. The No. 5 and No. 6 bearings support the turbine.

The JT8D engine has six general sections:

- Air inlet section
- Compressor section
- Fan discharge section
- Combustion section
- Turbine and exhaust section
- Accessory drive section

Air Inlet Section

As shown in Figure 7-2-4, the air inlet section is the most forward section of the engine. This section forms the air inlet for the engine and houses the inlet guide vanes. The purpose of the vanes is to direct the incoming air at the proper angle

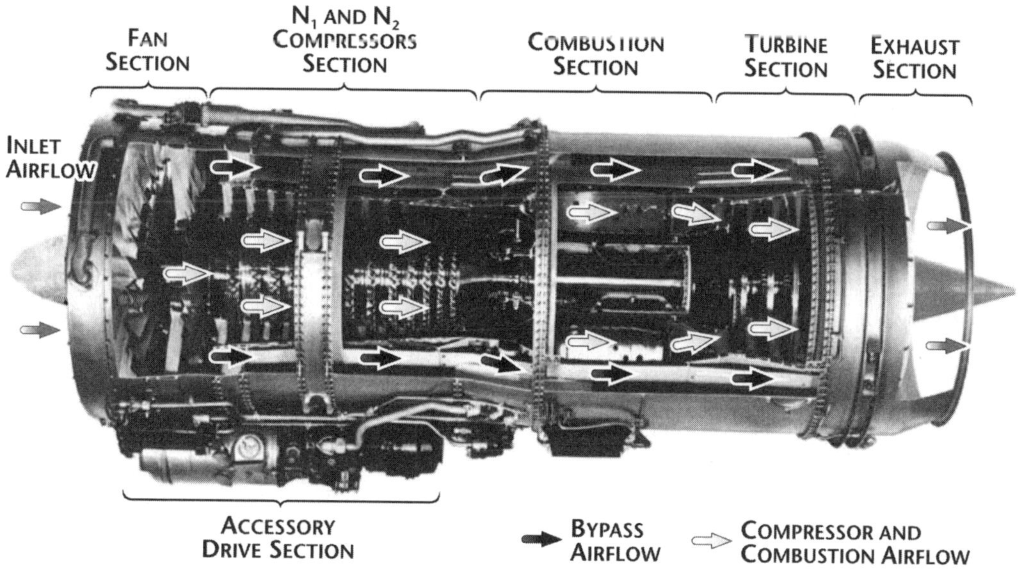

Figure 7-2-3. JT8D arrangement and airflow

Pratt & Whitney photo

to the first fan stage. The vane at the bottom of the air inlet is thicker than the other vanes in order to accommodate engine tubing.

Compressor Section

The front-compressor section and the fan section of the JT8D engine are both part of the same rotating assembly. In the engine, the air passes through the last row of rear-compressor blades at a high velocity. The motion is both rearward and circular in pattern around the engine.

Two rows of radial, straightening exit-guide vanes at the entrance to the diffuser case slow the circular whirl pattern and convert the whirl-velocity energy to pressure energy. After passing through these straightening vanes, the air still has a strong rearward velocity. This velocity is so high that it would be nearly impossible to maintain a flame in its airstream. A gradually increasing cross section of the air passage decreases the velocity of the airflow and at the same time converts the velocity energy to pressure energy.

Fan Discharge Section

The fan is comprised of the outer ends of the first two compressor blades. These two blades are enclosed by the front and rear fan cases. Figure 7-2-3 illustrates the arrangement of the JT8D engine with respect to position of units and airflow.

Figure 7-2-4. Air inlet showing stationary inlet guide vanes on a JT8D engine
Pratt & Whitney photo

The N_1 (low-pressure) compressor partially compresses the air entering the engine before the air is delivered to the N_2 (high-pressure) compressor. While primary air flows through the core of the engine, secondary air from the fan is passing through the fan duct surrounding the engine. In this engine, the primary air and secondary air are divided.

Combustion Section

The combustion section of the JT8D engine is of the cannular type. This means that individual combustion chambers are arranged around the engine inside a single annular chamber.

Turbine and Exhaust Section

The turbine section includes the turbine front case, the turbine rear case, an inner case and seal, four stages of turbine-nozzle vanes, the two turbine rotors with four stages and the coaxial drive shafts. The first-stage turbine-nozzle vanes are coated with a thermal barrier material and air-cooled.

The front-compressor drive-turbine rotor includes the front-compressor drive-turbine shaft, three turbine stages and the spacers and air seals between the disks.

Twelve tie rods secure the disks and spacers to each other and to the rear flange of the rotor shaft. The blades for the second, third and fourth turbines are secured in the disks by fir-tree slots and rivets.

The turbine exhaust case, constructed of welded steel, is the most rearward section of the basic inner engine. It is bolted to the rear flange of the turbine case and decreases from front to rear in order to increase the velocity of the exhaust gases.

The turbine exhaust case and fairing assembly act as the structural supports for the No. 6 bearing and its support rods. The thermocouples for the EGT and the pressure sensors for the EPR are also located in this area.

Accessory Drive Section

The JT8D incorporates two areas on the engine designed to accommodate accessory and components drives. The first is the front accessory drive housing, which is mounted on the front of the inlet case. This area incorporates an external pad for mounting the N_1 tachometer generator.

The other unit is the accessory and components drive gearbox mounted under the

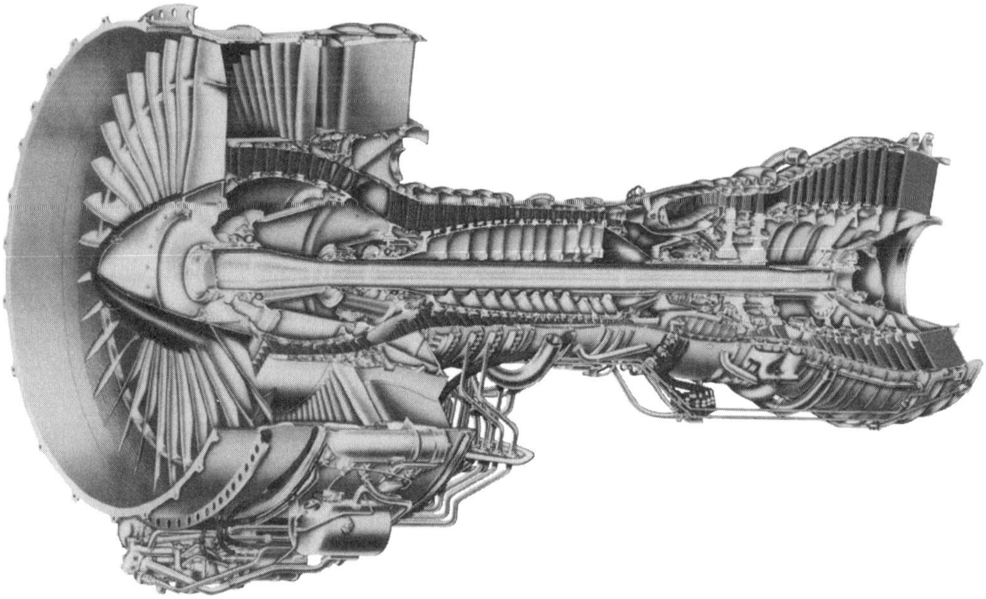

Figure 7-3-1. Pratt & Whitney 2037 high bypass turbofan engine cutaway

Image courtesy of Pratt & Whitney

engine. It has one drive pad for both the fuel pump and fuel control, plus drive pads for the constant-speed drive, starter and hydraulic pump. Other units driven from this section are the N_2 tachometer, oil pressure pump and oil scavenge pumps. An oil pressure relief valve, oil strainer and bypass valve are also included in this section.

Section 3

Pratt & Whitney 2000 Series Turbofan Engine

The Pratt & Whitney 2037 turbofan engine, shown in Figure 7-3-1, has improved design features and materials that contribute to engine efficiency, reliability, lower fuel consumption and improved maintainability. It is one of the PW2000 family of high-bypass turbofans with maximum thrust ratings from 37,000 to 43,000 lbs. The PW2037 engine is designed to power the Boeing 757 aircraft. The general specifications for the Pratt & Whitney 2037 turbofan engine are as follows:

- Length 133.7 in.
- Diameter, fan tip 78.5 in.
- Diameter, fan case 85.0 in.
- Diameter, turbine exhaust case 49.0 in.
- Weight 6,675 lb.
- Takeoff thrust, sea-level 37,000 lb.
- Overall pressure ratio 30:1
- Bypass ratio 5.8:1
- Fan pressure ratio 1.70:1
- Total airflow 1,193 lb./sec.

The Pratt & Whitney 2037, a twin-rotor, high-bypass-ratio, axial-flow turbofan engine, designed for use with commercial and military transport aircraft, is shown in Figure 7-3-2. The single-stage fan and four-stage low-pressure compressor are driven by a five-stage turbine at the rear of the engine. A two-stage turbine drives the twelve-stage high-pressure compressor through a hollow shaft that is coaxial with the low-pressure compressor drive shaft. The two rotors are supported by five main bearings.

Figure 7-3-2. Pratt & Whitney 2000 series engine side view

Fan and Compressor Section

The fan has thirty-six wide-chord, single-shroud blades. The airfoils (blades and vanes) are controlled-diffusion airfoils that permit higher Mach numbers without a loss of efficiency and are used in both the compressors and the turbines. The thicker leading and trailing edges of the airfoil enhances continued serviceability by increasing resistance to airborne particle erosion.

Variable stators are employed in the first five stages of the high-pressure compressor to increase compressor efficiency, control surge and eliminate compressor stall. These stators provide stability over the entire operating envelope by controlling the aerodynamic loading on the compressor stages.

Electron-beam welding joins the disks and spacers in the high-pressure rotor. This technique, used instead of bolted joints, eliminates leakage and improves clearance control by stiffening the rotor.

Combustion Section

The engine has an annular combustion chamber with twenty-four single-pipe air-blast fuel nozzles. The combustor design provides improved heat transfer from the lower lip, which reduces thermal stress. In addition, the design provides uniform discharge of the cooling air to the inner surface of the downstream burner wall.

Turbine Section

The high-pressure turbine blades are single-crystal castings. These blades provide high creep strength, high-thermal limits and increased low-cycle fatigue life. They are also resistant to oxidation and high-temperature corrosion.

The outer air seals for the high-pressure turbine are of an abradable, nonmetallic material. These seals improve performance by reducing blade tip clearances during operation. They also improve performance retention and reduce the risk of turbine blade damage.

The high-pressure turbine disks and the last high-pressure compressor disk are produced from fine-mesh PW1100 powder-metal. Compared to conventional forged disks, the powder-metal disks offer higher tensile strength, greater stress-rupture resistance and longer low-cycle fatigue life.

The low-pressure turbines increase in diameter substantially from the first stage to the last stage as illustrated in Figure 7-3-3.

This flow-path configuration is designed to provide the best possible aerodynamic performance. The large mean diameter and smooth gas-flow transition from the high-pressure turbine is more efficient than the smaller mean diameter turbines used on earlier engines.

Figure 7-3-3. The low-pressure turbine stages increase in diameter from early stages to the later stages.

Figure 7-4-1. Pratt & Whitney 4000 series engine being prepared for a test run. *Pratt & Whitney photo*

Fuel Control Section

The Pratt & Whitney 2037 engine is controlled by a full-authority electronic control (FADEC). All of the engine variables, including starting, fuel flow, variable stator positioning, acceleration and deceleration, are regulated by the FADEC. The automated thrust eliminates the need to continually readjust throttle settings during takeoff and climb. The FADEC reduces engine maintenance time by eliminating the requirement for engine trimming.

Section 4

Pratt & Whitney PW4000 Engine Series

Pratt & Whitney's PW4000 commercial jet engine series is a high-bypass-ratio turbofan engine. The PW4000 engine is a two-spool engine and has a nominal bypass ratio of 5:1. The PW4000 engine, seen in Figure 7-4-1, consists of several fan diameters: the 94-inch, 100-inch and 112-inch fan engines. PW4000 is the basic series designation. Specific models change the last two digits to indicate the thrust rating. For example, the PW4084 is an 84,000 lb. thrust engine, whereas the PW4098 is a 98,000 lb. thrust engine. Thrust developed by the PW4000 engine series ranges from 56,000 lb, with the 112-inch fan having capability of over 100,000 lb of thrust. This wide range of thrust ratings makes the engine ideal for current and new versions of the Boeing 747, 767, 777, the Airbus A300, A310, A330 and Boeing/McDonnell Douglas MD-11 wide-body aircraft.

The 94-inch fan diameter PW4000 engine series specifications are as follows:

- Length 132.7 in.
- Fan case diameter 97 in.
- Fan tip diameter 93.4 in.
- Weight 9,200 lb.
- Turbine exhaust case diameter 53.4 in.

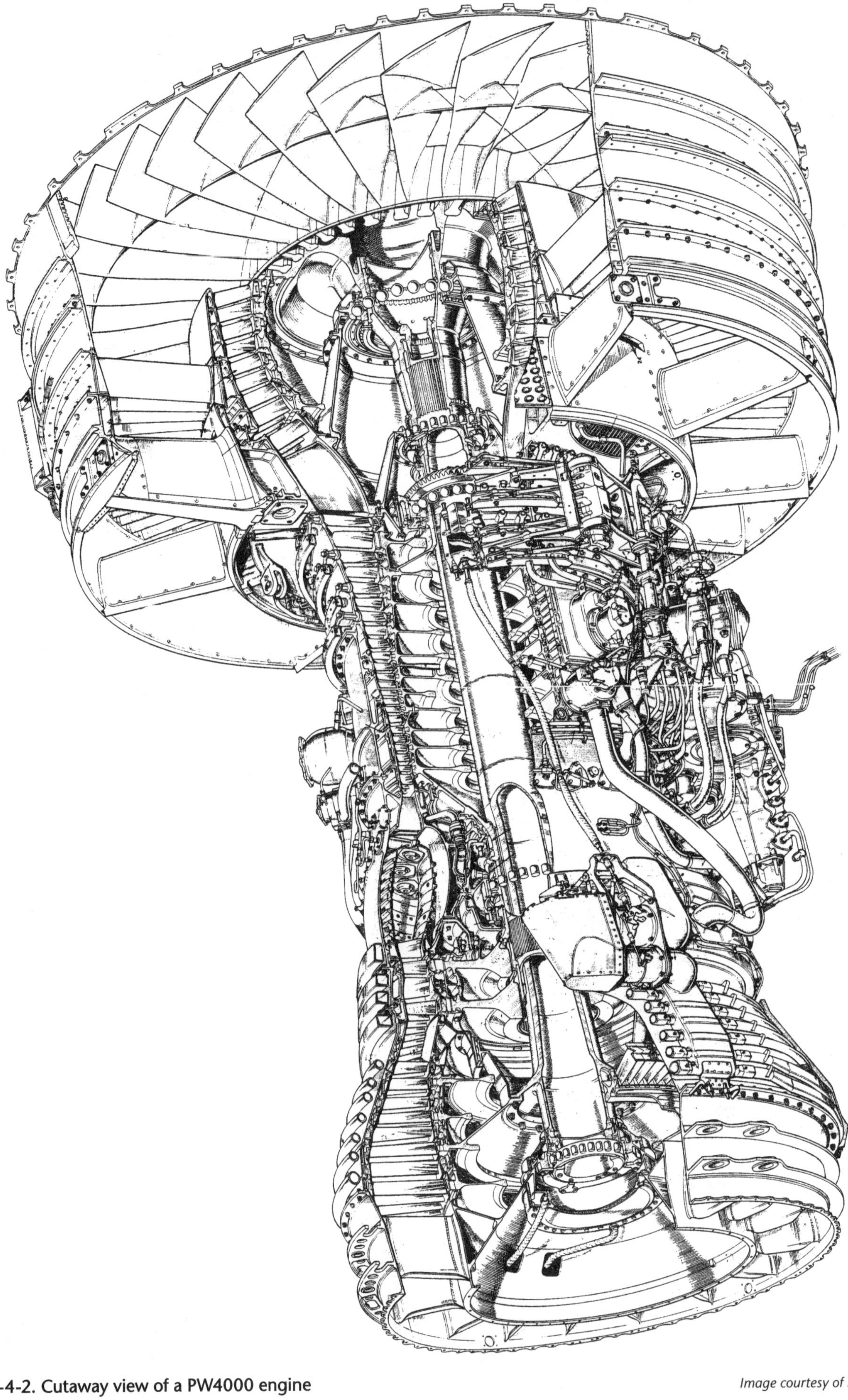

Figure 7-4-2. Cutaway view of a PW4000 engine

Image courtesy of Pratt & Whitney

Figure 7-4-3. A 94-inch diameter fan engine mounted in a test area.

• Combustor type	Annular
• Takeoff thrust sea-level static	56,000 lb.
• Total airflow	1,705 lb./sec.
• Fan pressure ratio	1.72:1
• Bypass ratio	5.0:1
• Overall pressure ratio	28.1

The PW4000's higher rotational speed coupled with a simplified design permits a large-scale reduction in the number of engine parts. The basic construction and nomenclature of the engine are discussed starting from the front of the engine. Even though each model has some differences, the basic systems and construction of the engines are similar, as is seen in Figure 7-4-2 and 7-4-3.

94-inch Fan Engine

Fan and Low-pressure Compressor

The compressor inlet cone, also referred to as the nose cone or spinner, is mounted to the very front of the engine and serves as an aerodynamic fairing. The nose cone provides for smooth airflow into the engine. It is constructed of Kevlar and epoxy resin with a polyurethane coating. Two cone segments are used: the rear segment, which is bolted to the front of the low-pressure compressor (LPC) hub and the front segment, bolted to the rear cone segment. The complete assembly is pre-balanced to reduce vibration.

There are twelve vent holes for anti-icing air, equally spaced around the rear of the cone segment, allowing the anti-icing air to vent back to the fan duct.

The next component is the fan that is the first stage of the LPC rotor. It compresses the air that flows into the engine. The LPC first stage, shown in Figure 7-4-4, has thirty-eight wide-chord fan blades and a single-part span shroud. Each blade is moment-weighted for balance and individually marked. The fan blades are installed into the LPC hub in dovetail slots, which hold the blades radially while a split-ring

Figure 7-4-4. Wide chord fan blades and the first stage LPC of the PW4000

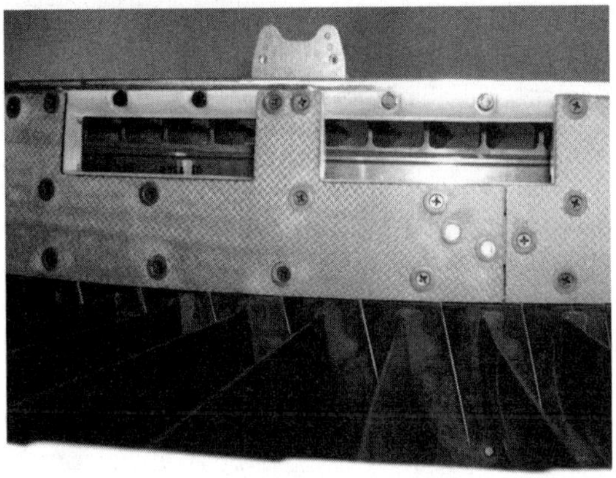

Figure 7-4-5. Bleed valve at the 2.5 station showing the air exit to the fan air stream

blade lock holds them axially. The fan blades can be replaced as moment-weighted pairs or individually, if the replacement blade is within the required moment-weight. Each fan blade has a rubber seal below the blade platform to prevent air leakage.

At the entrance to the primary gas path, the first stage of the stator assembly is located aft of the fan blades. The fan exit fairing divides the primary (core) and secondary (fan) airstreams. The remaining stages further increase the pressure of the primary airstream. The LPC includes a five-stage rotor and stator assembly (stages 1, 1.6, 2, 3 and 4). Supported by the No. 1 ball bearing, the LPC rotor is on the front compressor hub and turned by the low-pressure turbine. The fan exit fairing is attached to the fan exit inner case assembly which supports the LPC stator assembly.

The fan case makes a flow path for the fan discharge air and is the part of the engine structure that supports the nacelle inlet cowl. An inlet cowl contains the fan blade tip rub strips that prevent blade tip wear. The fan blade containment ring prevents the fan blades from exiting the engine radially should they break. Fan exit guide vanes are used to straighten the discharge air before it goes into the thrust-reverser fan air duct.

The 2.5 bleed valve is attached to the fan exit inner case at the LPC exit. The 2.5 bleed air goes out of the fan exit inner case through fourteen slots, to the fan air stream. This is shown in Figure 7-4-5.

The intermediate case is the primary structural component of the engine; an example is shown in Figure 7-4-6. It has the supports for three main engine bearings. These are the No.

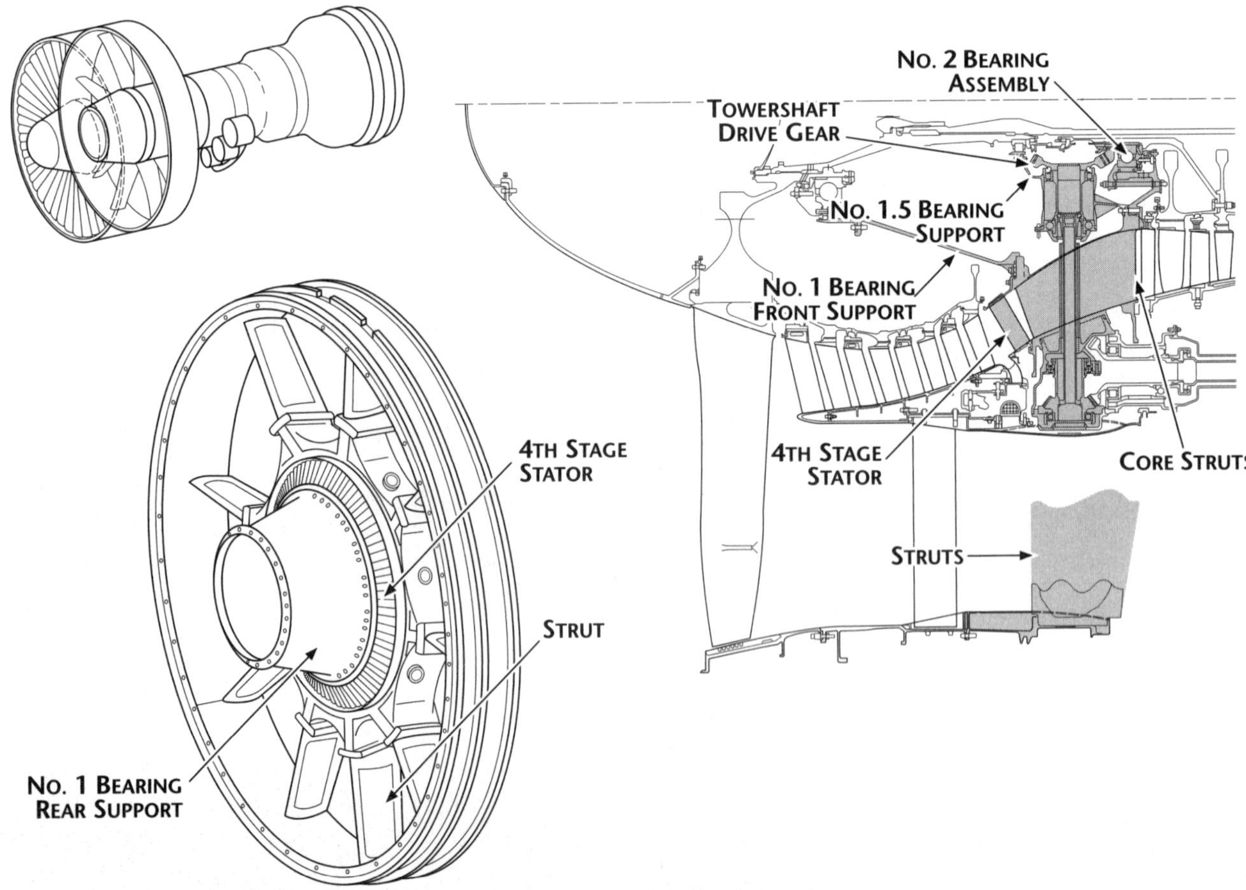

Figure 7-4-6. The intermediate case is a primary structural component of the engine.

1 bearing (LPC), No. 1.5 (LPC/LPT shaft) and the No. 2 bearing (HPC). The intermediate case also includes the fourth-stage compressor stator assembly.

High-pressure compressor. The high-pressure compressor (HPC) increases the pressure of the primary air from the low compressor and sends it into the diffuser. The HPC has an eleven-stage rotor and stator assembly. The first set of airfoils is the inlet guide vane (IGV) assembly.

Each of the first four stator stages has variable vanes moved by a unison ring assembly, shown in Figure 7-4-7. The HPC rotor is supported at the front by the No. 2 bearing and at the rear by the No. 3 bearing. The HPC is turned by the HPT.

The HPC turns the tower shaft that drives the angle and main gearbox. The HPC supplies eighth-stage bleed air for aircraft use. The ninth-stage bleed air is used for engine stability, rotor cooling and No. 1.5 bearing seal pressurization.

There are two bleed valves that can bleed ninth stage air from the compressor if needed. One is used during the starting of the engine to relieve pressure in the later stages of the compressor as the engine spins up during starting. The other ninth stage bleed valve can be used for compressor stability. This valve can bleed off compressor pressure if a compressor stall is about to occur.

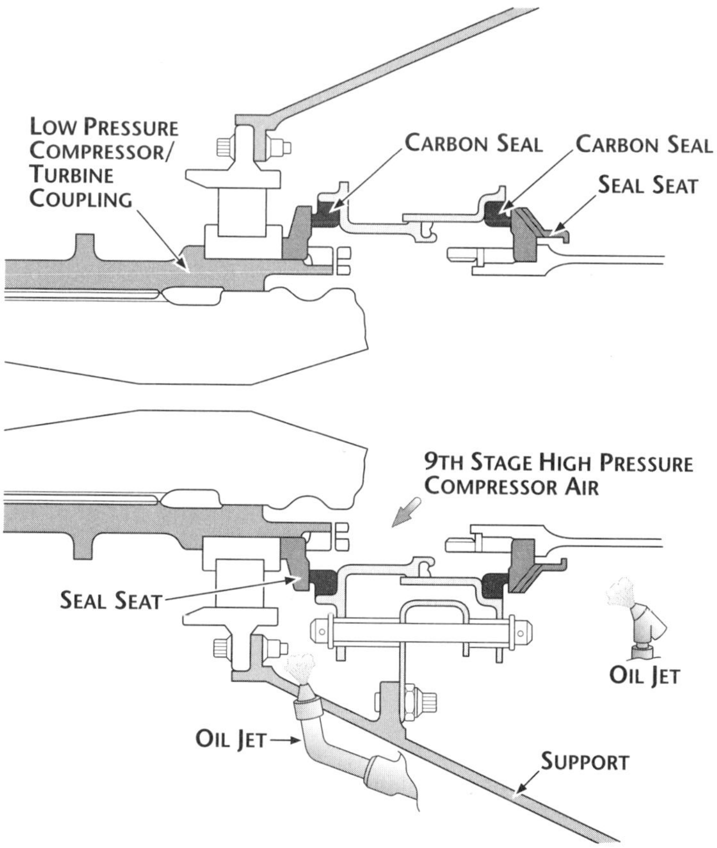

Figure 7-4-8. The bearing chambers are pressurized with bleed air to prevent oil leakage.

Figure 7-4-7. Variable stator vane's unison rings

Ninth stage air is also bled into the HPC compressor interior to cool and stabilize the internal temperature of the HPC. A small amount of air under pressure is allowed to leak across the seal into the bearing compartment and prevent the oil from escaping in the opposite direction into the engine areas. This is shown in Figure 7-4-8.

The twelfth-stage bleed air is used to cool the No. 3 bearing, cool parts of the turbine and provide for the No. 3 bearing seal pressurization. Twelfth stage air is routed through an air to air heat exchanger which uses fan air to cool the twelfth stage air. It is then sent to the No. 3 bearing buffer.

This buffer duct surrounds the No.3 bearing compartment, preventing overheating of the bearing as shown in Figure 7-4-9. Twelfth stage is air is also used to cool the HPT by passing twelfth stage air through internal passage ways in the turbine vanes and blades.

The fifteenth-stage bleed air is used to balance the thrust load on the No. 2 bearing, for muscle

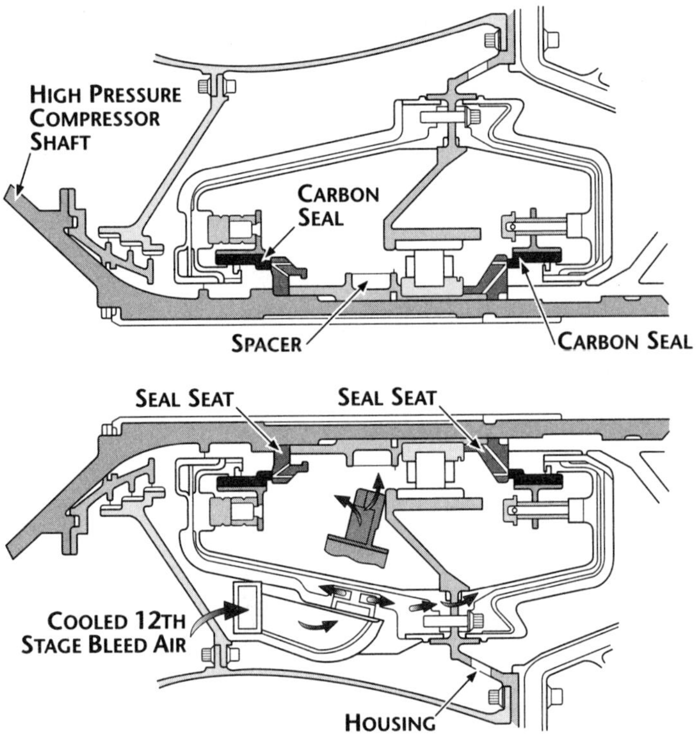

Figure 7-4-9. The No. 3 bearing buffer duct is pressurized with bleed air.

pressure to control engine valves and for airflow sensing. It is also used in the aircraft as well for the No. 3 bearing seal pressurization and to cool parts of the turbine.

The thrust loads on the No. 2 bearing are caused by the tendency of the spinning compressor and fan to pull themselves through the engine. A thrust bearing prevents this from happening, but thrust loads are applied to the bearing.

To offset some of the thrust load, the bleed pressure acts upon the surface area of the turbine disk to push in the opposite direction. Fifteenth stage air is also used to pass through the internal areas of the first stage turbine inlet guide vanes, which provides cooling of the vanes and other turbine components.

A diffuser straightens the airflow from the compressor exit, increases the pressure and reduces the velocity of the primary air, which is sent into and around the combustor, where the fuel is mixed with air. The diffuser case is attached with bolts to the high-pressure compressor rear case.

Combustion Section

Part of the combustion chamber is shown in Figure 7-4-10. Primary gas path air enters the combustion chamber for the addition of heat energy (burning fuel), dilution and cooling. Cooling air from the diffuser flows around the inner and outer chamber walls. The gas path flow also enters the chamber, through small holes, into each segment. Then it flows against the inner surface of the combustion chamber as a cooling film.

This action prevents the combustion chamber from being subjected to temperatures that would be harmful to its surface. This cooling film prevents the combustion gases from coming into contact with any of the surfaces of the combustion liner. The dilution occurs in the latter part of the combustion chamber. The temperature of the flame gases must be reduced before entering into the turbine guide vanes. By mixing compressor air with the hot burning gases, the temperature of the gases entering the turbine section will be reduced.

The combustion chamber has eight fuel injector manifolds that transmit fuel to the twenty-

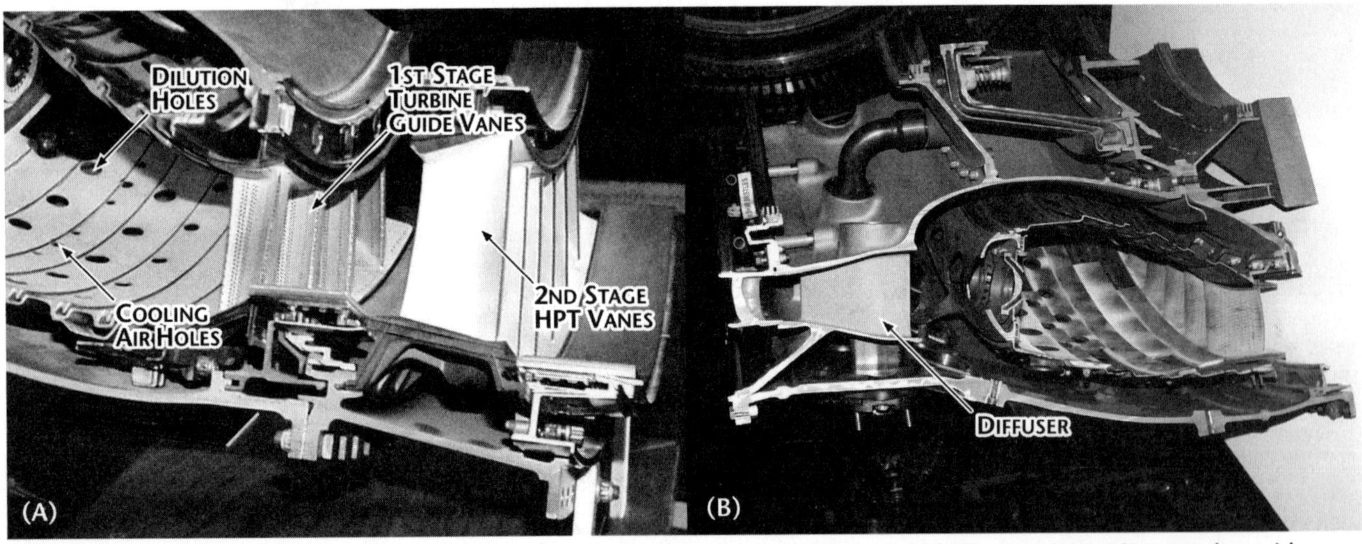

Figure 7-4-10. (A) Combustion chamber showing air cooled turbine inlet guide vanes and (B) ceramic coatings on the guide vanes and combustion chamber.

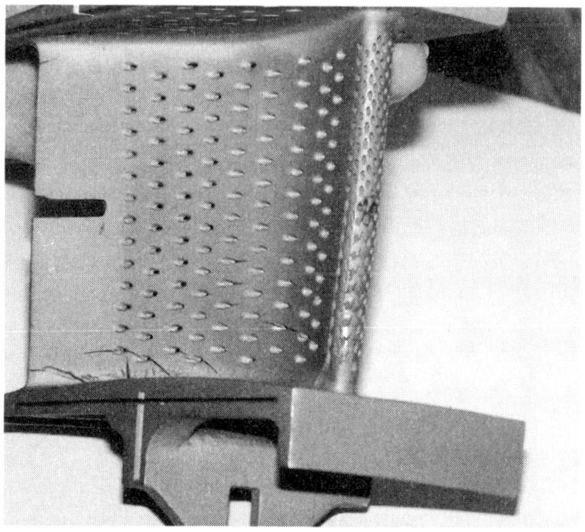

Figure 7-4-11. Compressor discharge air enters the turbine guide vane and exits out the holes in the vane.

four fuel injectors, which are attached around the diffuser case. The combustor also includes two igniter plug bosses, which provide ignition for combustion. The combustion chamber is an annular design with double-pass cooled louvers formed by two parts: the outer combustion chamber and the inner combustion chamber.

Air from the gas path flow (compressor discharge) also enters the internal passages of each turbine inlet guide vane. This is shown in Figure 7-4-11. As it passes out through a pattern of holes in the surface of the vane, it causes a protective air film on the surface of the vane, preventing it from being subjected to high temperatures.

The gas path air goes into the annular cooling duct that operates as a metering nozzle, then goes out of the nozzle and flows against the turbine rotor disk surface. There are honeycomb seals that interface with the first-stage turbine rotor, keeping leakage of the cooling air used for the first-stage turbine rotor and blades to a minimum.

Any air that is bled from the gas path will require extra fuel to produce it. Therefore the least amount of air bleed from the engine will increase the overall efficiency of the engine.

Turbine Section

High-pressure turbine. The high-pressure turbine (HPT), seen in Figure 7-4-12, supplies the force to turn the high-pressure compressor. It includes one case and vane assembly, two disk and blade rotor assemblies and one rotating inner air seal. The components that are air-cooled in the HPT are the first-stage disk and blade assembly, second-stage disk and blade assembly, second-stage vanes and inner air seal. The second-stage turbine vanes (twenty-one vane cluster assemblies, two vanes per cluster) are cooled internally by twelfth-stage HPC air that enters the cooling air annulus through cooling air ports.

Turbine nozzle guide vanes send hot gases from the combustion chamber to the first-stage turbine blades at the correct angle and speed. The cooling duct sends cooling air to

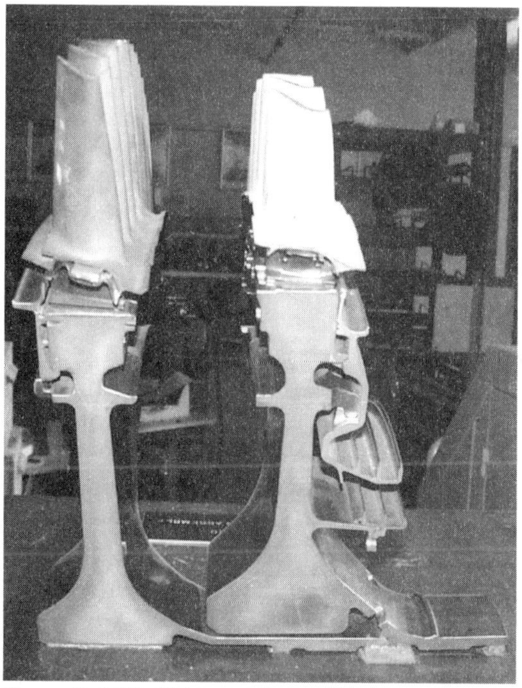

Figure 7-4-12. Cutaway view of high-pressure turbine blades and disk

Figure 7-4-13. Low-pressure turbine blades and disk

Figure 7-4-14. The struts in the turbine exhaust case straighten the primary airflow.

the first-stage turbine rotor and blades. The sixty first-stage turbine blades are made via a single crystal-casting process. The eighty-two second-stage turbine blades are made via a directional-solidification casting process. Both of these casting processes are used to make the blades stronger and more heat-resistant. Abradable ceramic outer air seal segments form a shroud around the blade tips.

The turbine nozzle build group includes the inner combustion chamber liner, the first-stage HPT cooling duct and 17 first-stage HPT nozzle guide vane cluster assemblies (two vanes per cluster).

Low-pressure turbine. A low-pressure turbine (LPT) section is shown in Figure 7-4-13. The low-pressure turbine supplies the force to turn the low-pressure compressor, including the fan, through a drive shaft. The low-pressure turbine

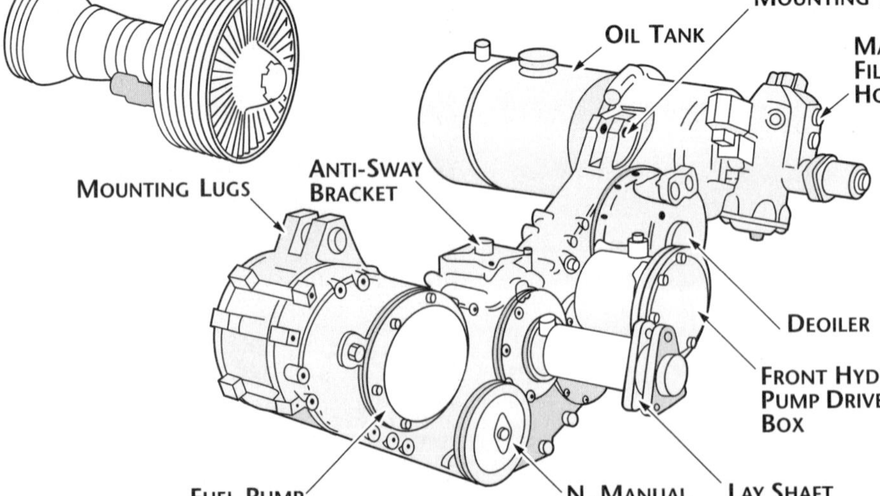

Figure 7-4-15. The accessory gear box transfers power to the mail gearbox through the lay shaft.

has four stages. Internal cooling air from the HPC ninth stage is supplied to the LPT to reduce the temperature in this area.

As energy is used by each turbine stage, the amount of energy available to the next stage becomes less. To provide for each turbine stage to produce the same amount of power, the latter stage blades must have a larger area to absorb the same amount of energy.

Exhaust Section

The turbine exhaust case (TEC) supports the No. 4 bearing and holds the exhaust nozzle and plug. The TEC has attachment points for the rear-engine mount and for ground-handling tools. The struts make the primary airflow straight before it enters the area of the exhaust plug and nozzle and has opening and attachment points for four probes: two $T_{T\,4.95}$ probes and two combination $P_{T\,4.95}/T_{T\,4.95}$ probes. The turbine exhaust case can be seen in Figure, 7-4-14.

Accessory Gearbox Section

The HPC drives a tower shaft connected to the angle gearbox (AGB) which through a lay shaft drives the main gearbox (MGB). The AGB is installed at the rear of the intermediate case at the six o'clock position and is supported by two mount lugs. The lay shaft transfers power from the AGB to the main gear box, as shown in Figure 7-4-15. Most of the main gearbox accessory drives are modules that can be easily put into or pulled out of the MGB. The main gearbox drives the accessories for the engine and aircraft.

The engine accessories mounted on the main gear box are the oil pump assembly, air turbine starter, generator, fuel pump, hydraulic pump. The aircraft may require other accessories as well.

The MGB housing is an aluminum casting that contains a chip detector used to detect gear wear in the main accessory gear box. Many of the components attached to the main accessory gear box are line-replaceable units. These are shown in Figure 7-4-16.

PW4000 Systems

Active clearance control. The PW4000 series of engines incorporates an active clearance control (ACC) concept that controls the clearances between the turbine blade tips and turbine case. Clearance control is achieved by impinging cold air from the fan duct on the outside of the hot turbine case. This controls case dimensions and results in tighter clearances, reduced blade tip losses and improved fuel efficiency. Active clearance control is based on the fact that metals contract when cold and expand when heated. This is accomplished by using cold fan air on the surface of the turbine case.

The clearance between the turbine blade tips and the shroud that surrounds them is critical to the efficiency of the engine. This blade tip clearance must be adequate to allow for full power (maximum thrust) when the blades are at their hottest and centrifugal force is at its highest in order to prevent any contact with the shroud.

As the engine speed is reduced (in cruise flight) and the inlet air temperature is greatly reduced (at high altitude), the clearance becomes excessive. To reduce this clearance, the turbine case is shrunk by the cool fan air. The excessive clearance is also reduced at high altitudes and lower power settings (cruise flight).

There should be some clearance between the turbine blade tips and the turbine shroud. At no time should the turbine blade tips come into contact with the turbine shroud. ACC is used on both high-pressure turbines (HPT) and low-pressure turbines (LPT) to improve fuel efficiency in the cruise range.

Another type of ACC is used on the inside of the high-pressure compressor rotor or drum. The compressor rotor consists of all the rotor stages placed together. There is generally a hollow area inside the drum. Under high power low altitude operation it sends cooling air into the compressor drum, preventing it from fully expanding. It is designed to provide ACC by slowing the flow of cooling air into the compressor rotor.

The high-pressure compressor disk or drum is uniformly expanded by reduction of this cooling

Figure 7-4-16. The main gearbox drives most of the airplane and engine accessories.

Figure 7-4-17. Turbine case cooling system ducts and valves cool the case during engine operation.

air. This expansion then reduces the rotor blade to seal clearances. This system is needed because of the same problem as in the turbine blades.

To have correct clearance during takeoff, the clearance at cruise is too wide. This system closes the clearance somewhat during cruise operation, thus improving efficiency. This system is not part of the turbine case cooling system. Many engines do not use this type of ACC.

Figure 7-4-18. A 2.5 position bleed transition ring type of valve and actuator

Turbine case cooling. This system, shown in Figure 7-4-17, is not used during high power settings and low altitudes. The FADEC unit, which senses aircraft altitude, ambient temperature and power setting, controls the valves that allow fan air to flow onto the turbine cases.

The compressor rotor is designed to provide ACC without impinging cold air on the compressor case. The high-pressure compressor disk is uniformly expanded with hot engine air to reduce rotor-to-stator-seal clearances and thus improve efficiency on some engine models.

The turbine case cooling (TCC) system's components include cooling air manifolds, which are attached to brackets on the outside of the HPT case. They control the flow of fan air through those manifolds to cool the HPT case, with air holes on the turbine case side only, which reduces its diameter during cruise flight. This action in turn reduces the HPT blade tip clearances, thus increasing the engine's efficiency at cruise flight. Ceramic abradable outer air seals are used in the high-pressure turbine to minimize operating clearances and further improve operating efficiency and provide higher and improved turbine life.

Compressor airflow control. The compressor airflow control system increases compressor stability during starting, transient and reverse thrust operation. The system uses a series of bleed valves and variable inlet guide stator vanes. This first bleed valve in the gas path flow is the 2.5 bleed valve. The 2.5 position refers to the engine station at which the valve is located. The 2.5 bleed valve is a 360° translating ring type of valve that bleeds fourth-stage airflow through bleed ports into the fan air stream.

This valve, shown in Figure 7-4-18, is a modulating valve and can be closed, open or modulating between closed and open. The valve is controlled by the FADEC unit through a fuel-actuated actuator which—through a bell crank—adjusts the position of the valve. This bleed valve allows for large quantities of air to be released quickly. When open, this bleed valve makes an opening at this station almost all the way around the engine.

There are two 2.9 bleed valves. One is a start bleed and the other a stability bleed. Both are spring-loaded open and closed by P_{S3} pressure (sometimes called muscle pressure). The FADEC unit controls these valves by using solenoids to control muscle air pressure to the valves. Feedback is provided to the FADEC unit by temperature sensors in the valves. If the valve is open, the bleed air will increase the temperature

Figure 7-4-19. A 2.9 bleed valve is used for either starting or stability bleed.

exiting the valve. The FADEC unit receives a signal from the sensor that the valve is open. A 2.9 bleed valve can be seen in Figure 7-4-19.

The variable stator vane control system, shown in Figure 7-4-20 provides maximum compressor performance while preventing compressor

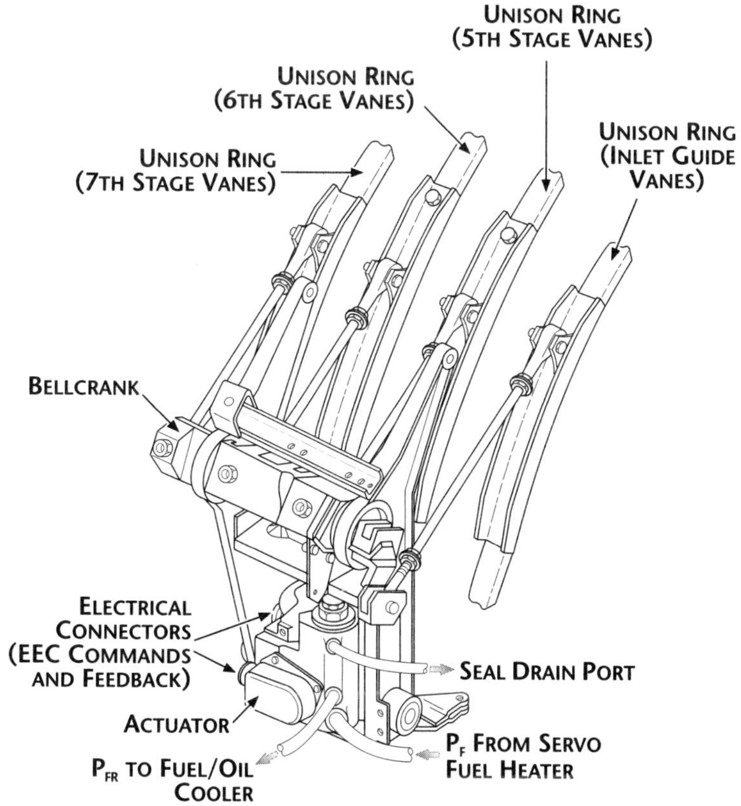

Figure 7-4-20. A set of variable stator vanes, actuator and unison ring connections

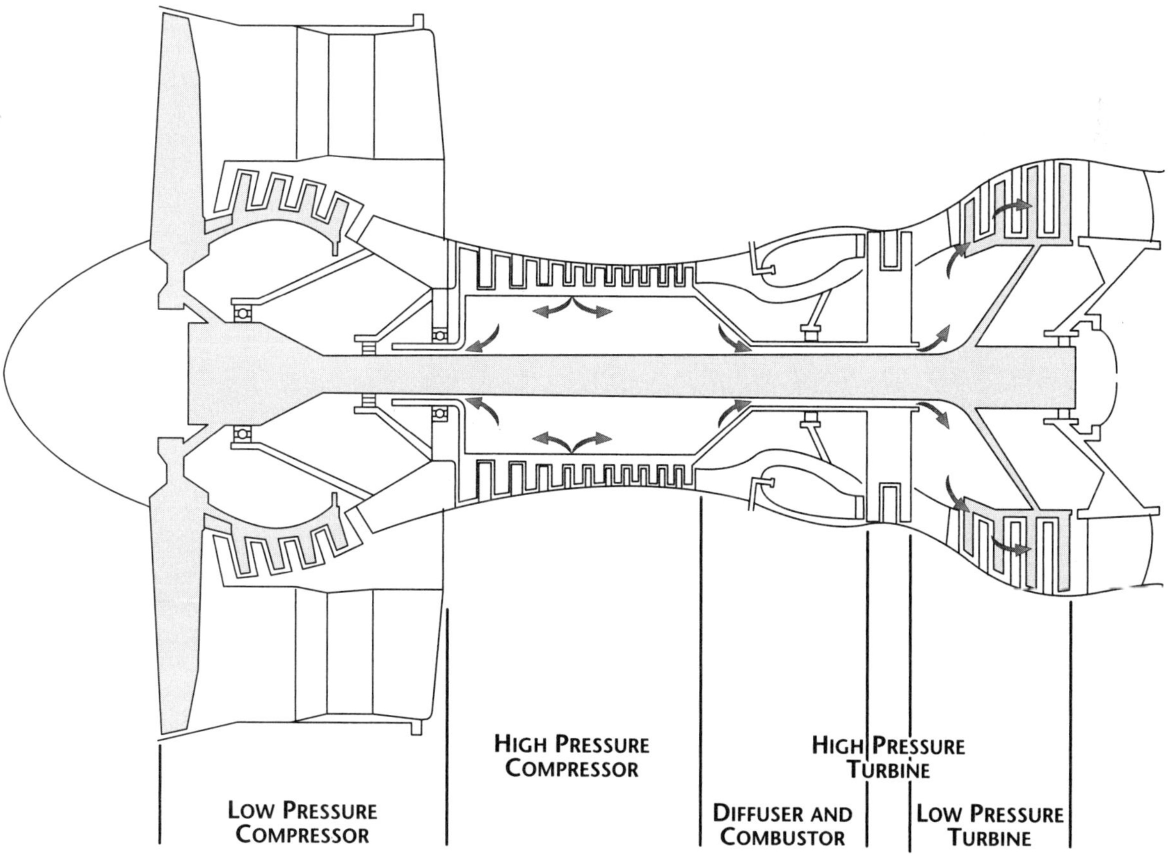

Figure 7-4-21. HPC secondary airflow control system

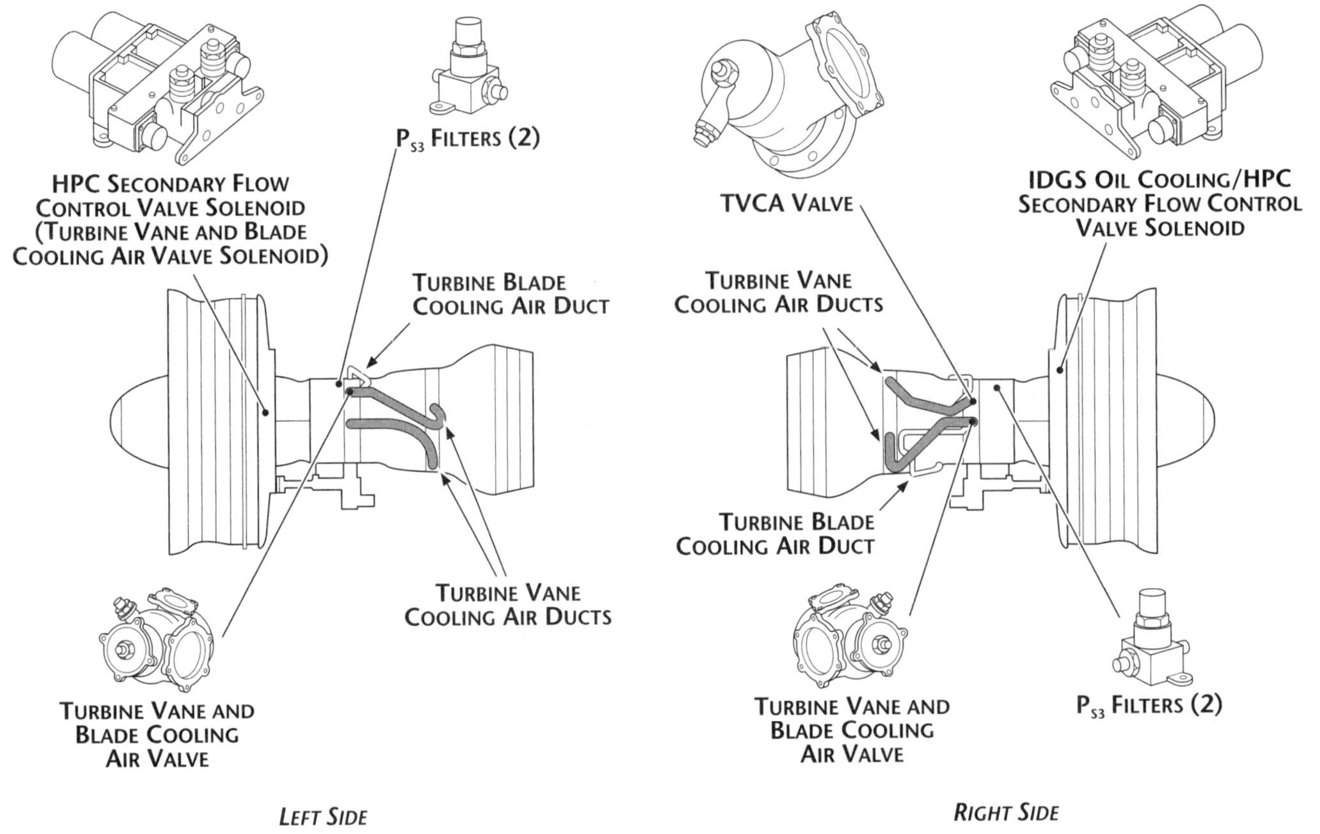

Figure 7-4-22. A turbine vane blade cooling air system

Figure 7-4-23. TVBCA control valve and cooling air ducts direct air to control the turbine blade clearances.

surge. It also aids in the engine starting process. During engine start, the vanes are normally in the open position until 15% of N_2, at which time they are closed. At engine speeds above 40% of N_2, the vanes start to modulate open as N_1 and N_2 increase in speed. The vanes should be full open at high power settings. By redirecting the airflow to enter the rotating compressor blades, the optimum angle can be used as the air flows into the compressor blades.

The variable stator vane bell crank, hydraulic (fuel) actuator unit and unison rings position the variable inlet guide vanes plus the fifth, sixth and seventh-stage vanes in their correct position. The FADEC unit commands the actuator's torque motor, to put the vanes in their correct position. The HPC secondary flow control system allows ninth-stage air to flow into the high-pressure compressor drum for cooling, shown in Figure 7-4-21. Then it flows on through the space between the rotating shafts into the interior low-pressure turbine areas for cooling and thermal stability.

Turbine vane and blade cooling air. Cooling of the HPT blades and vanes is handled by a system of ducts and valves that allow compressor bleed air to pass through interior areas of the engine for cooling. Even though the air is heated by compression, it is still cool compared to temperatures in the combustion and turbine section. By using this bleed air to cool some hot section components, the internal operating temperatures of the engine can be higher, increasing engine efficiency.

These blades typically operate in temperatures of more than 2,000°F. Improved internal cooling schemes minimize the amount of air diverted from the compressor to cool the blades. The more air diverted from the compressor, the lower the engine's efficiency will be. So if the cooling can be accomplished with as small an amount of bleed air as possible, engine efficiency increases.

The turbine blade and vane cooling air system (TVBCA), shown in Figure 7-4-22 and 7-4-23, is used to send twelve-stage compressor bleed air to the HPC second-stage turbine components for cooling under all engine operating conditions. Valves that control a portion of the cooling air can be closed to enhance cruise performance. This performance enhancement can be done at cruise power settings because the engine is at a lower power setting, high altitude and lower temperatures.

The TVBCA system has three valves (phase three engines) that are spring-loaded open and closed by P_{S3} air pressure. The P_{S3} air (muscle pressure) is controlled through the FADEC unit by 28-volt DC solenoids. The valves are closed

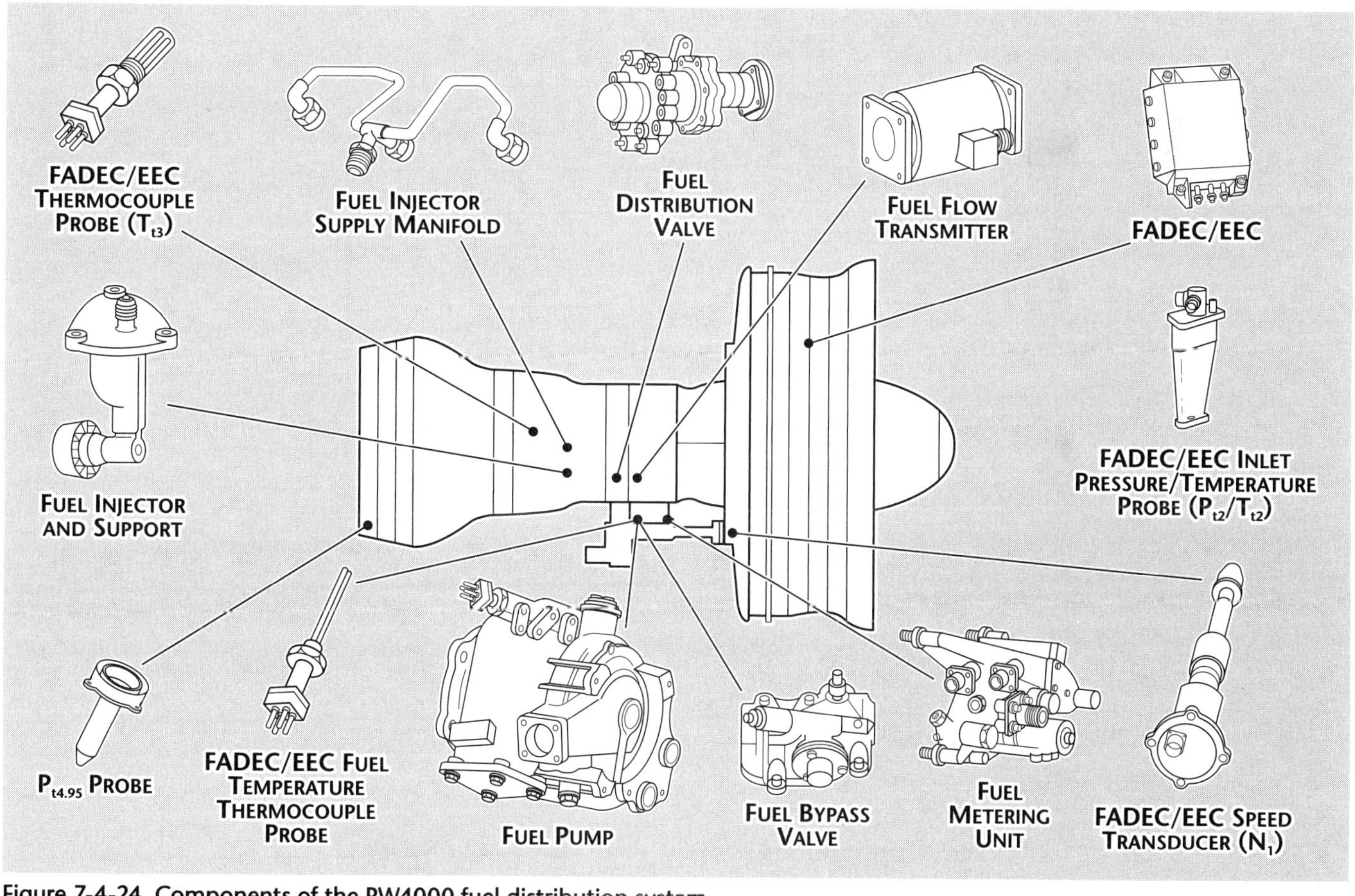

Figure 7-4-24. Components of the PW4000 fuel distribution system

by pneumatic pressure during cruise power settings and altitudes. These valves are failsafe to the open position or maximum cooling. P_{S3} filters clean the air used to operate these valves.

Fuel System

The fuel distribution system supplies ice-free filtered fuel at the pressure and flow rates that are necessary to meet all engine operating requirements. The components of the fuel distribution system are shown in Figure 7-4-24. Fuel flows from the aircraft fuel tank to the fuel pump boost stage inlet, as shown in Figure 7-4-25. The boost pump stage discharge fuel flows to the fuel/oil cooler. It flows through the fuel/oil cooler, then is returned to the fuel pump for filtering and sent on to the main stage of the fuel pump.

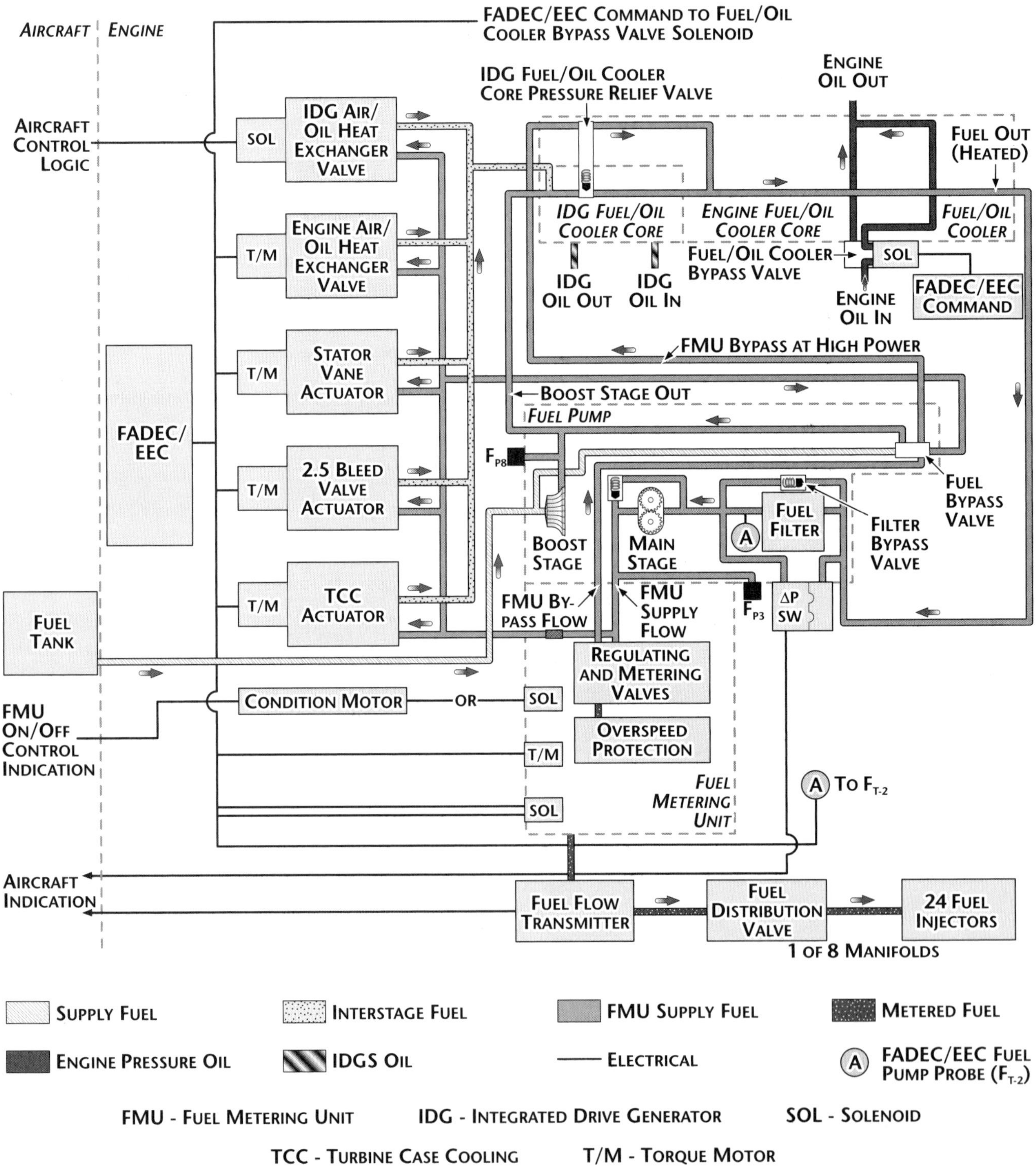

Figure 7-4-25. Fuel system schematic for PW4000 engines

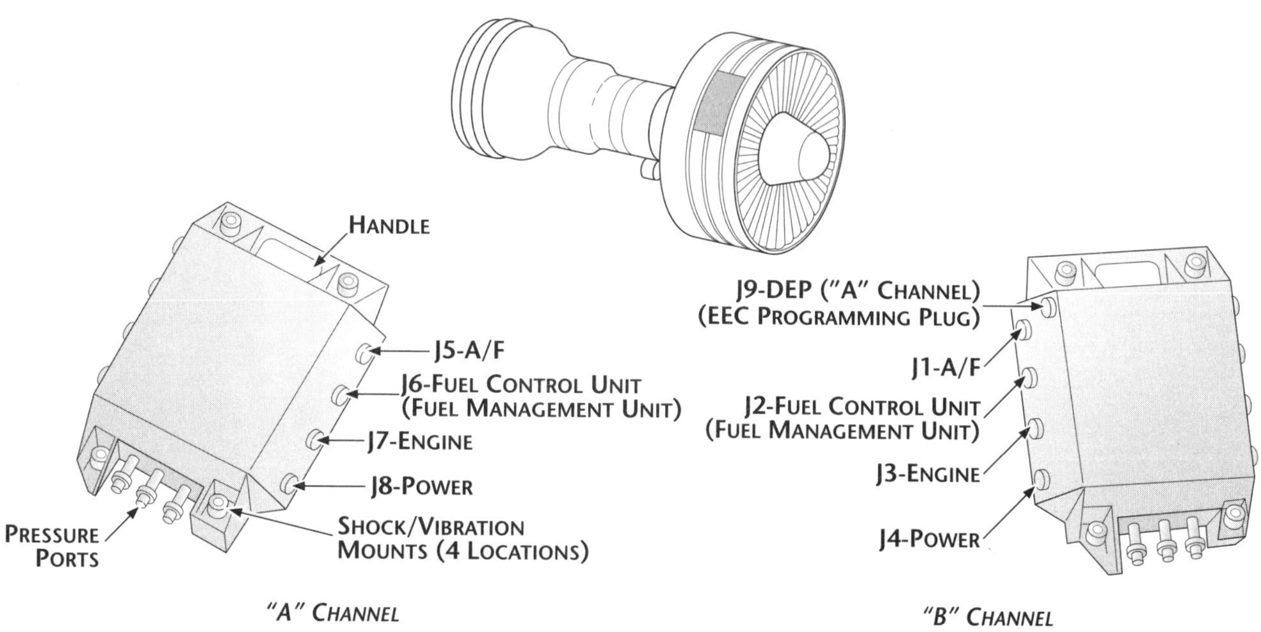

Figure 7-4-26. FADEC control channels A and B create a redundant set of controls for safety.

The fuel flows from the main stage pump to the fuel metering unit. At the fuel metering unit some of the fuel becomes servo fuel (P_f) and flows to the interface components. such as units that actuate the VSV, TCC actuators and other systems. This servo fuel pressure is used as actuation pressure for engine systems.

Engine-metered fuel flows through the fuel flow transmitter and on to the fuel distribution valve. Some fuel bypasses back to the fuel pump inter-stage flow. After passing through the distribution valve, the fuel flows through the fuel manifolds and on to the fuel injectors. This is where it is injected into the combustion chamber and is converted to heat energy. The FADEC unit receives aircraft and engine information that it uses to schedule fuel flow through an electronic interface with the fuel metering unit. The fuel metering unit has a torque motor that is controlled by the FADEC unite to schedule the correct amount of fuel that flows to the engines combustion section through the fuel nozzles.

FADEC Control System

The FADEC is the primary interface between the engine and the aircraft. It increases the efficiency of the engine by keeping more precise control of the engine's functions. It also provides accurate control of engine functions such as compressor bleeds, variable stator vanes, cooling air flows, IDG oil cooling and fuel heating which increases the engine's overall efficiency.

The FADEC unit also enhances several operational functions such as starting, idle, acceleration, deceleration, compressor stability and thrust level control. The FADEC unit protects the engine by limiting engine speeds, thrust, over-boost and combustion pressure.

By sensing the engine speeds and pressures, the FADEC unit can keep engine parameters within approved limits. Redundancy is built into the control system by using two separate channels in the FADEC, with inputs and outputs for each channel. The channels are labeled channel A (blue) and channel B (green) and include maintenance monitoring, self-test and fault isolation seen in Figure 7-4-26 and 7-4-27.

The FADEC programming plug is attached to the engine and must remain with the engine even if the FADEC unit is replaced. The information programmed into the plug includes engine thrust rating, engine performance package and the variable stator vane schedule.

Figure 7-4-27. Programming plug installed in the FADEC unit

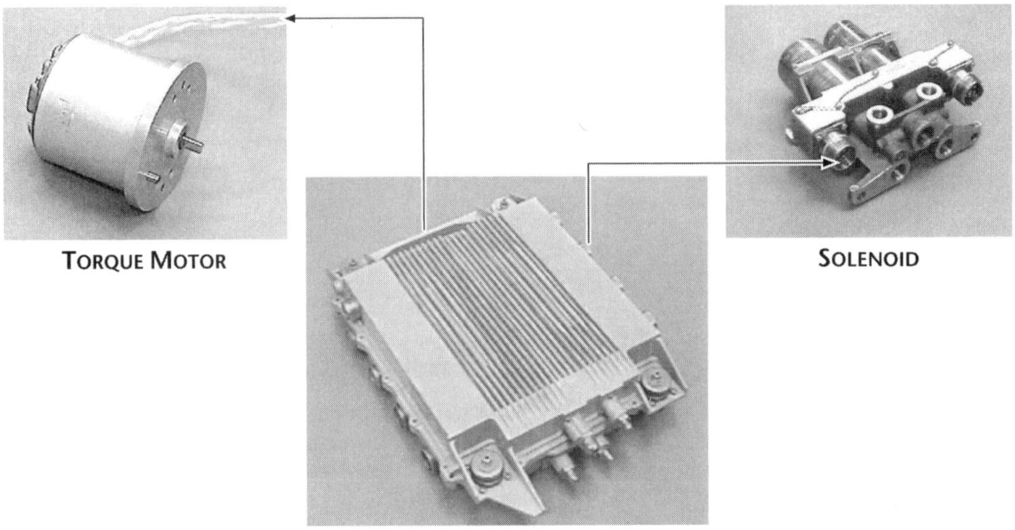

Figure 7-4-28. Output components for the FADEC unit, torque motors and solenoids

The way the FADEC uses physical movement to command engine components to a different setting is through torque motors and solenoids as shown in Figure 7-4-28. Some of the engine systems controlled by a torque motor require a modulation rotational motion. The solenoid-controlled components are either turned on or off by controlling the flow of muscle pressure to the unit being controlled.

Oil Pressure Subsystem

The expansion space in the oil tank is pressurized to approximately 6 p.s.i. to assure a positive flow of oil to the oil pump. Excess pressure is vented to the main gearbox (MGB) through a check valve. The oil flows from the tank down to the pressure stage in the lubrication and scavenge oil pump shown in Figure 7-4-29.

Figure 7-4-29. Oil system pressure and scavenge pump

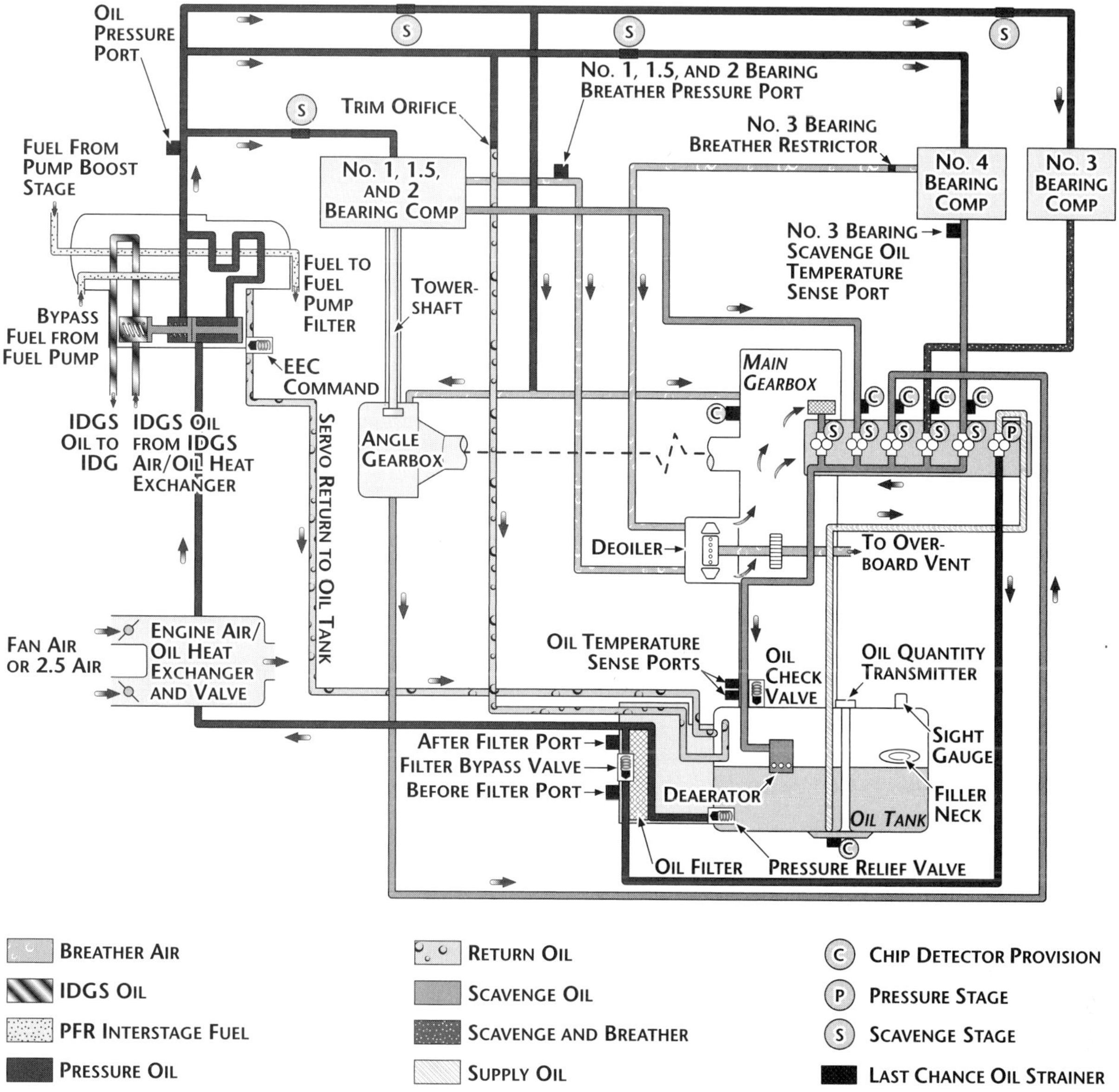

Figure 7-4-30. Oil system for the PW4000 engine

The pressure oil pump pressurizes the oil and sends it to the main oil filter. If the oil pressure before the filter is greater than approximately 540 p.s.i. some of the oil goes through a pressure relief valve back to the oil tank. This would be an abnormal situation as normally the oil pressure will not reach this pressure. This is a relief valve not a pressure-regulating valve. This system's pressure is based mainly on the pump speed and overall restriction to flow. An oil system schematic is shown in Figure 7-4-30.

If the filter is clogged, a filter bypass valve opens to permit the oil to go around (bypass) the filter. This will assure that the engine will receive oil even if it is unfiltered. The filter housing has ports to sense the oil pressure before and after the filter. They are used to measure the pressure differential across the filter to detect clogging. A filter bypass is normally sent as an alert for the flight crew through the EICAS system. Some engines use an indicator on the filter which pops out, indicating a filter by-pass. This pop-out warning does not send any warning to the flight crew but can be noticed by maintenance crews. An indicator on the filter will pop out as a visual warning for filter bypass.

The pressurized oil flows from the filter housing to the engine air/oil heat exchanger. The air/oil heat exchanger has an internal bypass valve that opens if the oil pressure difference is greater than approximately 60 p.s.i.d across the heat exchanger. This permits the oil to bypass the air/oil heat exchanger if the oil is cold (thick), or if the heat exchanger core is clogged.

The FADEC controls the flow of cooling air through the air/oil heat exchanger valves. It increases the flow of cooling air if the fuel

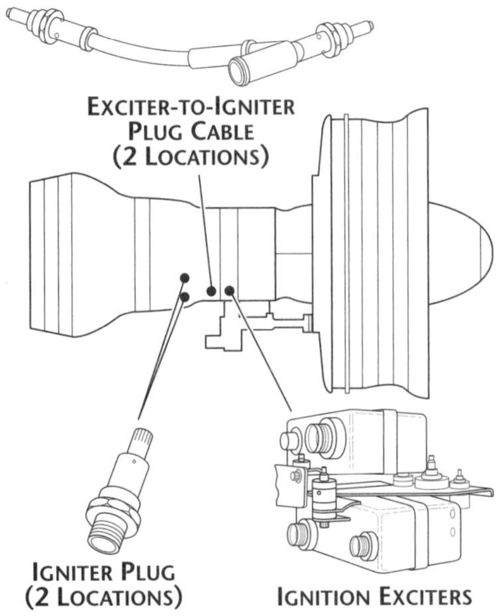

Figure 7-4-31. A dual ignition system

temperature is greater than a specified value. This decreases the oil temperature; thus the oil gives less heat to the fuel in the fuel/oil heat exchanger.

The oil goes from the engine air/oil heat exchanger to the fuel/oil cooler bypass valve. This valve causes the oil to bypass the fuel/oil cooler under FADEC control in case the fuel temperature is greater than a specified value. The function of the fuel/oil cooler is to heat the fuel and cool the oil. Some of the oil from the fuel/oil cooler goes through a sized oil pressure trim orifice. It bypasses some of the oil back to the oil tank to control rate of flow in the system.

Oil from the fuel/oil cooler which is not bypassed through the trim orifice flows through the last chance oil strainers. These strainers are mounted externally on the engine and remove particles from the oil if the oil filter is bypassed. This protects the bearing oil nozzles from clogging.

After the pressurized oil goes through the last chance filters, it flows to the No. 1, 1.5 and 2 bearing compartment (intermediate case), No. 3 bearing compartment (diffuser case) and No. 4 bearing compartment (exhaust case) through the angle gearbox (AGB) to the MGB. The nozzles in the main bearing compartments and in the gearboxes send the oil, at correct flow rates,

Figure 7-4-32. Capcitor discharge ignition exciters mounted on the engine

to the different bearings, seals and accessory drive splines.

Oil scavenge subsystem. After the oil has performed its function (lubrication, cleaning and cooling) in the bearing compartments and gearboxes, the scavenge subsystem returns that oil to the tank.

The lubrication and scavenge oil pump, shown in Figure 7-4-29 has five scavenge pump stages. They pull the scavenge oil from the bearing compartments and gearboxes. The five scavenge pump stages send the scavenge oil to the de-aerator in the oil tank. The oil tank de-aerator separates the air from the scavenge oil and sends the air into the oil tank cavity to be vented to the MGB through the oil check valve. This allows the hot, de-aerated scavenge oil to return to the oil tank.

Oil breather subsystem. The breather subsystem removes air from the bearing compartments, separates the breather air from the oil and vents the air overboard. The breather air from the No. 4 bearing compartment (in the exhaust case) mixes with the scavenge oil from that bearing compartment. This mixture flows to the scavenge pump and then it is pumped to the oil tank de-aerator.

The air in this mixture goes from the de-aerator to the oil tank cavity, where it is pressurized to about 6 p.s.i. through the oil check valve, then on to the MGB. Next it goes through the de-oiler and the air is vented overboard. The breather air from the other two bearing compartments flows to the gearbox de-oiler. The de-oiler spins and uses centrifugal force to cause a separation of the oil from the air. The oil goes into the MGB and mixes with the MGB scavenge oil, which is pumped to the oil tank de-aerator. The air from the de-oiler goes through ducts and is sent overboard to ambient air through the nacelle cowl.

Ignition System

The ignition system, seen in Figure 7-4-31, supplies high energy through the igniters to ignite the fuel/air mixture during starting and low-intensity ignition situations. The components of the system are fairly simple: ignition exciters, igniter cables, igniter plugs and ignition switches.

There are two separate ignition systems. Normally they are labeled system 1 or 2, with both systems used under normal starting. Selecting one or both ignition systems supplies electrical power through the engine fuel switches to the engine for ignition. Two capacitor discharge-type ignition exciters mounted on the engine as shown in Figure 7-4-32, provide the high voltage for igniter operation.

Figure 7-4-33. Engine igniters installed on the engine

The igniters, shown in Figure 7-4-33, protrude into the combustion section and provide the spark needed for lighting the fuel/air mixture during engine starting. The exciter box and cables are fan-air cooled using sheet metal cooling shields to assure proper cooling. This arrangement is shown in Figure 7-4-34.

Engine Indication System

The engine indicating and crew alerting system (EICAS) is used to sense, transmit and display engine operating parameters, seen in Figure 7-4-35. The FADEC receives input from selected

Figure 7-4-34. Fan air cooling system for the exciters

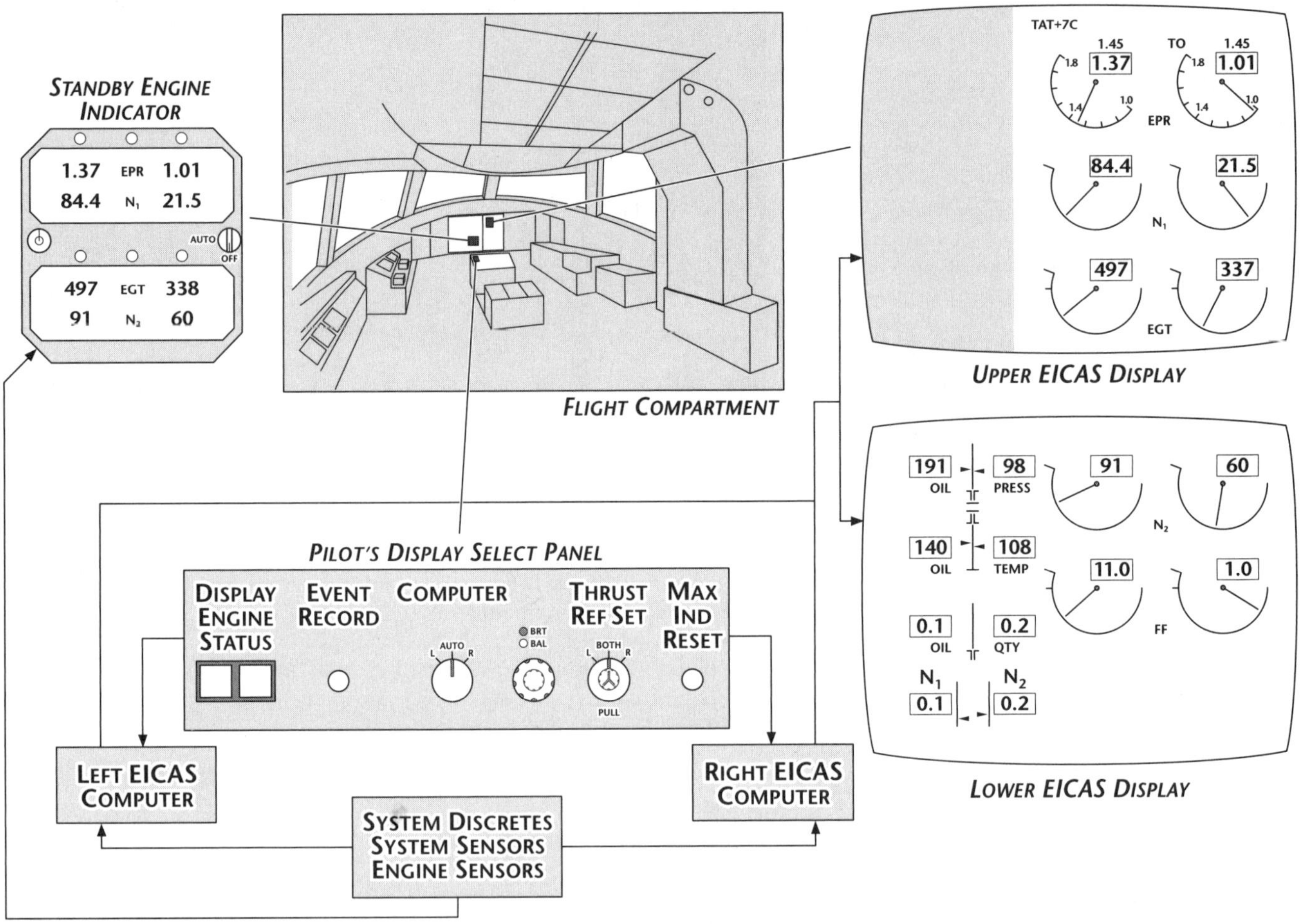

Figure 7-4-35. EICAS engine display and system

Figure 7-4-36. View of the basic nacelle configuration showing the engine cowls
Photo courtesy of Pratt & Whitney

aircraft and engine components and sensors then outputs the data to the aircraft system (central maintenance computer) for display on the flight deck and maintenance control panel.

Nacelle Configuration

The basic nacelle configuration, shown in Figure 7-4-36, consists of the inlet cowl, fan cowl, reverser cowl, core cowl, exhaust nozzle and exhaust plug. The inlet cowl is attached to the A flange of the engine and is anti-iced by passing warm bleed air through the leading edge. Its interior is used to reduce the noise level from the fan. This is accomplished by using noise absorbing materials on the inter liner.

The fan cowls are mounted to the aircraft's strut and allow access to the fan case. The reverser cowl has the reverser mechanism that includes the blocker doors and cascade vanes and it is generally opened by a hydraulic actuator. The core cowl allows access to the core of the engine. The core or primary nozzle mounts to the T flange, which is one of the last flanges on the engine. The nozzle performs

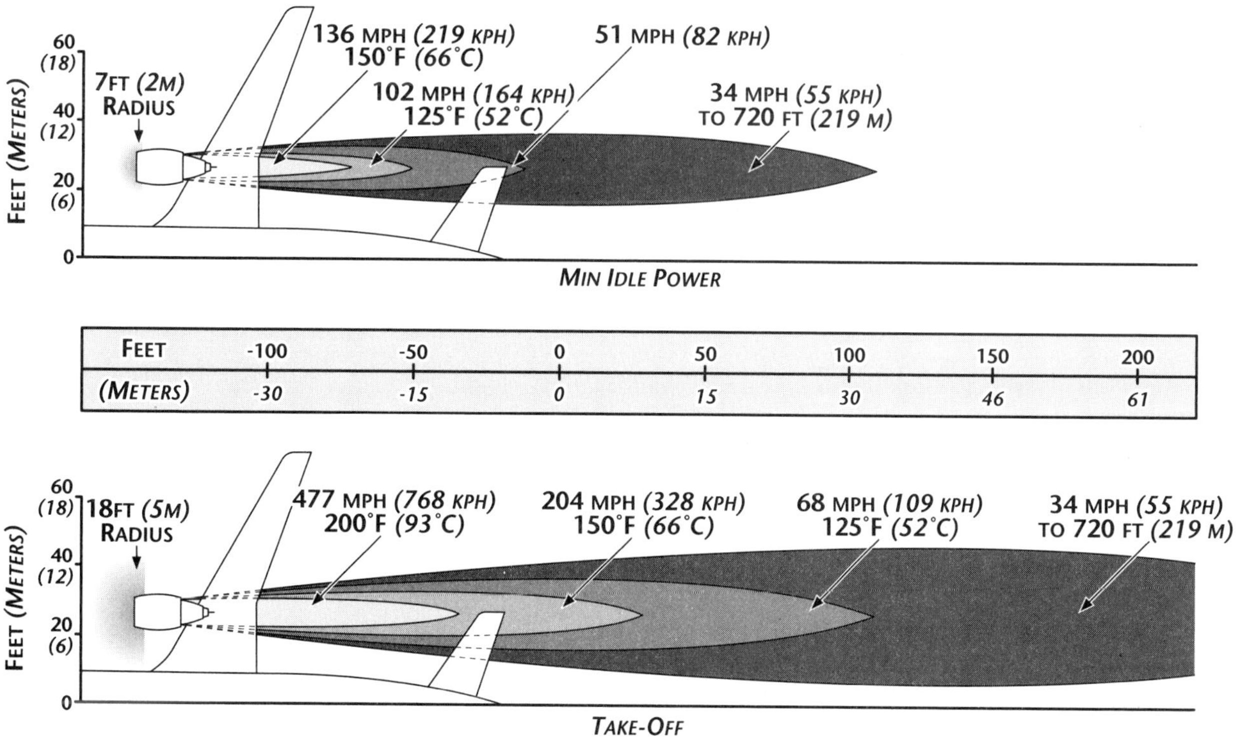

Figure 7-4-37. Intake and exhaust hazards

the same function as it had in other engines, of increasing the primary air flow exhaust velocity. The exhaust plug forms a divergent duct and reduces turbulence inside the nozzle. It also protects the No. 4 bearing from the hot gases in the exhaust.

Engine Ground Operations

After performing maintenance or an overhaul, it is necessary to test run the engine. Typical maintenance operations such as replacing or repairing engine components, assuring performance and troubleshooting require a test run.

During engine testing, safety precautions should be observed. Figure 7-4-37 shows the intake (suction) danger areas to avoid during operation. The exhaust dangers of high temperature/pressure/velocity gases must be taken into account before operations can be accomplished.

Ambient temperature and pressure should be noted during an engine test. During ground testing it is important that the operator be aware of wind direction and velocity.

In Figure 7-4-38, the wind direction velocity and direction limits are listed. High starting and operational exhaust temperatures will be encountered if these wind limits are not taken into account. After providing adequate starter duct air pressure, fire detection and observing ground personnel hazard areas, the following is a generalized operational procedure. Always refer to the manufacturer's current information for operating any turbine engine.

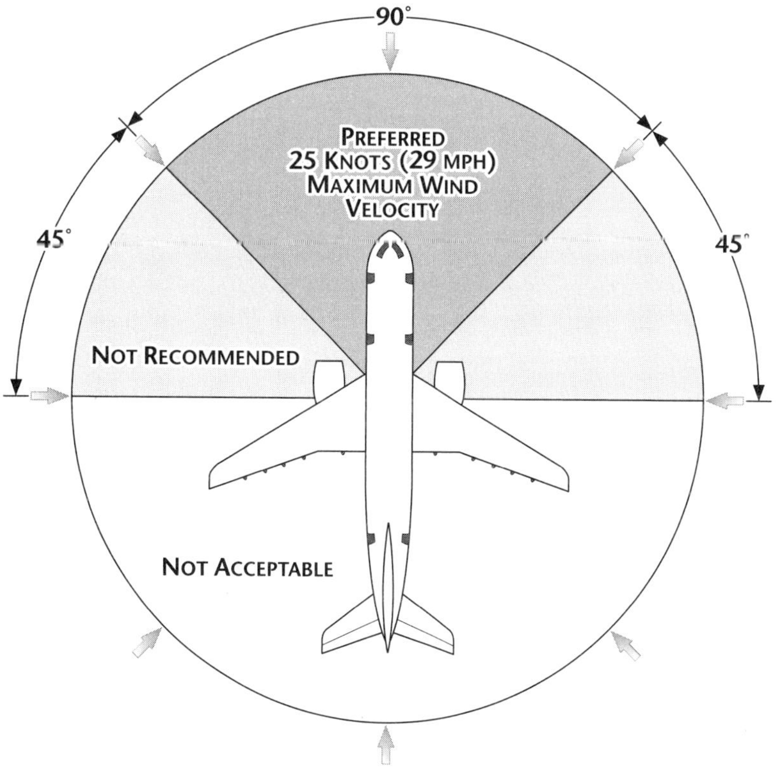

Figure 7-4-38. Wind direction and velocity limits

Figure 7-4-39. Engine start selector panel

Typical starting procedure. Always refer to the approved checklist for the specific model engine and aircraft being operated.

- Push in and rotate left or right engine start selector, shown in Figure 7-4-39, to the GND position. The selector will be magnetically held in position and the ignition system will be armed.
- As the bleed air regulating valve closes, an amber L (or R) ENGINE START VALVE light cycles off-on-off as the starter shutoff valve opens when the engine N_2 begins to rotate. It is important for the APU to maintain duct pressure, since this is where the starting energy for N_2 rotation is drawn.
- The engine fuel control switch (left or right) should be selected to the RUN position at 15% N_2. This is the minimum speed at which fuel can be turned on to the engine. Some engine manufacturers recommend waiting until maximum motoring speed is reached, then selecting run.
- When moving the fuel control switch to the run position, the ignition system energizes and the spar valve and condition motor actuates to turn the fuel on.

The operator must observe the following events:

- EGT and rate of increase
- N_2 speed
- Starting fuel flow
- N_1 rotation
- Oil pressure

The start selector switch releases to AUTO at 50% N_2 and the ENGINE START VALVE light cycles off-on-off at 50% N_2. A satisfactory start will include oil pressure indication required at fuel pressurization (fuel turned on). Light-off should take no more than twenty seconds after the fuel is turned ON. The engine should continue to accelerate to idle r.p.m. and the EGT must not exceed the start limit of 535°C (hot start).

Unsatisfactory starting occurrences include:

- Immediate light-off when the fuel is commanded ON could be a sign of excess fuel being in the engine before the starting sequence was begun.
- If there is no oil pressure indication when the fuel should be turned on, abort the start.
- Make sure of N_2 rotation. N_1 should start to rotate generally before the fuel is turned on. The point of N_1 rotation in the starting sequence can vary somewhat.
- When the engine lights-off but fails to reach idle r.p.m., a hung start has occurred. Abort the start.
- If light-off has not happened within the twenty-second time limit after turning the fuel on, abort the start.
- An impending hot start generally deals with excess fuel flow just as the fuel is switched on.
- If the engine acceleration is too slow to idle r.p.m., the start fuel schedule for start could be incorrectly set.

Typical shutdown procedure. The normal shutdown procedure is to allow the engine to operate at idle r.p.m. for five minutes. Then the fuel control switch can be switched off. This time delay will assist the engine in lowering its temperatures and temperature gradients within the engine. In the case of an emergency, retard thrust lever to idle and turn the engine fuel control switch off.

If a hot start has occurred, move the engine fuel control switch to the off position and motor the engine with the starter until the EGT goes below 180°C. If EGT exceeds start temperature limit of 535°C, the duration of the over-temperature (in seconds and peak temperature) must be recorded in the engine log for maintenance. If the starter must be re-engaged, the N_2 must be below 20% before re-engaging the starter.

Section 5

Rolls-Royce Trent Series Engine

The RB211 was initially developed to power a variety of commercial airliners; it can be found on the Lockheed L-1011, the Boeing 747, 757 and 767. The newer version of the RB211 series of engines is the Trent engine series. It is one of the engines certified for use on the Boeing 777. General specifications are as follows:

- Length 172 in.
- Fan tip diameter 97.4 in.
- Weight 13,100 lbs.
- Combustor type Annular
- Takeoff thrust sea level 90,000 lbs.
- Total airflow 2,597 lbs/sec
- Bypass ratio 4.9 to 1
- Overall pressure ratio 37.42:1

The basic construction and nomenclature of the engine is explained beginning with the front of the engine. An example of engine layout is shown in Figure 7-5-1. The engine has several basic modules. The Trent is an example of the traditional Rolls-Royce three-spool axial flow front fan high bypass turbofan, seen in Figure 7-5-2.

Compressor Section

Fan and low-pressure compressor. The first stage consists of the front fan acting as the low-pressure compressor. The fan has a composite nose cone. Twenty-six titanium alloy hollow wide-chord blades start the airflow into the engine. A steel shaft coupled to the low-pressure turbine drives the fan. Just behind the fan is an outlet guide vane ring used for straightening the airflow.

The fan blades are designed for easy replacement in the event of FOD damage. The blades can be individually changed without the use of special tooling: only the nose cone and a fan blade retaining ring must be removed. The fan blades can then be slid forward out of the fan assembly. A replacement blade (of the correct type) is then installed.

The low-pressure fan case incorporates a blade containment ring in case of fan blade failure.

Intermediate-pressure compressor. The low-pressure compressor feeds into an eight-stage intermediate-pressure (IP) compressor. A drum of welded titanium discs creates the rotor assembly. The compressor uses titanium compressor blades. A titanium shaft connected to the intermediate turbine drives this assembly. The intermediate-pressure compressor also utilizes single stage titanium variable inlet guide vanes.

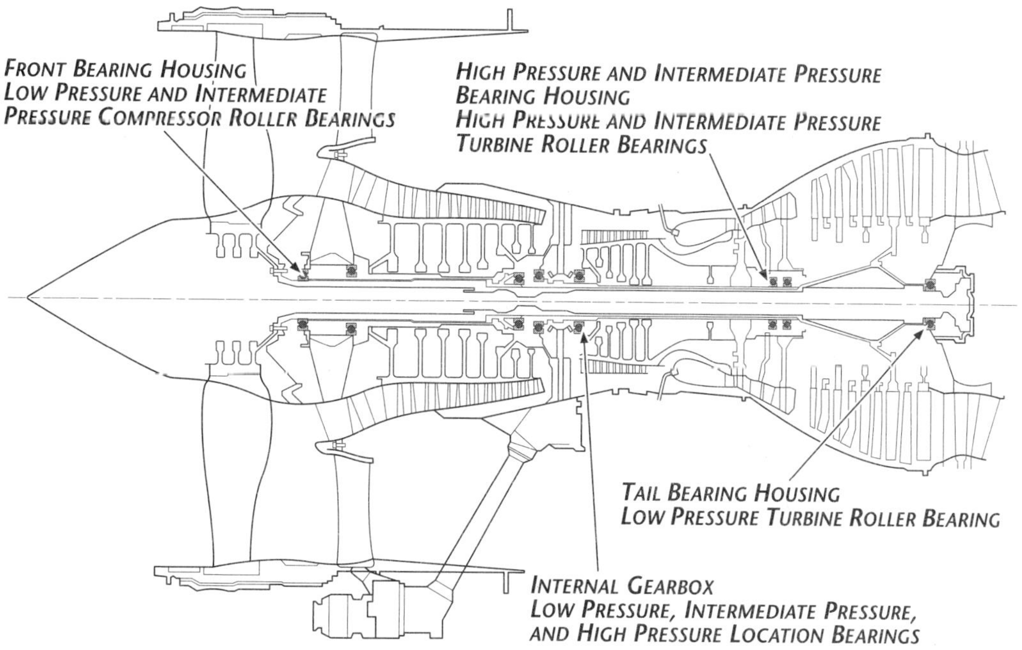

Figure 7-5-1. Rolls-Royce Trent series engine layout

High-pressure compressor. The high-pressure compressor is the final section of the complete compressor. The HP compressor rotor is a six-stage welded assembly. On these discs are mounted a combination of titanium and nickel alloy compressor blades.

Combustion Section

The Trent combustion chamber is of the fully annular type. It features an outer casing and a nickel alloy combustor. It also has an inner combustion case which serves to contain high-pressure compressor delivery air. Some of the high-pressure compressor delivery air is fed into the liner at various points along its length. This type of delivery aids in efficient and stable combustion and provides for proper cooling at the liner outlet.

Fuel is injected through the twenty-four fuel spray nozzles containing annular atomizers. High-energy igniter plugs in the combustion chambers provide ignition. The ignition unit has a high-and a low-energy position. The high-energy position is used for ground and air starting, whereas the low-energy output is used when automatic and continuous operation modes have been selected.

Turbine Section

High-pressure turbine. The high-pressure turbine is the first stage in the turbine section. It drives the high-pressure compressor. It is mounted on bearings and blade cooling is by both convection and film methods. The film air is supplied both through holes in the disc and through the blade shank. The blades use a conventional fir-tree mounting.

Intermediate-pressure turbine. The second turbine stage drives the intermediate-=pressure compressor. Like the high-pressure turbine, it is a single stage. Fir-tree blade mounting is again used.

Low-pressure turbine. The low-pressure turbine is the third and final turbine section. It drives the fan (acting also as the low-pressure compressor). This stage again has nickel alloy blades, but the lower temperatures at this point permit the use of steel turbine discs. The LP casing is cooled by fan stream air to control expansion and maintain consistent rotor blade tip clearances (ACC).

Accessory Section

Engine accessories are driven by a radial drive from the HP shaft to a gearbox on the fan casing. This drive assembly is mounted in the intermediate case just ahead of the high-pressure compressor. An integrated drive generator, hydraulic pumps and engine-related systems are powered from the gearbox.

Thrust Reverser Section

For most engine installations, Rolls-Royce provides a complete powerplant system. It includes the core engine, thrust reverser, cowling, noise suppression, fan cowling and exhaust duct. The reverser system is a cold-stream system with no reversing of the core engine gases. The hydraulically-actuated reverser cowl moves aft, exposing the reverser cascades. At the same time, blocker

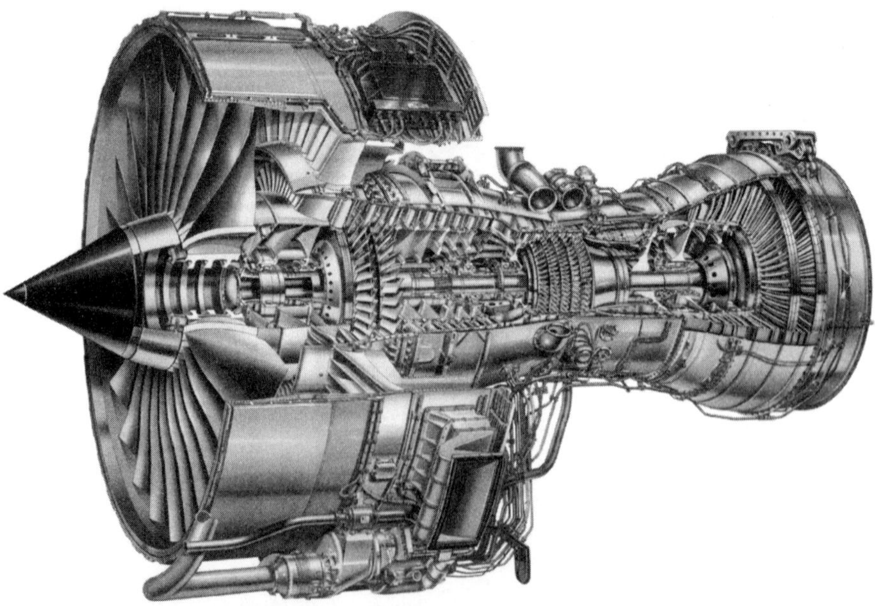

Figure 7-5-2. A three spool Rolls-Royce Trent 700 engine *Image courtesy of Rolls-Royce*

doors move into place, diverting the fan air through the cascades. The EICAS system also gives a visual indication by displaying the letters REV in yellow while the cowls are translating aft. The letters change to green when fully deployed. The oil and fuel delivery system is somewhat similar to other large fan engines.

These engines are typical of some of the more common turbofan engines in service. Although there are differences, most large turbofan engines have similar types of systems and operate in a similar manner.

Chapter 8

TURBOPROP engines

The turboprop is one application of the basic gas turbine engine. It uses a gas turbine engine to turn a reduction gear system which in turn drives the propeller.

Since the gas turbine engine must turn at high r.p.m. to develop its power, a means of reducing the r.p.m. must be used. This is done using a reduction gear box that reduces the r.p.m. at the propeller. The propeller can rotate only at slower speeds (1,800 r.p.m. to 2,750 r.p.m. maximum). The length of the propeller is also a consideration. The larger the diameter propeller, the slower it must rotate. This keeps propeller tip speeds below the speed of sound. Despite this limitation, the turboprop still has a major place in aviation. A turboprop allows for the use of shorter runways and is a good choice for shorter flights. Most propeller-driven aircraft are limited to speeds of about 400 m.p.h. Over the years, this type of engine has proven to be a most efficient power source for aircraft operating in a wide variety of speed ranges.

Learning Objectives

- *Turboprop Overview*
- *PW PT6 Series*
- *Compressor Section*
- *Turbine Section*
- *Propeller Control*
- *Honeywell TPE331*
- *Anti-ice System*
- *Negative Torque Sensor*
- *PW100 Family*

Section 1

Turboprop Overview

Turboprop engines provide the best specific fuel consumption (SFC) of any gas-turbine engine. They perform well from sea level to comparatively high altitudes of 20,000 feet and higher. The sections of a turboprop engine are similar to those of any gas turbine, however there are some key differences. The most important difference is found in the design of the turbine section. In a normal gas turbine engine the turbine section extracts only enough energy from the hot gases to drive the compressor and accesso-

Left: Many commuter airlines use turboprop-powered aircraft. *ATR photo*

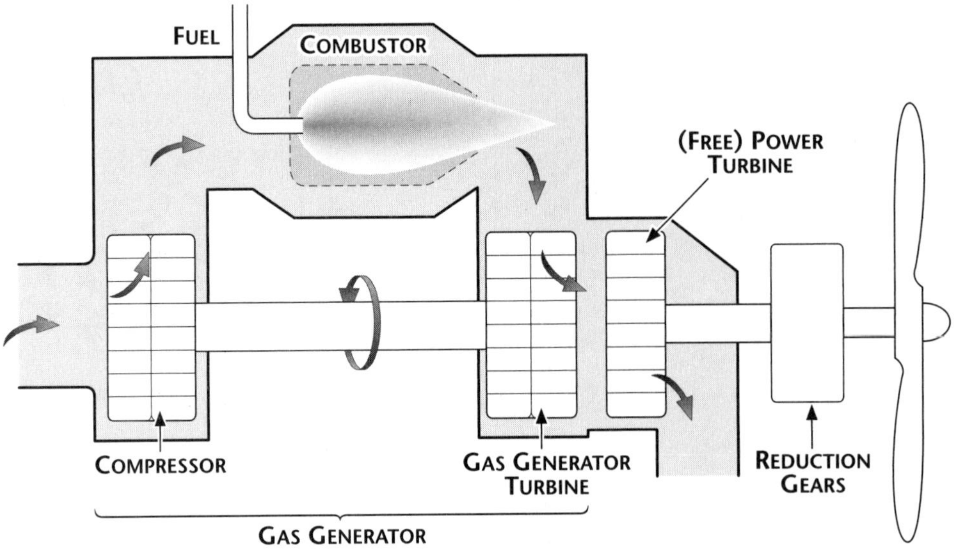

Figure 8-1-1. Free turbine arrangement in a turboprop engine

ries. The turboprop engine has a turbine section which extracts as much as 75% to 85% of the total energy to drive the propeller.

A turboprop engine is rated in shaft horsepower (SHP) delivered to the propeller shaft. For example, a turboprop engine can extract 3,460 SHP for the propeller and produce 726 lbs of thrust. The thrust is developed from exhaust gases passing out of the exhaust nozzle. When the SHP and thrust from the nozzle are combined, this is called equivalent shaft horsepower (ESHP). The total ESHP is given as 3,750 ESHP. To convert lbs of thrust to horsepower, thrust is divided by 2.5.

$$\text{ESHP} = \text{SHP} + \frac{\text{thrust HP}}{2.5}$$

$$\text{ESHP} = 3{,}460 + \frac{726 \text{ lbs. of thrust}}{2.5}$$

$$\text{ESHP} = 3{,}750$$

The high level of energy extraction is due to the design of the blades in the turbine section. The compressor, combustion section and the turbine (which drives the compressor) comprise the gas generator or gas producer. The function of the gas generator is to produce the high-velocity gases used to drive the power turbine, which in turn drives the propeller through the reduction gears. The gas generator section's main function is to convert fuel energy into high-speed exhaust gases in order to drive the power turbine. The primary effort of the turboprop engine is directed toward driving the propeller. One method of accomplishing this is to use a free turbine.

Free turbine. A free turbine is not mechanically connected to the gas generator; instead, an additional turbine wheel is placed in the exhaust downstream from the gas generator. This type of turbine wheel is referred to as a power turbine. It is shown schematically in Figure 8-1-1.

Fixed turbine. A fixed turbine is used to convert high-speed rotational energy from the gas generator into usable shaft horsepower; illustrated in Figure 8-1-2. The gas generator in this illustration has an additional turbine wheel. In both types, the additional turbine utilizes the excess hot gas energy (energy in excess of that required to drive the engine's compressor section) to drive the propeller.

In a fixed turbine shaft engine, the turbine shaft and compressor are mechanically connected to

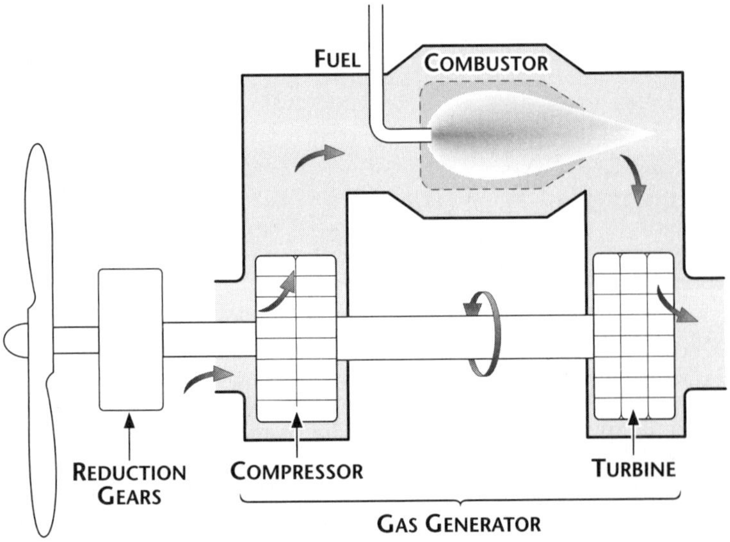

Figure 8-1-2. Fixed turbine arrangement in a turboprop engine

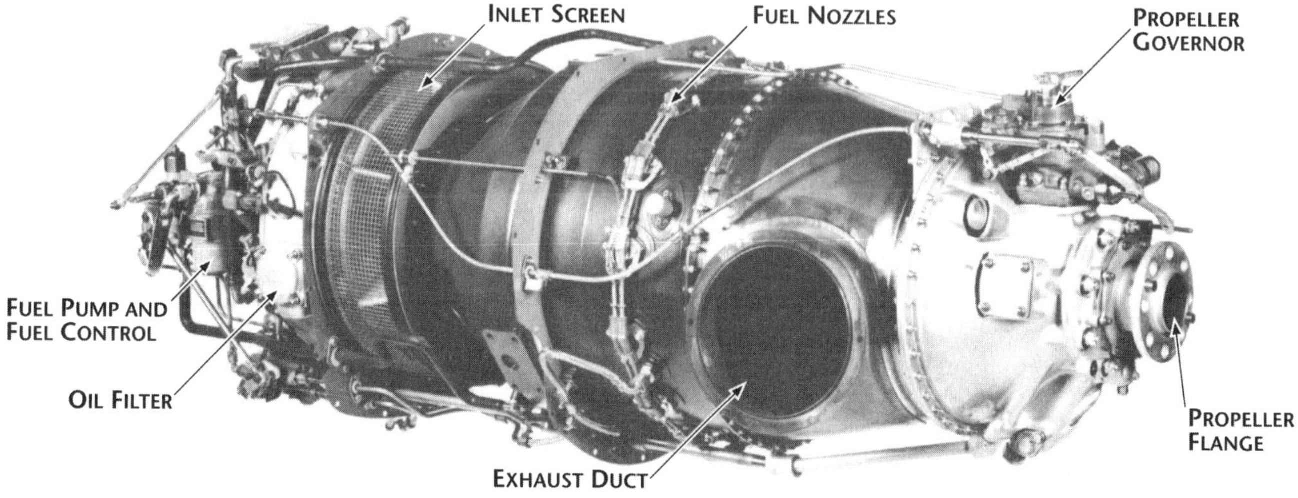

Figure 8-2-1. Pratt & Whitney PT6 engine showing the major components

Photo courtesy of Pratt & Whitney

Figure 8-2-2. Pratt & Whitney PT6 engine cutaway

the propeller reduction gearbox and propeller. In a fixed turbine type of engine, turning the propeller will turn the complete engine. In the free turbine, the added turbine drives the propeller though the reduction gearbox. Turning the propeller only turns the power turbine wheel. This allows the high-speed low-torque rotational energy which is transmitted through the gearbox from the turbine to be converted to the low-speed high-torque power required to drive the propeller.

Because the propeller must be driven by the gas generator part of the engine, a complex propeller control system is necessary to adjust the propeller pitch for the power requirements of the engine. At normal operating conditions, both the propeller speed and engine speed must be coordinated in order to maintain the correct power setting.

Section 2

Pratt & Whitney Canada PT6 Series of Engines

The PT6A is a lightweight, free-turbine engine, designed for use in fixed or rotary-wing aircraft (helicopters). The PT6A engine is also produced in a turboshaft version which can be used as an APU. A photograph of the engine is shown in Figure 8-2-1. The PT6 powerplant cutaway is shown in Figure 8-2-2.

One of the most popular light turboprop engines ever manufactured, the PT6 powers more than fifty aircraft types. These include the Beechcraft King Air series, Beechcraft 99 and 1900 series, Cessna Caravan and Conquest, DeHavilland

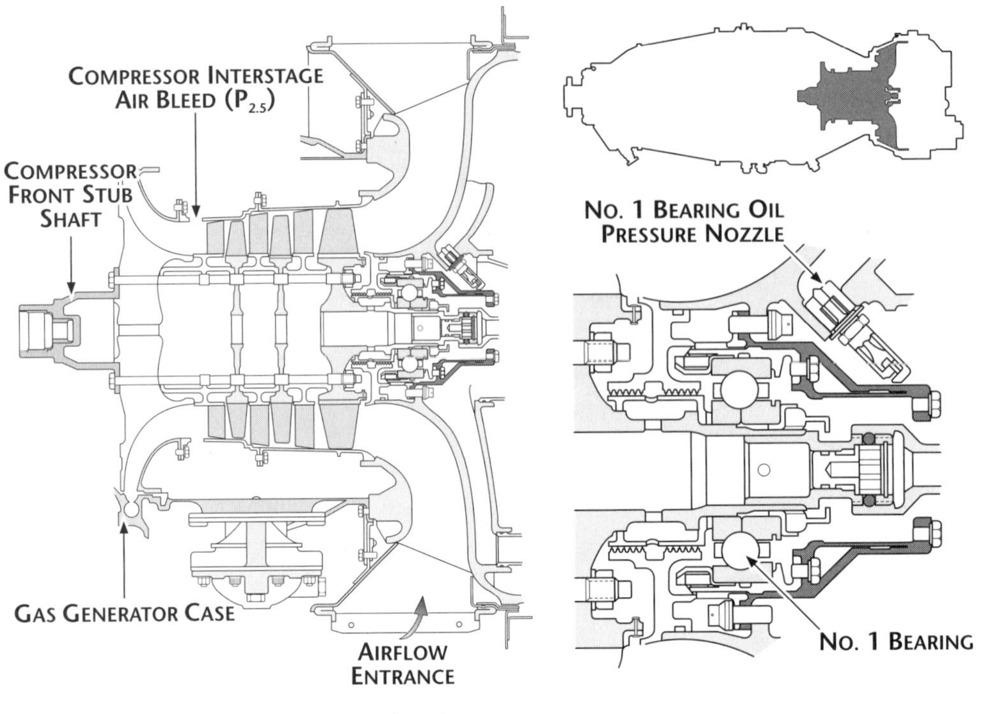

Figure 8-2-3. Compressor rotor and No. 1 bearing area

Twin Otter and Dash 7, Piper Cheyenne, Pilatus PC-9 and PC-12, Shorts 330 and 360 as well as agricultural and other aircraft.

Horsepower for the PT6-series ranges from approximately 400 to 1,970 SHP. The engine utilizes two independent turbine sections: a compressor turbine, driving the compressor in the gas generator section; and a power turbine (two-stage in larger-model engines), driving the output shaft through a reduction gearbox. The compressor and power turbines are located in the approximate center of the engine with their respective shafts extending in opposite directions. This feature provides for simplified installation and inspection procedures.

Figure 8-2-4. PT6 compressor section with axial and centrifugal stages

Inlet Section

As can be seen in Figure 8-2-3, inlet air enters at the rear of the engine through an annular plenum chamber formed by the compressor inlet case. The compressor inlet case is a circular aluminum-alloy casting, the front of which forms a plenum chamber for the passage of compressor inlet air. The rear portion consists of a hollow compartment which forms the integral oil tank. The complete compressor and stator assembly is fitted into the center rear portion of the gas generator case which forms the compressor housing. The assembly is secured in this position by the impeller housing at the front and the compressor inlet at the rear. The intake is screened to preclude the ingestion of foreign objects.

Airflow path through the engine. Air enters at the rear of the engine and turns 90°, entering the axial part of the compressor. After flowing through three stages of compression, the air flows into the centrifugal stage and turns 90° again. The airflow path then travels through diffuser tubes and into the combustion area, turning yet another 90°. The air enters the annular combustion chamber and turns 180°. Combustion takes place and the air is turned 180° by the large and small exit ducts.

The air flows into the first stage of the turbine inlet guide vanes and into the compressor turbine. Enough energy is taken from the airflow to turn the compressor. The air then continues to the power turbine inlet guide vanes and through the power turbine which turns the reduction gears and propeller. The air turns another 90° and flows out of the engine through the exhaust duct. The air path can be traced by using the cutaway diagram in Figure 8-2-2.

Bearing locations. The No. 1 bearing, which supports the rear of the compressor assembly in the inlet case is a ball bearing type. A short hollow steel coupling with ball lock and internal splines at each end extends the compressor drive to the accessory input-gear shaft. The ball lock, incorporated at the front end of the coupling, prevents end thrust on the two accessory input-gear shaft roller bearings.

The No. 1 bearing, bearing support and air seal are contained within the compressor inlet-case center-bore. The bearing support is secured to the inlet-case center-bore flange by four bolts. A special nut and shroud washer retains the No. 1 bearing outer race in its support housing.

A puller groove is provided on the rear face of the No. 1 bearing split inner race to facilitate its removal. The bearing and seal arrangement is shown in Figure 8-2-3. The airflow (gas path) is then directed forward to the compressor.

The No. 2 roller bearing with two air seals is positioned in the center bore of the gas generator case and supports the front of the compressor and the attached turbine. The bearing has a flanged outer race secured in the support housing by four bolts.

The front and rear air-seal stators with their spiral-wound gaskets are each secured in the center bore of the case by eight bolts. An oil nozzle with two jets, one in the front and the other in the rear of the bearing, provides lubrication.

Compressor Section

The compressor consists of three axial stages, combined with a single centrifugal stage, assembled as an integral unit (combination compressor). The rotating compressor blades add energy to the air passing through them by increasing its velocity and pressure. A row of stator vanes located between each stage of compressor rotor blades diffuses the air, converting velocity into pressure and directing it at the proper angle to the next stage of compression. The compressor rotor and stator assembly is shown in Figure 8-2-4.

First-stage rotor blades are made of titanium to improve impact resistance, while the second and third stages are made of stainless steel. The rotor blades are dovetailed into their respective disks with a clearance between the blade and disk to allow for heat expansion. This also causes a clicking sound during compressor run down. Axial movement of the rotor disks is limited by the inter-stage spacers placed between the disks.

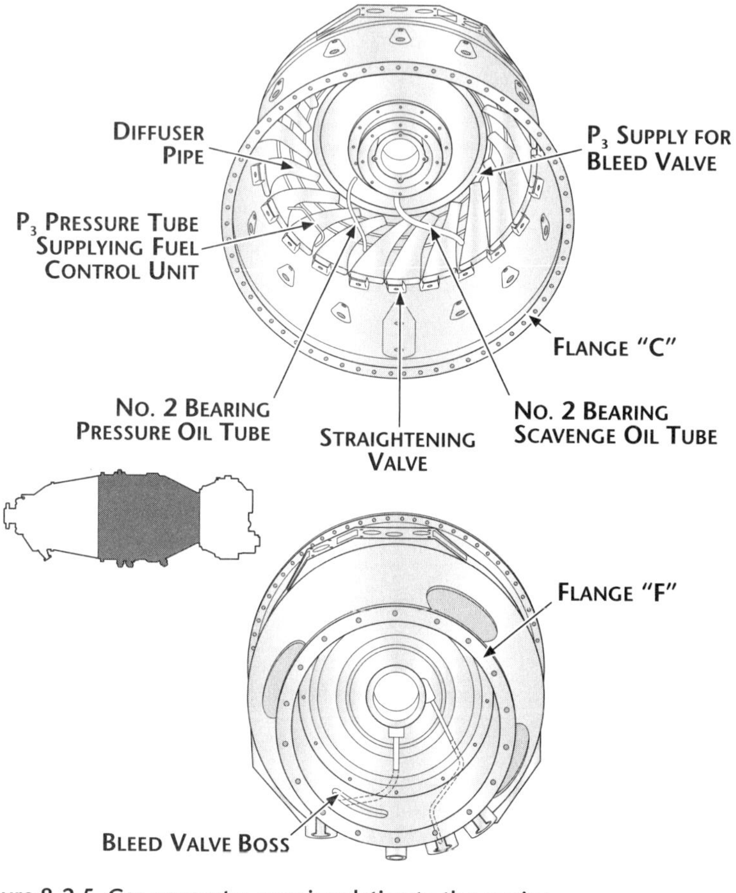

Figure 8-2-5. Gas generator case in relation to the engine

The airfoil cross section of the first-stage blades differs from those of the second and third stages, the latter two being identical. The length of the blades differs in each stage, decreasing from the first to the third stage. The first- and second-stage stator assemblies each contain forty-four vanes and the third stage contains forty vanes. Each set of stator vanes is held in place by a circular ring with the vane outer ends protruding through and brazed to the ring. Part of each ring also provides the shrouds for the adjacent set of compressor blades.

Airflow. The air flows into the single stage centrifugal compressor, then passes through diffuser tubes (diffuser vanes in older-model engines) which turn the air 90° in one direction and also convert velocity to pressure. The gas generator case, shown in Figure 8-2-5, is attached to the front flange of the compressor inlet case and encloses both the compressor and the combustion section. The case con-

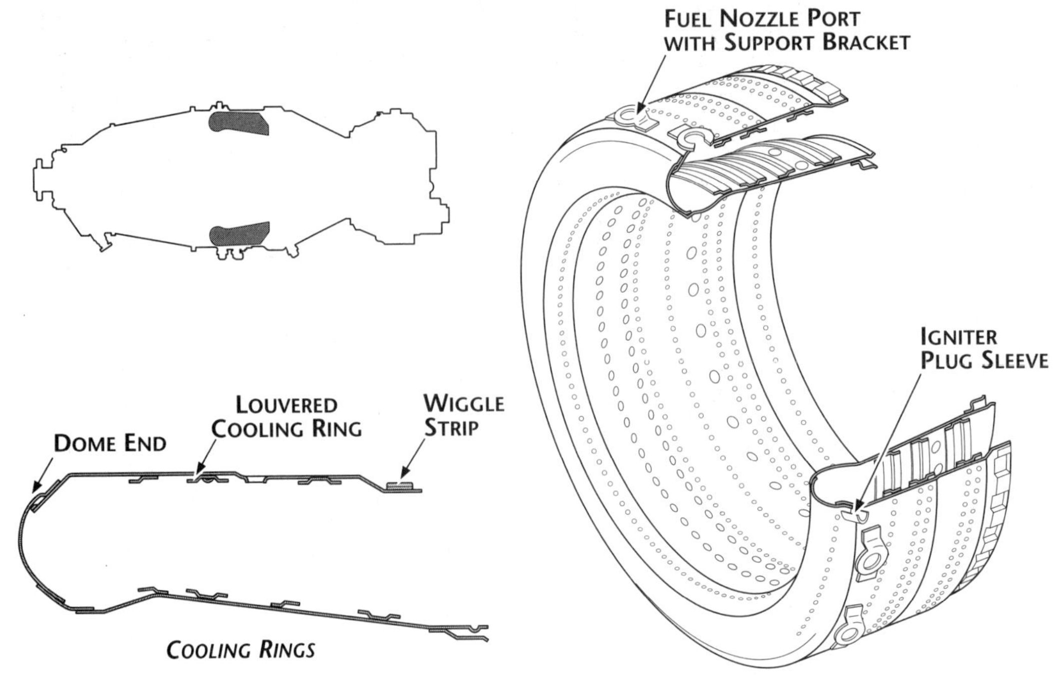

Figure 8-2-6. Annular combustion case surrounds the turbine wheels

sists of two stainless-steel sections fabricated into a single structure. The rear inlet section provides housing support for the compressor assembly.

The fourteen radial vanes brazed inside the double-skin center section of the gas generator case provide a pressure increase to the compressed air as it leaves the centrifugal impeller.

The compressed air is then directed through seventy straightening vanes, welded inside the gas generator case diffuser and out to the combustion chamber area through a slotted diffuser outlet baffle. The diffused air then passes through straightening vanes to the annulus surrounding the combustion chamber.

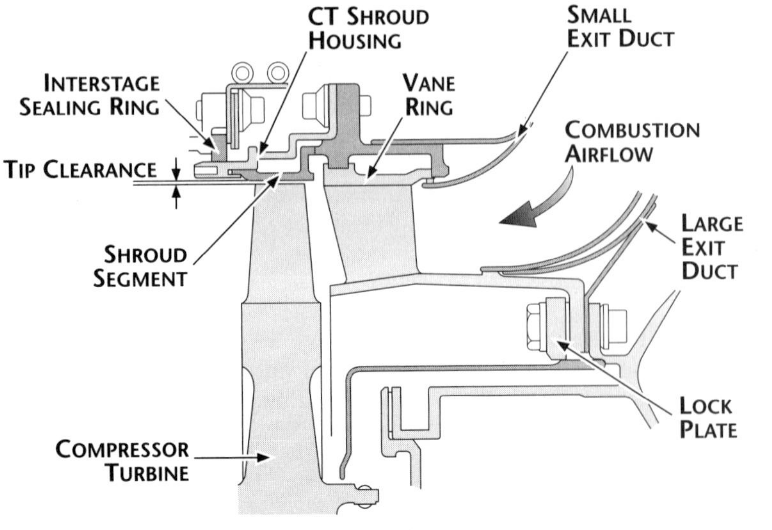

Figure 8-2-7. The compressor turbine vane assembly is downstream from the combustion case.

Combustion Section

The combustion chamber is formed by the gas generator case and the rear end of the exhaust duct assembly. The combustion chamber liner, located in the combustion chamber, is an annular, reverse-flow unit with perforations of various sizes which provide for the entry of cooling air. This cooling air prevents the flame from coming into contact with the liner, by forming a layer of air between the flame and the liner.

The combustion chamber liner, as shown in Figure 8-2-6, consists primarily of an annular, heat-resistant steel liner open at one end. Best fuel/air ratios for starting and sustained combustion are made possible by the series of straight, plunged and shielded perforation in the liner.

Combustion airflow. Cooling rings located opposite the perforations control the direction of airflow. The perforations ensure an even temperature distribution at the compressor turbine inlet. The flow of air changes direction to enter the combustion chamber liner, where it reverses direction and mixes with the fuel. The resultant hot gases expand and flow through the liner, reverse direction (180°) in the exit duct. The location of the liner outside the turbines eliminates the need for a long shaft between the compressor and the compressor

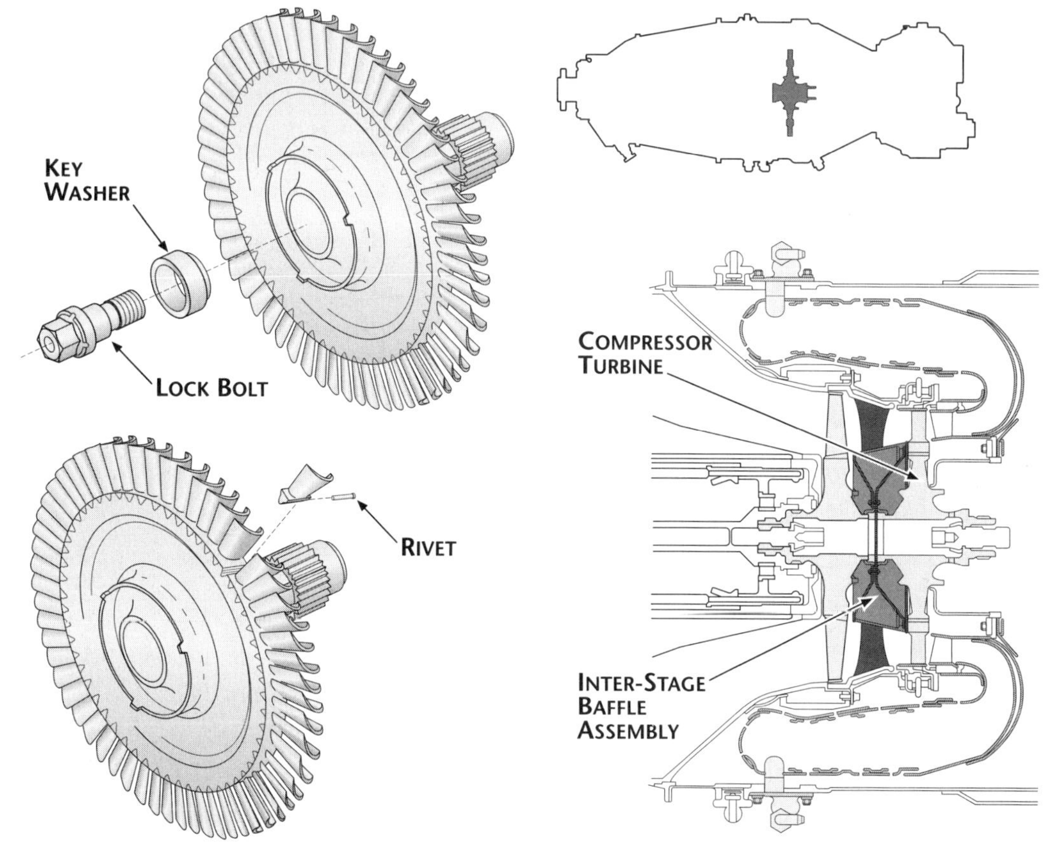

Figure 8-2-8. Compressor turbine wheel and location on the PT6 engine

turbine, thus reducing the overall length and weight of the engine.

Turbine Section

The gas path air passes through the compressor turbine inlet guide vanes to the single-stage compressor turbine. The guide vanes ensure that the expanding gases impinge on the turbine blades at the correct angle with minimum loss of energy. The still-expanding gases are then directed forward to the power turbine inlet guide vanes and on to the power turbine section, which in turn drives the propeller shaft through a planetary reduction gearbox.

Guide vanes. The compressor turbine vane assembly (guide vanes), shown in Figure 8-2-7 consists of twenty-nine cast-steel vanes located between the combustion chamber exit ducts and the compressor turbine. The vanes are cast with individual dowel pins on the inner platforms which fit in the outer circumference of the vane support. Sealing is ensured by a ceramic fiber cord packing located on the outer diameter of the support which is secured to the center bore of the gas generator case by eight bolts.

The outer platforms of the vanes are sealed with a chevron packing and fit into the shroud housing and exit duct. They are secured to the center bore by twelve bolts. The shroud housing extends forward and forms a runner for two inter-stage sealing rings. The inter-stage sealing rings provide a power seal and an internal mechanical separation point for the engine. Fourteen compressor turbine shroud segments located in the shroud housing act as a seal and provide a running clearance for the compressor turbine.

The compressor turbine consists of a two-plane, balanced turbine disk with blades and classified weights. This turbine drives the compressor in a counterclockwise direction. The assembly is secured to the front stub-shaft by a simplified center lock bolt. A master spline is provided to ensure that the disk assembly is always installed in a predetermined position to retain proper balance. The disk has a reference circumferential groove for checking disk growth when required.

The fifty-eight blades in the compressor turbine disk are secured in fir-tree serrations machined in the outer circumference of the disk and held in position by individual tubular rivets, shown in Figure 8-2-8. The blades are made of cast-steel alloy and have squealer tips.

A squealer tip is designed to minimize blade damage or pickup if the blade should come into

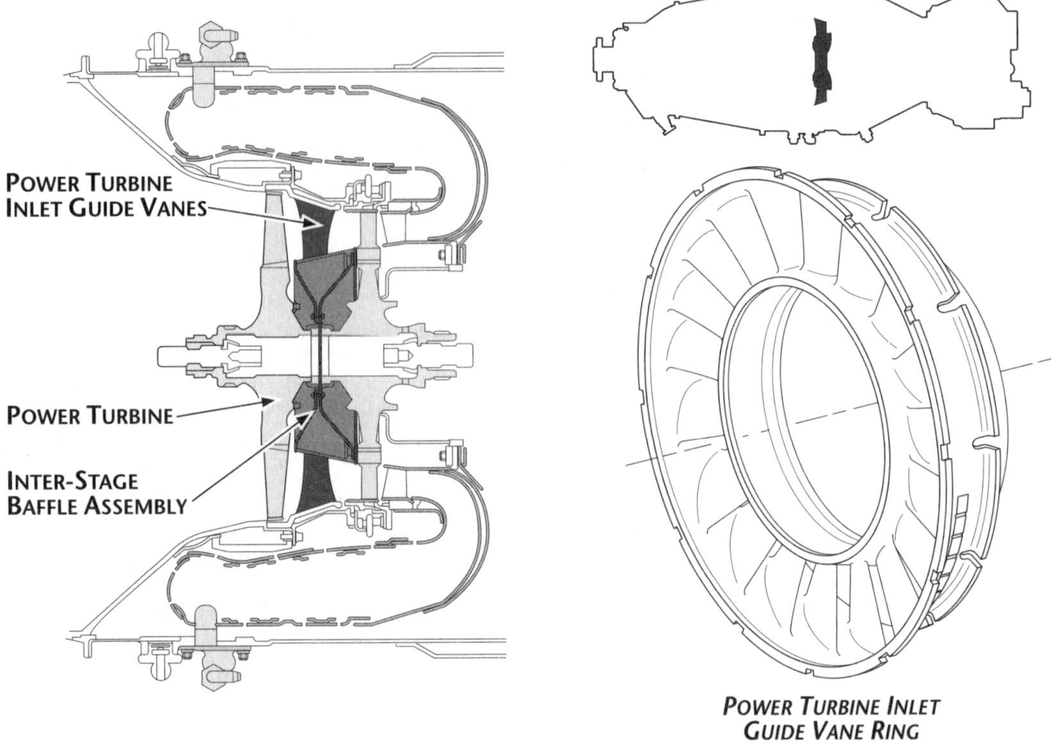

Figure 8-2-9. The power turbine wheel is after the compressor turbine

contact with the shroud segments during operation. It will also make a loud squealing noise that can be heard by operating personnel. The squealing noise alerts personnel that there is a problem in the turbine section. A small rotor machined on the rear face of the turbine disk provides a sealing surface to control the flow of turbine-disk cooling air.

Inter-stage baffle. The compressor turbine is separated from the power turbine by an inter-stage baffle, shown in Figure 8-2-8, which prevents turbine gases from transmitting heat to the turbine disk faces. The baffle is secured to and supported by the power-turbine ring. The center section of the baffle includes small circular-lipped flanges on the front and rear faces. The flanges fit over mating rotor seals machined on the respective turbine disk faces to provide control of cooling airflow through the perforated center of the baffle. After passing through the compressor turbine, the gas path air is directed into the power turbine guide vanes.

Between the compressor turbine and the power turbine is a ring which holds the power-turbine

Figure 8-2-10. PT6 turbine disk with master spline

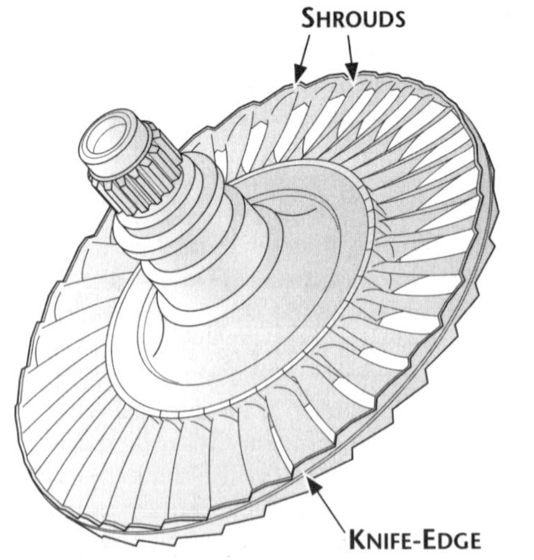

Figure 8-2-11. Shrouded turbine blades used on the PT6 power turbine

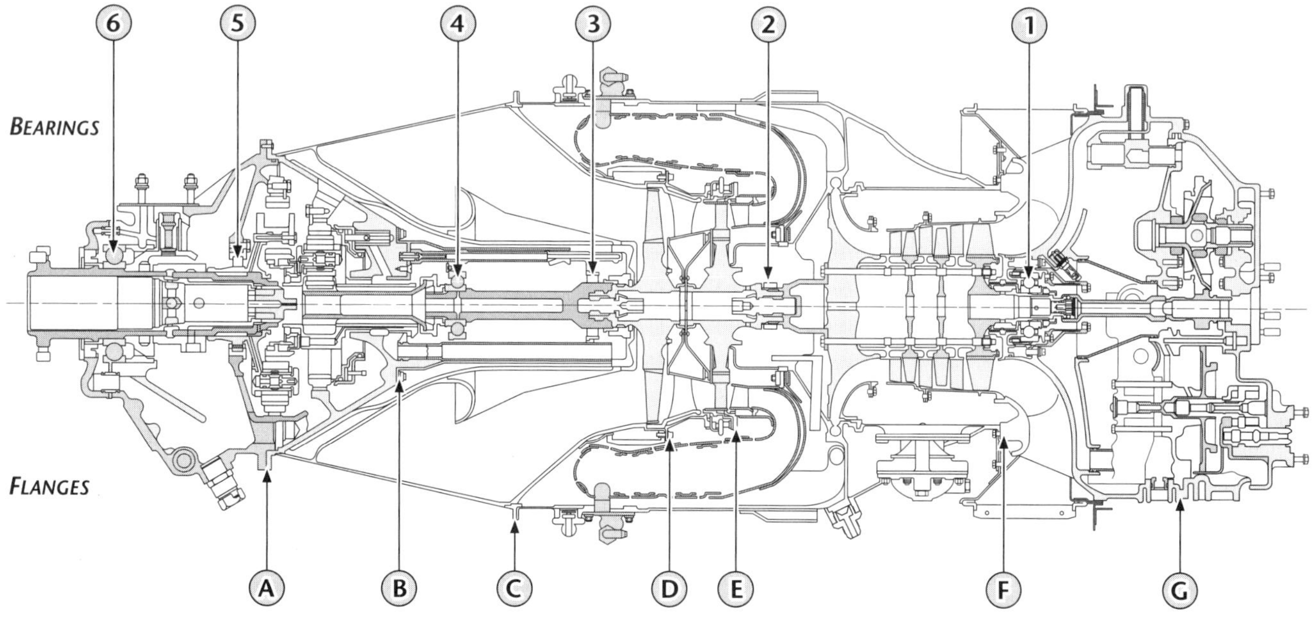

Figure 8-2-12. Engine bearing locations and engine flange locations

guide vanes. Depending on the model of the engine, either the vanes are separately cast and fitted into the inter-stage baffle rim by means of integral dowel-pin platforms or they are cast integrally with the turbine-vane ring. The position of the vane ring can be seen in Figure 8-2-9.

The stator housing with the enclosed vane assembly is bolted to the exhaust duct and supports two sealing rings at flange D. The rings are self-centering and held in position by retaining plates bolted to the rear face of the stator housing.

The power-turbine disk assembly, which consists of a turbine disk, blades and classified weights, drives the reduction gearing through the power-turbine shaft in a clockwise direction. The disk is manufactured with close tolerances and incorporates a reference circumferential groove to permit disk-growth. The turbine disk is splined to the turbine shaft and secured by a single center lock bolt and key-washer. The compressor turbine and power turbine use very similar bolts and washers to retain the turbines. This arrangement is shown in Figure 8-2-8.

A master spline, seen in Figure 8-2-10, ensures that the power-turbine disk is always installed in a predetermined position to retain the original balance. The required number of classified weights is determined during balancing procedures. The weights are riveted to a special flange located on the rear face of the turbine disk.

The power-turbine blades differ from those of the compressor turbine in that they are cast complete with notched and shrouded tips. See Figure 8-2-11. The forty-one blades are secured by fir-tree serrations machined in the rim of the turbine disk and held in place by means of individual tubular rivets. The blade tips rotate inside a double knife-edge shroud and form a continuous seal when the engine is running. This reduces tip leakage and increases turbine efficiency.

The power-turbine disk and shaft assembly is supported and secured in the power-turbine shaft housing by two bearings. The No. 3 bearing is a roller type and can be seen at the rear of the power-turbine shaft seen in Figure 8-2-12. The No. 4 bearing is a ball type and is at the forward end of the power-turbine shaft.

The exhaust gases from the power turbine are directed through an annular plenum into the atmosphere via twin opposed ports provided in the exhaust duct, shown in Figure 8-2-13.

Figure 8-2-13. PT6 exhaust duct and housing

All engine-driven accessories, with the exception of the propeller governor, power turbine over-speed governor and power turbine tachometer-generator, are mounted on the accessory gearbox at the rear of the engine shown in Figure 8-2-14. These components are driven off the compressor by means of a coupling shaft that extends the drive through a conical tube in the center section of the oil tank, shown in Figure 8-2-15A and B. The rear location of accessories simplifies any subsequent maintenance procedures.

Inter Turbine Temperature Measurement

Inter-turbine temperature (ITT) or T5, seen in Figure 8-2-16, is monitored by an integral set of thermocouple probes, a bus-bar and a harness assembly installed between the compressor turbine and the power turbines, with the probes projecting into the gas path. A terminal block mounted on the gas generator case (exhaust case in late-model engines) provides a connection point to cockpit instrumentation.

Propeller Reduction Gear Box

The propeller shaft is driven from the power turbine through a two-stage, planetary reduction gear having a ratio of 15:1. The power turbine turns at 33,000 r.p.m.; therefore the propeller turns at 2,200 r.p.m. The reduction gearbox embodies an integral torquemeter device which is instrumented to provide an accurate indication of engine power (ft-lb. of torque). The reduction gearbox, shown in Figure 8-2-17, consists of two magnesium-alloy castings bolted to the front flange of the exhaust duct. The speed reduction gear box has two stages of planetary reduction gears.

The first stage of reduction is contained in the rear case. The first-stage reduction sun gear consists of a short, hollow steel shaft which has an integral spur gear at the front end and is externally splined at the rear end. The external splines engage the retainer coupling by which the first-stage sun-gear shaft and the power-turbine shaft are joined.

The first-stage ring gear is located in helical splines provided in the first-stage reduc-

Figure 8-2-14. The engine accessory section is on the rear of the engine.

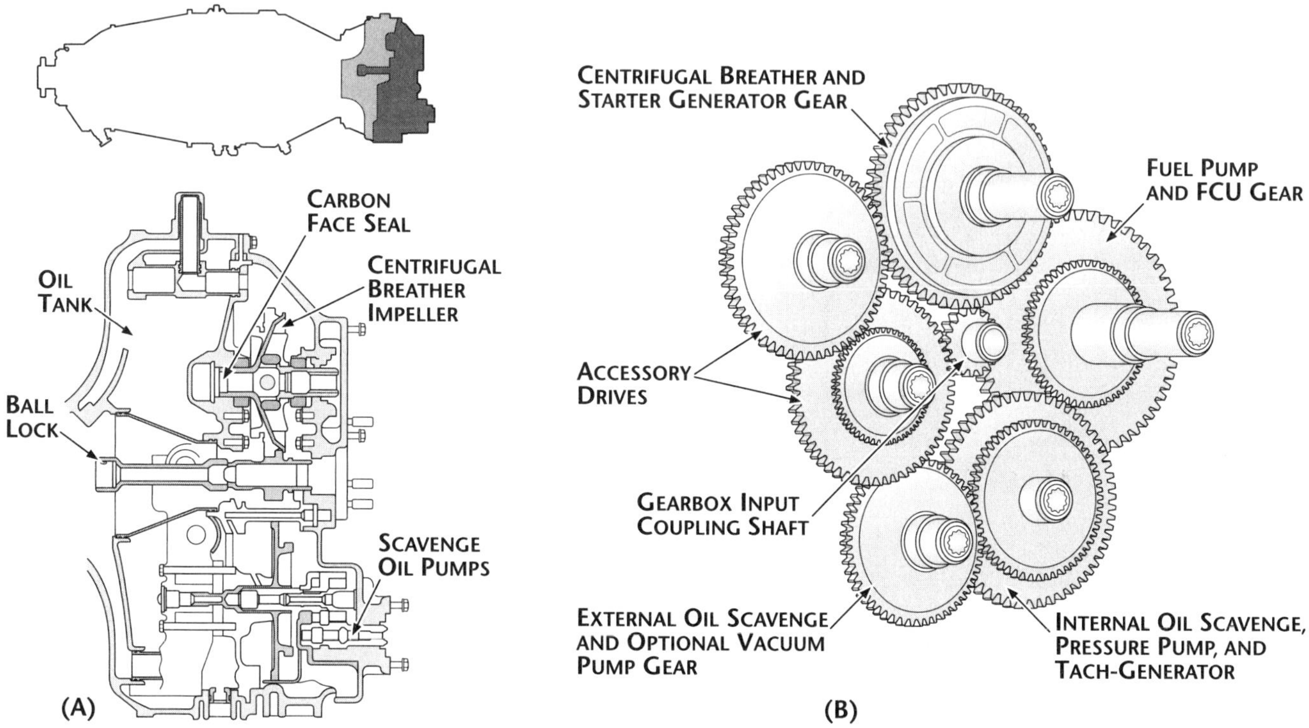

Figure 8-2-15. (A) A diagram of the accessory gearbox and (B) gear train which are located to the rear of the engine.

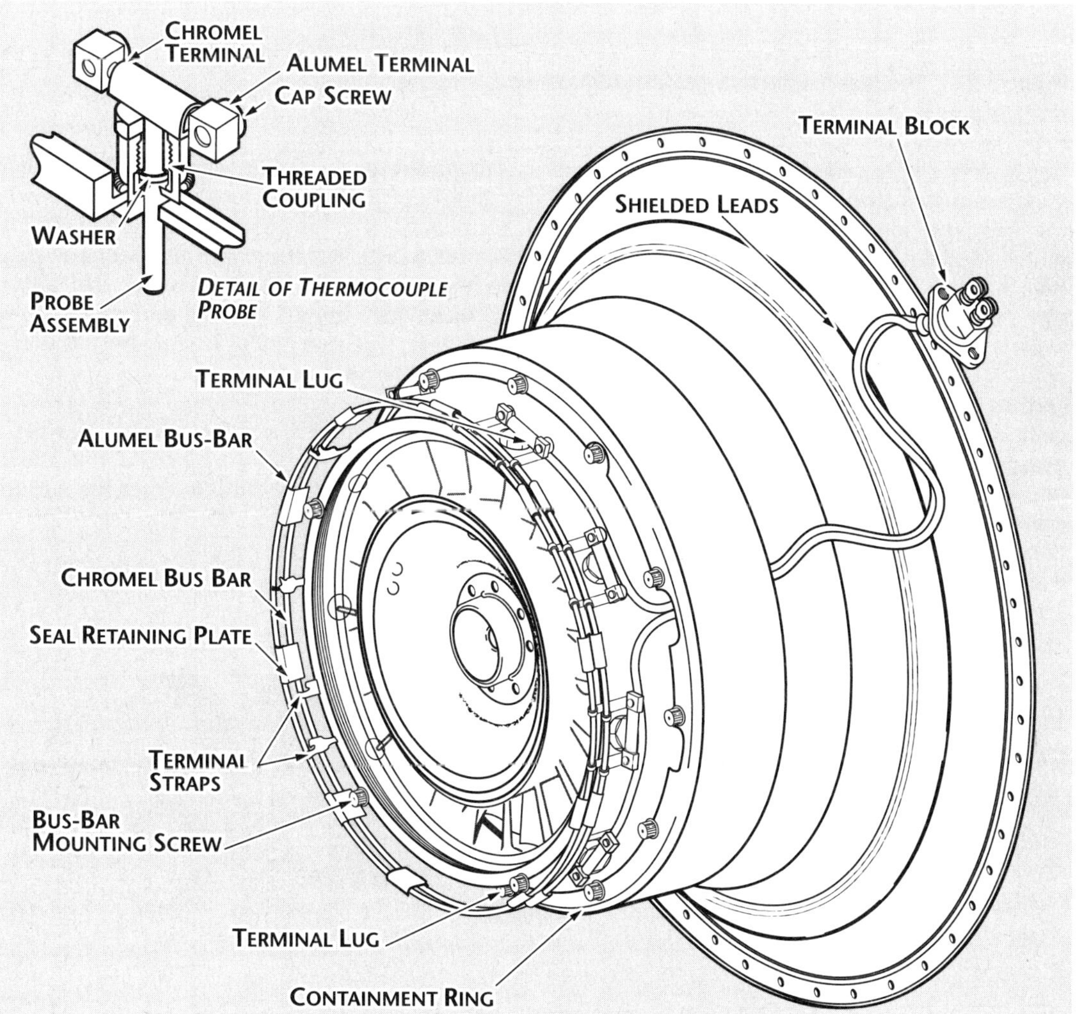

Figure 8-2-16. A PT6 turboprop engine's T5 inter-turbine temperature thermocouples.

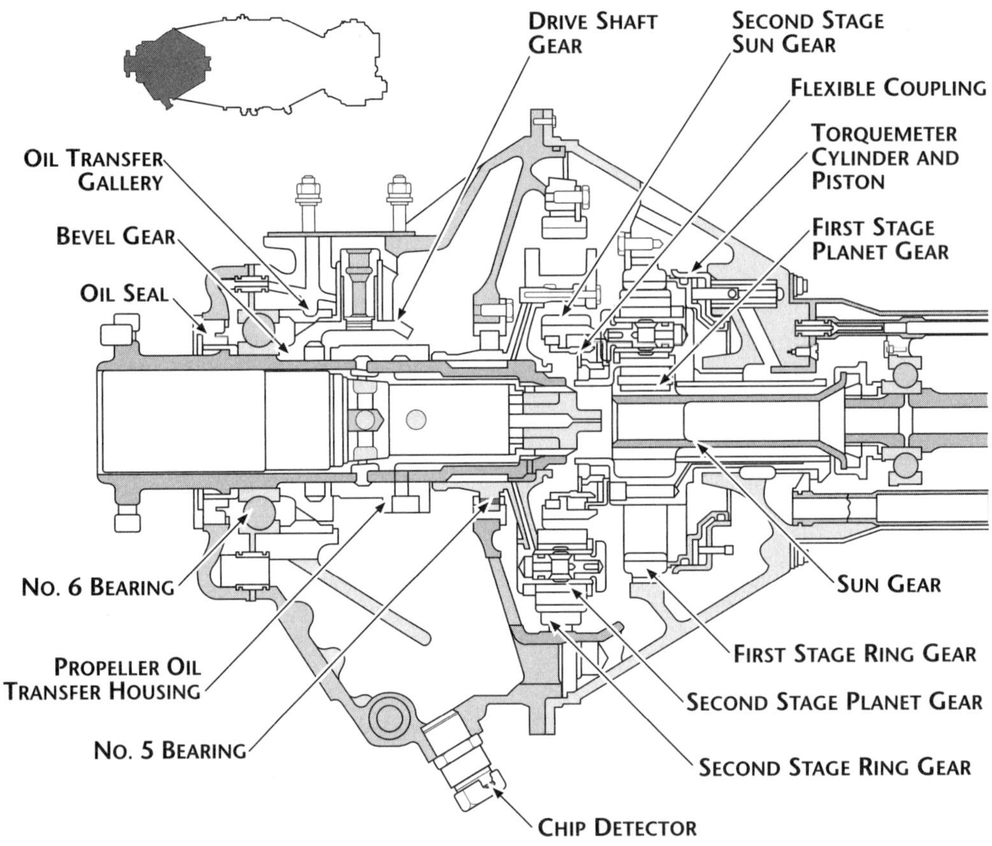

Figure 8-2-17. The speed reduction gearbox reduces r.p.m. for the propeller.

tion-gearbox rear case. The torque developed by the power turbine is transmitted through the sun and planet gears to the ring gear, which is opposed by the helical splines. Thus, the ring gear cannot rotate, but the planet-gear carrier is caused to rotate. The ring gear moves a short distance axially because of the helical splines, shown in Figure 8-2-18. The helical splines are set at an angle allowing the ring gear to move slightly forward and aft. This movement is used to operate the torquemeter which determines the torque force being exerted by the engine.

Torquemeter. The torquemeter mechanism consists of a torquemeter cylinder, torquemeter piston, valve plunger and spring shown in Figure 8-2-19. Rotation of the reduction-gear first-stage ring gear is resisted by the helical splines which impart an axial movement to the ring gear; this movement is transmitted to the torquemeter piston.

This in turn moves a valve plunger against a spring, opening a metering orifice and allowing an increased flow of oil to enter the torquemeter chamber.

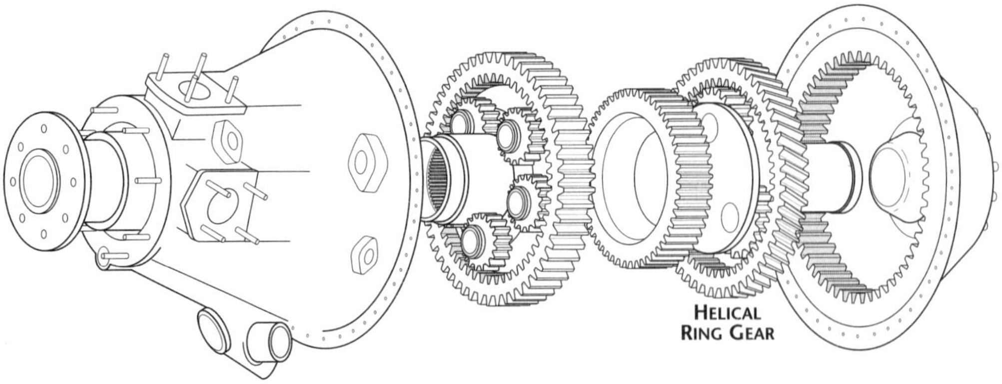

Figure 8-1-20. The helical ring gear arrangement on the PT6 engine is part of the torquemeter.

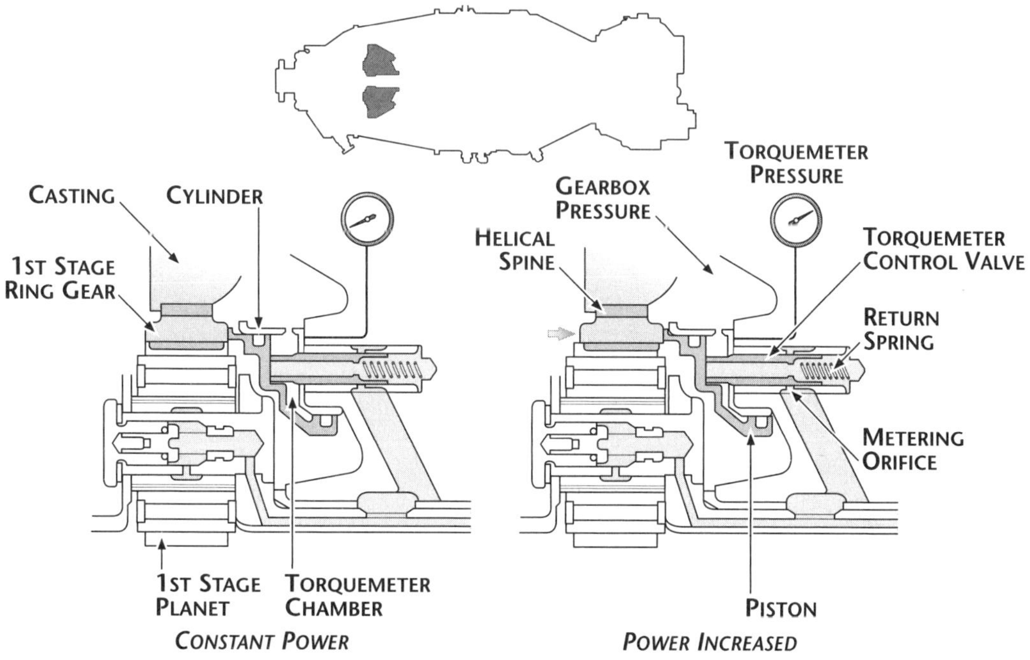

Figure 8-2-19. Torquemeter system components and operation

This movement will continue until the oil pressure in the torque chamber balances the force on the ring gear caused by the torque being absorbed by the gear and the propeller blades. Any change in the power control lever setting will recycle the sequence until a state of equilibrium is again achieved.

Hydraulic lock in the torquemeter is prevented by allowing the oil to bleed continuously from the pressure chamber into the reduction-gear casing through a small bleed hole provided in the top of the torquemeter cylinder. Because the external oil pressure within the reduction gearbox may vary and affect the total oil pressure on the torquemeter piston, the internal pressure is measured.

The difference between the torquemeter oil pressure and the reduction-gearbox internal oil pressure accurately indicates the torque being produced. The two pressures are internally routed to bosses located on the top of the reduction-gearbox front case where connections can be made to suit individual cockpit instrumentation requirements.

The second stage of reduction gearing is contained in the reduction-gearbox front case. The first-stage planet carrier is attached to the second-stage sun gear by a flexible coupling, which also serves to dampen any vibrations between the two rotating masses.

Air Bleed Systems

The PT6A engine has three separate air-bleed systems:

- Compressor bleed control
- Bearing compartment air seal and bleed system
- Turbine-disk cooling system

A fourth system, sometimes referred to as customer bleed, is available as an optional source of high-pressure air for use in operating auxiliary airframe equipment. A mounting flange located on the gas generator case is provided for external connections.

Compressor bleed control. The compressor bleed valve automatically opens a port in the gas generator case to spill inter-stage compressed air ($P_{2.5}$), thereby providing antistall characteristics at low engine speeds (less than 80% Ng,). This action allows the airflow in the compressor to remain at a constant velocity, preventing compressor stall. At low compressor speeds the airflow tends to slow down in the last stages of the compressor. By allowing some of the air in the back part of the compressor to bleed overboard at low compressor speeds, compressor stall is prevented.

The port closes gradually as higher engine speeds are attained. The compressor bleed valve, located on the gas generator case at the seven o'clock position and secured by two bolts, consists of a piston-type valve in a ported housing. This bleed valve is illustrated in Figure 8-2-20.

The piston assembly is supported in the bore of the housing and is guided by a seal support plate, guide pin and guide-pin bolt, the latter holding the piston assembly together. A roll-

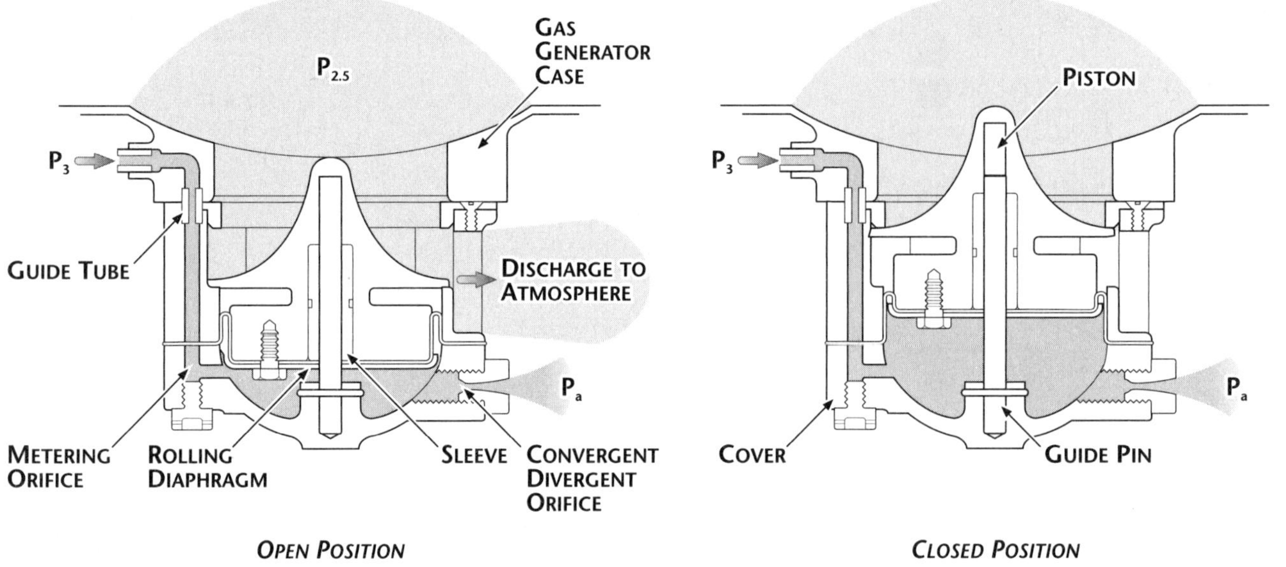

Figure 8-2-20. PT6 compressor bleed valve operation

ing diaphragm permits the piston full travel in either direction, to open or close the port, while at the same time effectively sealing the compartment at the top of the piston.

A port in the gas generator case provides a direct passage for the flow of compressor air ($P_{2.5}$) to the bottom of the bleed valve piston. Compressor discharge air (P_3) is tapped off and applied to the bleed valve through a nozzle (fixed orifice) in the bleed-valve cover, then passed through an intermediate passage and out to the atmosphere through a metering plug.

The control pressure between the two orifices acts upon the upper side of the bleed-valve piston so that when control pressure is greater than $P_{2.5}$, the bleed valve closes. In the closed position, the inter-stage air port is sealed by the seal support plate which is forced against its seat by

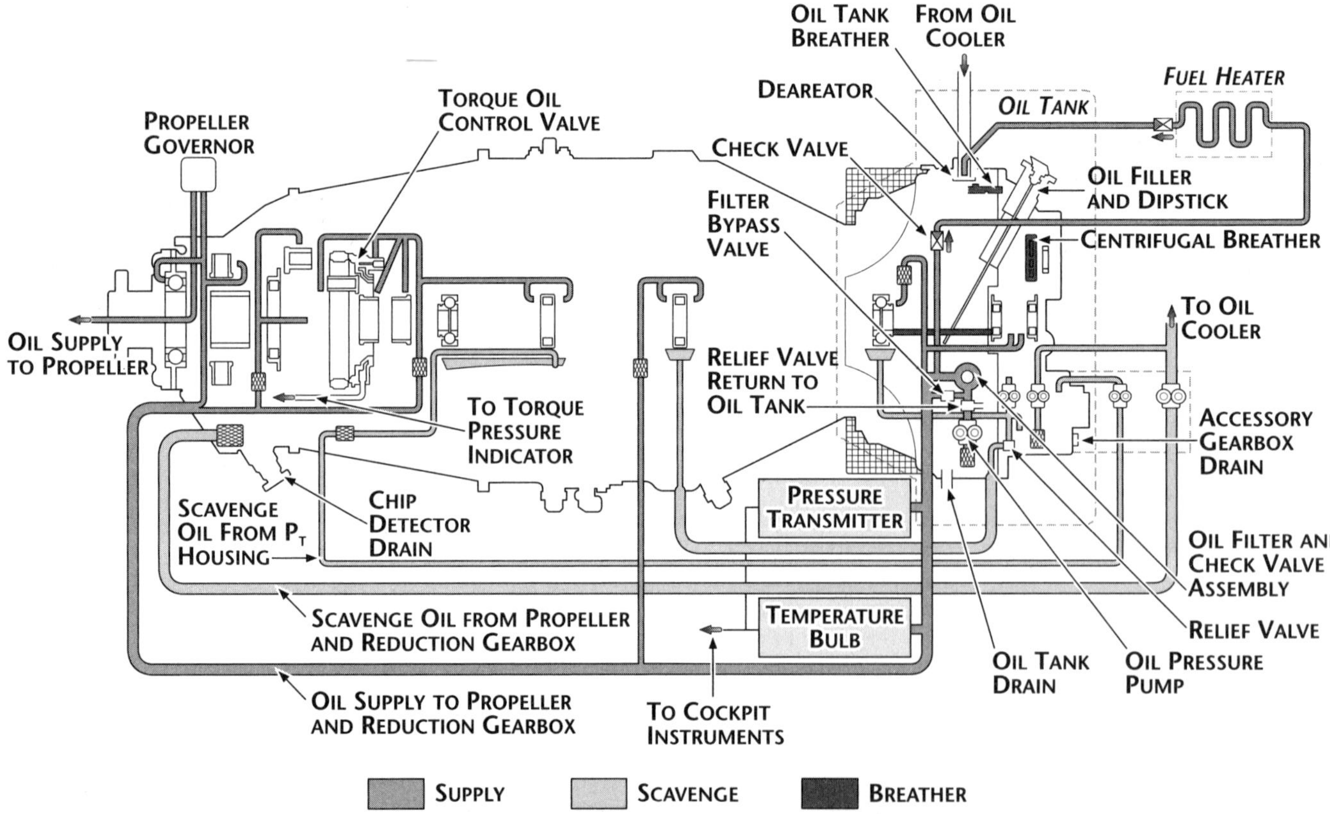

Figure 8-2-21. Typical oil system diagram which shows the oil pressure and scavenge systems.

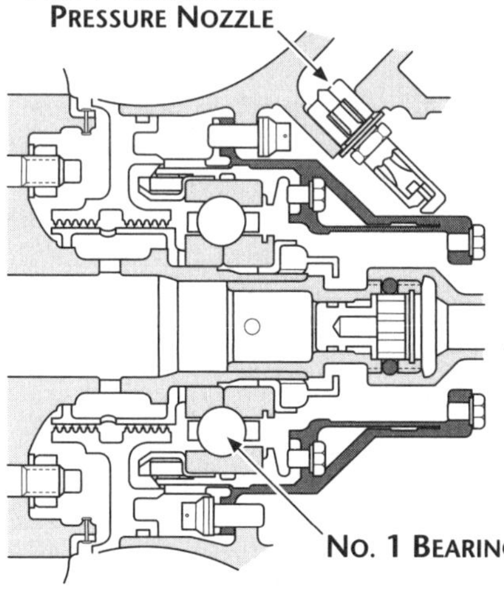

Figure 8-2-22. Number 1 bearing arrangement

the effect of control pressure. Conversely, when the control pressure is less than $P_{2.5}$, the bleed valve opens and allows inter-stage pressure ($P_{2.5}$) to be discharged to the atmosphere.

For calibration purposes, the control pressure is measured by installing a suitable fitting in the valve cover and varying the diameter of the metering plug and/or nozzle orifice. The calibration should be such that control pressure exceeds $P_{2.5}$ when the overall compressor ratio (P_3/P_2) is 3.70. The P_2 is the compressor inlet pressure.

Bearing compartment air seal. Pressure air is utilized to seal the first, second and third bearing compartments and to cool both of the turbine disks. The pressure air is used in conjunction with air seals which establish and control the required pressure gradients. Air pressure is used in turbine engines to prevent oil from leaking into areas where it is not required or where it would be detrimental to the operation of the engine.

The air seals used on the engine consist of two separate parts. One part takes the form of a plain rotating surface. The corresponding part consists of a series of stationary expansion chambers (the labyrinth) formed by deep annular grooves machined in the bore of a circular seal. The clearance between the rotating and stationary parts is kept as small as is consistent with minimum clearance requirements.

Turbine disk cooling system. The compressor turbine disk and power turbine disks are both cooled by compressor discharge air bled from the slotted diffuser baffle area down the rear face of the outer exit duct assembly. The air is then metered through holes in the compressor turbine vane support into the turbine baffle hub where it divides into three paths.

Some of the air is metered to cool the rear face of the compressor turbine disk and some to pressurize the bearing seals. The balance is led forward through passages in the compressor turbine hub to cool the front face of the compressor turbine. A portion of this cooling air is also led through a passage in the center of the inter-stage baffle where the flow divides. One path flows up the rear face of the power- turbine disk while the other is led through the center of the disk hub and out through drilled passages in the hub to the No. 3 bearing air seals and front face of the power-turbine disk.

The cooling air from both turbine disks is dissipated into the main gas stream flow to the atmosphere. The bearing cavity leakage air is scavenged with the scavenge oil into the accessory gearbox and vented to the atmosphere through the centrifugal breather.

Lubrication System

The typical lubrication system for the PT6 engine is shown in Figure 8-2-21. The engine governor oil system provides lubrication for all areas of the engine, including pressure for the torque meter and power for propeller pitch control. The compressor assembly No. 1 bearing area is shown in Figure 8-2-22. An oil nozzle fitted at the end of a cored passage provides lubrication to the rear of No. 1 bearing at approximately the one o'clock position. Other cored passages are provided for pressure and scavenge oil.

The oil pressure regulating valve and the engine main oil filter, with check-valve and bypass-valve assemblies, are located on the right side of the inlet case at the one and three o'clock positions. A fabricated conical tube complete with a preformed packing is fitted in the center of the oil tank compartment to provide a passage for the coupling shaft which extends the compressor drive to the rear accessories.

The pressure oil pump is driven by an accessory drive which is located in the bottom portion of the integral oil tank and is secured by four bolts to the accessory diaphragm. During operation, oil from the oil tank, the accessory gear box, is picked up by the main oil pressure pump and forced through the main oil filter, as shown in Figure 8-2-21.

The filter is a disposable cartridge type or a cleanable metal type. If the filter should be come clogged, the oil flows through a bypass valve. A check valve is incorporated in the end of the filter housing, thus making it possible to change the filter without draining the oil tank, as shown in Figure 8-2-23.

The oil pressure regulating valve is located on the gear case above the filter cover. The pressure

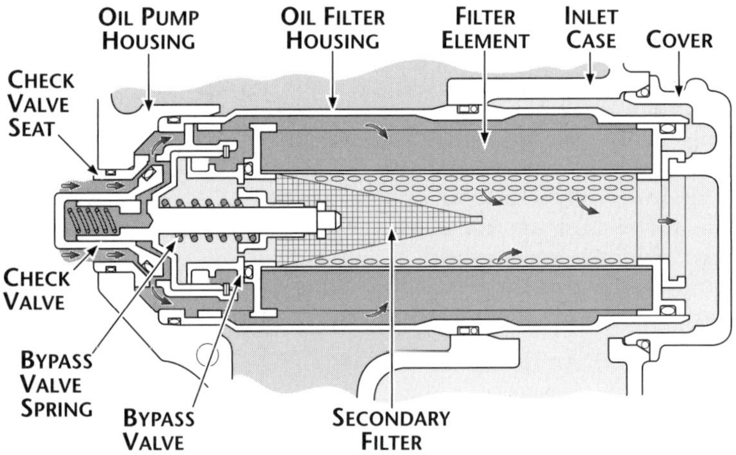

Figure 8-2-23. Oil filter and check valve

regulating valve is adjusted at the factory and no further adjustment is usually required. Oil released by the regulating valve is returned to the tank.

Lubricating oil is carried to all parts of the engine through a system of tubes and passages. Thus, pressure oil reaches all bearings, gears and other moving parts requiring lubrication. The oil reduces friction, cools the engine parts and cleans the engine by removing foreign particles to be picked up by the oil filter.

Scavenge oil is drained into sumps and is pumped back to the oil tank. Oil from the reduction case scavenge pump and the accessory case scavenge pump is routed through an oil cooler if the engine installation in the aircraft requires such a cooler.

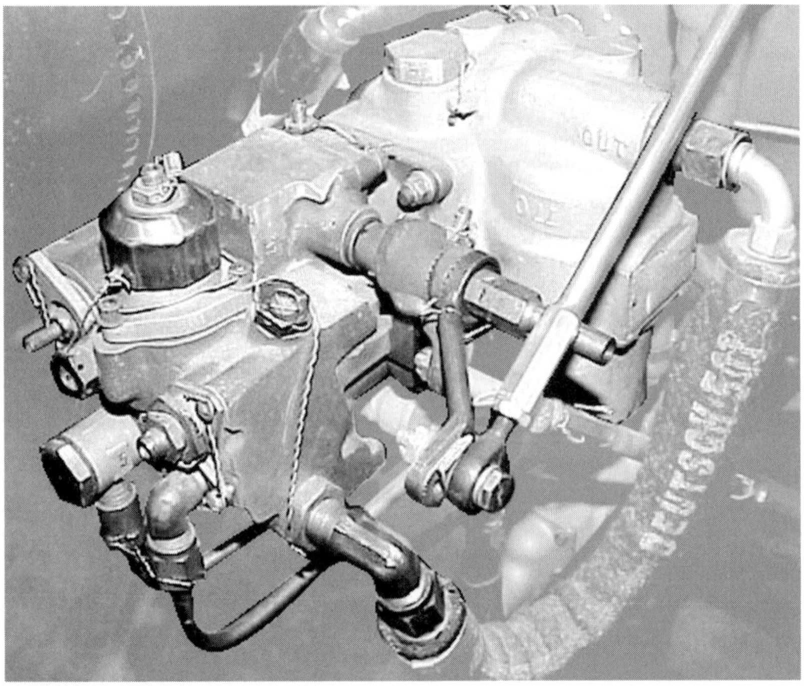

Figure 8-2-24. The fuel control and pump are mounted to the rear of the engine.

Some installations include a fuel heater through which the fuel is heated by engine oil.

The fuel heater is a simple heat exchanger with an automatic temperature control. Instruments for monitoring the oil system include a temperature gauge and a pressure gauge. The normal operating pressure is 65 to 85 p.s.i.g. with a minimum of 40 p.s.i.g. Normal operating temperature of the oil is 74°C to 80°C. Always refer to the operating manual for proper pressure and temperature values.

Fuel System

The fuel system supplies the engine from the aircraft fuel tanks through a boost pump mounted in the tank. This boost pump operates during all engine operations. Fuel is then further pressurized by an engine-driven fuel pump. The rate of flow to the fuel manifold is then controlled by the fuel control unit (FCU). These components can be seen in Figure 8-2-24. Fuel is injected into the combustion chamber liner through fourteen simplex nozzles. The fuel is supplied by a dual manifold (single on early engine models) is seen in Figure 8-2-25). It consists of primary and secondary transfer tubes and adapters. A schematic of the complete system is shown in Figure 8-2-26.

System components. The engine-driven fuel pump is mounted to the accessory section with the fuel control mounted at the rear of the fuel pump. Fuel from the aircraft system enters the fuel pump and is filtered. The high pressure fuel is filtered again before entering the fuel control. Both filters have a bypass valve that will bypass fuel if the filter becomes clogged.

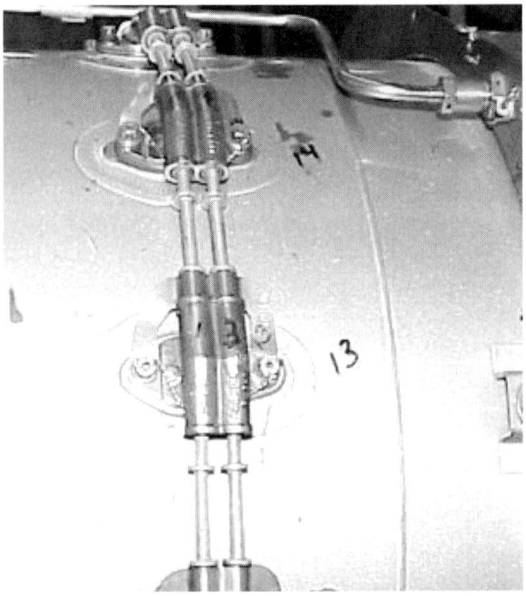

Figure 8-2-25. PT6 primary and secondary fuel manifolds

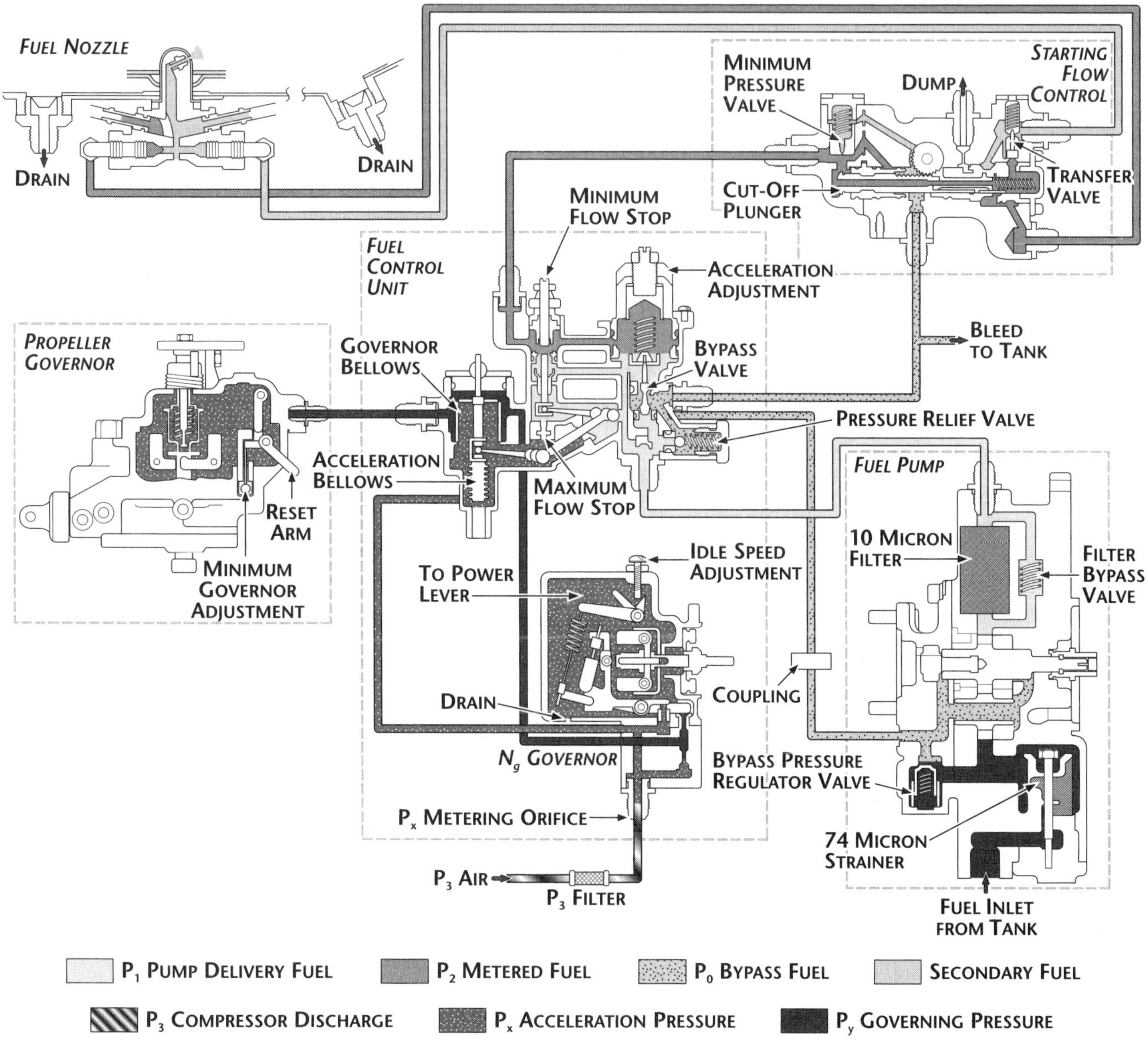

Figure 8-2-26. The engine fuel system meters fuel to the engine.

The engine parameters that are used to schedule the fuel to the engine are:

- Power lever position
- Compressor discharge air pressure (P_3)
- Compressor speed (Ng speed)
- Inlet temperature

The fuel control and fuel pump for the PT6A turboprop engine in Figure 8-2-27 includes:

- Gear-type or a vane-type fuel pump
- 74-micron inlet filter
- Fuel control unit (FCU)
- Power-turbine governor
- Automatic fuel dump valve
- Fuel manifold adapter assembly
- Fuel nozzles

The function of the system is to provide the correct amount of fuel for all operating conditions and to limit fuel as necessary to avoid damage to the engine, compressor stall and flameout.

Fuel control. The fuel pump is mounted on the accessory gearbox and is driven through a splined coupling. Another splined coupling shaft extends the drive to the FCU, which is bolted to the rear face of the fuel pump. Fuel from the aircraft boost pump enters the fuel pump through the filter and flows into the pump chamber. Fuel from the pump is delivered at a high pressure to the FCU through a 10 micron filter. Both the inlet filter and the outlet filter have bypass valves to permit fuel flow if the filters should become clogged.

Figure 8-2-27. PT6 fuel control and fuel pump

The fuel control unit is classed as a pneumatic type since the primary actuating element is a pair of bellows which respond to varying air pressures. The controlling parameters for the fuel control unit are:

- Power-lever position
- Compressor discharge pressure (P_3)
- Compressor inlet temperature (T_2)
- Compressor r.p.m. (N_g)

If the r.p.m. of the propeller exceeds a limit, the propeller overspeed governor will take over and slow the gas generator. This governor is sometime called a fuel topping or N_f governor. As compressor pressure and inlet temperature vary, the fuel control will set the metering valve to deliver the correct amount of fuel to the engine through the use of differential bellows.

An additional governor supplies an input signal to prevent over-speeding of the power turbine when the propeller governor is not in control of power-turbine speed (N_f). The automatic fuel dump valve (combustion drain valve) allows fuel from the bottom of the combustion chamber to drain at shutdown to eliminate the possibility of fuel collecting in the combustion chamber.

Ignition System

Two spark igniters, or glow plugs, which protrude into the combustion liner, ignite the fuel/air mixture. The igniters are normally used only during starting of the engine. The flame in the combustion section is self propagating after being lit. The ignition system is a capacitance discharge ignition system that uses a 9 to 30 DC volt input.

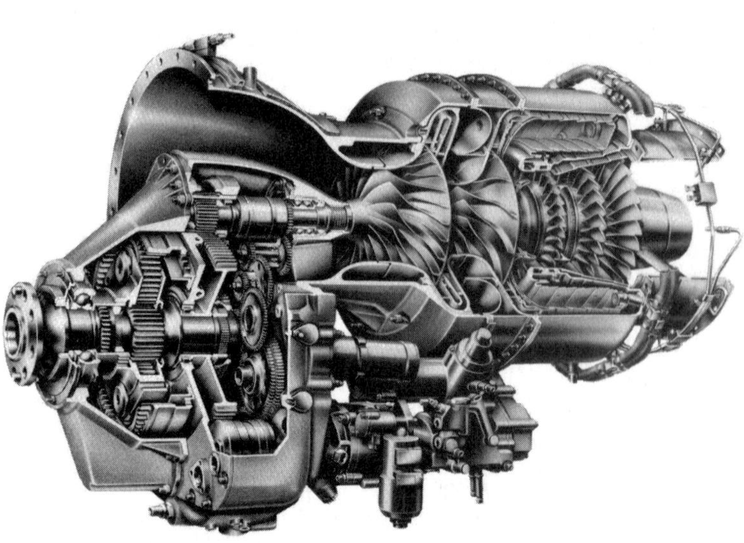

Figure 8-3-1. TPE 331 engine cutaway view *Image courtesy of Honeywell*

Section 3

Honeywell TPE331 Turboprop Engine

The Honeywell TPE331 turboprop engine is illustrated in Figure 8-3-1. The TPE331 engine is a single-shaft (spool) engine that has one

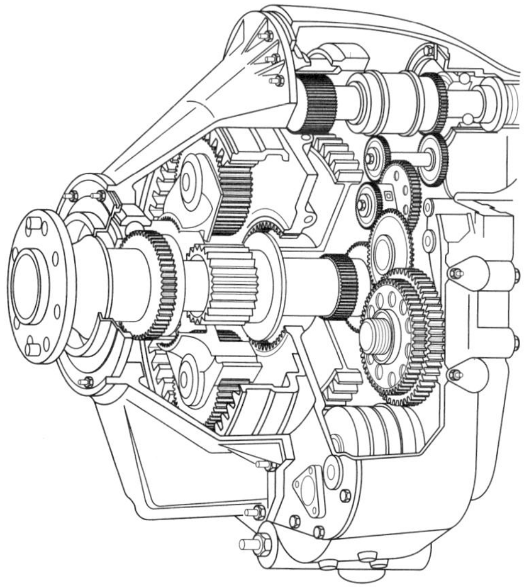

Figure 8-3-2. TPE 331 speed reduction gearbox cutaway

main rotating assembly that includes the compressor turbine and an internal speed reduction gearbox, shown in Figure 8-3-2. Horsepower ranges from around 700 to 1,700. A larger version of the engine is the Dash 12 and Dash 14 which produce the higher end horsepower ratings.

The main rotating group of the power section drives the propeller through a gear train within the gearbox which provides the necessary speed reduction at the propeller. Since this engine is a fixed turbine engine, a method of locking the propeller in approximately zero pitch is needed. This position makes the propeller blade angle flat to the plane of rotation as shown in position B of Figure 8-3-3. In this blade position, the load on the engine during starting is reduced as much as possible. After the engine has started, the propeller blades are released from the zero pitch locks also shown in C of Figure 8-3-3.

A two-stage centrifugal compressor is located on the main shaft in the forward section of the engine. To the rear of the compressor section is the three-stage turbine that extracts power from the hot, high-velocity gases and delivers the power through the main shaft to both the compressor and the propeller reduction gears. The turbine is surrounded by the reverse-flow annular combustor. The engine is of modular construction to simplify repair and maintenance procedures.

During operation of the TPE331 engine, air flows from the inlet to the first stage of the centrifugal compressor. From the first stage the air flows outward and then is routed through ducting back toward the center of the second-stage centrifugal compressor. From the second stage the pressurized air flows outward and back around the outside of and into the annular combustor. Atomized fuel injected through nozzles in the rear of the combustor is ignited and the resulting hot gases flow forward, then turn inward and flow to the rear through the three-stages of turbine blades and vanes. After most of the energy is absorbed by the turbine section, the exhaust gases are ejected out the rear of the engine.

Propeller Control System

The propeller control system for the TPE331 series of engines, shown in Figure 8-3-4, is similar to those for other turboprop engines only while operating in the governor r.p.m. range. During flight, the system propeller governor automatically adjusts propeller pitch to maintain a constant propeller speed. As engine power is increased through movement of the power lever (propeller r.p.m. increases to the max governor setting), propeller pitch increases as the propeller governor moves to release oil from the pitch-changing mechanism in the propeller hub. As the propeller

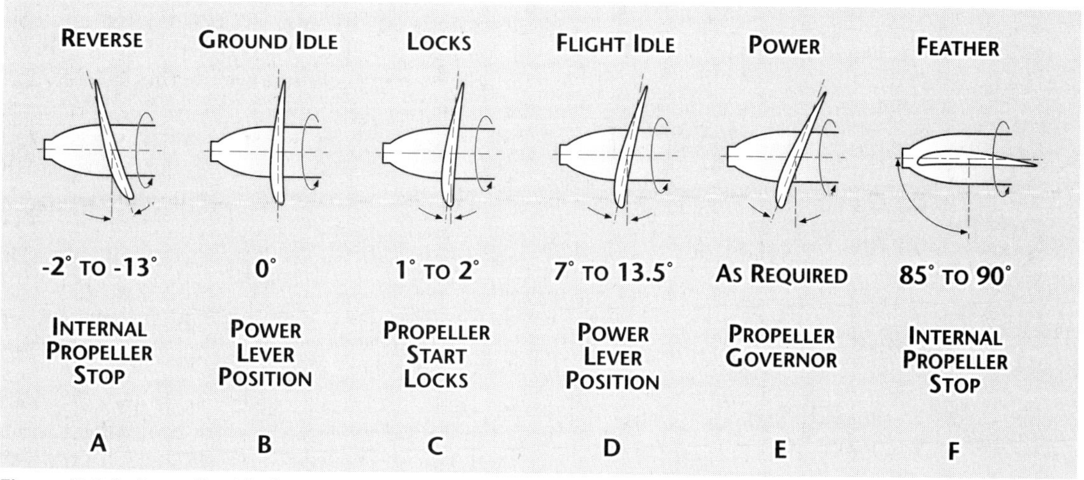

Figure 8-3-3. Propeller blade positions for all ground and flight settings

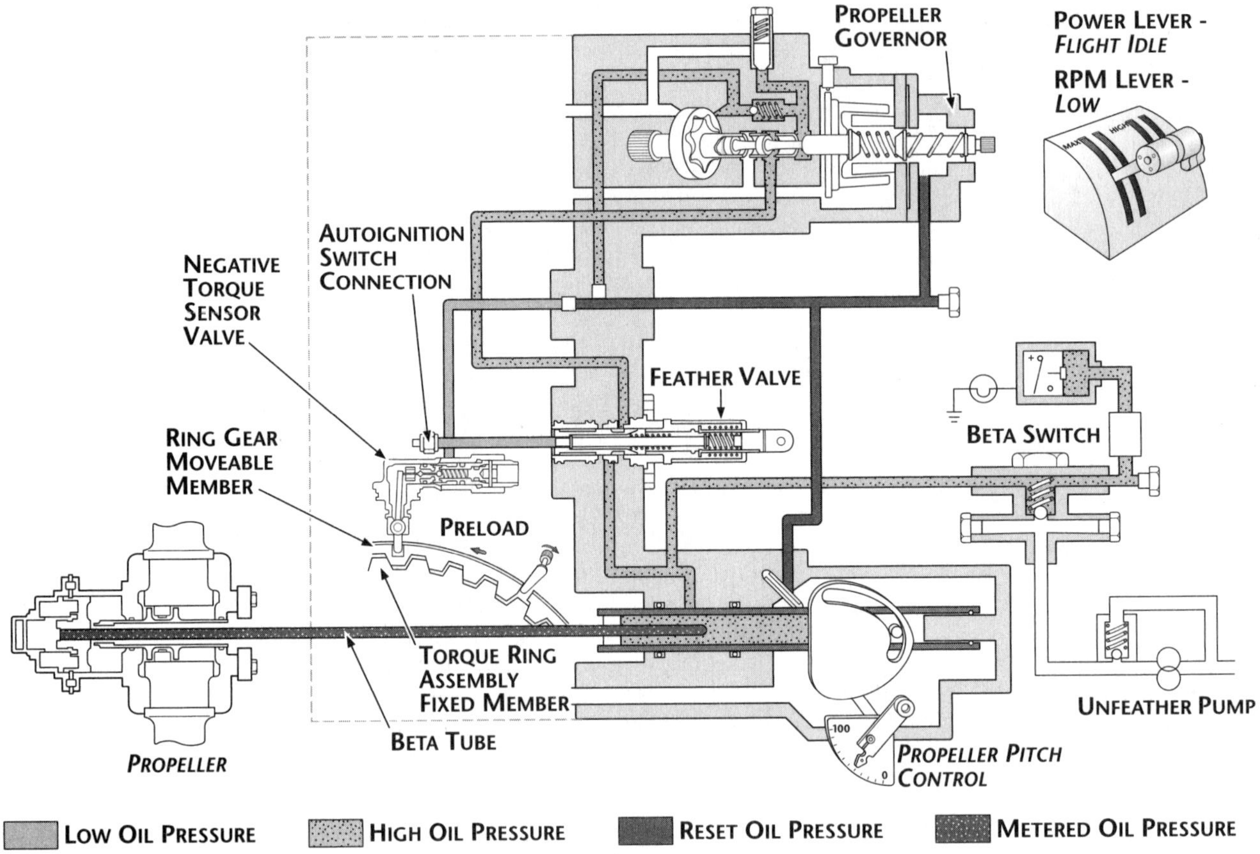

Figure 8-3-4. The propeller control system is hydraulically actuated.

pitch increases, it will reach a point that is torque (horsepower) limited. For ground operations (beta mode), the propeller control system provides for reverse and positive thrust during taxiing.

The propeller pitch-changing mechanism is actuated hydraulically and is designed for both feathering and reverse pitch thrust. Hydraulic pressure moves the propeller toward low pitch; however, high pitch and feathering are accomplished by means of coil springs and counterweight force, illustrated in Figure 8-3-5. This means that when oil is released from the propeller, it will move toward high pitch. Conversely, when oil pressure is directed to the propeller, it will travel toward low pitch and reverse.

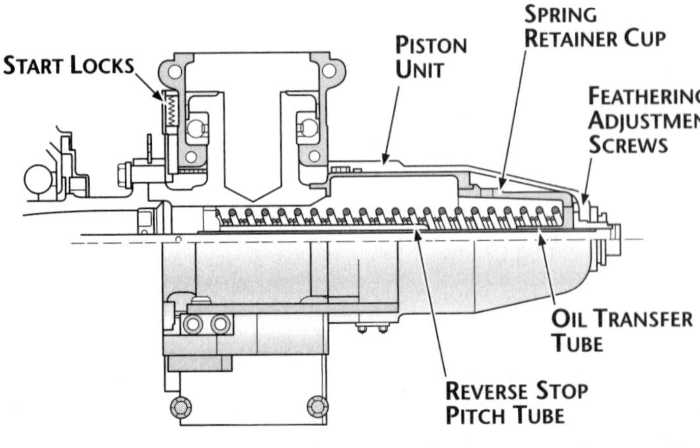

Figure 8-3-5. Typical TPE331 propeller arrangement

Cockpit controls. Cockpit-operated controls include the power lever, condition lever (engine r.p.m. lever), manual feather control and unfeather switch. Since the management of both fuel and propeller blade angle is involved when the levers are moved in the cockpit, it is essential that the aircraft and engine controls be interconnected precisely so that selections made in the cockpit provide the correct corresponding positions of the controls. As mentioned earlier, the propeller must be removed from the start locks. The propeller control must be moved toward reverse angle position. This action will cause the propeller blade to move in the reverse direction. This reverse blade angle will release the locks and the locks will be held away from the blades the by centrifugal force until engine shutdown.

With the locks removed, the propeller blades can move freely from positive to reverse thrust. With the condition lever (speed lever) in the low speed position, see Figure 8-3-6, the propeller blade position setting is accomplished by the propeller pitch control through the power lever.

The propeller pitch control is located on the accessory case directly in line with the center of the propeller. A tube, called the beta tube, is connected to the propeller pitch change mechanism and moves back and forth as the propeller changes pitch. The other end of the beta tube is contained inside the propeller pitch control. When low pitch or reverse pitch is called for by the power lever, the beta tube allows oil pressure from the propeller governor to flow into the propeller which will move the blade angle to low pitch or reverse. If a higher pitch is required to taxi forward, the oil pressure is dumped from the propeller. The beta tube also provides for feedback by moving to a neutral position when the correct blade pitch is accomplished as requested by the power lever.

During takeoff, the speed lever is set in the high speed position or 100% r.p.m. As the power lever is moved toward maximum power the propeller governor will allow the propeller r.p.m. to increase to a certain limit. At this point the blade angle will increase to hold the r.p.m. at the preset limit. With the blade angle increasing, torque will rise because the propeller is absorbing the power and converting it to thrust. The power lever is advanced until the torque or temperature limits are reached. On a hot day at sea level, the temperature limits may be met before the torque limits. A cold day at sea level, the torque limit will tend to limit takeoff thrust.

Negative torque sensor. The system includes a torque sensor, shown in Figure 8-3-7 to detect negative torque, that is, a situation in which the engine is being rotated by the wind-milling propeller or the engine has stopped creating power. When the negative torque signal (NTS) is produced, the system automatically feathers the propeller by using the feathering valve. The feathering valve will dump oil from the propeller and cause it to move into the feather position. This action will cause the engine rotation to cease and reduce aircraft drag. The unfeathering pump is used to produce pressure to move the blades from the feather position to low or zero pitch until the locks engage (static) and hold the propeller blade angle in low pitch in flight.

Anti-ice System

Anti-icing for the TPE331 engine, seen in Figure 8-3-8, involves an electrically actuated system controllable by the pilot. The inlet anti-icing system employs warm bleed air from the second-stage compressor. This air is directed through a forward manifold to an anti-icing shield surrounding the outer side of the air inlet. The air then flows rearward and is discharged into the engine nacelle. The inner wall of the air inlet is a part of the gearbox case and is warmed by engine oil.

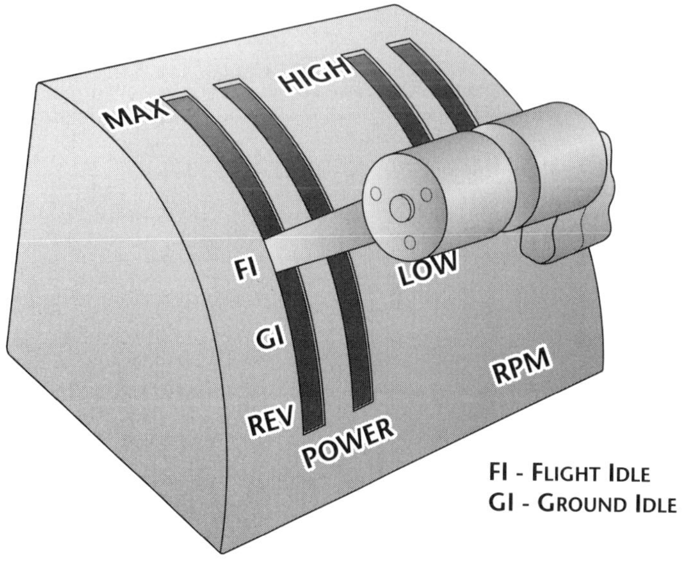

Figure 8-3-6. The engine control panel has the power lever and condition (speed) lever.

Fuel System

The fuel system for the TPE331 engine, shown in Figure 8-3-9, is designed to pressurize and

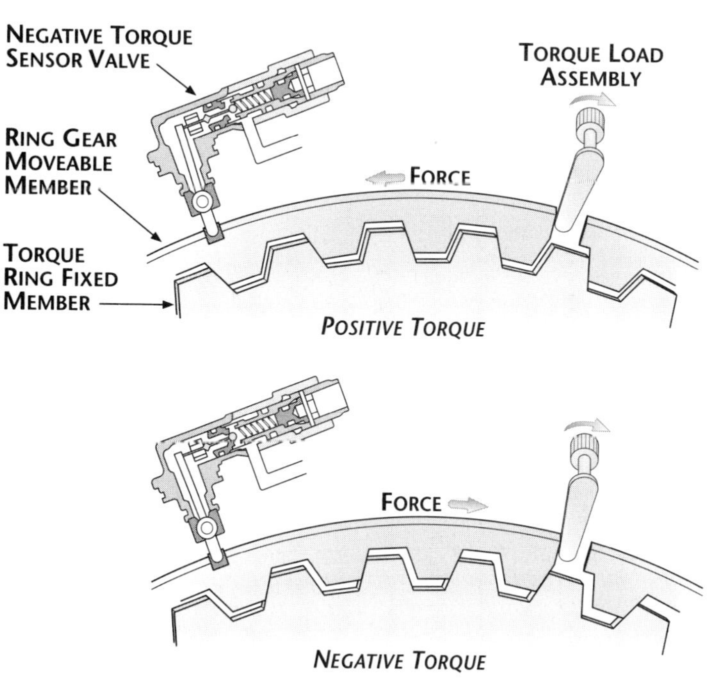

Figure 8-3-7. Engine torque sensor showing positive and negative torque situations

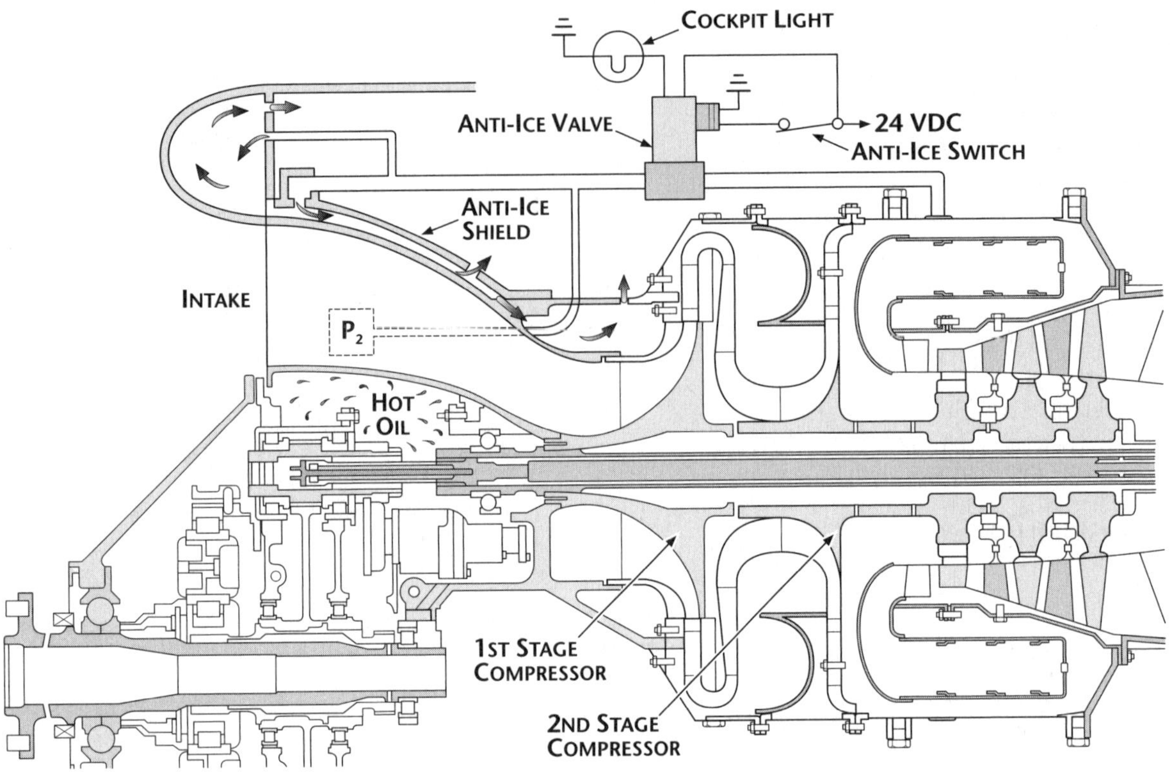

Figure 8-3-8. The anti-icing system and operation use a combination of hot oil and hot air.

regulate the fuel as it is directed to the nozzles that atomize it as it is injected into the rear of the combustor. The fuel control unit is coordinated with the propeller control to provide the correct amount of fuel to meet the speed and power requirements of the engine. The system includes:

- Fuel control unit
- Solenoid valve
- Flow divider
- Fuel nozzle
- Manifold assembly
- Oil/fuel heat exchanger

The system automatically controls fuel flow for variations in power-lever position, compressor

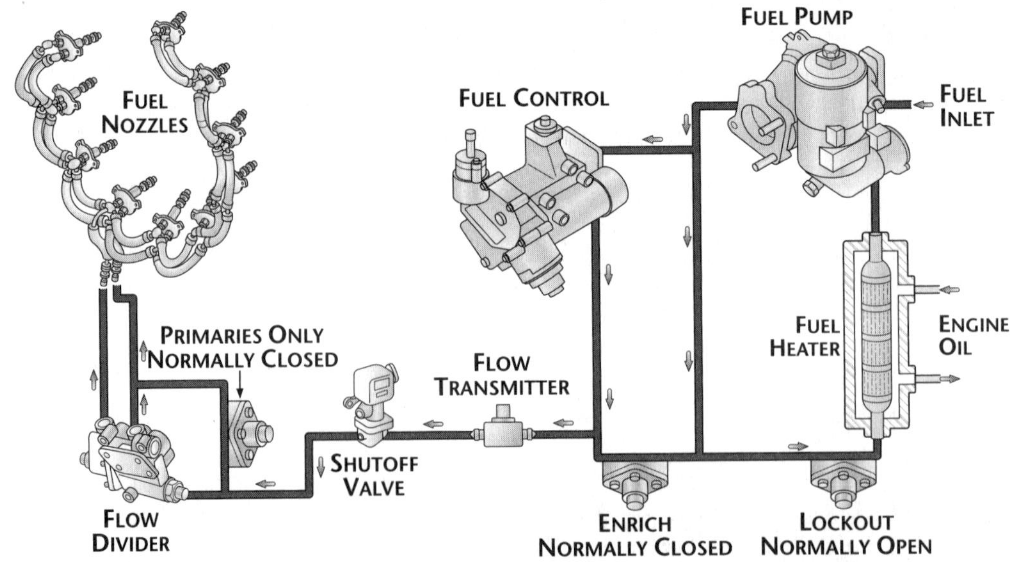

Figure 8-3-9. The fuel system meters fuel to match power demands from the cockpit.

discharge pressure and inlet-air temperature and pressure. The solenoid valve is actuated automatically to open during starting and to close on engine shutdown. It is manually closed when the propeller is feathered.

Section 4

Pratt & Whitney Canada PW100 Turboprop Engine

The Pratt & Whitney Canada PW100 series of engines, seen in Figure 8-4-1, is widely used in regional airline industry. The engine series offers power ranges from 1,800 to 6,680 shaft horsepower with over 5,500 engines produced. The PW-100 is a multi-spool engine incorporating a single stage low pressure centrifugal compressor attached to its corresponding low pressure turbine. The high pressure signal stage centrifugal compressor is driven by the high pressure turbine. The two stage power turbines turn the propeller shaft through a propeller reduction gear box. The basic layout of the engine is shown in Figure 8-4-2. Electronic engine control with mechanical backup allows ease of pilot operation and system redundancy.

Examples of the aircraft that utilize this engine are the ATR42 and 72, the Q-series Dash 8, the Casa C295, the Dornier 328, the EMB 120 Brasilia, the Fokker 50 and 60 and the British Aerospace ATP. The PW150A, a growth derivative of the current PW100 family of engines uses advanced technology and can develop 7,500 horsepower.

This engine is designed to increase reliability, durability and economics. As with all engines, a reduction in fuel consumption, noise and emissions are always being improved. The engine uses a FADEC (Full Authority Digital Electronic Control) fuel control system and EMS (engine monitoring system). This is one of several turboprop engines that develop high horsepower ratings in the 5,000 to 6,000 horsepower range. General Electric and Rolls-Royce also have engines in this and higher horsepower ranges.

Figure 8-4-1. Pratt & Whitney engines produce from 1,800 to 6,680 SHP.

Photo courtesy of Pratt & Whitney

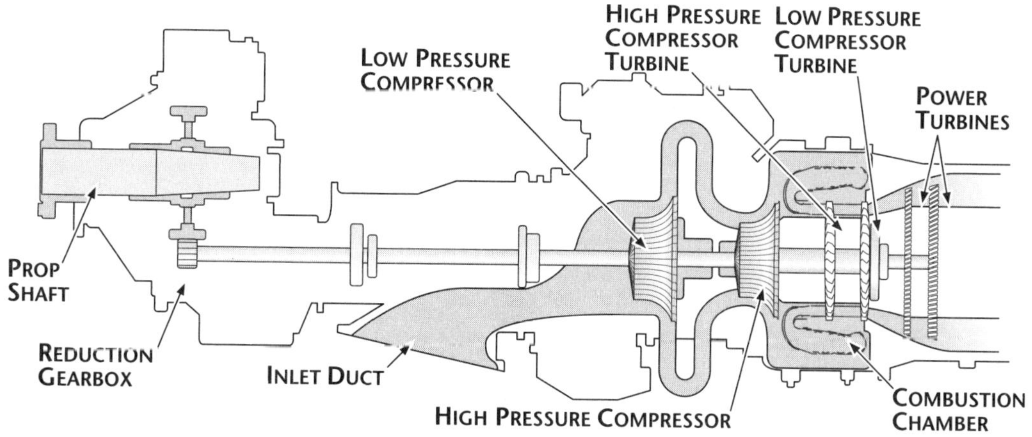

Figure 8-4-2. The engine design reflects many of the innovations developed on other turboshaft engines.

AIR
3520
H-515
2·5 L.

Chapter 9

TURBOSHAFT engines & APUs

A gas-turbine engine that delivers its power through a shaft is referred to as a turboshaft engine. Turboshaft engines are very similar in many ways to turboprop engines. They use a turbine located in the exhaust stream to capture thrust energy and convert it to rotary motion. The primary difference between the two engines is in their output shaft speeds. Turboprop engines operate around 2,000 r.p.m., while turboshaft engines operate above 6,000 r.p.m.

Additionally, reduction gearing is required for turboprop engines to keep the propeller tip speed from exceeding the speed of sound. Some turbines are available in both turboshaft and turboprop versions. The turboshaft engine may produce some thrust but it is primarily designed to produce shaft horsepower (SHP).

The turboshaft engine has the same basic components found in a gas turbine engine (gas generator), with the addition of an extra turbine wheel or wheels to absorb the power of the escaping gases from the gas generator. The output shaft may be coupled directly to the gas generator turbine or the shaft may be driven by a turbine of its own (free turbine), located downstream of the gas generator in the exhaust stream. The free turbine is the most common because it allows the gas generator to be started independently of the power turbines.

Turboshaft engines are primarily used in helicopter and auxiliary power unit applications. An auxiliary power unit (APU) is a stand-alone unit that is not the main powerplant.

Smaller gas turbine APU engines are used mostly on large transport aircraft and business aircraft. They are designed to provide an aircraft with electrical or pneumatic power to perform several on-board functions, making the

Learning Objectives

- *Auxiliary Power Units*
- *Honeywell GTCP 85*
- *Operation*
- *APU Operation*
- *Rolls-Royce 250*
- *Engine Operation*
- *Inflight Power Loss*

Left: Turboshaft engines power most of the modern helicopter fleet.

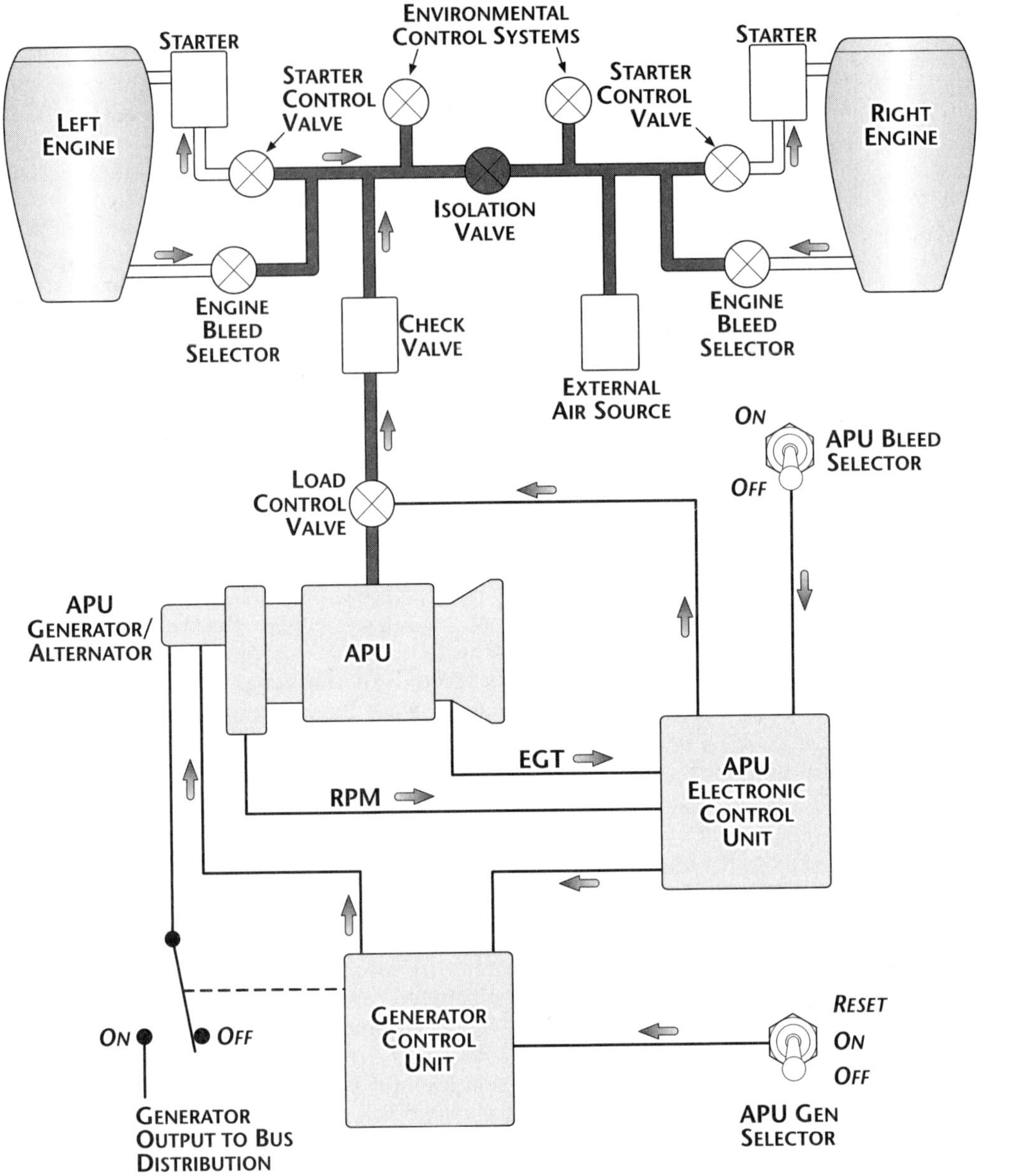

Figure 9-1-1. The APU system, connected to an aircraft system and engines, provides electrical and pneumatic power on the ground.

aircraft more independent of ground support equipment. APUs can provide either auxiliary, electric, or pneumatic power on the ground or electrical power in flight if needed.

Section 1

Auxiliary Power Unit (APU)

An auxiliary power system, such as the one shown in Figure 9-1-1, supplies electrical and pneumatic power for most transport category aircraft. Its purpose is to provide high-pressure bleed air to drive the main engine's air turbine starters and to mechanically turn a generator to provide electrical power while on the ground.

The APU is generally mounted in the tail cone of the aircraft. See Figure 9-1-2. On the ground, electrical and pneumatic power is available for such uses as lighting, onboard electrical systems, ventilation (heating and air-conditioning) and main engine starting. This APU power makes the airplane independent of ground support equipment. Pneumatic and electric power is available on most large aircraft in flight up to a specified altitude for emergency power. The new Boeing 787 is bleed air free. Its APU drives two electrical generators that provide power to all the aircraft systems that before used pneumatic (engine bleed air) power. Even engine starting will be accomplished by using electrical power.

The APU is started using a 24-28 volt battery that is on board the aircraft. Although there are many different types and sizes of APUs,

Figure 9-1-2. An APU installation in the tail of a large transport aircraft

the basic function remains the same: providing electrical and pneumatic power. Electrical power can also be provided independently of, or in combination with, pneumatic power. Electrical power has priority at all times. The APU is temperature-limited during pneumatic loading by the use of a fuel control-connected thermostat and temperature-sensitive load control valve thermostat. The load control valve is used to meter the amount of bleed air allowed for aircraft systems. The pneumatic load control valve will move toward closed if the APU exhaust temperature is near the limit.

Honeywell GTCP 85 Series APU

The GTCP 85 series APU is used in many transport type aircraft. Figure 9-1-3 illustrates a cutaway view of the GTCP 85 gas turbine APU. This design incorporates a two-bearing engine with a rotating group assembly of a single-piece first stage impeller, next to a second stage impeller connected to a turbine wheel which drives the assembly, as shown in Figure 9-1-3.

This APU is a self-contained power source that requires only fuel and electrical power for operation, which is provided by onboard aircraft systems. The starting, acceleration and operation of the engine is controlled by an integral system of automatic and coordinated pneumatic and electromechanical controls. Minimal airframe external controls and instruments are used for initiating engine starts and observing engine operation.

Compressor Section

The engine cutaway in Figure 9-1-3 shows a two-stage centrifugal compressor and a single-stage

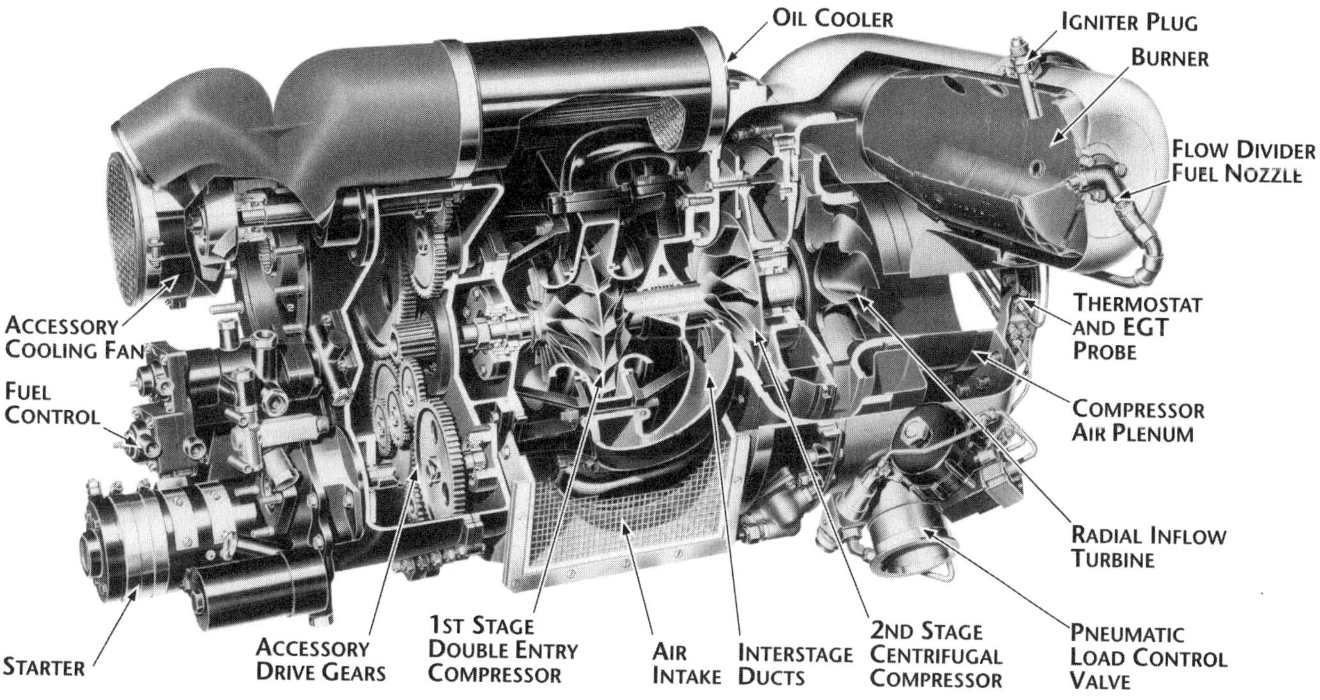

Figure 9-1-3. Cutaway view of a Honeywell GTCP 85 series APU

Image courtesy of Honeywell

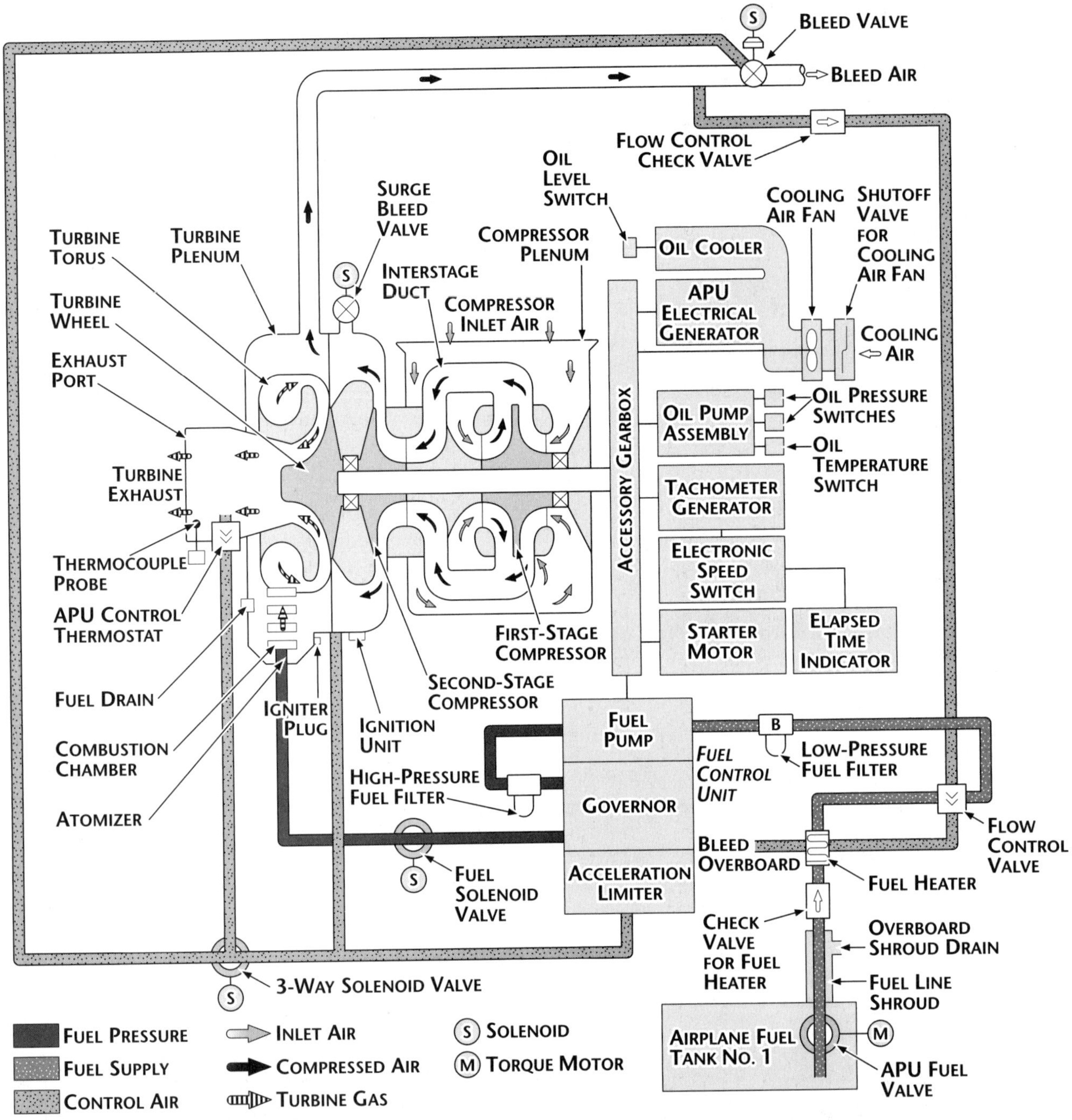

Figure 9-1-4. APU schematic showing airflow and engine systems

radial inflow turbine rotating on a common shaft. At the APU compartment the airflow splits into two paths: the engine intake airflow and the cooling airflow. The accessory cooling air, using a fan driven by the engine gearbox, cools the accessories. The flow of cooling air is controlled by a shutoff valve that is pneumatically operated and then exhausted overboard through a hole in the lower shroud, as shown in Figure 9-1-4.

The compressor impellers are attached pneumatically through inter-stage ducts. At the second-stage impeller, the air velocity is further increased and discharged through the second-stage diffuser, where velocity is decreased and total pressure is increased. The pressure rise from ambient to second-stage discharge is approximately 3:1. The pressure rise represents the contribution of pneumatic energy provided by the compressor section to the engine power cycle.

Turbine Section

The turbine plenum assembly encloses the turbine components and provides a receiver for compressor discharge air. Combustion takes place within the combustion liner. An atomizer injects fuel into the center of the liner, where it is mixed with air and lit by an igniter plug.

A combustion chamber provides a place for mixing and burning the fuel and air at the correct rate. See Figure 9-1-5. First, sufficient air is supplied through specially designed holes in the combustion liner to aid the combustion process. Then, as the flame progresses down its length, additional air is added to dilute this burning mixture in order to reduce the gas temperature, as overheating can damage the APU turbine inlet guide vanes. The holes in the liner are designed to produce efficient burning, while ensuring that the gases cool properly before reaching the inlet guide vanes and turbine. A torus assembly directs the combustion gases to a turbine nozzle that directs the gases at the proper angle and speed onto the turbine blades. See Figure 9-1-6.

The turbine assembly consists of two major pieces: the turbine wheel and turbine nozzle assemblies. The nozzles are convergent ducts; gases flow from a larger to a smaller area, causing an increase in air velocity. Air entering the turbine nozzle is directed against the outer blade tips of the turbine wheel. Since the air is moving at high velocity, it imparts a force against the blade tips, which produces a torque to rotate the wheel.

The air then flows toward the hub, where it must turn again and push against the exducer (radial outflow) blades, thus yielding more of its energy before escaping through the exhaust duct. Some APU's incorporate a load compressor driven by a free turbine that drives the compressor that provides the air pressure for aircraft systems. In this system the APU has a gas generator that provides the expanding gases that drive across the load turbine which in turn drives the load compressor.

Accessory Section

A mechanically driven generator and other accessories necessary for APU operation (fuel control, oil pump, etc.) are mounted on an accessory gearbox and are connected to the compressor/turbine shaft through a gear-reduction system. Depending upon the aircraft, the APU drives one or two generators that are generally identical to the engine-driven generators. The APU generators are usually capable of supplying all or most of the electrical load needed by the airplane.

APU Operation

Normal operation. During operation of the APU, a condition known as IDLE will exist when the APU operates at full speed (100% r.p.m.) and no load is applied to the APU. No load means no pneumatic or electrical power is extracted from the APU. When power is extracted from the generator, a load is imposed on the shaft that causes the compressor and turbine r.p.m. to slow down. Additional increases in load will produce further decreases in shaft r.p.m. (called droop).

To keep the APU unit on speed, the turbine will have to produce more power to match the load. To do this, the fuel control will sense the drop in r.p.m. and increase the fuel flow, which will bring the APU r.p.m. back to the starting point. As this process happens, the EGT will increase with each addition of fuel. The other condition that will cause the EGT to rise is extracting bleed air. Because this action reduces the amount of air flowing through the engine, the EGT temperatures will increase. This increase in EGT is limited at a certain temperature by a thermostat placed in the exhaust air stream. At the maximum temperature the thermostat bleeds fuel control compressor discharge air away form the fuel control. Since the fuel control is using this pressure to schedule

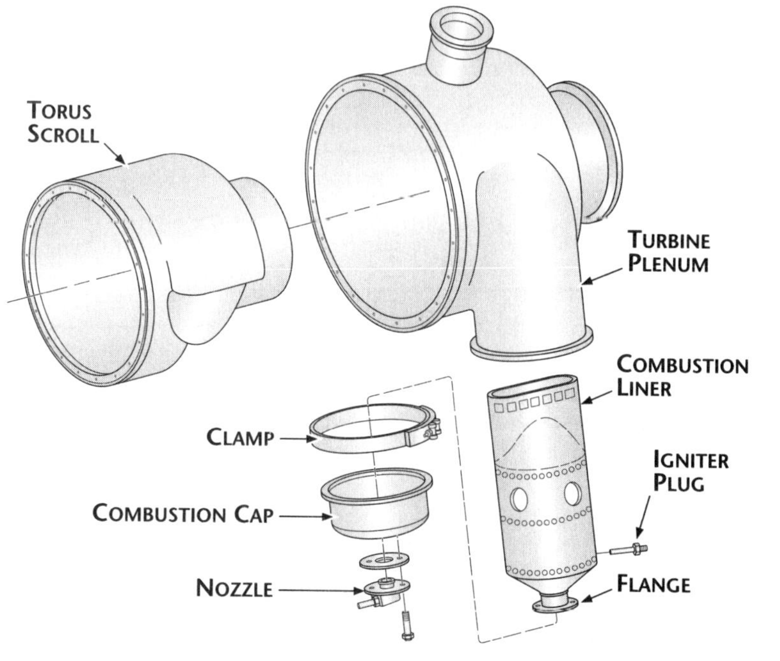

Figure 9-1-5. The combustion section feeds into the torus scroll before the turbine.

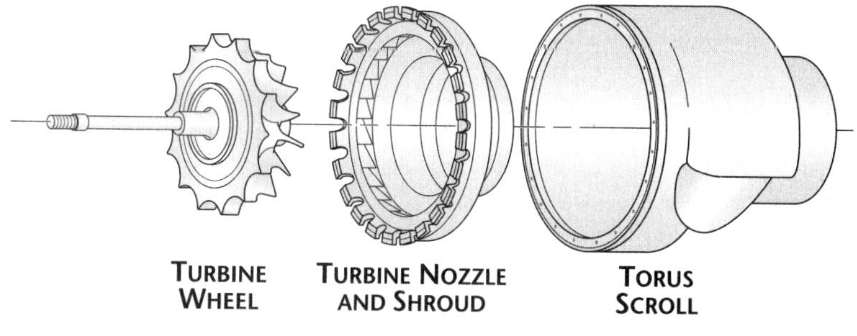

Figure 9-1-6. The turbine section includes the torus scroll, the nozzle and turbine-wheel.

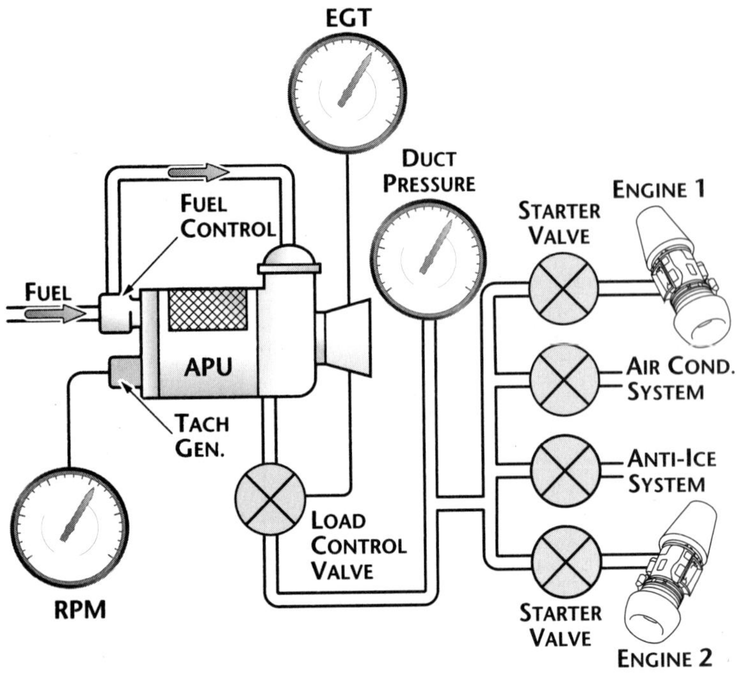

Figure 9-1-7. EGT, duct pressure and r.p.m. are the controlling factors during startup and operation.

the fuel flow, this action limits any additional fuel to the engine.

Starting Sequence

Switches on the APU control panel in the cockpit operate the APU. Sometimes the APU can be controlled from a ground-accessible control panel. In order to initiate the APU's start cycle, all pertinent switches and controls must be in their proper positions as specified in the aircraft checklist. This includes fuel shutoff valves, electrical controls, doors, etc. The main airplane battery switch must be ON to operate the APU. This battery is provided with a battery charger that is disconnected during APU starter engagement. Power for normal charging is provided by the aircraft's electrical system.

The start switch is moved to the start position momentarily and the switch is spring-loaded to return to the run position when released. This action energizes relays that open fuel valves and doors and the starter relay that carries heavy current to the starter. When the starter has cranked the engine to sufficient speed, oil pressure from the lubrication pump will build (3±5 p.s.i.) to close the oil pressure sequence switch. This completes a circuit and energizes the ignition and the fuel solenoid, which opens to permit fuel into the combustor. The fuel ignites from the spark provided by the igniter plug. Light-off (combustion) normally occurs from 10% to 20% r.p.m. When combustion has started, the EGT gauge in the cockpit will show an increase in exhaust gas temperature.

The pressure rise produced by the heat of combustion increases the velocity of airflow through the turbine, which begins producing power to assist the starter in accelerating the engine. Airflow is still too low, however, for the turbine to do the job alone. Acceleration will not continue without the assistance of the starter. Therefore, during the early stages of light-off and acceleration, the operator must pay very close attention to the exhaust gas temperature and r.p.m., to ensure the APU is accelerating smoothly. This acceleration is accomplished by increasing fuel flow to the combustion chamber. At 50% r.p.m., the speed switch operates and the power to the starter is disconnected.

As the APU increases speed to about 95% r.p.m., the APU is then ready to supply electrical and pneumatic power. The APU supplies heated, compressed air. As this energy is extracted from the compressor section, the available pneumatic energy to the turbine section is reduced. This will increase the exhaust temperatures because of reduced airflow as mentioned earlier. Figure 9-1-7 illustrates this operation.

Bleed air. APU air used for aircraft systems passes through a pneumatically actuated load bleed air valve (load control valve). The load-control thermostat controls the opening of the load control valve. As more bleed air is demanded, more air is taken from the compressor section, causing the APU to tend to slow down. The governing section in the fuel control senses a reduction in speed and increases fuel flow to keep speed essentially consistent. As more fuel is added, EGT rises; at a certain point, the load-control thermostat will prevent further opening of the load-control valve. This limits the amount of air being bled and ensures that the maximum EGT is not exceeded.

The newer models utilize the latest technology in hot section materials and an electronic temperature control (ETC) system that limits hot section temperatures based on aircraft need and ambient conditions. The electronic temperature control provides engine operating temperature limits for two operating modes: main engine start (MES) and environmental control system (ECS) operation. Under the original design, exhaust gas temperature (EGT) was limited at a constant maximum temperature. In the dual mode electronic design, the EGT limit can increase from a set maximum temperature for environmental control systems operation to a slightly higher temperature for main engine starting.

Only 5% of the APU operating time is used for main engine start. This limits the time the engine is subjected to higher temperatures.

Oil and fuel system. The APU oil system is a self-contained system made up of independent supply, pumps, regulator, cooler, filters and indicator.

The fuel control system, shown in Figure 9-1-8, consisting of a fuel control unit, fuel pump, acceleration control and governor. Fuel is supplied from a main tank through the fuel shutoff valve. Fuel from the fuel control unit enters the combustion chamber through the fuel solenoid valve and fuel nozzle. Fire detection and extinguishing systems are also installed to provide fire protection for the APU.

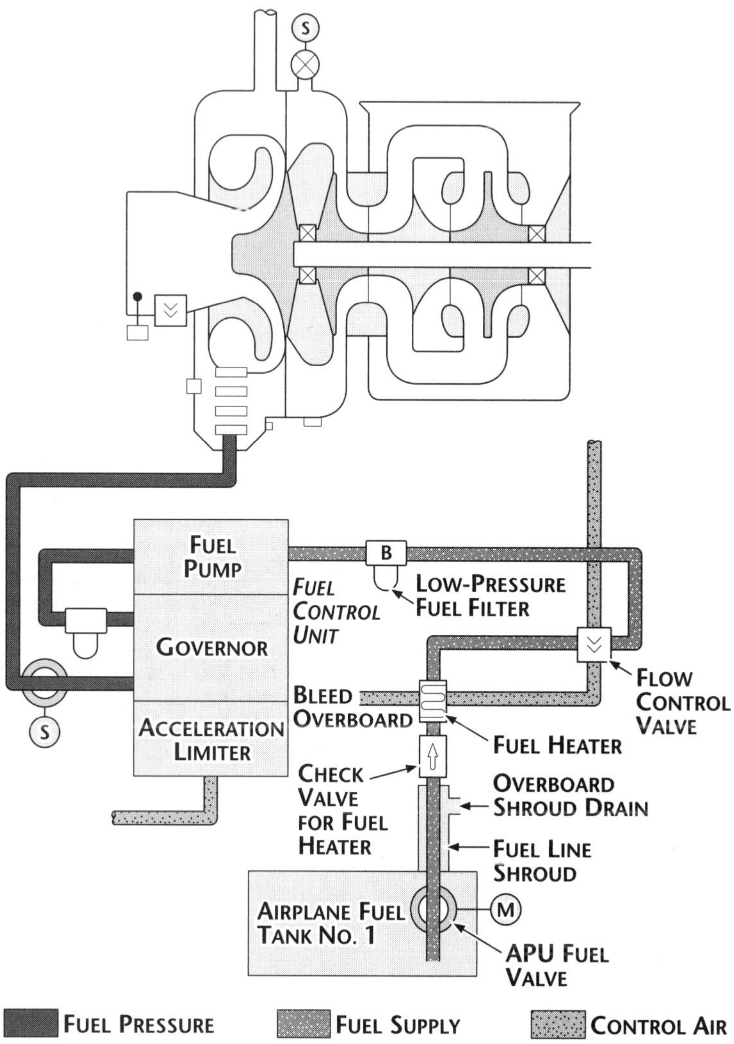

Figure 9-1-8. The fuel control system helps to control the APU output.

Section 2

Turboshaft Engines

Rolls-Royce 250 Series Turboshaft Engine

The Rolls-Royce (Allison) 250 turboshaft series of engines has a long history. The Rolls-Royce 250 series turboshaft engine is one of the most popular helicopter powerplants in the world. Over 23,000 engines have been manufactured since production started in 1958. During that time, several engine types have been produced. The engine has been modernized and updated over the years and powers the Bell Jet Ranger and 222 series, the MD Helicopters 500 & 600 series, as well as the Sikorsky S-76. With the addition of a propeller and a reduction drive gearbox, the engine has also been used to power a number of small turbo-prop aircraft. The 250 is available with power output ratings ranging from 318 SHP to more than 700 SHP. The general specifications for the engines can be found in Table 9-2-1.

The Rolls-Royce 250 series turboshaft engine, shown in Figure 9-2-1, features a free power turbine. A free turbine engine has no mechanical connection between the gas generator turbine and the power turbine. This connection is formed by an air link that will rotate the power turbine due to the gas generator gas flow. The engine consists of a combination axial-centrifugal compressor, a single can type combustor

GENERAL SPECIFICATIONS	
Weight	280 lb
Power/weight ratio takeoff	2.89:1
Airflow takeoff	6.1 lb/sec
Pressure ratio takeoff	9.2:1
Takeoff horsepower	715
Fuels	JP-4, JP-5, ASTM-1655, Jet A, A1, B
Oils	MIL-L-7808, MIL-L-23699
PERFORMANCE AT 100% r.p.m.	
Power output shaft	9,598 r.p.m.
Gas producer rotor	51,000 r.p.m.
Power turbine rotor	30,908 r.p.m.

Table 9-2-1. Performance and specifications model RR 250 – C40B (with FADEC)

Figure 9-2-1. A Rolls-Royce 250 series turboshaft engine

Photo courtesy of Rolls-Royce

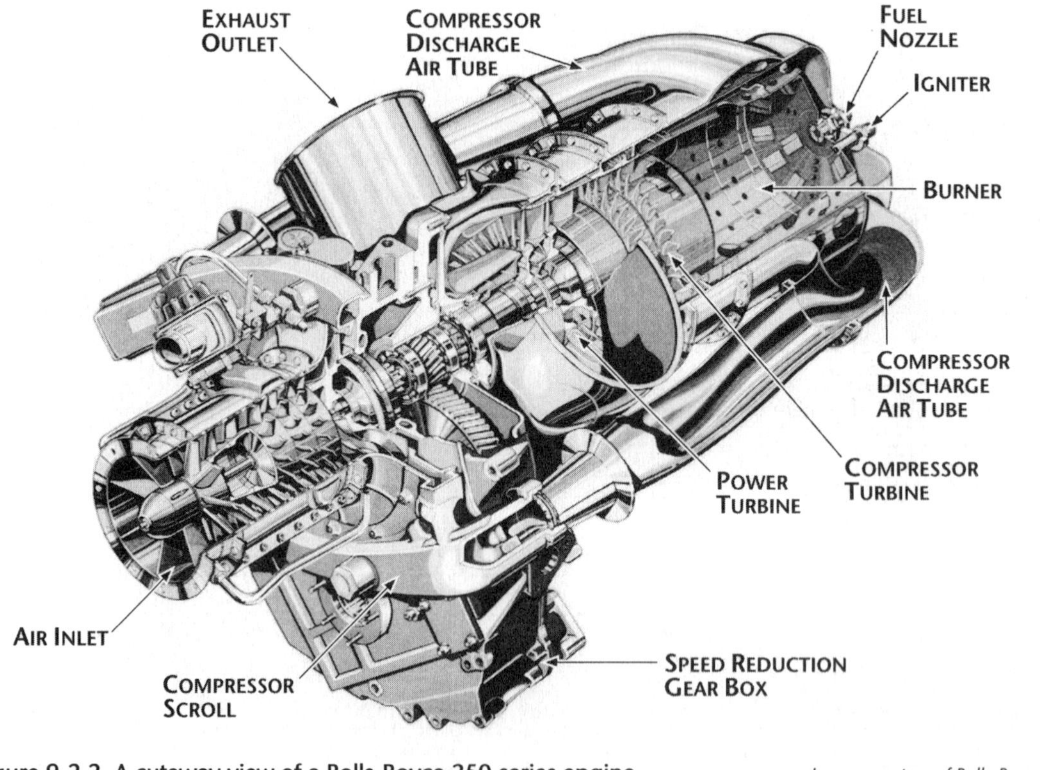

Figure 9-2-2. A cutaway view of a Rolls-Royce 250 series engine.

Image courtesy of Rolls-Royce

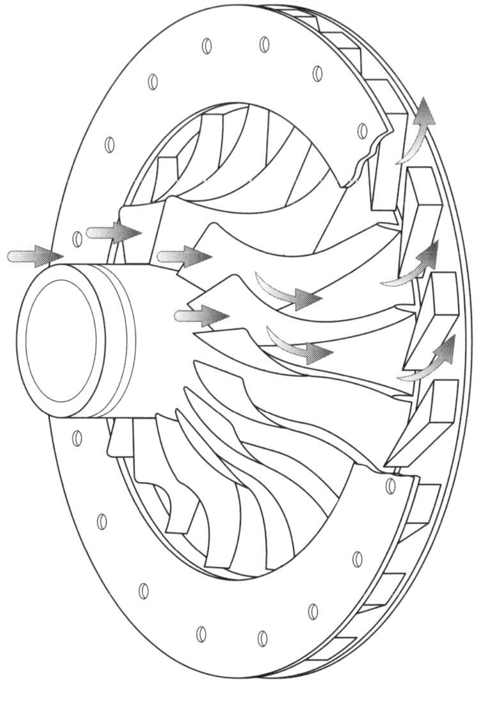

Figure 9-2-3. An impeller and diffuser showing flow through the compressor

and a turbine assembly. It has a two-stage power turbine, an exhaust collector and an accessory gearbox. The accessory gearbox incorporates a gas producer gear train and a power turbine gear train. A cutaway view of the engine can be seen in Figure 9-2-2.

Compressor Section

The compressor assembly consists of a compressor front-support assembly, compressor rotor assembly, compressor case assembly and compressor diffuser assembly. See Figure 9-2-3. The compressor section consists of a compressor front support, case assembly, rotor wheels with blades (for the axial compressor section), centrifugal impeller, front diffuser assembly, rear diffuser assembly, diffuser-vane assembly and diffuser scroll.

Some models of the Rolls-Royce 250 engine do not include the six-stage axial compressor section. On these models, all compression is accomplished by means of the centrifugal compressor. Air enters the engine through the compressor inlet and is compressed by the axial and centrifugal compressor sections. The air then passes through the scroll-type diffuser into two external ducts which convey it to the combustion section at the rear of the engine. The compressor is driven directly by the gas producer turbine at speeds of more than 50,000 r.p.m. Figure 9-2-4 illustrates airflow and gas flow through the Rolls-Royce 250-C20B engine.

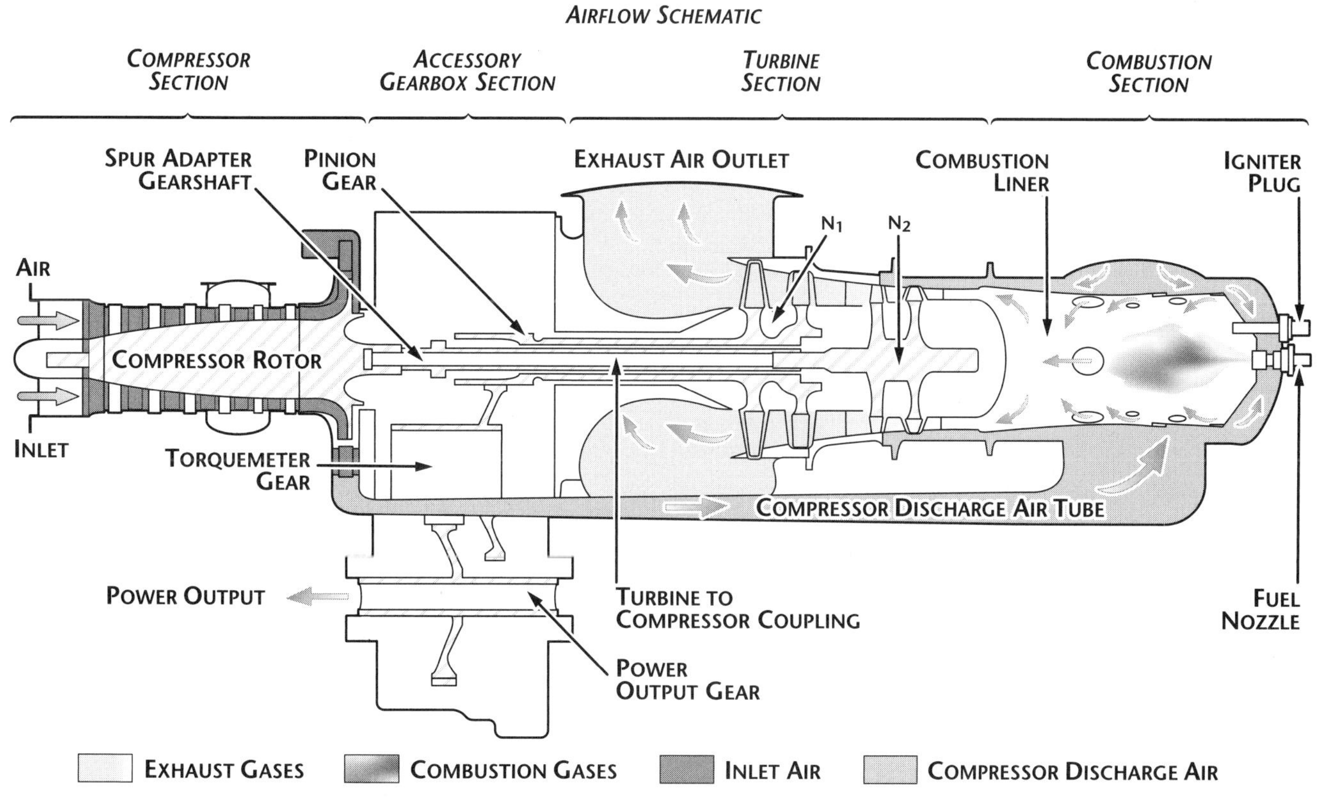

Figure 9-2-4. Airflow and sections through a Rolls-Royce 250 series engine

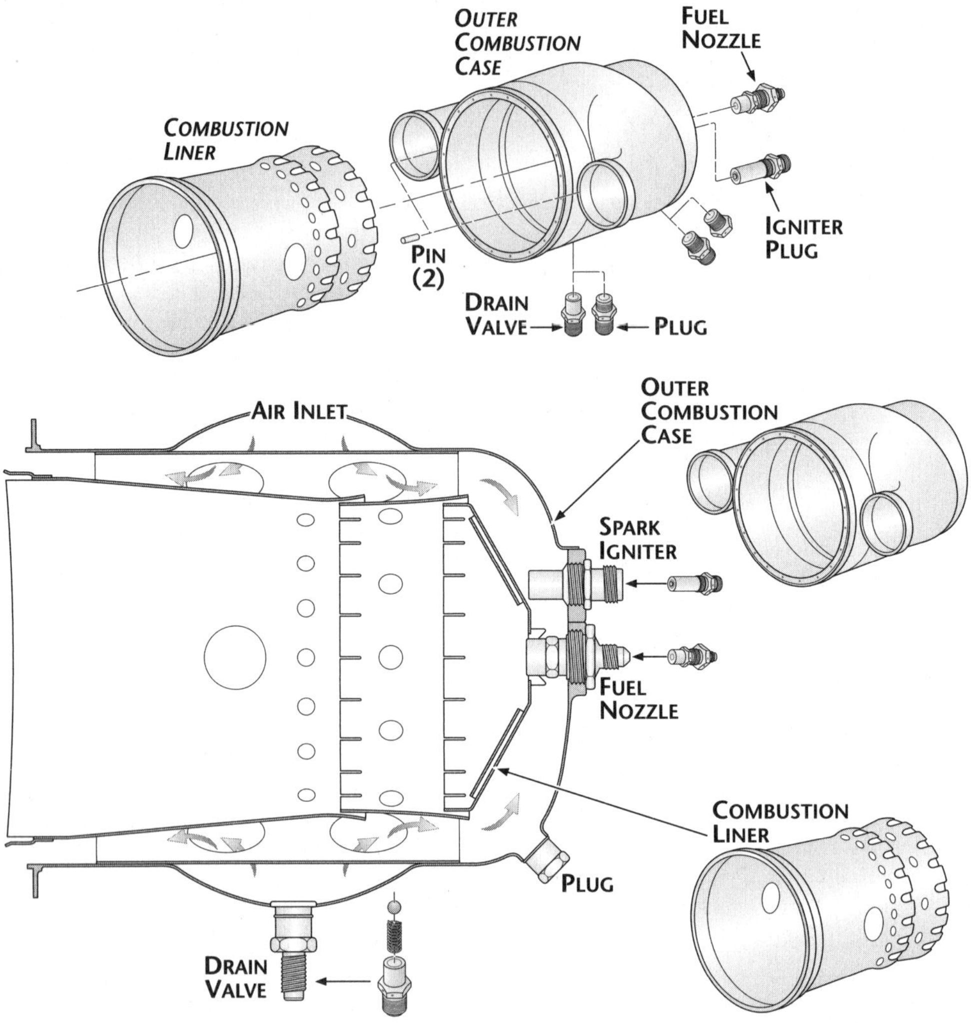

Figure 9-2-5. Rolls-Royce 250 series combustion section components and outer combustion case.

Combustion Section

The combustion section, illustrated in Figure 9-2-5, is located at the rear of the engine. A fuel nozzle and igniter are mounted in the aft end of the outer combustion case. The combustion assembly is comprised of the combustion outer case and a combustion liner. The combustion outer case is stainless steel with four tapped bosses for mounting the burner drain valve and plug, a fuel nozzle and an igniter. The burner drain valve threads into the boss nearest the gravitational bottom, while the other boss is plugged.

The fuel nozzle and igniter are on the rear side of the combustion outer casing; they thread into their respective bosses and extend into the combustion liner dome. The fuel nozzle positions and supports the aft end of the combustion liner and the igniter locates the combustion liner in a circumferential position. The combustion outer casing is flanged on the front for mounting to the gas producer turbine support, seen in Figure 9-2-6.

Compressed air from the two external ducts enters the combustion liner at the aft end through holes in the liner dome and skin. The air is mixed with the fuel sprayed from the fuel nozzle and combustion takes place. The hot gases move forward out of the combustion liner to the first-stage gas producer turbine nozzle.

The combustion liner must provide for rapid mixing of fuel and air and it must control the flame length and position such that the flame does not contact any metallic surface of the liner.

Turbine Section

The turbine assembly of the engine, seen in Figure 9-2-7, incorporates the components necessary for the development of power and the exhausting of gases. The turbine is mounted between the combustion section and the power and accessory gearbox. The turbine assembly has a two-stage gas-producer turbine and a two-stage power turbine.

Power to drive the compressor is furnished by the gas-producer turbine through a direct drive. The power turbine converts the remaining gas energy into power that is delivered to the power pads of the engine. The power turbine drives the output shaft through the reduction-gear train. Exhaust gases from the power turbine are directed into the exhaust collector, which provides for exhaust flow through two elliptical ducts at the top of the engine.

Accessory Section

The main power and accessories drive-gear trains are enclosed in a single gear case which is shown in Figure 9-2-8. This gear case serves as the structural support for the engine. All of the engine components, including the engine-mounted accessories, are attached to it.

Accessories driven by the power-turbine gear train are the power-turbine governor and an airframe-furnished power-turbine tachometer generator.

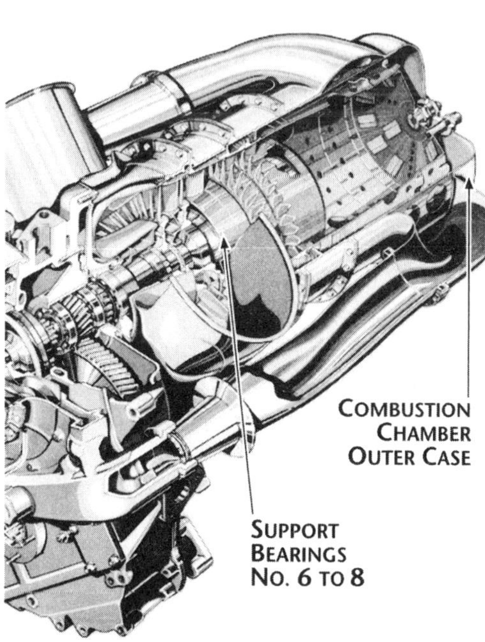

Figure 9-2-6. Cutaway view detailing the combustion outer casing flange and gas producer turbine support

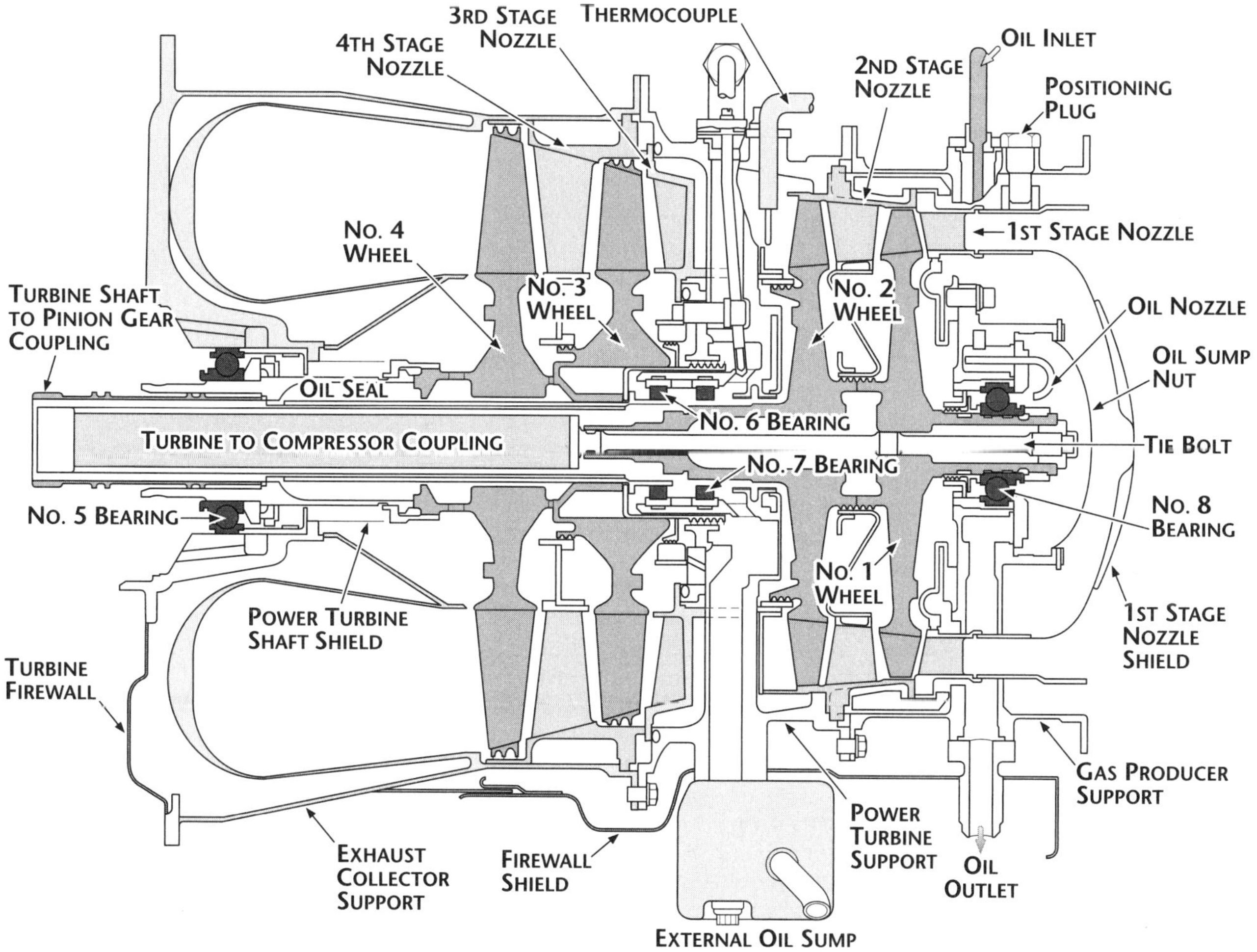

Figure 9-2-7. Rolls-Royce 250 engine turbine section

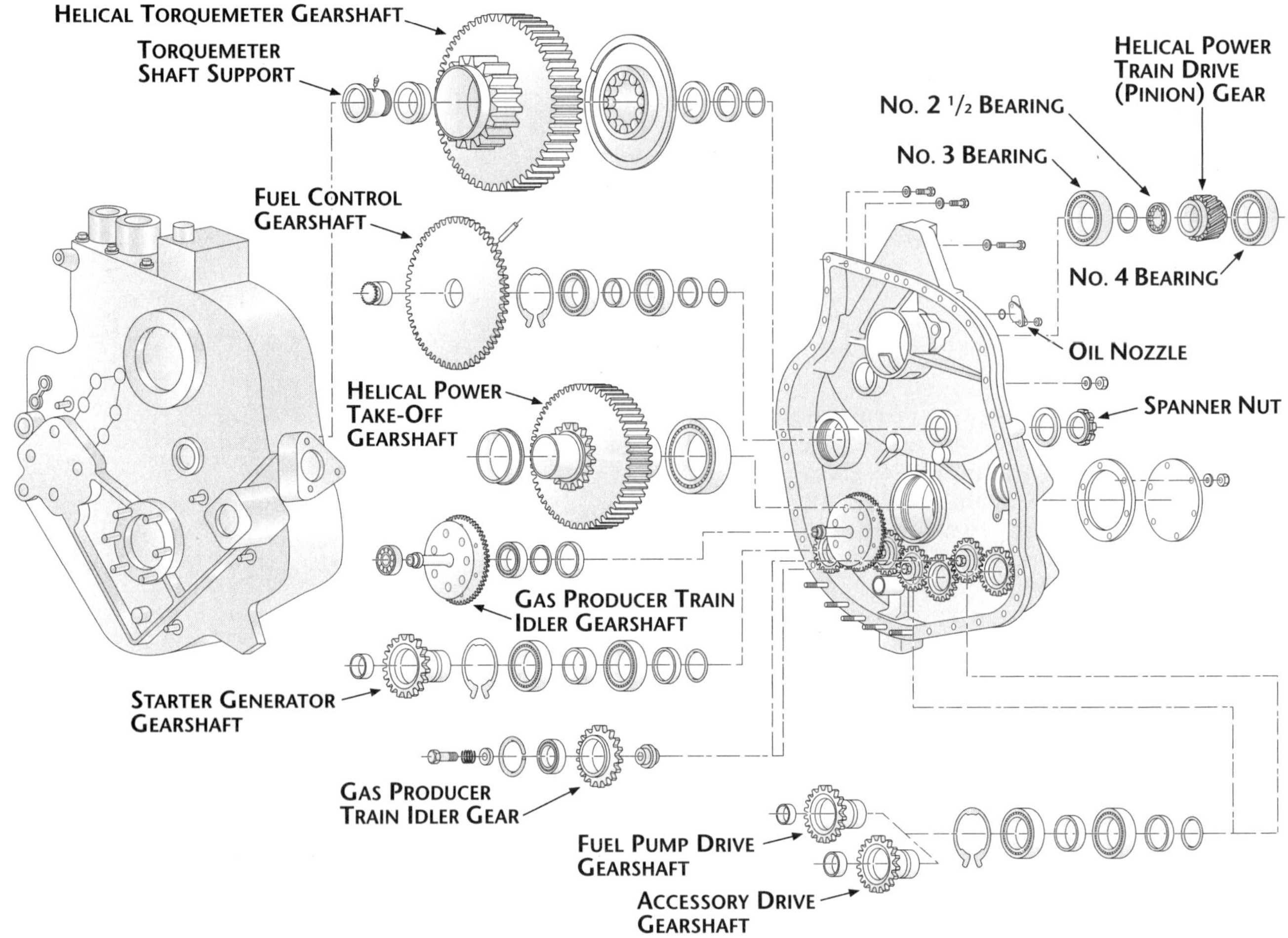

Figure 9-2-8. Rolls-Royce 250 engine accessory gearbox assembly

The gas producer gear train drives the compressor, fuel pump, gas producer fuel control and an airframe-furnished gas producer tachometer generator. The starter drive and a spare drive are part of the gas producer drive train.

Fuel System

The fuel system is illustrated in Figure 9-2-9. The components of the system are a fuel pump, a gas producer fuel control, a power-turbine governor and a fuel nozzle.

The fuel control and the governor are located schematically in the system between the fuel pump and fuel nozzle. The actual flow of fuel in the system involves only the pump, gas producer fuel control and fuel nozzle.

Lubrication System

The lubrication system for the Rolls-Royce 250-C20 turbine engine is shown in Figure 9-2-10. This is a dry-sump system utilizing a pressure pump and a scavenge pump. Two metal chip detectors are included in the system to aid in discovering wear problems within the engine. The oil tank and the oil cooler are both airframe-furnished.

Transmission

The main rotor of a helicopter turns at speeds of 300 to 400 r.p.m. on most makes of helicopters. At the same time, a typical helicopter turbine engine may operate with an output shaft r.p.m. of 6,500. Due to this difference in r.p.m., helicopters require a transmission to reduce engine speed down to the speed required by the main rotor and the tail rotor.

Engine Operation

A minimum starter load is always desirable when an engine is being started. An engine must be able to be cranked without the helicopter rotor imposing any load on the starter. Helicopters powered by reciprocating engines incorporate a clutch system that enables the starter to crank the engine and not the rotor. This clutch system also allows for a gradual stress-free pickup of rotor momentum while the system is being engaged. Helicopters powered by the Series 250 engine do not incorporate a clutch system, because the free-turbine design permits the starter to crank the gas producer system without any helicopter rotor load on the starter.

When a Series 250 engine is started, N_2 N_R speed will not begin to increase when the starter cranks the engine. The speed of N_2 N_R gradually increases, as N_1 speed increases to idle r.p.m. Thus, a free turbine allows for stress-free pickup of rotor momentum and permits cranking of an engine with the rotor imposing no load on the starter.

Ground idle. If the engine is running at stabilized ground idle and takeoff power is required, the operator must move the twist grip from GROUND IDLE to FULL OPEN. When this is done, the gas producer fuel control governor spring is reset from the N_1 ground idle r.p.m. setting to the N_1 overspeed governor setting. This setting results in an increase in N_1 r.p.m., an increase in N_2 r.p.m. to 100% and an output of approximately 70 SHP with the collective-pitch at its minimum setting. On free-turbine installations, it is not necessary for the operator to coordinate the twist grip with the collective-pitch control. As the collective-pitch control is pulled up, the rotor pitch changes such that the rotor power requirements increase. Thus, rotor r.p.m. will tend to droop. As N_2 droops, the power-turbine governor senses the droop and initiates the necessary action to cause the gas producer fuel control to increase fuel flow. As the fuel flow increases, N_1 r.p.m. increases and expansion through the power turbine increases. Thus, the power turbine develops more power, which is delivered to the rotor system to prevent excessive N_2 r.p.m. droop.

The characteristics of the power-turbine governor are such that as the helicopter rotor system power requirements increase, N_2 N_R r.p.m.

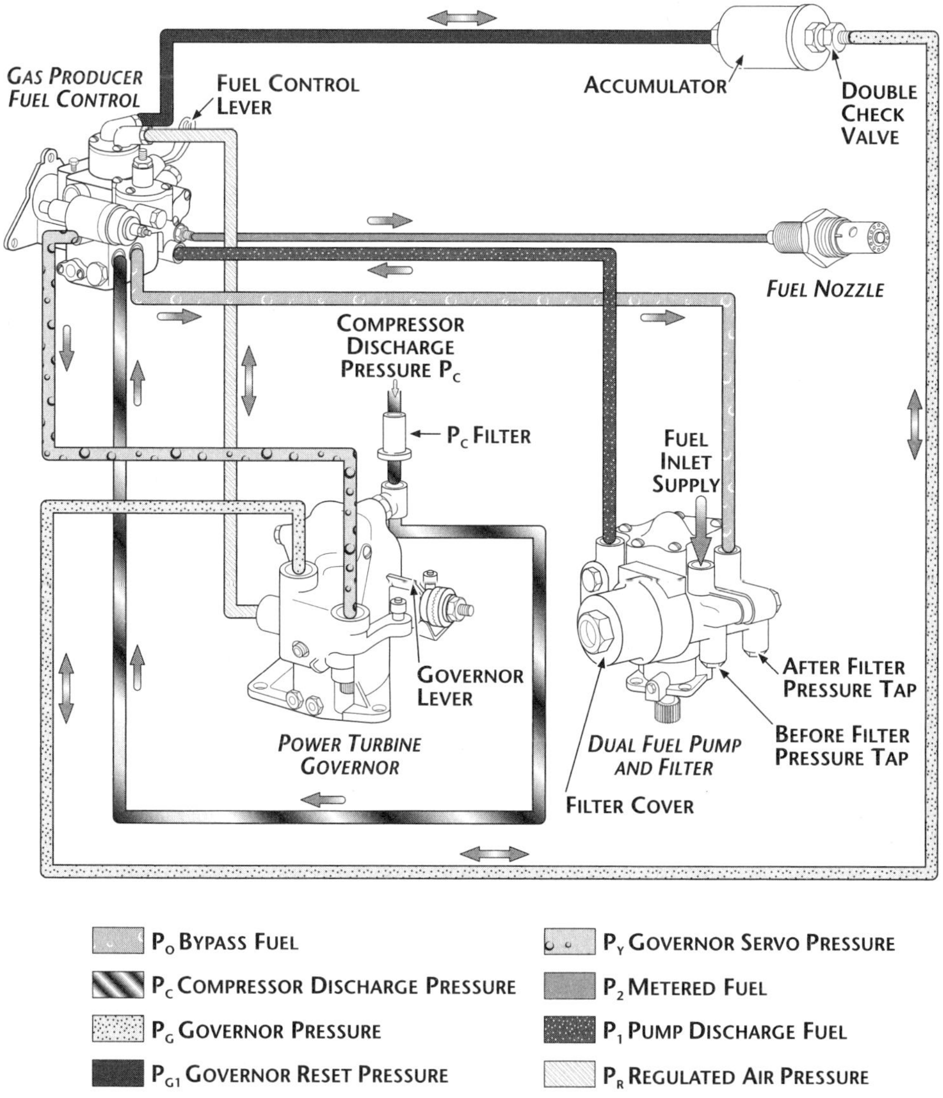

Figure 9-2-9. The fuel system for Rolls-Royce 250 meters fuel to one fuel nozzle.

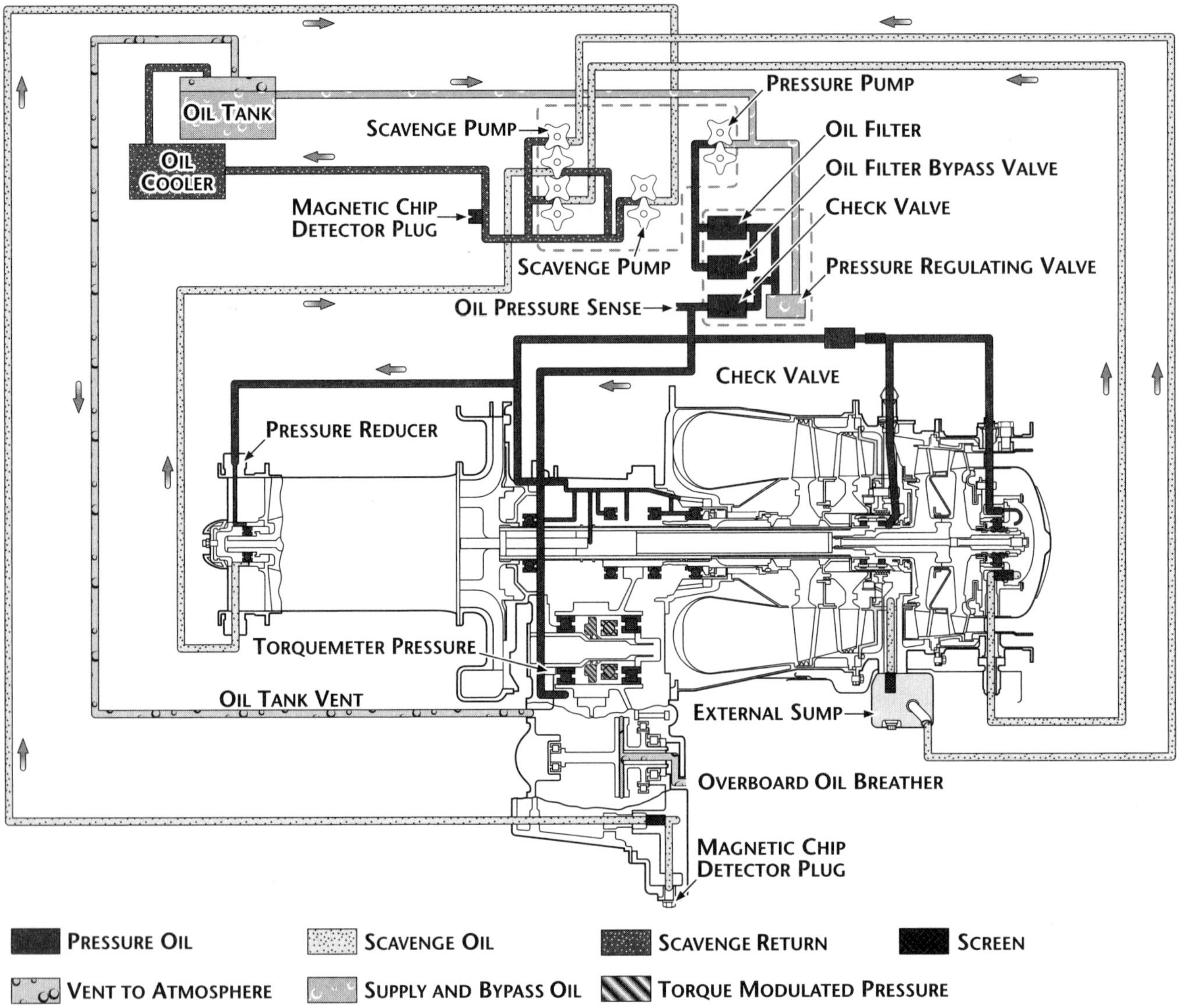

Figure 9-2-10. The dry sump lubrication system has a four-stage gear pump. Three stages are on the scavenge side and one is on the pressure side.

tends to decrease and if the rotor system power requirements decrease, then N_2 N_R tends to increase. On helicopters, it is highly desirable to vary rotor system power requirements without having a change in N_2 N_R r.p.m., as described in the previous paragraph. Therefore, in order to prevent N_2 N_R rpm variation when a power change is made, the helicopter manufacturer provides a droop compensator which acts on the power-turbine governor in such a way that the N_2 N_R r.p.m. holds constant while power to the rotor system is varied.

The droop compensator resets the power-turbine governor spring during power changes, so that the resulting stabilized N_2 N_R following a power change is the same as it was before the power change. Thus, when the operator increases collective, the power delivered to the rotor system increases and the stabilized N_2 N_R r.p.m. remains the same.

Beep switch. If the operator wishes to operate the engine at a different N_2 N_R r.p.m., the power-turbine governor must be reset by some means other than the droop compensator. For this purpose, the helicopter manufacturer provides an electric beeper system. By means of a manually positioned beeper switch, the beeper system can reset the power-turbine governor so that N_2 N_R r.p.m. will be governed at a different speed.

In-flight Power Loss

In the event of an engine failure during flight, a helicopter can usually make a safe autorotational landing without damage to the helicopter or injury to its passengers. An autorotation is a condition of flight in which the helicopter rotor (N_R) speed and the resultant lift are derived entirely from the airflow up through the rotor system.

If an engine fails or if a power loss occurs such that powered flight is no longer possible, the pilot must immediately initiate autorotation by moving the collective-pitch lever down to select minimum rotor pitch. As the helicopter descends, the airflow up through the rotor will maintain N_R speed, the overrunning clutch will prevent the rotor system from delivering power to the engine and the N_2 N_R tachometer indicator needles will (should) split.

Engine failure warning. The natural pilot response to loss of altitude is to increase the collective pitch. If the loss of altitude is due to an engine failure and the pilot increases collective pitch, N_2 N_R r.p.m. will rapidly decrease and a soft autorotational landing may be impossible.

When an engine fails on a helicopter powered by a reciprocating engine, there is a significant change in sound level. Thus, the pilot is warned of the engine failure by the change in sound level. On gas-powered helicopters an engine failure in flight is not easily detected, for there is very little sound-level variation at the time of power loss. For this reason, helicopters powered by turbine engines should be equipped with engine failure warning systems.

Chapter 10

INSPECTION & maintenance

Section 1

Maintenance Requirements

Learning Objectives:

- Maintenance Requirements
- Line Maintenance
- Modular Maintenance
- Maintenance Programs
- Engine Wash
- Overhaul Practices
- Corrosion of Turbine Engines
- Sulfidation
- Standard Practices
- Bearing Inspections

Maintenance programs and processes have evolved over many years. The first generation of formal air carrier maintenance programs was based on the premise that each functional part of a transport aircraft engine needed periodic disassembly and inspection.

This is known as a hard time (HT) inspection program. As the industry gathered more information on engines, it was apparent that some parts of an engine could remain in service longer than others. These findings led to the development of on-condition (OC) and reliability control (RC) philosophies of maintenance.

On-condition Maintenance

General application of the hard time process became obsolete as the industry matured and aircraft became more complex. The industry realized that each component or part did not require a scheduled overhaul on a fixed-time basis to ensure acceptable reliability. The OC process was assigned to components on which a determination of continued airworthiness could be made by visual inspection, measurements, tests or other means without disassembly and inspection or overhaul.

Reliability Control

The OC process evolved into the method of control which is referred to as reliability control (RC) and includes the third maintenance process category, referred to as condition monitoring (CM).

Left: **Visual inspection of an Airbus A310 engine during an overnight stop**

Photo courtesy of Lufthansa

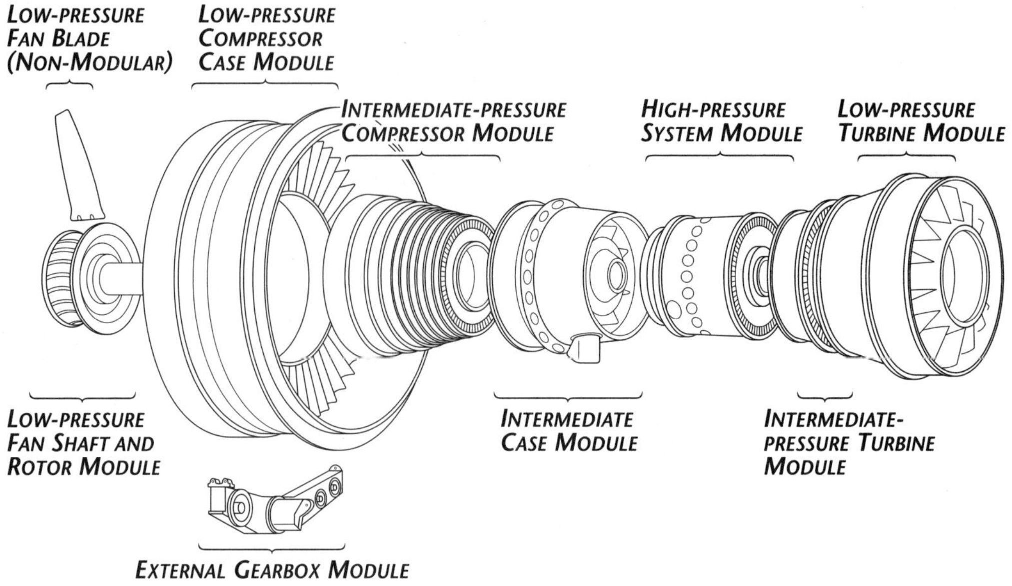

Figure 10-2-1. The Rolls-Royce Trent engine is an example of a modular engine.

This new method of control was oriented toward mechanical performance rather than predicting failure points which was the case with earlier maintenance processes. Reliability control's major emphasis is maintaining failure rates below a predetermined value of an acceptable level of reliability. The analytical nature of reliability management identifies aircraft, powerplants, components and systems that do not fit the HT or OC process categories. The CM process category does not require services or inspections, but mechanical performance is monitored and analyzed.

Time Between Overhauls

Time between overhauls (TBO) was originally used for turbine engines to determine when an engine needed to be overhauled. Older engine designs still use the TBO requirement. Many of these engines are now maintained under an on-condition maintenance program that can extend the overhaul intervals. The length of time between overhauls varies between different engine types, the type of operation and the utilization and climatic conditions under which the engine is operated. Operational experience with the engine can also be factor in the TBO interval.

The maximum time an engine can remain installed in an aircraft is limited to a period agreed upon by the aircraft operator, engine manufacturer and airworthiness authority (FAA/EASA). Rotating disks of the turbine and compressor are often time- or cycle-limited parts and are replaced automatically at overhaul. During overhaul, it is generally found that other assemblies of the engine are mechanically sound and could continue in service for a much longer period.

Older engines. Many engines which were type certificated before 1980 used only the HT process. No maintenance programs were developed under the OC or CM process. Since 1980, many operators have developed maintenance programs centered on the OC process.

An operator must have an approved scheduled maintenance program for each engine model operated. In addition to procedural information, the program must provide scheduling information or intervals for cleaning, adjusting, testing and lubrication of each engine part. The degree of inspection, applicable wear tolerances and the work required at these periods must also be included in the program.

These inspections and other required tasks may be scheduled on an opportunity basis, whereby the task is performed in conjunction with such opportunities as scheduled shop visits, engine removal for cause, product improvements, AD accomplishment or other maintenance functions. These OC programs must be approved by the manufacturers and the FAA/EASA before they can be implemented.

Cycles

Cycles are used to determine when to overhaul a turbine engine. For engines in normal airline usage, a cycle is defined as an engine start and stop. Other manufacturers use any flight consisting of one takeoff and one landing, regardless of length of flight and whether or not the thrust reversers were used on landing. A touch-and-go (landing and takeoff) is sometimes included in this definition. Operating cycles will give a better indication of engine wear than operating hours because engines are stressed more during start-up and maximum thrust operations than during cruise flight conditions.

Start counters. Some auxiliary power units (APUs) have a start counter that records the number of starts. The number of starts, not the operating hours, determines when the engine must be inspected or overhauled.

It is very important that the number of cycles and/or operating hours of life-limited parts are recorded accurately in the permanent record or computer database.

Section 2

Line Maintenance

The inspection and maintenance requirements are not the same for all types of turbine engines. Each manufacturer has established maintenance schedules for its engines. Smaller aircraft could be maintained under 14 CFR part 91 requirements and typically have a progressive type of inspection schedule. This means that the total inspection requirement for the engine is divided into different phases to limit the downtime of the aircraft.

Modular Maintenance

Newer modular engine designs and improved inspection and monitoring techniques have replaced the TBO as the primary reason for overhaul of many large turbine engines. Typically, the engine will be monitored and sections containing life-limited parts will be replaced as needed. Some modern turbine engines have been on the wing for more than 20,000 hours before being overhauled or replaced.

Modular maintenance is applicable to most modern high-bypass-ratio turbofans and is generally a part of maintenance procedures. Engines of this type are assembled in build groups or modules which enable rapid and efficient removal, repair or replacement. Figure 10-2-1 illustrates this concept. Modular construction has several important benefits:

- Decreased turnaround time for repair
- Lower overall maintenance costs
- Reduced spare engine holdings
- Maximum life achieved from each module
- Savings on transport costs
- Ease of transport and storage
- On-wing test capability after any module change

Maintenance Programs

Air carriers monitor and analyze their maintenance programs and adjust inspection requirements and intervals accordingly. Aircraft engines in commuter aircraft that fly many short routes need more frequent maintenance than engines installed in large aircraft which fly long routes, because the commuter aircraft will have many more flight cycles per time period than the larger aircraft. The maintenance inspection schedule is based on flight hours, cycles, flight conditions, age of the engine and environmental conditions. The maintenance schedule can be adjusted by the air carrier after approval of the engine manufacturer and the airworthiness authority.

Scheduled Inspections

Periodic service check. During the periodic service (PS) check the engine is visually inspected and its maintenance log book is checked for entries and daily maintenance needs. The PS check can be performed overnight or during downtime during the flight day.

A check. The A check is more detailed than the PS check and is performed about once a week or after 100 flight hours. The engine check usually includes the following tasks:

- Visually inspect the engine exhaust and rear turbine stages for damage.
- Visually inspect the thrust reverser for damage and check for sound operation of the translating cowls and other moving components of the system.
- Check and fill the engine oil tanks as required. Record the amount of oil added in the inspection log.
- Inspect and service the constant-speed drive as necessary.

B check. The B check is more thorough than the A check and is done approximately once a month (after about 300 to 500 flight hours). Besides specific service performed on the aircraft, a detailed series of systems and operational checks on the engine are performed. The B check on the engine includes the following:

- Visually inspect all cowling, fan and first-stage compressor blades.
- Apply approved lubrication to cowl latches.
- Service oil system, including oil filter and screen. Visually check for appearance of

Figure 10-2-2. The latest borescopes are equipped with LCD screens.

metal contamination in both, as an indicator of abnormal wear.

- Check oil quantity, carefully following the manual directions for the time interval after engine shutdown.
- Check the CSD and starter oil, servicing as required and recording quantities added in the inspection log.
- Check the ignition system for operation, observing all precautions to avoid potentially lethal voltage.
- Inspect thrust reversers, paying close attention to the deflector doors or cascade vanes for the presence of cracks.
- Check for sound operation and security of the translating cowls.

C and D checks. The C and D checks are extensive in scope and type-specific in procedure. They are scheduled based on flight hours and cycles and they require many man-hours to perform. The D check focuses primarily on the airframe and is generally performed once every six years. The aircraft will be completely disassembled and inspected for corrosion and structural defects. Depending on the history of the engine, it may have an extensive inspection or some of the modules can be replaced. In some instances the engine may be overhauled

Figure 10-2-3. A combustion chamber viewed with a borescope.

or replaced. These checks are performed at facilities which are approved and equipped for this type of heavy maintenance.

Maintenance performed on the engine when it is installed on the aircraft is often called on-wing maintenance. This includes either scheduled or unscheduled maintenance as well as component changes, inspections and routine service.

Many air carriers operating commercial aircraft use line checks or numbered intervals—Number 1 check—as well as A, B, C and D checks for their maintenance scheduling. The engine maintenance requirements are performed during the scheduled aircraft inspections.

Unscheduled Inspection

An unscheduled inspection is performed when the engine is subjected to unusual stress or operating conditions, when operating limitations have been exceeded, or when the engine performs below standard. The following are examples of conditions requiring unscheduled maintenance:

- Performance deterioration
- Over-speed
- Over-temperature
- Over-torque
- Immersion in water

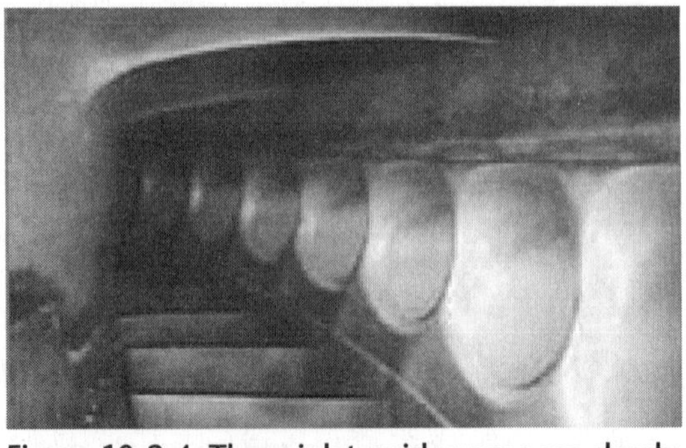

Figure 10-2-4. These inlet guide vanes are clearly seen with a borescope.

- The engine is dropped
- Material ingestion (ice, rocks)
- Bird strike
- Chip detector circuit completion or debris in oil filter
- Heavy/hard landing

Inspection Tools for Line Maintenance

One of the first steps in these inspections is a close visual inspection using a borescope.

Borescope Inspection

The borescope is an optical device which lets an operator inspect areas of the engine without removing or disassembling it. Access is gained through special ports or openings created by removal of engine components. The fiberscope and videoscope, seen in Figure 10-2-2, have the added advantage of making photographs or videos of the inside of the engine. This information can then be stored on a computer as a record of the engine condition.

The ability to document results is essential in aviation, in order to allow discussion or monitoring of the progression of small cracks and blisters with colleagues who may be located elsewhere. If any unacceptable damage is found during the borescope inspection, the engine may need to be disassembled. A satisfactory borescope inspection, when used with other analytical tools, can increase the operating life of the engine.

A borescope or similar equipment is used to perform hot-section inspections to determine engine deterioration, as shown in Figures 10-2-3 and 10-2-4. Using the borescope is more practical and economical than disassembling the engine to inspect the hot section parts. Frequent removal and installation of the engine section, components and assemblies may result in damage to parts and/or distortion of sealing surfaces which can cause gas leaks and performance loss. Operators of borescope equipment require training, experience and practice to be able to determine defects and analyze what they are looking at.

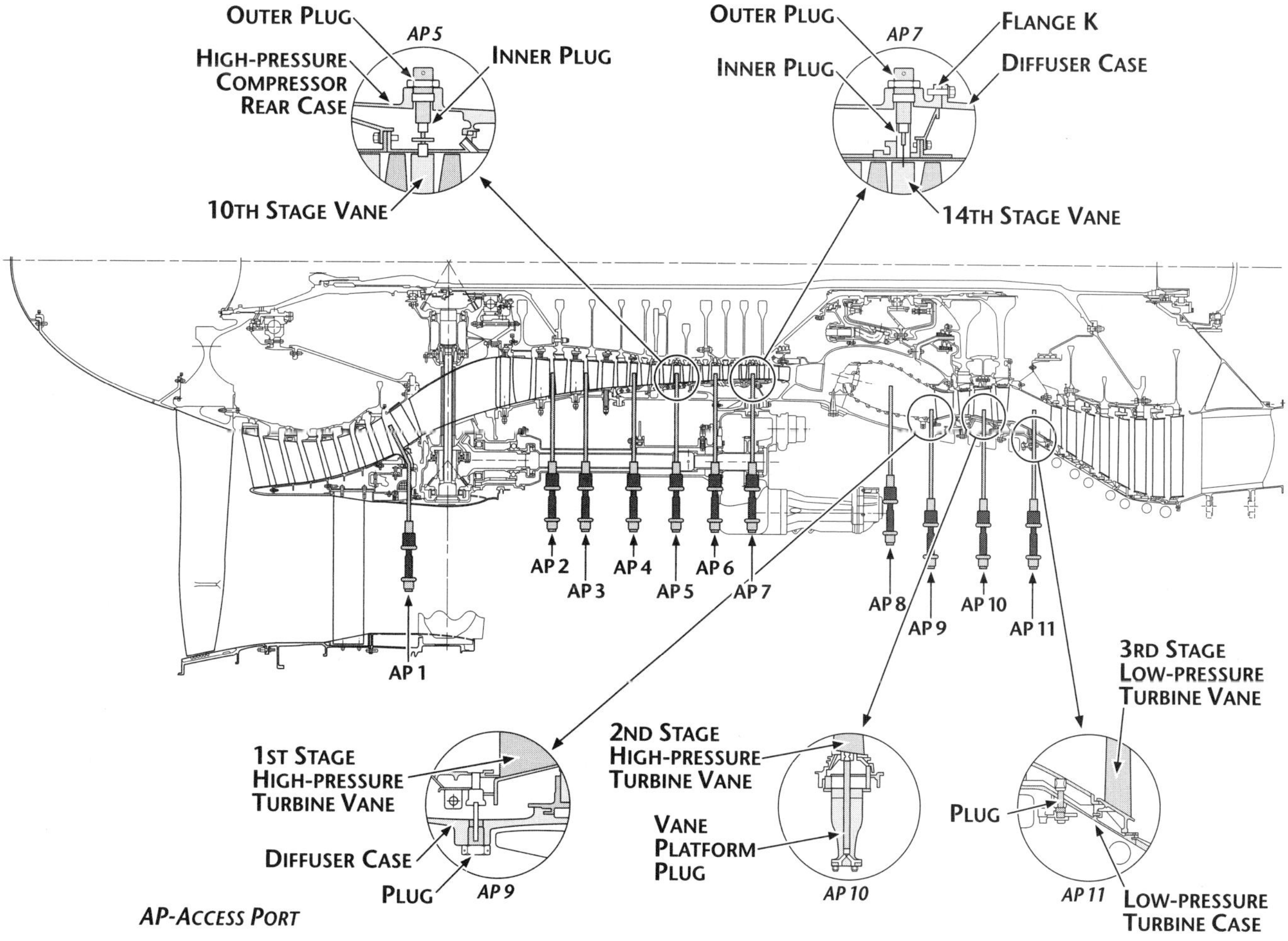

Figure 10-2-5. Engine areas that are viewed by a borescope

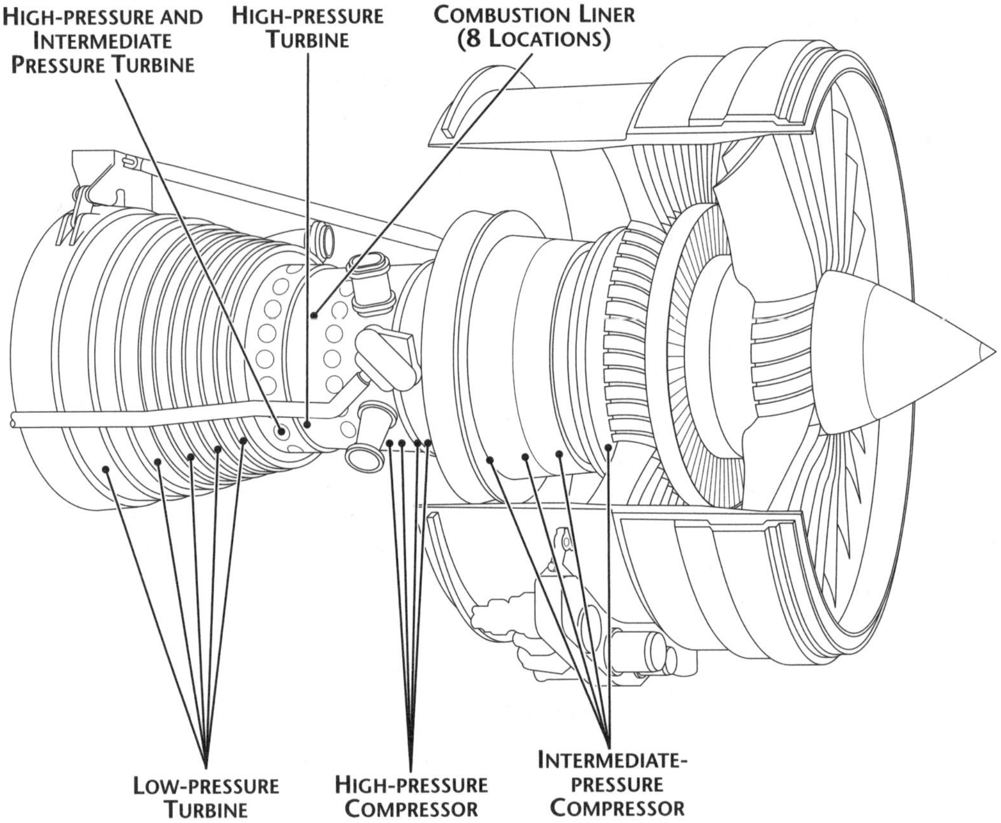

Figure 10-2-6. Borescope access ports

Many engines have specific openings where the borescope can be inserted into the engine for inspections. Some of these are shown in Figures 10-2-5 and 10-2-6.

Figure 10-2-7. Cutaway of a PT6 hot section

Maintenance Practices

Much of the line maintenance on a turbine engine consists of replenishing fluids and correcting minor discrepancies. During periodic inspections, one of the most common inspections is the hot section inspection.

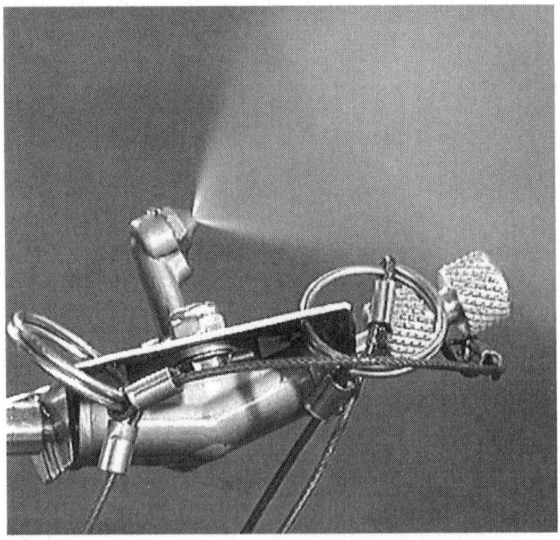

Figure 10-2-8. Along with tests of the ignition system and visual examination of surfaces for cracking, warping, corrosion, and heat distress, fuel nozzles are checked for leaks during a hot section inspection.

Hot-section Inspection

The hot section of a turbine engine includes the combustion can and liner as well as the turbine nozzle and vanes. Deterioration of the hot section components affects the performance of the entire engine. When less energy is extracted from the hot gas stream the compressor, fan or propeller have less power to draw upon.

Before disassembly of the engine for a hot-section inspection, it is important to make a record of engine performance. An engine run-up and performance check will be performed before and after the inspection to compare the performance of the engine. These before and after figures are also compared to the baseline performance of the engine when it was new. Even when an improvement in performance is found, the engine may still be marginal when compared to the baseline figures. One of the misconceptions is that the performance of the engine will improve after a hot-section inspection.

A scheduled hot-section inspection is performed primarily to determine the condition of the parts. If the parts meet inspection criteria, they are reinstalled in the same condition and the engine performance should be the same as before the inspection. If a hot-section inspection is performed due to performance problems and the parts are found to be marginal or defective, then installation of new parts should improve performance.

Inspection intervals. Hot-section inspection intervals are scheduled on either an on-condition or time-in-service basis. The use of borescope equipment and other ongoing inspection procedures allows operators to utilize an on-condition schedule for hot-section inspection which can result in longer on-wing service and significant monetary savings. The hot-section includes the combustion chamber, liners and the turbine section, all of which are inspected with a borescope or are disassembled from the engine in order to perform the inspection. The hot section can be seen in Figure 10-2-7.

During disassembly, care must be taken to identify the location of components critical for reassembly. Due to the specific nature of disassembly and inspection methods, only a brief description of the inspection procedures is discussed below.

> **CAUTION:** *Do not mark any part of the hot section with a pencil or ink marker that contains lead or graphite since both will cause corrosion. Only use markers specified by the manufacturer.*

Figure 10-2-9. Determining turbine blade tip clearance during a hot section inspection

Upon disassembly (following manufacturer's instructions), all of the components in the hot section are visually inspected for cracks, distortions, corrosion and evidence of excessive temperatures. Cracks in the combustion chamber may not be reason enough for rejection, but should be noted so they can be referenced during the next inspection steps.

Erosion of coatings on compressor-turbine vane rings and shroud segments, for instance, must be evaluated with particular emphasis on the underlying parent material. Where parent material has been lost, component replacement is usually the next step.

As part of an inspection, the fuel nozzles are checked for leaks and operation and the ignition system is checked for resistance. A flow check on a nozzle is shown in Figure 10-2-8.

Shroud tip clearance. One of the most critical dimensions within the hot section is the turbine blade-to-case shroud clearance, which is shown in Figure 10-2-9. As total operating time accumulates on the turbine section, this dimension increases. This leads to higher EGT readings and lower efficiency. Correcting this problem requires the selection of new shroud segments, seen in Figure 10-2-10, which are classified on thickness. Following selection and temporary installation of the segments and the turbine wheel, the turbine tip clear-

Figure 10-2-10. Vanes are often numbered to better illustrate and document the variances in blade tip clearances, as well as for correct replacement.

ance is again checked. Grinding of the shroud segments is performed on the inside circumference of the segments to achieve the precise tip clearance required. The grinding process is shown in Figures 10-2-11 and 10-2-12 .

Turbine blade blending. If minor blade damage is found, it can be repaired in the field. Blending out minor nicks and abrasions is usually part of a hot section inspection. Operations must be carried out from tip to root and not crossways. Major damage may still be repairable, but is not repairable in the field. Consult the engine manufacturer's maintenance manual before performing any repairs. Always follow the manufacturer's recommendations and guidelines when performing a hot section inspection.

Fuel Control Trimming

Fuel control trimming, sometimes called engine trimming, is required when a fuel control has been replaced, the flight crew indicates that the engine parameters are not within limits or an engine performance check during an inspection reveals that the engine parameters are not within limits.

The process of fuel-control trimming checks engine r.p.m. against fuel flow, engine pressure ratio (EPR) and power lever positions. For engines equipped with variable compressor stator vanes, additional information on the position of the vanes at specified power set-

Figure 10-2-11. The grinding wheel is attached via the axial adjuster only after blanking material has been installed over the vanes and other moving parts, protecting them from dust and debris.

tings is considered as well. Over accumulated hours of operation, compressor and turbine efficiency are affected by wear and contamination. The EGT tends to increase relative to a specified EPR value and will eventually indicate that trimming of the fuel control is necessary to maintain engine efficiency.

Engine trimming. Several adjustments can be made to turbine engines equipped with a hydro-mechanical fuel control in order to achieve optimum engine performance. This is shown in Figure 10-2-13. Most hydro-mechanical fuel controls have adjustments for minimum and maximum governing speeds, idle speed, acceleration and fuel flow. Adjustments to the fuel control can be made only when the engine is shut down. Once the adjustments have been made, the engine must be started and run up to various settings to check its performance.

Before starting the aircraft, it should be headed into the wind. The engine run should be performed in an area of the airport that is designated for high-power engine runs. The outside air temperature and the barometric pressure must be measured at the engine intake to make corrections to standard-day, sea level conditions. Always adjust the fuel control in accordance with the maintenance instructions.

EEC Equipped Engines

Turbine engines equipped with an engine electronic control unit (EEC) do not have a requirement for fuel control trimming and no adjustments can be made by the technician to the fuel metering unit (FMU). The EEC is a computer that controls the operation of the engine and is shown in Figure 10-2-14. The EEC controls the engine with servo motors that adjust the governor and fuel flows. The EEC receives feedback from the control motors and sensors to keep the engine operating at its most efficient settings. There is an EEC maintenance switch that supplies power to the EEC during maintenance operations and checks. The EEC can be operated in two modes:

- Normal mode
- Alternate mode

In the normal mode, the EEC sets engine thrust or power based on the EPR readings. When the alternate mode is selected, the N_1 is used to set power and thrust.

EEC programming. The EEC is designed to control all possible configurations of the engine regardless of individual characteristics. To provide interchangeability of the EEC, the following specific engine information must be made available to the EEC.

- Engine serial number
- Thrust rating
- EPR/thrust trim relationship
- Turbine gas temperature trim
- Engine baseline performance
- Engine health monitoring
- N_1 modifier trim

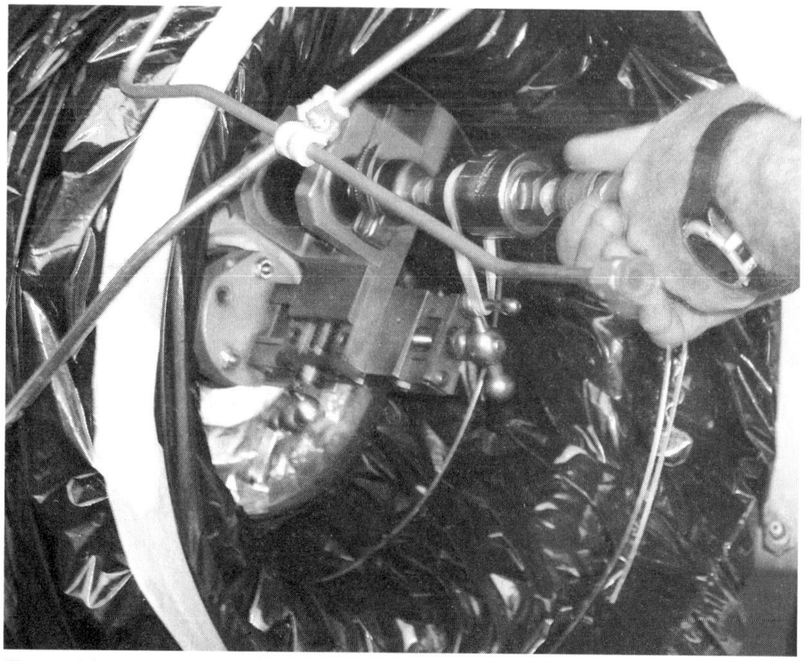

Figure 10-2-12. Grinding the shroud segments

Figure 10-2-13. Some fuel controls have adjustments for trimming the engine.

Figure 10-2-14. Engines with electronic engine controls have no provision for trimming the fuel control.

This is achieved by a dual channel memory device known as the EEC programming plug, seen in Figure 10-2-15. This device plugs into the EEC and is programmed with the relevant engine data which is used by the EEC to correctly operate the engine. The programming plug remains with the engine throughout its operational life and not with the EEC.

Compressor and Turbine Wash

The interior of a turbine engine needs to be cleaned periodically to remove dirt and salt deposits from the gas path.

Engines that operate in dirty, dusty or corrosive environments are washed more often than engines operated in a clean environment. Most of the contamination that accumulates in the compressor section comes from air pollutants in flight at altitudes from sea level to 5,000 feet. The contaminants can be salt from costal areas, to particulate matter in industrialized areas, to herbicides and pesticides near agricultural operations.

These contaminants eventually impinge on the airfoil surfaces of the compressor rotors, stators and diffusers and result in a reduction in aerodynamic efficiency of the compressor and thus a loss of horsepower. Some manufacturers recommend washing or rinsing the engine daily, if the engine has been operating in dirty or salty environment.

Power recovery. The interior of the engine should be rinsed with clean, demineralized, deionized or distilled water. If the engine's performance is low, a soap solution could be used to recover the engine performance. This is often called a power recovery wash. After these washes the engine performance can increase as much as 10%.

The compressor wash procedure is different for each engine type and the following discussion is only a general description of a compressor wash procedure. Consult the maintenance manual before washing a turbine engine. Figure 10-2-16 shows the type of equipment used for washing a turboshaft engine.

Preparation for Engine Compressor Wash

Before the compressor wash, several procedures must be carried out to prevent damaging the engine:

- Disconnect any pressure-sensing lines and cap all openings to avoid contamination of the fuel control or bleed valves.
- Do not perform an engine wash below 35°F.
- Make sure that the engine is cool before starting the wash procedure.
- Most engines use a wash ring or wand to introduce the water or soap into the compressor. Do not spray the water directly into the compressor. A solid stream of water or soap may cause excessive stress on the compressor blades.
- Connect the compressor wash ground equipment to the wash ring and secure the hoses.

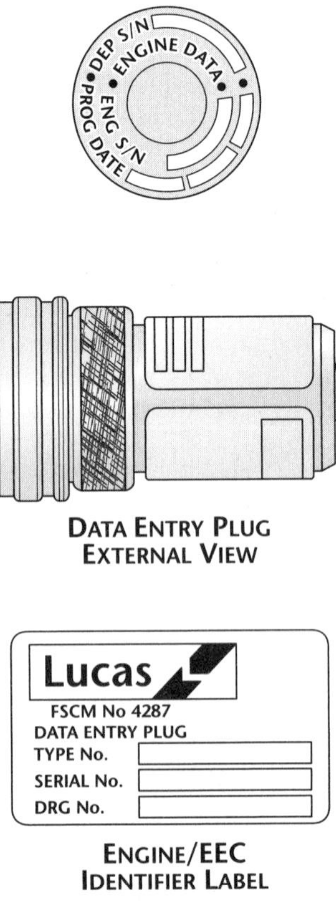

Figure 10-2-15. Data entry plug

Figure 10-2-16. (A) A compressor wash can be a daily occurrence on engines that are operated in a salty environment. (B) Compressor wash kits are self-contained for ease of use.

- Connect a suitable external power source to the aircraft.
- Disable the ignition system by pulling the circuit breakers.
- Turn off all fuel valves and pumps.
- Close all bleed valves.

Engine washing procedure. The exact procedure for washing an engine is stipulated in the maintenance manual. The following is a very general description of the procedure:

- Mix the soap and water in accordance with the manufacturer's recommendations.
- Motor the engine with the starter.
- Introduce the water or soap solution into the compressor.
- Never exceed the maximum starter time or the starter will overheat. Observe the starter-duty cycle to give the starter sufficient time to cool.
- When using a soap solution, a specific soak time may be stipulated.
- If a soap solution is used, the engine must be flushed with clean, demineralized water to rinse off the soap.
- After the wash is completed, remove the wash equipment.
- Connect all lines and remove all caps and plugs.
- Perform a ground run to dry the engine and make sure it operates correctly.
- Any water or soap left in the engine could cause corrosion or freeze in cold weather.

Section 3

Overhaul Practices

Off-wing Maintenance

The term off-wing maintenance refers to engine maintenance once an engine is removed from the aircraft. This is normally done in a shop or any other appropriate facility such as a certificated repair station. Off-wing maintenance can be an engine overhaul or a major inspection. During overhaul, the engine is disassembled so that the internal parts can be inspected for condition or renewal and replacement of deteriorated parts. In addition, those parts that would not remain in a serviceable condition until the next overhaul are replaced.

New generation engine designs use the modular design process. This concept is based on the on-condition monitoring of the modules. This means that no life-limit is set for the entire engine, but only for certain parts or modules of the engine. Modules that contain life-limited parts can be replaced by similar assemblies and the engine can be returned to service with minimum delay. The removed modules can then sent out for overhaul to an approved agency or repair station.

General Procedures

Since overhaul procedures and requirements are different for each manufacturer, always use the applicable engine overhaul manual. A general discussion of accepted overhaul practices must include some of the following information:

METHOD	ADVANTAGES	DISADVANTAGES
VISUAL	• Inexpensive • Highly portable • Immediate results • Minimum training • Minimum part preparation	• Surface discontinuity only • Generally only large discontinuities • Misinterpretation of scratches
EDDY CURRENT	• Portable • Detects surface and subsurface discontinuities • Moderate speed • Sensitive to small discontinuities • Thickness sensitive • Can detect many variables	• Surface must be accessible to probe • Rough surfaces interfere with test • Limited to electrically conductive materials • Skill and training required • Time consuming for large areas
MAGNETIC PARTICLE	• Can be portable • Inexpensive • Sensitive to small discontinuities • Immediate results • Moderate skill involved • Detects surface and subsurface discontinuities • Relatively fast	• Surface must be accessible • Rough surfaces interfere with test • Part preparation required • Semi-directional requiring general orientation of field to discontinuity • Ferro-magnetic materials only • Part must be demagnetized after test
ULTRASONIC	• Portable • Inexpensive • Sensitive to small discontinuities • Immediate results • Little part preparation • Wide range of materials and thickness can be inspected	• Surface must be accessible to probe • Rough surfaces interfere with test • Highly sensitive to sound beam discontinuity orientation • High degree of skill required to set up and interpret • Couplant usually required
X-RAY AND ISOTOPE RADIOGRAPHY	• Detects surface and internal flaws • Portable • Can inspect hidden areas • Permanent test record is obtained • Minimum part preparation	• Must conform to federal and state regulations for handling and use • Safety hazard • Very expensive • Slow process • Highly directional, sensitive to flaw orientation • High degree of skill and experience required for exposure and interpretation • Depth of discontinuity not indicated
LIQUID PENETRANT	• Portable • Inexpensive • Immediate results • Moderate skill involved	• Discontinuities must be open to surface • Possibility of misinterpretation • Limited to non-porous materials

Table 10-3-1. Advantages and disadvantages of NDI techniques

Disassembly

During disassembly the various sections or modules of the engine are separated. Further disassembly is down to the component level. Initial documentation about the condition of the module is part of the process. Some general procedures are:

- Be aware of engine parts that contain hazardous materials and use appropriate personal protection equipment if parts containing asbestos are ground, sanded, drilled, scraped or cut.
- To ensure correct reinstallation, tag and mark all parts, clips and brackets as to their location.
- During removal of tubes or engine parts look for indications of scoring, burning or other conditions.
- Tag unserviceable parts and units for investigation and possible repair.
- To facilitate reinstallation, observe the location of each part during removal.
- Suitable plugs, caps and other coverings must be used to protect all openings as they are exposed.
- To protect the critical areas of engine parts (such as compressor and turbine disks) against scratches and nicks, tools contacting these areas must be covered with a protective material.

Cleaning

The primary purpose of cleaning is to remove contaminants that may conceal minor cracks and defects which, if not detected, could lead to failure of a component or part. Engine com-

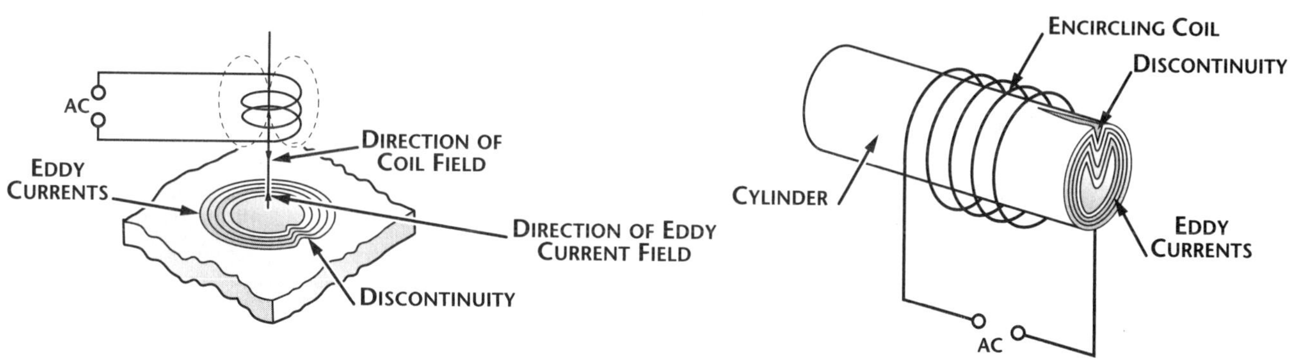

Figure 10-3-1. Discontinuities such as cracks change the conductor's permeablilty and disrupt the induced eddy currents.

ponents or parts must be cleaned to perform required inspection and repair.

CAUTION: *Many cleaning solutions are harmful to skin or clothing; always use adequate protection. Certain solutions are corrosive and/or toxic and other solutions emit harmful vapors. Always read the Material Safety Data Sheet (MSDS) before using the cleaning solution and use adequate protection.*

General Cleaning Procedure

- Wear rubber gloves, apron or coveralls and face shield or goggles when working with or near solvents.
- Use only the manufacturer's approved chemicals and procedures for cleaning.
- Use the least toxic of available cleaning materials to satisfactory complete the work.
- Perform all cleaning operations in well-ventilated work areas.
- Ensure adequate, usable fire fighting and safety equipment is available.
- Use a stiff bristle brush for any cleaning operation. Do not use steel or brass brushes.
- Ensure that cleaning agents are thoroughly removed from all parts after cleaning.

After cleaning, many parts need to be protected against mishandling and corrosion. The maintenance manual's recommendations for preserving and protecting parts should be followed carefully.

Inspection

All components are visually inspected and dimensionally inspected after cleaning to determine their general condition. The dimensional inspection consists of measuring specific components to ensure that they are within the limits and tolerances of the overhaul manual.

After the visual inspection and dimensional inspection, components are inspected with a nondestructive testing method to reveal cracks and flaws that cannot be detected visually. The detection of cracks, especially on rotating parts such as compressor and turbine disks, is very important because failure to detect them could result in crack propagation during engine operation and eventually lead to component failure.

Non-destructive Testing

There are several non-destructive testing (NDT) methods used to detect flaws and defects that cannot be found during a visual inspection. The most commonly used methods are: eddy current, magnetic particle, ultrasonic, X-ray and liquid penetrant inspection. The advantages and disadvantages of each type are listed in Table 10-3-1.

Eddy current inspection. Eddy current inspection is a non-destructive technique that is used to find discontinuities on or near the surface of a metallic part. The method works on the principle of eddy currents—currents that are generated within a conductive material when put in close proximity to the dynamic magnetic field—around a current coil. When alternating current is applied to a coil, a magnetic field is induced around the coil that expands and contracts at the frequency of the applied current. If an electrically conductive material is placed within the influence of this alternating magnetic flux field, eddy currents are generated within the material on and slightly below the surface of the conductor. This is illustrated in Figure 10-3-1.

The electrical properties of the test material affected by the flux field become part of and have influence on, the inductive circuit of the coil. Because surface or subsurface discontinuities affect the eddy current flow and are reflected back through the inductive circuit of the coil, the circuit can be monitored to show the presence of discontinuities within the test material.

Magnetic particle testing. Magnetic particle testing will indicate surface or near surface

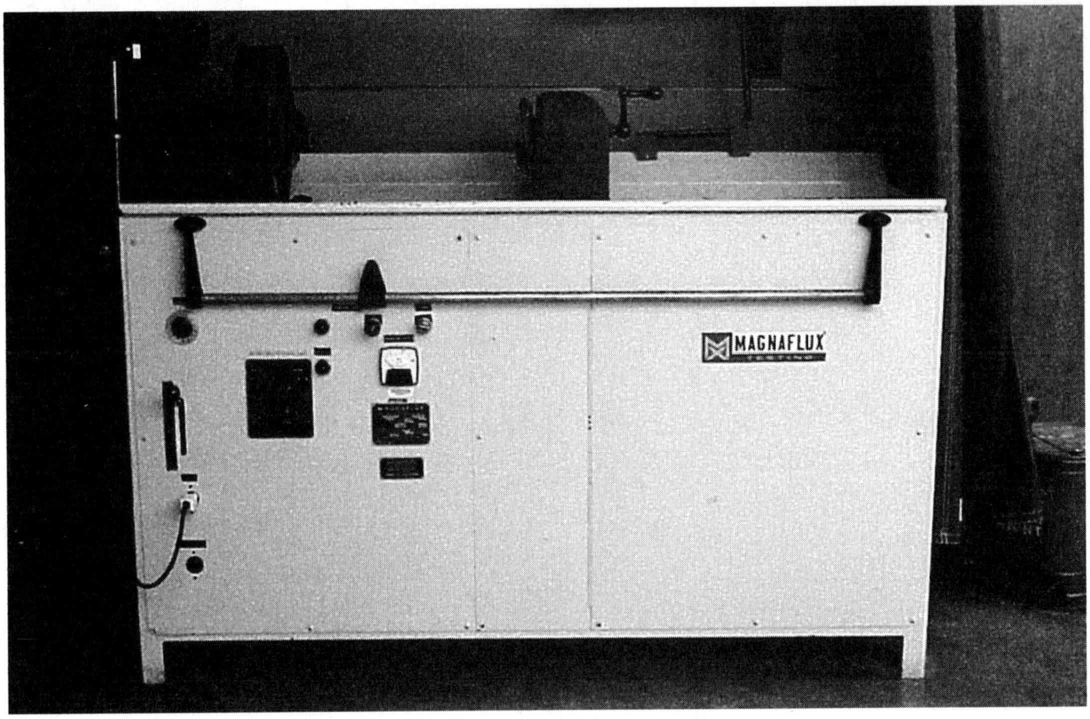

Figure 10-3-2. Magnetic particle inspection is used on ferrous metals.

defects in ferro-magnetic parts (parts which can be magnetized) and may be performed on assembled or disassembled parts. The test is accomplished by inducing a magnetic field in the part and applying a dry powder or liquid suspension of iron oxide particles. Local magnetic poles formed by defects in the part attract the oxide particles so they many be viewed and evaluated by color contrast or fluorescence under black light. A magnetic particle inspection station is shown in Figure 10-3-2.

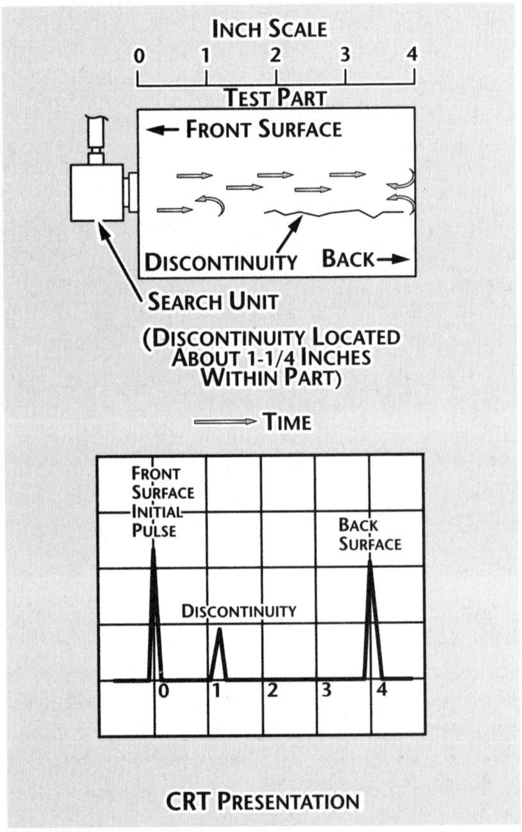

Figure 10-3-3. Typical ultrasound display for contact inspection

Ultrasonic testing. Ultrasonic testing is a nondestructive test method suitable for the inspection of most metals, plastics and ceramics for surface or subsurface defects. Ultrasonic inspection requires access to at least one surface of the part. Inspection of the parts is accomplished by inducing ultrasonic energy into the part through a contacting probe and picking up reflections of the sound from within the part. Discontinuities create an early or abnormal reflection of the ultrasonic energy, as shown in Figure 10-3-3. The detected ultrasonic reflections are electronically displayed on a monitor and interpreted for indications of defects.

X-ray and isotope radiography. X-ray and isotope radiography is a nondestructive test method suitable for the inspection of all types of materials. It is used when the other types of nondestructive methods are not suitable.

An X-ray or isotope machine is used to pass radiation through the object and produces an image on film. When processed, the film becomes a radiograph or shadow picture of the object. Since more radiation passes through a thin object or where there is a void or a space or the density of the material is lower, the corresponding area on the film is darker. The diagram in Figure 10-3-4 illustrates this principle. The radiograph is read or interpreted for defects or damage by specially trained technicians. Fine cracks or delaminations are difficult to detect using radiographic inspection methods.

Liquid penetrant inspection. Liquid penetrant inspection is a nondestructive test method used to detect small surface cracks that are not visible with the naked eye. For liquid penetrant to be effective, the material must be nonporous and the crack must be open to the surface. Liquid penetrant can be used for a variety of materials including metals, plastics and glass. Two types of liquid penetrant inspection methods are used: fluorescent liquid penetrant inspection which uses a black light and a fluorescent liquid and the visible liquid penetrant inspection. The visual type uses a colored penetrant and a contrasting developer.

Identification of Metal Particles

During a turbine engine inspection, it is not uncommon to find small metal particles. Several tests are available to determine the type of metal particles found in the engine. This is helpful in troubleshooting and identifying defective parts. These tests are detailed in Table 10-3-2.

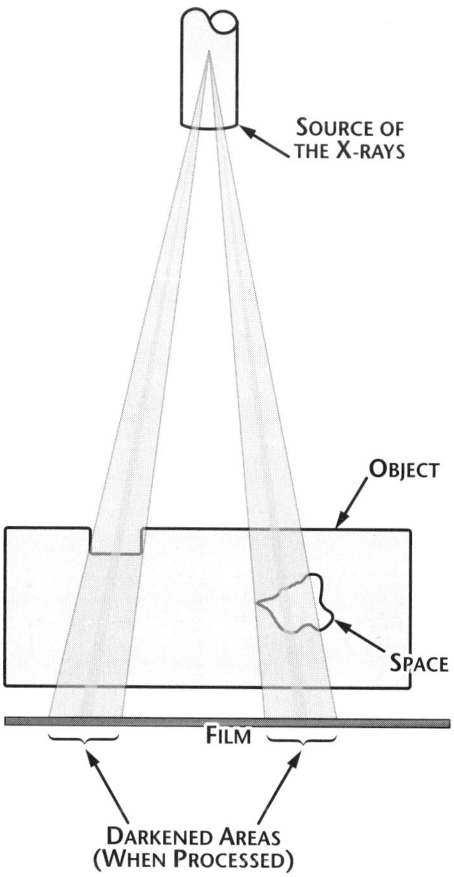

Figure 10-3-4. The radiation that passes through a discontinuity (a thinner area) retains more energy and creates a darker image on the film.

Compressor and Turbine Blade Inspection

The compressor section of the turbine engine has one primary purpose: to supply enough air in sufficient quantity to satisfy the requirements of the engine. Since all of the air must pass through the compressor, any dirt, stones or debris that are picked up off the ground also pass through. In turbofan engines the fan sec-

PARTICLE	METHOD OF IDENTIFICATION
STEEL	A permanent magnet can be used to isolate steel or iron particles.
MAGNESIUM	A simple test to determine magnesium is to burn the particle. Magnesium will burn with a bright flash.
CADMIUM	A simple test to determine cadmium is to place the particle in an ammonium nitrate solution. If the particles dissolve in this solution they are cadmium.
TIN	Heat a soldering iron to 5,000°F. If the particle melts on the tip it is tin.
ALUMINUM	When a particle of aluminum is placed in a 50% solution by volume, of hydrochloric acid it will disintegrate and form a black residue.
SILVER	When silver is placed in nitric acid it reacts slowly and produces a white fog in the acid.
BRONZE	Bronze or copper in nitric acid produces a bright green cloud.
TITANIUM	Place the suspect material and a known piece of titanium on a white plate: 1. Add several crystals of ammonium bifluoride and 5 to 10 drops of water to each piece and let stand for 20 to 30 minutes or until the solution becomes slightly discolored 2. Add 2 to 3 drops of 1:1 sulfuric acid (1 part water, 1 part concentrated acid). Let stand 20 to 30 minutes or until solution is further discolored. 3. Add 3 to 4 drops of hydrogen peroxide, if titanium is present a yellowish cloud will develop. 4. Add 2 to 3 drops of concentrated phosphoric acid and stir to discharge any yellow color due to iron. Any light yellow to orange coloration indicates titanium.

Table 10-3-2. Identification of metal particles

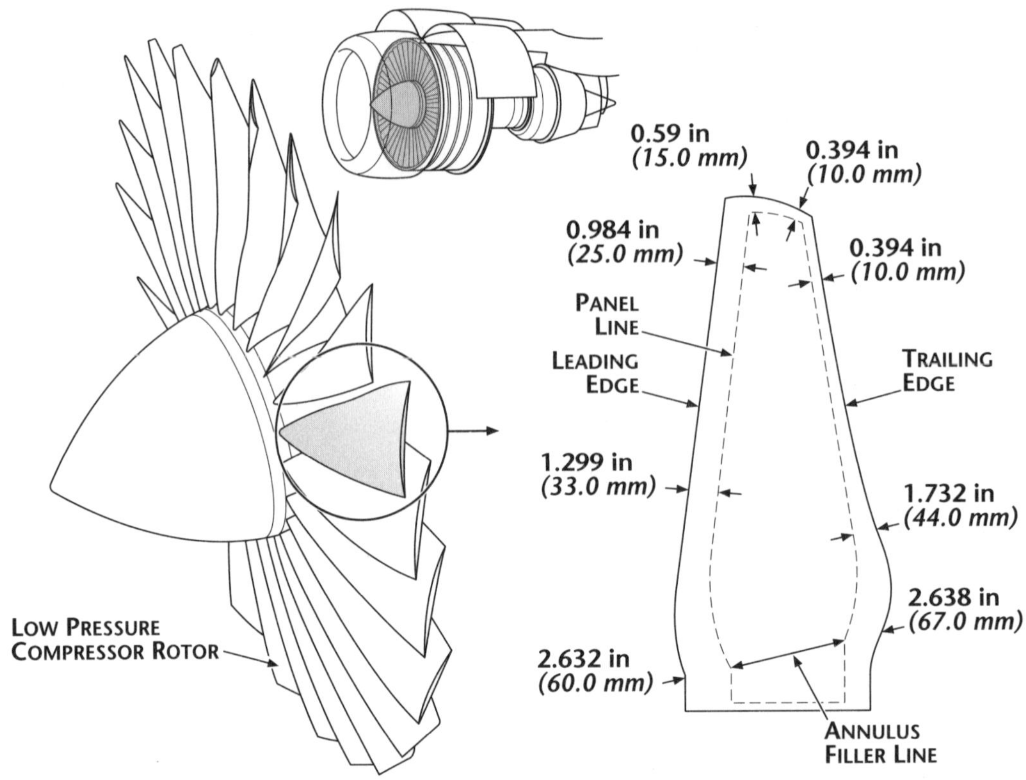

Figure 10-3-5. Inspection areas and dimensions of low pressure compressor blades

tion acts as a centrifugal separator before the air reaches the core of the engine.

Damage to these initial stages of the compressor can affect the overall efficiency of the engine by changing the dynamics of the air stream. Additionally, when a piece of a blade breaks off it tends to migrate aft and increases the damage to the compressor.

Inspecting, repairing or replacing compressor blades in the field as well as at overhaul is a fairly common maintenance function. Most manufacturers have specific guidelines for field repair of the blades. The material discussed in this section is general in nature and should not be used to repair any specific compressor or turbine blades.

Blade Defects

The fan blades are susceptible to damage due to foreign matter which is drawn into the engine intake and to fatigue failure due to high centrifugal forces and resonant vibration. Figures 10-3-5 and 10-3-6 indicate possible damage limitations to a low pressure compressor rotor.

Compressor blades. Compressor blades are susceptible to damage from rocks, stones and other foreign matter which can be drawn into the engine. The ramp, taxiways and runway are often filled with tiny particles and aircraft with low engine installations will be especially susceptible to drawing in tiny particles. Typical repair limitations are illustrated in Figure 10-3-7.

The repair techniques and tools that are used to blend out any damaged areas must be approved by the manufacturer for use on the blades. The amount of material removed must be kept within the limits stipulated in the maintenance manual. When blades are replaced, they must be moment weight matched in order to preserve the dynamic balance of the section.

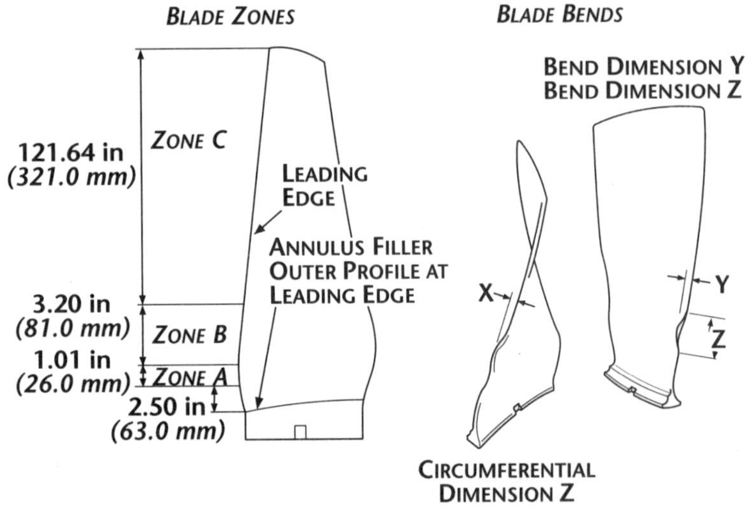

Figure 10-3-6. Damage area of low pressure compressor blades

Maximum Allowable Repair Limits (Inches)				
Blade Area	Steel Blades		Titanium Blades	
	Stages		Stages	
	1 Through 4	5 Through 9	1 Through 4	5 Through 9
A	5/16 R	1/4 R	5/16 R	1/4 R
B	1/32 D	1/32 D	1/32 D	1/32 D
C	5/32 D	1/8 D	5/32 D	1/8 D
D	0.008 D	0.005 D	None	None
E	1/32 D	1/32 D	1/32 D	1/32 D

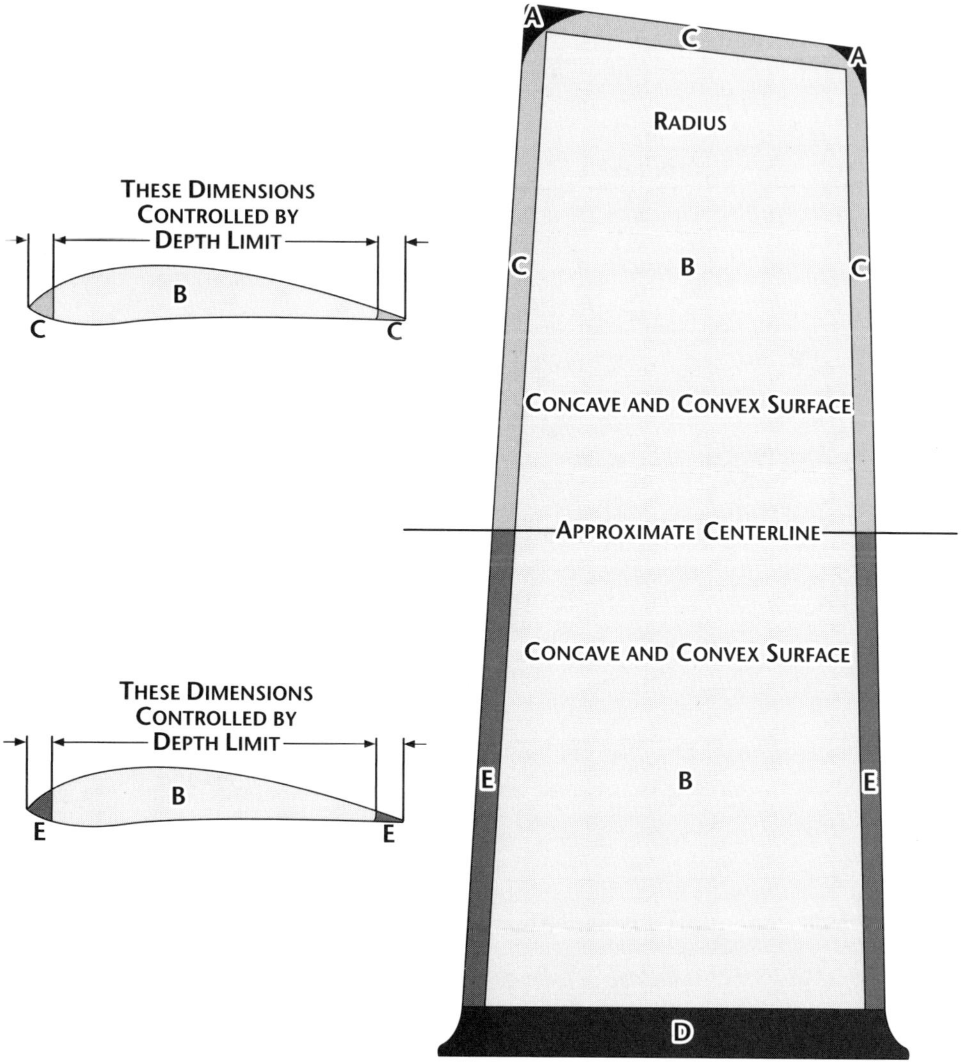

CAUTION: ***The limits referred to in areas C and E pertain to local, isolated, damaged areas only. They must not be interpreted as authority for removal of material all the way across the tip and the leading or trailing edges, as might be done in a single machining cut.***

Figure 10-3-7. Compressor blade damage limitations

Moment weight is defined as the mass of the blades multiplied by the distance from the engine centerline to the center of gravity of the blade. Weighing opposite blades does not take into consideration the location of the blade's CG relative to each other. If the CG of several blades is changed, then the CG of the disk will shift, creating a dynamic imbalance which results in vibrations and accelerated wear.

Turbine blades. Turbine blades are susceptible to damage by the high temperature of the

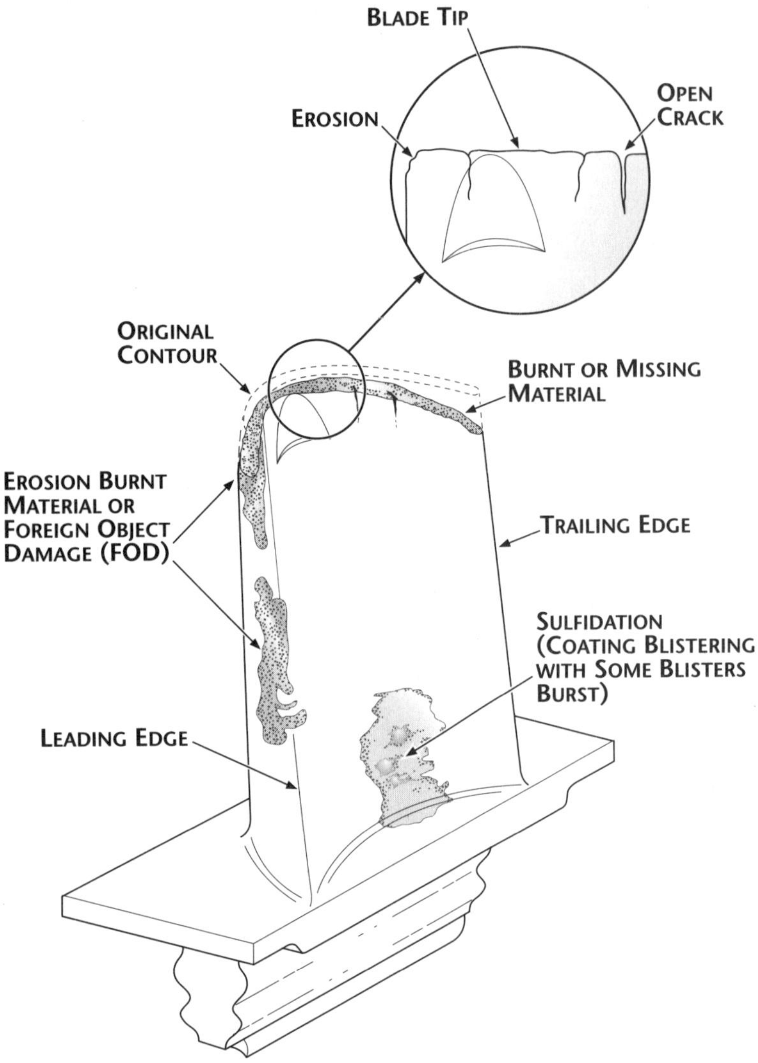

Figure 10-3-8. Compressor turbine (CT) blade damage. This is an example of unacceptable damage.

gas flow and high centrifugal forces. Inspection limitations for a turbine blade in a PT6 engine are illustrated in Figure 10-3-8.

Turbine blades are subjected to high temperatures and centrifugal forces. During engine operation, the blades will increase in length, which could cause them to break. This increase of length (growth) is called creep. There are three phases of creep as illustrated in Figure 10-3-9.

- Primary creep - the initial growth of the blades is quick but it slows down.
- Secondary creep - the growth is directly related to the operation time.
- Tertiary creep - The growth will increase till the blades break.

Due to the critical nature of the turbine blades, they are not reparable in the field. When the turbine section is overhauled, the blades are replaced rather than repaired.

Repair

All repairs to the component parts must result in a part which is still within the serviceable specifications for the engine.

- Before starting a repair, make sure that all required cleaning, stripping, inspecting and testing has been accomplished.
- When repairing engine parts, make sure that critical markings on each part are masked and will not be removed during the repair process. Critical markings can include part number, serial number, heat code, run out, residual unbalance and growth.

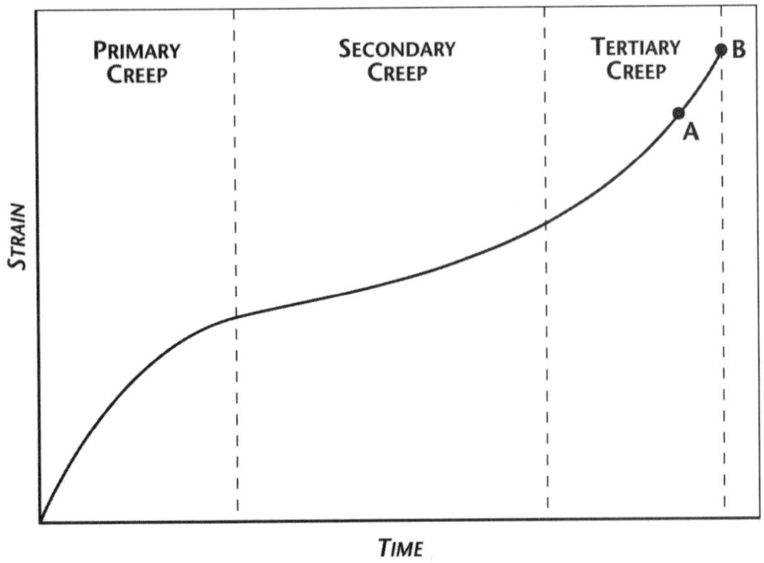

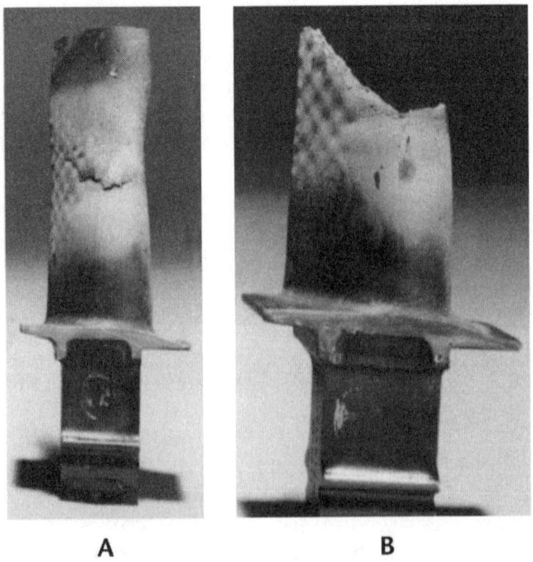

Figure 10-3-9. Blade creep can result in failure of the turbine blades

Assembly

The assembly process is one of the most critical phases of an engine overhaul. All of the components are assembled into their subassemblies and sections. The sections are then assembled to become a complete engine. Setting the clearances between the sections is a critical step in the assembly process. The shafts must be aligned with the bearings and to the engine centerline for the compressor and turbine to rotate freely. Some general items are:

- Extreme care must be taken to prevent dust, dirt, safety wire, nuts, washers and other unwanted objects from entering the engine. If anything is dropped, the assembly procedures must be stopped until the dropped articles are located.
- Before assembly or installation of any part, be sure it is completely clean.
- Do not use tapes on engine parts except where absolutely necessary, such as masking during a blasting or repair operation. Test results have shown that tapes and residues can cause surface attack and/or reduction in tensile ductility. The effect gets more severe as the temperature increases.
- Replace all rubber parts and packings that have been removed at overhaul.
- Safety wire, lockwashers, spring tension washers and cotter pins must never be reused. All safety wire and cotter pins must fit snugly in their holes.

Section 4

Corrosion of Turbine Engines

While corrosion on the exterior of a turbine engine is uncommon, it is treated much the same as corrosion on the airframe. First the limits are established for the area and then the corrosion is removed and the area treated with corrosion preventative compounds and sealed. The effects of corrosion to the inside of a turbine engine are quite different and require special inspections and techniques.

Interior Corrosion

Corrosion to the interior of the engine is critical in terms of the loss of efficiency and the potential for failure of components. The compressor section is subject to some surface corrosion, however, it is the turbine section that is of major concern. Due to the high temperatures and the sulfur content of fuel there are two types of corrosion that are common for turbine engine hot sections:

Figure 10-4-1. Advanced sulfidation is shown on these turbine blades.

- High temperature alloy corrosion
- Sulfidation

High Temperature Alloy Corrosion

This type of corrosion in the turbine section may be identified by metal loss or pitting, but more commonly appears as local swelling or buildup due to greater volume occupied by the nickel oxides. These corrosion products vary in color from black to green and in the advanced state there will be cracking and flaking, referred to as exfoliation.

Care should be taken to distinguish between corrosion buildup and possible light brown or rust colored deposits, which are harmless combustion by-products. The latter are usually widespread over hot section components and while possibly affecting performance, will not directly affect the compressor turbine's mechanical integrity.

Sulfidation

Sulfidation is a common name for a type of hot corrosion which affects turbine area components. Sulfates form at engine operating temperatures when sodium and sulfur are present. Most aviation turbine fuels contain sulfur in sufficient amounts for sulfidation. Common sources of sodium are seawater, atmospheric pollutants and volcanic discharges. Sulfidation attack most often affects the compressor turbine blades, but sulfidation of power turbine blades and of non-rotating parts such as shroud segments is not uncommon.

Many turbine blades are coated with a protective layer and sulfidation will first degrade this coating. The loss of this coating will eventually lead to some loss of base alloy material. Upon disassembly and after the coating has been removed, inspection of the attacked blades may reveal that they are not suitable for repair by recoating. An example of sulfidation can be seen in Figure 10-4-1.

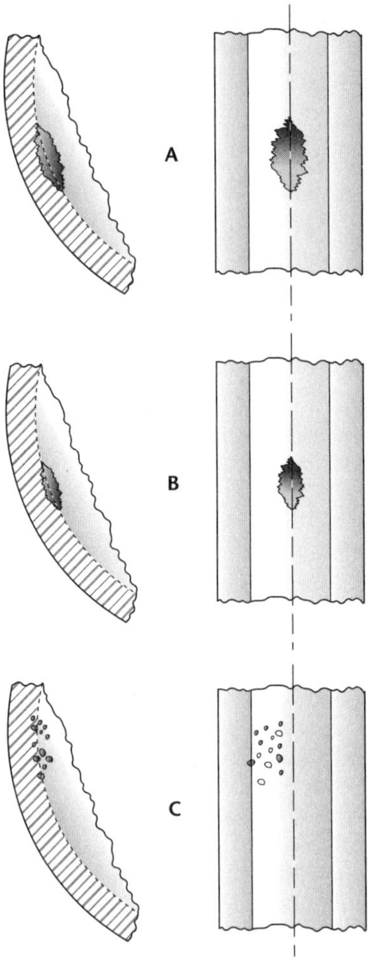

Figure 10-5-1. Three types of race surface deterioration: (A) Hard coarse foreign matter causes rounded depressions; (B) Overloads cause fatigue failure characterized by sharp jagged edges; (C) Etching causes hemispherical depressions.

In service, sulfidation may be characterized by the following four stages:

- Stage 1: Light Sulfidation - Slight roughening of the surface and localized breakdown of the protective surface layer. Alloy is not yet affected.
- Stage 2: Failure of the protective layer-Roughness of surface is more marked as the protective layer breakdown exposes the alloy to attack. Mechanical integrity is not yet affected.
- Stage 3: Severe sulfidation - Base material is attacked to significant depth, as evidenced by obvious buildup scale and some blistering. Mechanical integrity is now affected and parts are no longer serviceable.
- Stage 4: Catastrophic attack - Deep penetration of attack with large blisters of scale. Loss of structural material will lead to eventual component failure.

Frequent washing of the engine interior with demineralized water will help minimize sulfidation attack.

Section 5

Bearing Inspection

Bearings are a key element in any turbine engine. A thorough inspection is necessary during any disassembly. Not only will this prevent unexpected bearing failure, but it may also provide clues to other areas of the engine that need attention.

Determining Causes

Defective mounting, improper operating conditions and similar causes can usually be detected by visually inspecting the bearing.

Radial ball bearing. The condition of a bearing that has operated under a radial load can be recognized easily. When bearings are properly mounted, lubricated and operated under correct conditions, the path of the balls in the highly polished races shows as a dulled surface similar to a lapped surface, wherein the microscopically fine grinding scratches have been smoothed out. No appreciable removal of material from the surface is noticeable, as indicated by the fact that there has been no measurable decrease in the diameter of the balls, though their entire surface has been dulled.

Other indications that operating conditions have been satisfactory are the uniformity of the ball paths, their exact parallelism with the side of the races, indicating correct alignment and the centering of the ball track in the race, which indicates that the bearing carried a purely radial load. Normally, the outer race, if fixed, should carry load for less than half the circumference. This type of discrepancy is shown in Figure 10-5-1.

Thrust bearing. If operating conditions are correct, the balls in thrust bearings will have their entire surfaces dulled, their appearance just like the ball paths, but with one important exception. If a thrust load has been present continuously for the entire period of operation and if it was large enough relative to the radial load to keep the balls in contact at all times, the balls will show a circumferential band, indicating that:

- The balls did not normally spin or change their axis of rotation.
- The fatigue life of the balls has been reduced because of the small area of ball surface used.

- If the bands have appreciable depth there has been material wear caused by improper operating conditions.

If, when operating under conditions that cause circumferential bands, the bearing setting was disturbed or the loads were removed or shifted, the axis of spin of the balls would shift, causing immediate roughness or noisy operation if the balls have been worn appreciably. Figure 10-5-2 illustrates some of these conditions.

Damage caused by foreign matter. Ball bearings are particularly sensitive to dirt or foreign matter, which is always more abrasive, because of the very high unit pressure between the ball and race and the rolling motion that tends to entrap the pieces, particularly if they are small. This is the most common cause of damage to ball bearings. Foreign matter may get into the bearing during the initial assembly or during repairs. Dirt my also seep in from the atmosphere into the bearing housing during operation or it might even be carried in with the lubricating oil.

The character of the damage caused by foreign matter getting into ball bearings varies considerably with the nature of the foreign matter. Fine foreign matter or matter that is soft enough to be finely ground by the rolling action of the balls will have an effect that is the same as the presence of a fine abrasive or lapping material. The races become worn in the ball paths, the balls wear and the bearings become loose and noisy. The lapping action increases rapidly as the steel removed from the bearing surfaces contributes to more lapping wear.

Hard, coarse foreign matter such as iron or steel, metallic particles which can be introduced when assembling the machine, produces small depressions of a character considerably different than those produced by overload failure. Acid etching or corrosion jamming of the hard particles between the balls and the races may cause the inner race to turn on the shaft or the outer race to turn in the housing.

Water, acid, other corrosive materials or corrosives from deterioration of the lubricant produce a type of failure that is indicated by a reddish brown coating and etched holes over the entire exposed surface of the races. Frequently, the etching does not show on the ball path because the rolling action of the balls pushes the lubricant loaded corrosive away from the ball path. The corrosive oxides formed act as lapping agents that cause wear and produce a dull gray color on the balls and the ball paths, as contrasted with the reddish brown color of the remainder of the surface.

Effects of corrosion. Corrosion is one of the most serious problems encountered in bearings. It makes itself evident over the entire exposed surface of the race by developing small etched holes and is precluded by local staining of the race and ball. The etching is most often caused by condensation collecting in the bearing housing because of temperature changes. Moisture or water can get into the bearing through worn or inadequate seals during engine washes.

Damage caused by excessive preload or overload. Overload causes fatigue failure of the material as evidenced by the breaking out of the surface layer of steel. Such a failure starts in a small area, spreads rapidly and would eventually spread over both the races and the ball surfaces. Most frequently, failure starts on the inner race. A wide ball path is added indication of excessive loading.

Thrust load wrong direction. A thrust load in the wrong direction on an angular-contact ball bearing will make the balls ride on the edge of the race groove where it joins the shallow

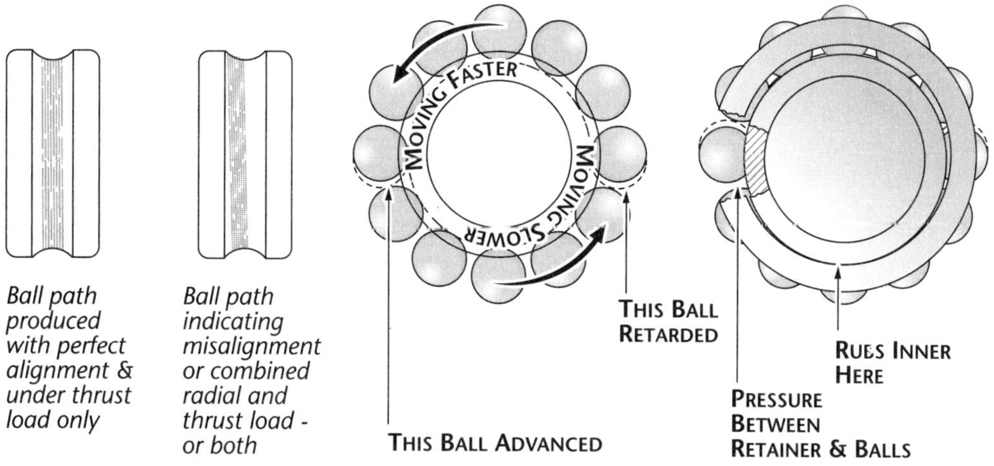

Figure 10-5-2. Conventional ball bearings that were misaligned when installed will show these wear patterns.

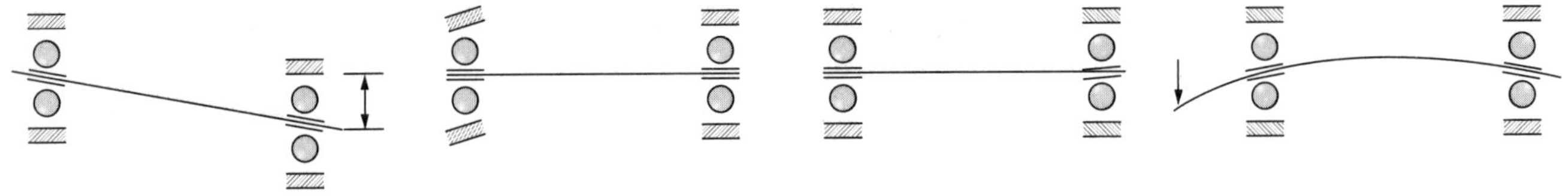

Figure 10-5-3. The most common types of misalignment

shouldered counterbore and thus breaks up the race surfaces. Under these conditions, the balls frequently break up or split, even though their material and heat-treatment was perfect.

Misalignment and off-square. On a conventional single-row bearing that had been subjected to off-square operating conditions, the outer race ball path clearly moves from the right hand side to the left and back again. The ball path can be a full 1/8-inch off-square in a three inch diameter raceway. The ring itself could tilt only about 1/64-inch, but produce a greater change in the ball path because of the change in contact angle. The inner race would have a very wide ball path since the ball wanders back and forth across nearly its full width.

Almost all separator failures in a standard single-row type of ball bearing can be traced back to an off-square condition of either the inner or outer race. The failure is caused by variations in ball speed jamming the balls into the separator pockets.

Ball speed variations caused by off-square operation produce the greatest effect when the balls are never free to readjust themselves, as in a tight bearing or in a bearing carrying mainly thrust loads. The variation in ball speed is then cumulative and the two side balls force the retainer downward until it strikes the inner or outer race. Outer race tilting can be easily determined in operation, being evidenced by the eccentrically operating retainer. With inner race cocking, the eccentricity of the retainer rotates with the inner race.

Four types of misalignment to which ball bearings may be subjected are shown in Figure 10-5-3. Out-of-line conditions rarely cause trouble. The exceptions occur only on long shafts where diameters are reduced to an absolute minimum, as on automobile rear wheels or airplane engine crankshafts.

Brinelling and False Brinelling

A few ball bearings are brinelled when putting them on the shaft by being struck with a severe blow or by extremely heavy pressure. This is rare, because most ball bearings have enough thrust capacity to permit forcing them onto the shaft by pressure against the outer race, provided the pressure is applied squarely. Exceptions to the rule are the smallest bearings and bearings with flatter races such as propeller shaft center support ball bearings and self aligning types. The rare occasions when regular single-row ball bearings are brinelled usually result from off-center blows or pressure when only three or four balls carry the entire load.

True brinelling. Extremely heavy impact loads, which may be of short duration, can cause brinelling of the bearing races and sometimes even fracture the race and ball. Brinelling of a bearing caused by off-center blow in mounting is typical, though rare. Such bearings frequently go unnoticed in operation because the load does not cause the ball path to reach the brinell marks on the races. However, the balls acquire similar depressions and will make the bearing sound noisy or catchy, as though it had several small pieces of foreign matter in it. Failure may result at the flat spots on the balls or will occur on the races if carrying heavy enough thrust load for the ball path to reach the brinell marks.

False brinelling. False brinelling occurs when bearings do not rotate for extensive periods. Loads may be relatively light but slight changes in the surfaces of the raceways result from even minute axial or rotational movements and these only appear under each ball.

False brinelling due to vibration without rotation. False brinelling pockets occur in the presence of vibration without rotation and can be deepened by abrasive foreign matter. Exposing the bearing surfaces to air will oxidize the microscopic metal particles freed by the vibrating movement and these oxides in turn provide the abrasive action that accelerates wear. False brinelling produces surface depressions far more rapidly when balls actually skid or slide on the race surfaces instead of just rolling. Examples of this are large axial vibrations in ball bearings or centrifugal forces on loose balls in controllable pitch propeller bearings.

THREAD SIZE (INCH)	TORQUE , LB- IN (NM)					
	OIL LUBRICATED			ANTI-SEIZE COATED		
	MIN.*		MAX.	MIN.*		MAX.
	TYPE I	TYPE II		TYPE I	TYPE II	
0.112 -40	4.5 (0.508)	5 (0.565)	6.0 (0.678)	3.5 (0.395)	4 (0.452)	4.5 (0.508)
0.138 -32	8.5 (0.960)	10 (1.130)	11.5 (1.299)	6.5 (0.734)	7.5 (0.847)	8.5 (0.960)
0.164 -32	16 (1.808)	20 (2.260)	22 (2.486)	12.5 (1.412)	15 (1.695)	16.5 (1.864)
0.164 -36	18 (2.034)	22 (2.486)	24 (2.712)	13.5 (1.525)	16 (1.808)	18 (2.034)
0.190 -24	#23 (2.599)	#27 (3.051)	30 (3.390)	16.0 (1.808)	19.5 (2.203)	21.5 (2.429)
0.190 -32	#24 (2.712)	#32 (3.616)	36 (4.067)	19.5 (2.203)	#23 (2.599)	26 (2.938)
0.250 -20	#50 (5.649)	#65 (7.344)	70 (7.909)	#37 (4.180)	#15 (5.084)	50 (5.649)
0.250 -28	#65 (7.344)	#75 (8.474)	85 (9.604)	#45 (5.084)	#54 (6.101)	60 (6.779)
0.3125 -18	#110 (12.428)	#135 (15.253)	150 (16.948)	#80 (9.039)	#95 (10.734)	105 (11.863)
0.3125 -24	#125 (14.123)	#150 (16.948)	170 (19.207)	#90 (10.169)	#110 (12.428)	120 (13.558)
0.375 -16	#200 (22.597)	#250 (28.246)	270 (30.506)	#140 (15.818)	#170 (19.207)	185 (20.902)
0.375 -24	#225 (25.422)	#275 (31.071)	300 (33.895)	#160 (18.078)	#190 (21.467)	215 (24.292)
0.4375 -14	325 (36.720)	375 (42.369)	425 (48.019)	#225 (25.422)	270 (30.506)	300 (33.895)
0.4375 -20	350 (39.545)	425 (48.019)	475 (53.668)	255 (28.811)	310 (35.025)	340 (38.415)
0.500 -13	500 (56.492)	600 (67.791)	650 (73.440)	340 (38.415)	400 (45.194)	450 (50.843)
0.500 -20	550 (62.142)	675 (76.265)	750 (84.739)	390 (44.064)	460 (51.973)	515 (58.187)
0.5625 -12	700 (79.089)	850 (96.037)	950 (107.336)	500 (56.492)	600 (67.791)	675 (76.265)
0.5625 -18	800 (90.388)	950 (107.336)	1,050 (118.634)	550 (62.142)	675 (76.265)	750 (84.739)
0.625 -11	1,000 (112.985)	1,200 (135.582)	1,300 (146.880)	675 (76.265)	800 (90.388)	900 (101.686)
0.625 -18	1,150 (129.933)	1,350 (152.529)	1,500 (169.477)	775 (87.563)	925 (104.511)	1,025 (115.809)
0.750 -10	1,700 (192.074)	2,100 (237.268)	2,300 (259.865)	1,200 (135.582)	1,450 (163.828)	1,600 (180.776)
0.750 -16	2,000 (225.970)	2,400 (271.164)	2,600 (293.760)	1,350 (152.529)	1,600 (180.776)	1,800 (203.373)
0.875 -9	2,800 (316.357)	3,400 (384.148)	3,700 (418.044)	1,950 (220.320)	2,350 (265.514)	2,600 (293.760)
0.875 -14	3,200 (361.551)	3,800 (429.342)	4,200 (474.536)	2,200 (248.587)	2,600 (293.760)	2,900 (327.656)
1.000 -8	4,200 (474.536)	5,100 (576.222)	5,600 (632.715)	2,900 (327.656)	3,500 (395.447)	3,900 (440.641)
1.000 -12	4,800 (542.327)	5,800 (655.312)	6,400 (723.103)	3,200 (361.551)	3,850 (434.991)	4,300 (485.835)
1.125 -7	5,900 (666.610)	7,200 (813.491)	7,900 (892.580)	4,100 (463.238)	4,900 (553.626)	5,400 (610.118)
1.125 -8	6,300 (711.804)	7,600 (858.684)	8,400 (949.072)	4,300 (485.835)	5,100 (576.222)	5,700 (644.013)
1.250 -7	8,400 (949.072)	10,100 (1,141)	11,200 (1,265)	5,800 (655.312)	6,900 (779.595)	7,700 (869.983)
1.250 -8	8,800 (994.266)	10,600 (1,197)	11,700 (1,321)	5,900 (666.610)	7,100 (802.192)	7,900 (892.580)
1.375 -6	11,000 (1,242)	13,300 (1,502)	14,700 (1,660)	7,600 (858.684)	9,100 (1,028)	10,100 (1,141)
1.375 -8	11,900 (1,344)	14,400 (1,626)	15,900 (1,796)	8,000 (903.878)	9,500 (1,073)	10,600 (1,197)
1.500 -6	14,700 (1,660)	17,700 (1,242)	19,600 (2,214)	10,000 (1,129)	12,000 (1,355)	13,330 (1,502)
1.500 -8	15,800 (1,785)	19,000 (2,146)	21,100 (2,383)	10,500 (1,186)	12,600 (1,423)	14,000 (1,581)
1.750 -5	23,200 (2,621)	27,900 (3,152)	30,900 (3,491)	15,800 (1,785)	19,000 (2,146)	21,100 (2,383)
1.750 -8	25,900 (2,926)	31,100 (3,513)	34,500 (3,897)	17,000 (1,920)	20,400 (2,304)	22,700 (2,564)
2.000 -4.5	35,000 (3,954)	42,000 (4,745)	46,600 (5,265)	23,800 (2,689)	28,500 (3,220)	31,700 (3,581)
2.000 -8	39,500 (4,462)	47,400 (5,355)	52,600 (5,943)	25,800 (2,915)	31,000 (3,502)	34,400 (3,886)

* Use type 1 minimum values where alignment of locking holes (cotterpins, safety wire, etc.) is requuied at assembly. Use type II minimum values where alignment of locking holes is not required at assembly.

For screws having screwdriver slots only (no external wrenching provisions) 22lb-in (2.486 Nm) minimum is permitted.

Table 10-6-1. Torques for free-spinning fasteners and for self-locking nuts on studs

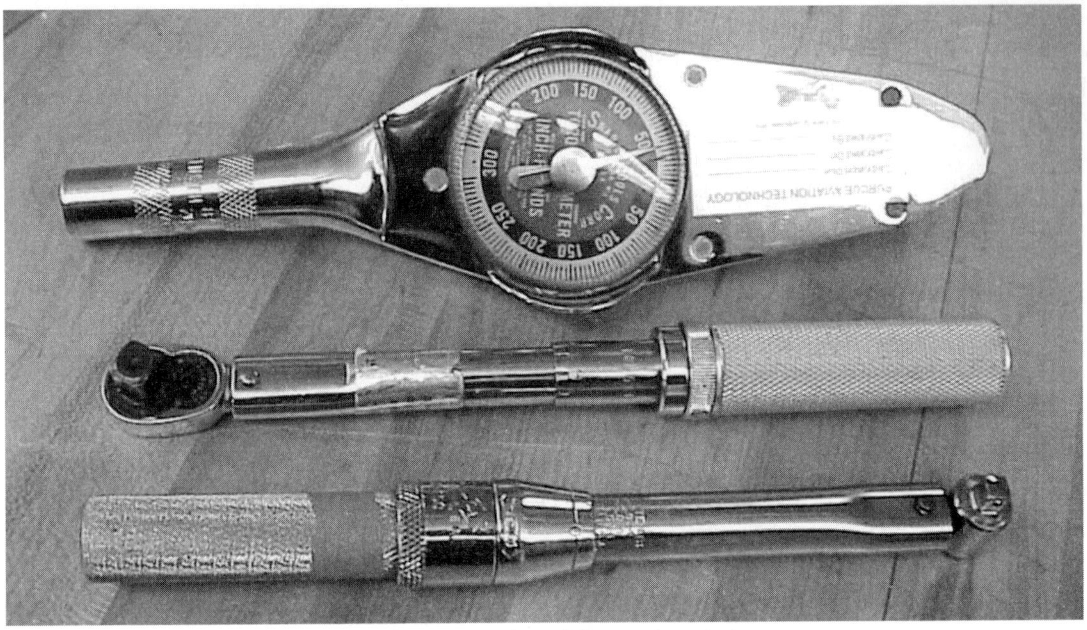

Figure 10-6-1. Examples of torque wrenches preferred for use in aviation

Heat Damage

Heat failures occur during medium and high speed operations. The initial cause is frequently obscured especially at the highest speeds and may be:

- Failure of lubricant by lubricant source being cut off, lubricant deterioration or contamination
- Excessive load
- Cramped bearings or tight bearings caused by expansion of inner race when pressing on a shaft or expansion of outer race when pressed into housings (radial) or by squeezing one bearing against another (axial)
- Off-square producing heat at retainer
- Heat from an external source

Sometimes the initial cause may be diagnosed by noting which parts showed the initial heating, the most heating or similar indications.

Heat will not only badly oxidize separators but will also soften the balls and races and particularly the balls because the heat cannot be conducted away from them as rapidly as from the races. Liberal lubrication may make continued operation possible for some time in spite of the partly softened balls and races.

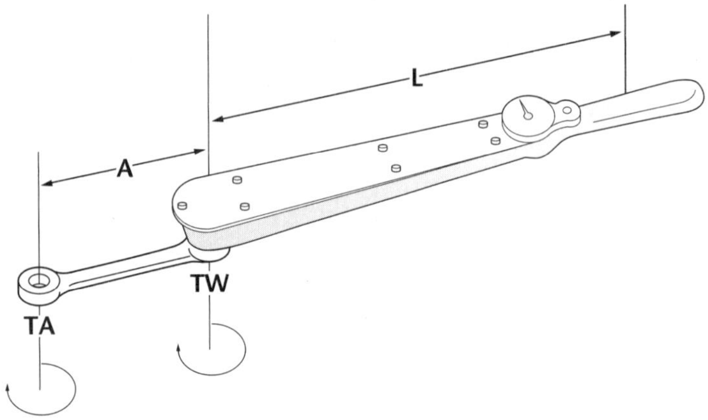

TW = Indicated Torque Value on Torque Wrench

TA = Actual Torque Value Applied to Fastener

L = Lever Length

Figure 10-6-2. Nonconcentric attachments to torque wrench

Section 6

Standard Practices

The engine manufacturer's maintenance manual contains a chapter where general information is found. This can include such topics as: general torque settings, preferred safety wiring methods, schematic symbols and wiring standards. The discussion that follows is typical of the information in the standard practices section of a maintenance manual.

Standard Torque Requirements

Torque measuring tools are used in the maintenance of most aircraft engines. Each threaded fastener is designed to operate at a specific torque. If installed either too tightly or loosely, both the

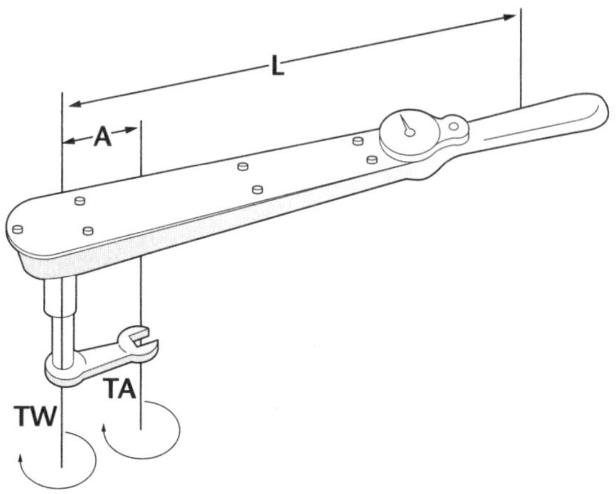

TW = INDICATED TORQUE VALUE ON TORQUE WRENCH

TA = ACTUAL TORQUE VALUE APPLIED TO FASTENER

L = LEVER LENGTH

A = ATTACHMENT LENGTH

$$TW = \frac{TA \times L}{L - A}$$

EXAMPLE

TA = REQUIRED TORQUE = 200 INCH LBS

L = 12 INCHES

A = 2 INCHES

$$TW = \frac{200 \times 12}{12 - 2} = \frac{2{,}400}{10} = 240 \text{ INCH LBS}$$

Figure 10-6-3. Torque wrench attachment offset reverse extension

fastener and the part may suffer damage or fail. By specifying the torque for a fastener, a designer can predict the strength and dependability of an assembly. If torque values are left to chance then there is no method of knowing when a fastener or assembly may fail. As a result, proper torque procedures are extremely important to the maintenance process.

Use standard torque values in locations where no specific torque is given in the maintenance manual. Standard torque tables are contained in the general practices section of the maintenance manual. Table 10-6-1 is a typical chart used for free spinning fasteners.

The application of torque should be slow and even for consistency and best possible accuracy. Pneumatic tools should never be used to tighten or torque a nut onto a bolt.

Torque Wrenches and Torque Application

Types of torque wrenches. There are several different types of torque wrenches: rigid frame or indicating dial type, audible indicating (click type) and flexible beam type. In aircraft maintenance applications, the rigid frame with the indicating dial and the audible click type torque wrench are used in preference to the deflecting beam type wrench. The audible indicating type wrench is preferred because of its ability to be used in places of limited access where it would be difficult to read a dial or scale while performing the tightening operation.

Typically, the torque wrench indicates in foot-pounds, inch-pounds or Newton meters, depending on the application. Choose the correct torque wrench for your application. When practical, the required torque value should be between 30% and 80% of the wrench's scale. The accuracy of most torque wrenches tends to decrease at the extremes of the range, with the best accuracy in the mid-range. Torque wrenches should be calibrated once a year or after they have been abused or dropped. Often, the calibration date is printed on the wrench for verification. Store the torque wrench in a dry place away from other tools. Several styles of torque wrenches are shown in Figure 10-6-1.

Extensions. Many torque wrench applications require the use of attachments such as adaptors and extensions to reach fasteners in places of limited accessibility. They may also be needed to position the wrench to move in the correct direction. This affects the actual torque value. Use the formula in Figure 10-6-2 for extensions that add to the length of the wrench.

Other types of extensions require the use of different formulas to compute the actual torque on the fastener. Use the formulas for extensions similar to those in Figures 10-6-3 and 10-6-4.

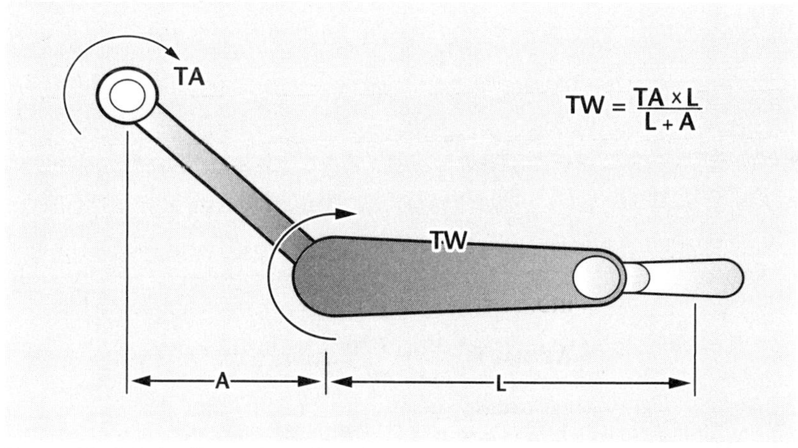

Figure 10-6-4. An illustration of angle extension torque wrench adjustment

Figure 10-6-5. Safety wire is available in one pound cans for easy use.

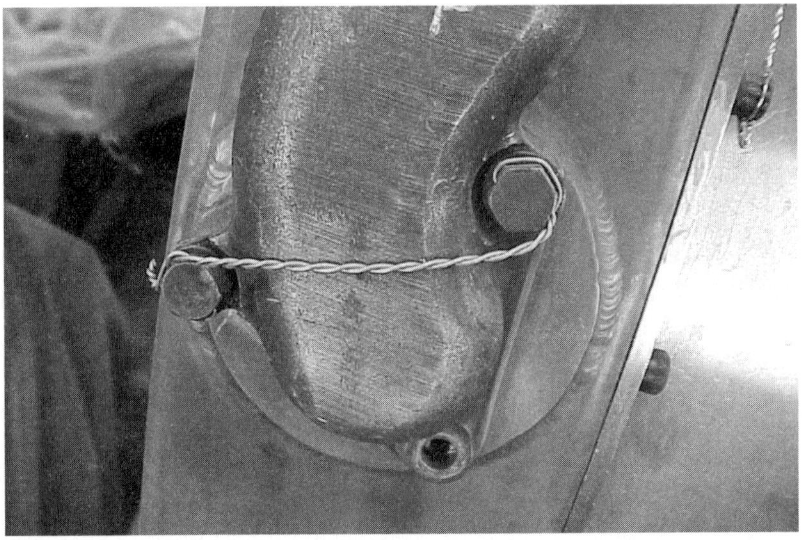

Figure 10-6-6. The double twist method provides a tight and neat safety.

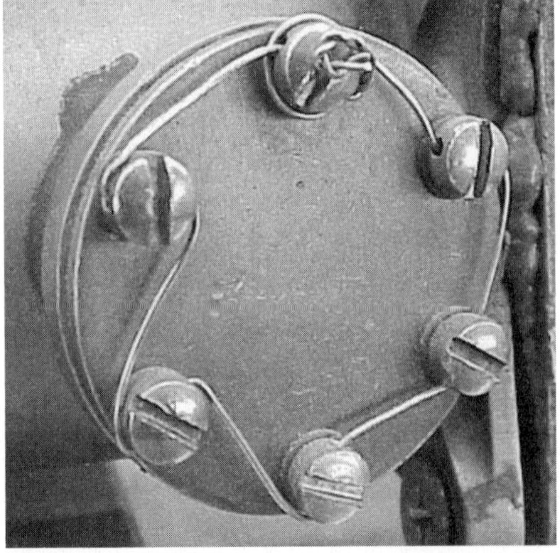

Figure 10-6-7. The single wire safety can be used on small screws.

Locking Devices

The use of locking devices is very common on turbine engines, as well as airframes. These devices prevent the inadvertent loosening of fasteners that hold the engine together as well as keeping the accessories from coming loose. Each of these devices is specific to its application and the manner in which they are used. It is understood that the locking device is not reusable once it has been removed since its locking ability may be impaired. Some of the most common devices are: safety wire, cotter pins, lockwashers and a variety of friction lock nuts.

Safety Wire Installation

Safety wire (also known as lock-wire) comes in many types and sizes. The terms safety wire and lockwire are interchangeable. The most commonly used safety wire material is stainless steel. Be sure to always check the part number on the roll of safety wire to verify that you are using the correct size and material for the job in question. Safety wire is used to secure bolts, screws, nuts, tube coupling nuts, hose connectors and electrical connectors. The part number in the maintenance manual will specify the correct type of safety wire that needs to be used. An example of safety wire is shown in Figure 10-6-5.

Installing safety wire. The following points on safety wiring are considered general information:

- The double twist method is normally used for all safety wiring applications unless otherwise specified. See Figure 10-6-6.

Figure 10-6-8. The maximum span between tension points should not be greater than 6 inches.

Figure 10-6-9. Safety wire should be tight to withstand vibration.

- Sometimes a single wire method is used to secure small screws which are placed closely together. Make sure that the pull exerted by the wire tends to tighten the screws. See Figure 10-6-7.
- The maximum span of safety wire between tension points must not be more than 6 inches. See Figure 10-6-8.
- The maximum length of wire used to lock one unit or a group of units in a series must not be more than 24 inches.
- Do not lock more than four units in a series with one continuous length of wire.
- The size of the safety wire shall be between 1/3 and ¾ of the hole diameter, except when using the single wire method. For single wire method, use the largest standard wire size that will fit the hole. Common wire sizes are: 0.020, 0.032, 0.041 and 0.047.
- All safety wires must be tight after installation, but not under so much tension that normal handling or vibration will break the wire. See Figure 10-6-9.
- The wire must be applied so that all pull exerted by the wire tends to tighten the nut or bolt.
- The loop of double wire shall pass around, not over, the head of the bolt or screw, unless clearance is a problem.
- When safetying nuts and bolts, tighten to the low side of the selected torque range and if necessary, continue tightening until a slot aligns with the safety hole.
- Twists should be tight and even and the wire between nuts as taught as possible without over-twisting. See Figure 10-6-10 and Table 10-6-2.

Double-twist method. This method of safety wiring is used for most applications.

- Cut a piece of wire that is long enough to secure the bolts. A wire too long is difficult to work with and becomes an eye hazard. Use safety goggles to prevent eye injury.
- Loop one part of the wire around the bolt head and run it below the other piece of

Figure 10-6-10. The twist in the wire should be even and tight.

SAFETY WIRE DIAMETER	0.020	0.032	0.041	0.047
TWISTS PER INCH	9 to 10	7 to 10	7 to 10	5 to 8

Table 10-6-2. Acceptable number of safety wire twists per inch

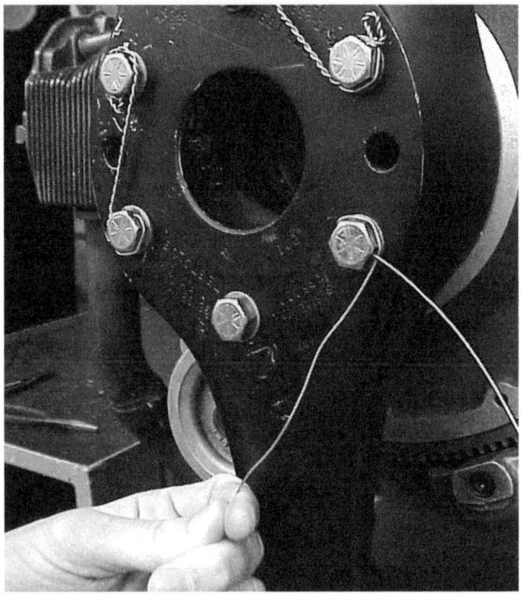

Figure 10-6-11. Start with the wire looped around the back of the bolt head.

wire and make a clockwise twist. See Figure 10-6-11.

- Place the wire pieces between your fingertips and start twisting the wire. Pay attention to the maximum number of twists per inch while twisting. If the loop around the bolt is loose you can use smooth duckbill pliers to twist the safety wire to tighten the loop.
- Twist the wire a little short of the hole of the opposing bolt, insert the top wire through the hole and loop the bottom wire around the bolt head. See Figure 10-6-12. You may use duckbill pliers to pull on both wires to tighten the safety wire.
- Run the wire that loops around the head under the wire that sticks out of the hole and start twisting counterclockwise.
- Make the pigtail about 1 inch long. See Figure 10-6-13. Put more pressure on the last few twists where you are going to cut the pigtail and bend it back towards the bolt head with needlenose pliers. This will prevent others from cutting themselves when performing maintenance on the aircraft.

Figure 10-6-12. Loop the wire so that it is held down by the twists.

Double check your work and verify that the safety wire is tight, that there are the correct number of twists per inch and that the pull exerted by the wire tends to tighten the bolts. See Figure 10-6-14.

Cotter Pins

Cotter pins are used to secure fasteners such as nuts, pins and rod ends. The bolt or pin must be drilled through the threaded end and a slotted or castellated nut is used. Cotter pins are often used in areas where high temperature prevents the use of a friction locking type of device. Always use a new cotter pin for each application.

Installation procedure. Below is the installation procedure for cotter pins.

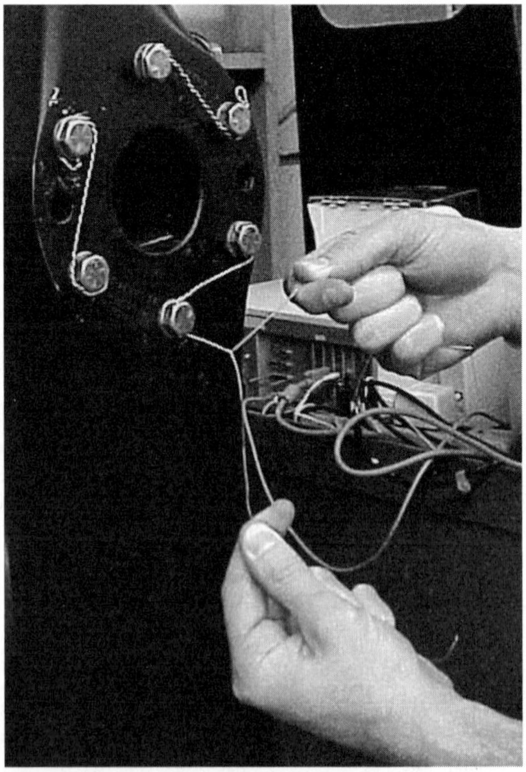

Figure 10-6-13. The pigtail should be about 1 inch long and neatly bent back.

- Torque the slotted nut to the low limit of the necessary torque. Continue to tighten the nut until a slot aligns with the hole in bolt shank. If a nut slot does not line up with the hole in the bolt shank before the maximum torque limit is reached, loosen the nut, install different thickness washer and repeat the procedure. If this still doesn't work, try another nut.
- Install the cotter pin with the head seated firmly in the slot of the nut. The axis of the eye must be at right angles to the bolt shank. Bend the cotter pin prongs so that the head and upper prong are firmly seated against the nut wrench flat. Figure 10-6-15 illustrates this technique.
- If necessary for clearance, cut off the upper prong level with the top of the bolt shank. Cut off the lower prong for clearance to the washer and a tight fit against the nut wrench flat. Do not let the lower prong rest on the washer.

Figure 10-6-14. The finished job should be consistent and all the wires should pull in the tightening direction.

Flat Lockwashers

The flat lockwasher is a one-time locking device used on torqued nuts when there is very little tolerance in the torque specification. They are bent up against the nut's wrenching flats and down into a drilled hole or over an edge. Flat lockwashers may be used once. New flat lockwashers must be used for each installation. The correct flat lockwasher will be specified in the maintenance manual by part number.

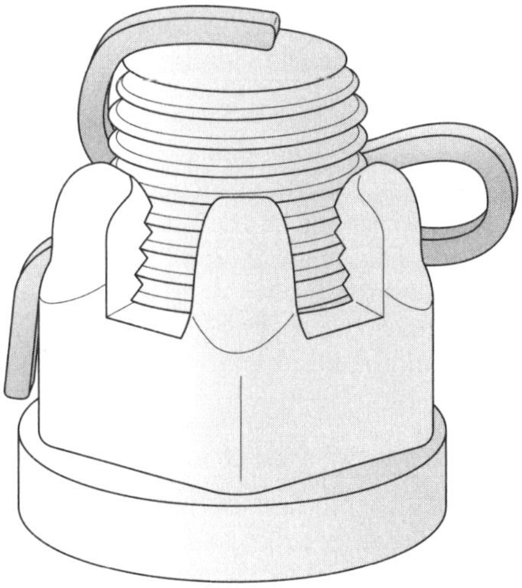

Figure 10-6-15. Cotter pins should be installed and bent over to keep the nut from turning.

Installation procedure. Below is the installation procedure for flat lockwashers:

- Once the proper lockwasher has been determined, position the outside diameter of the lockwasher over the locking hole and tighten the fastener to the required torque.
- While applying torque to the fastener and subsequent forming and bending operations, the correct position of the lockwasher must be maintained. Use a marker to mark the position of the periphery of the lockwasher in such a manner that any movement out of position can be detected.
- To form the locking arrangement, lightly tap or press the flat lockwasher into the hole with a conically tipped tool (center punch). Flat tipped tools must not be used.
- During the forming there must not be any cracking or shearing of the lockwasher at the locking hole. Bend the flat lockwasher so that one bent edge is in intimate contact with the wrenching flat on the fastener that is diametrically opposite the locking hole, as seen in Figure 10-5-16.

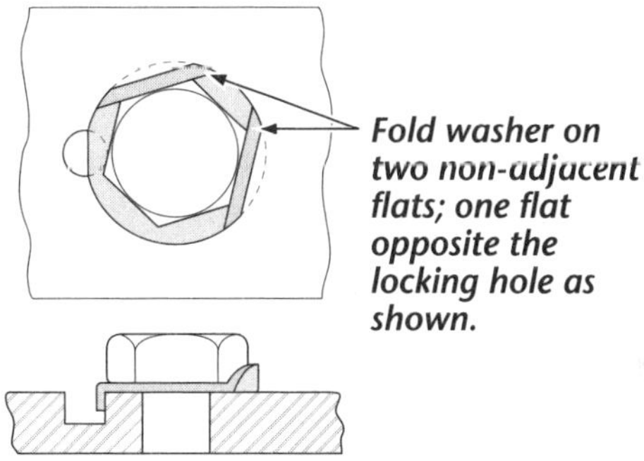

Figure 10-6-16. Flat lockwashers can only be used once.

Figure 10-6-17. Star lockwashers should only be used on top of a plain washer.

External Star Washers and Spring Lockwashers

Lockwashers may be used if self-locking or castellated nuts are not available. Sufficient friction is provided by the spring action of the washer to prevent loosening of the nut from vibration. Do not use if frequent removal is required or in areas exposed to the airflow. Always use a plain washer under the lockwasher. Figure 10-6-17 shows an internal and an external type of lockwasher.

NOTE: *Lockwashers are not to be used on primary structures, secondary structures or accessories where failure might result in damage or danger to aircraft or personnel.*

Bolts and Nuts

The bolts and nuts used in turbine engines have a permanent designation code. The code employs a letter C for corrosion resistant steel for normal application and H for heat-resistant alloys in hot section application. Never assemble a part coded with a C in a location which requires an H coded part and vice-versa. Never use cadmium plated nuts, bolts or any other cadmium plated part in the hot section of the engine due to the possibility that the plating may flake off, creating localized hot spots.

Figure 10-6-20. Castle nuts can be saftied with cotter pins or safety wire.

CAUTION: *Never use a locknut with a fiber insert in the hot section of the engine, since the fiber inset can melt or burn leaving no locking feature in the nut.*

Figure 10-6-18. These all-metal locknuts are suitable for high temperature areas.

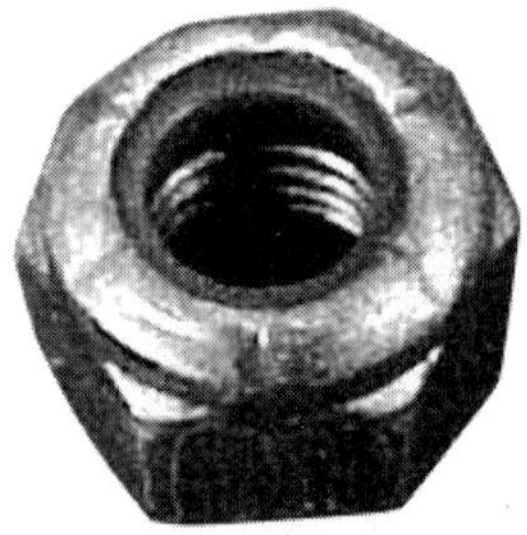

Figure 10-6-19. Fiber locknuts should never be used in areas wher the temperature exceeds 250°F.

Bolt code identification will usually appear on the top of the bolt head or on one side of the hex of a nut. Correct engine reassembly requires particular attention be paid to material requirements for nuts and bolts used in the engine hot section, where parts must be made of material resistant to high temperatures.

Locking Nuts

All metal type. Metal locknuts are constructed with the threads in the locking insert out-of-round with the load-carrying section. They are also made with a saw-cut insert and pinched-in thread in the locking section. Both of these create friction between the bolt and the nut and prevents loosening of the nut. In many instances, this friction must be compensated for when applying torque to the fastener. Several types of metal locknuts are pictured in Figure 10-6-18.

Fiber or nylon type lock nut. A fiber or nylon unthreaded ring provides the locking action of this type of nut. Because it has a smaller diameter than the nut it grips the bolt and prevents

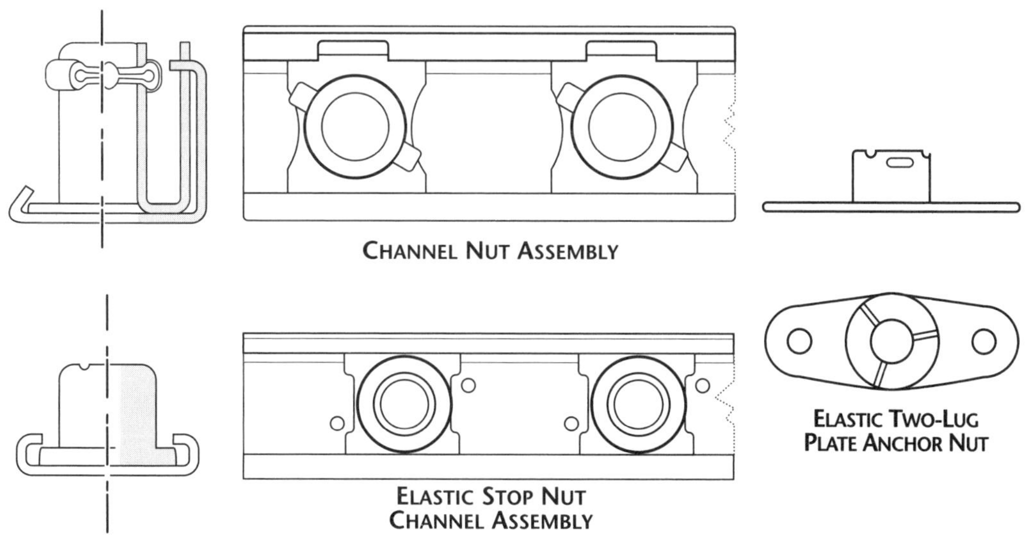

Figure 10-6-21. Self-locking nuts

the nut from becoming loose. They can not be used in areas where the temperature exceeds 250°F. After removal a fiber or nylon locknut can not be reused if it cannot meet the minimum prevailing torque values. An example is shown in Figure 10-6-19.

Castle nut. Castle nuts and castellated shear nuts are used with drilled shank bolts, hex-head bolts, clevis bolts, eyebolts and drilled-head studs. The castellated shear nuts are not as deep or as strong as the regular castle nut. These nuts are designed to be secured with cotter pins or safety wire. A castle nut is shown in Figure 10-6-20.

Nut plates. Nut plates are available in many different styles and sizes. In some types the nut moves around a little to account for a slight misalignment. This type is called a floating anchor nut. Most nut plates are riveted to the structure with small countersunk rivets but some are installed in channels and are called channel nuts. These channels are track-like bases with regularly spaced nuts which are either removable or fixed. The nut plates in Figure 10-6-21 and Figure 10-6-22 are typical of those used on engines.

Marking of Parts

Engine parts are marked for identification purposes as is stipulated in 14CFR part 45. Parts could be marked with part numbers, serial numbers, cycles and high or low balance points. Markings made on engine parts, assemblies or weldments must be easily read and must not be easily removed. Reidentification of parts, reapplication and/or relocation of part markings must be done adjacent to or in a location similar to that of, the original marking. Where reidentification or corrective marking is required, deletion of existing marking or portions thereof, can be necessary. Use an allowable marking method, draw a wavy line, loop, flat oval or Xs through the character(s) or symbol(s) to be deleted. Figure 10-6-23 shows typical markings on parts.

Approved methods for marking of parts are: electrolytic etch, metal stamping, vibration peening or engraving methods, which are shown in Figure 10-6-23. Temporary methods of marking parts are: electrolytic etch or the use of inks. Electric arc scribing, acid etching and soapstone are not suitable methods for marking jet engine parts.

> **CAUTION**: *Lead and/or metallic pencils or any marking method that leaves a deposit of carbon, zinc, copper, lead or similar residue must not be used. These deposits can cause a reduction in fatigue strength as a result of carburization or intergranular attack when the part is subjected to intense heat.*

Figure 10-6-23. Turbine engine parts can be marked in a variety of ways.

Figure 10-6-22. These metal nutplates have the same locking features as metal locknuts.

Figure 10-6-24. Pratt & Whitney JT9D wrapped and mounted on transport stand

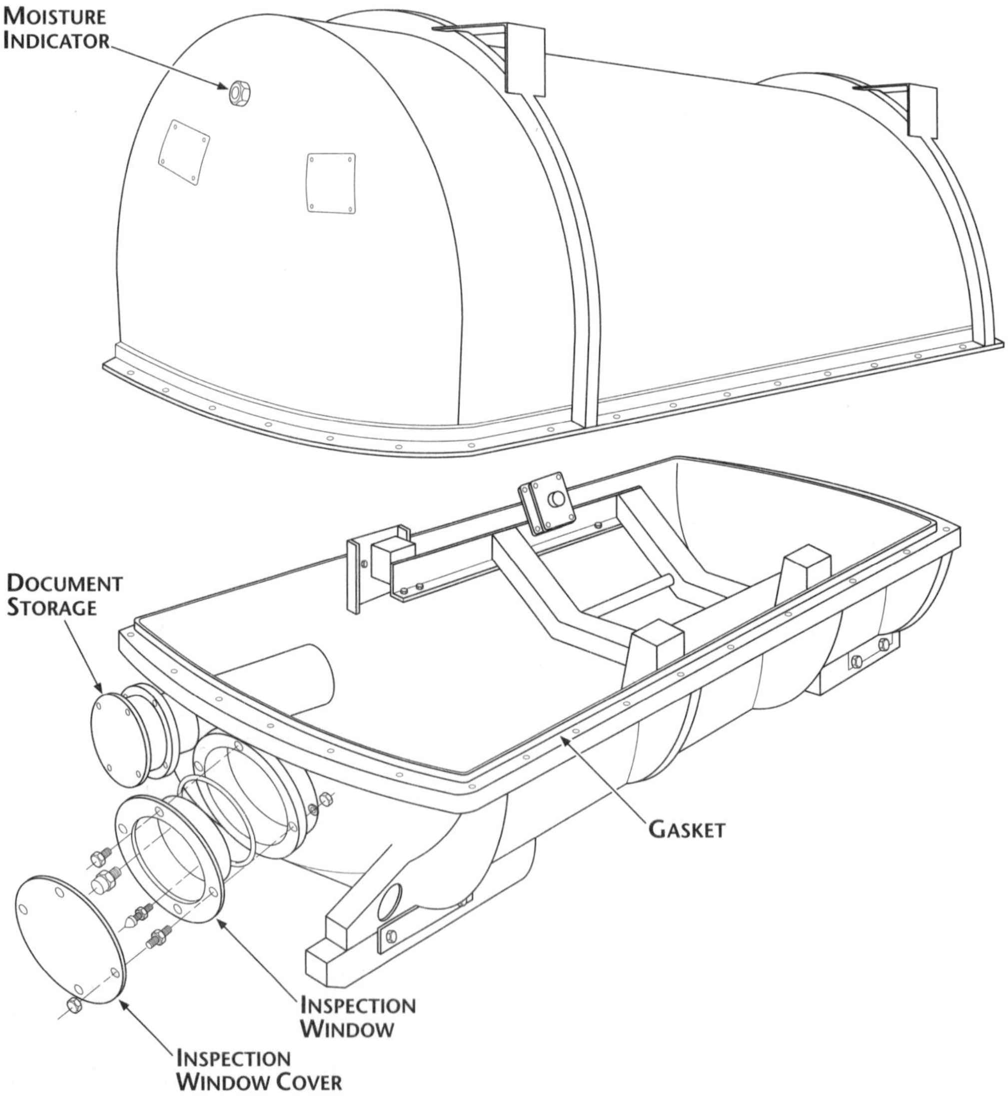

Figure 10-6-25. Metal storage and shipping container components

Transportation and Storage

At times it is necessary to ship turbine engines to and from overhaul facilities and maintenance bases. A turbine engine is essentially a series of heavy disks mounted on one or more shafts supported by bearings. Damage to the bearings and, in turn, to the discs is likely to happen if the proper shipping containers are not used. The larger the engine, the greater weight and the greater the risk of damage.

Engine Transportation

For an engine that is transported a long distance by truck, it is recommended that the truck have an air suspension system to avoid damage to the bearings of the engine. The engine should be installed in a shock-mounted transport stand that is made for the engine. Most engine manufacturers will provide, on loan, a shipping stand for their engines. Figure 10-6-24 shows an example of a shipping stand for a JT9D engine.

If the engine is moved around in the shop it is typically installed on an engine stand with pneumatic tires and shock absorbing casters to avoid bearing damage during movement. Never tow the engine at speeds higher than 5 miles per hour. The road surface must be smooth so avoid potholes, speed bumps and curbs.

Engine storage. The metal shipping and storage container shown in Figure 10-6-25 is used for long-term storage. The container is pressurized and bags of desiccant are tied to the engine to maintain the humidity within the container at a safe level for storage. A humidity indicator can be viewed from the outside. A safe level is indicated by a blue color, but if the indicator turns pink, an unsafe humidity level exists and the desiccant bags need to be replaced.

Troy Pedersen
Engine Technician

Chapter 11

FAULT analysis

Gas turbine engine maintenance practices include inflight engine performance monitoring as a means of detecting mechanical deterioration in engine gas paths. As components in the gas path such as turbine blades, inlet guide vanes and compressor components wear they will tend to change the operational values of the engine's parameters.

Engine condition monitoring (ECM) is used to aid in early detection of many different types of engine faults. This allows for advance planning of corrective maintenance procedures and reduces the potential costs of primary and secondary damage resulting from fully developed failures. It also reduces the risk of inflight shutdowns and flight cancellations.

Learning Objectives

- *Engine Condition Monitoring*
- *Engine Diagnostics*
- *Trend Analysis*
- *Vibration*
- *Engine Balancing*
- *Manufacturing Defects*

Section 1

Engine Condition Monitoring

The turbine engine characteristic of repeatedly producing its output at or very close to charted gas generator parameter values provides the basis for the engine condition trend monitoring system. The engine readings that are taken inflight are charted and compared to the values from an ideal engine. These curves can then be evaluated to determine the condition of the in-service engine.

The parameters used are pressure altitude (PA), indicated outside air temperature (OAT) or total air temperature (TAT), for a given torque (turboprop) or engine pressure ratio (EPR). As engine parameters change over engine operating time, a trend can be determined. In other words, the shift in certain engine parameters can be used

Left: **Fault analysis and troubleshooting can require many assets and sources.**

Photo courtesy Duncan Aviation

TREND PLOT INDICATION	PROBABLE CAUSE
One parameter moves	90% chance that it is an indicator error
Two parameters move	Equal chance that it is an indication or engine related problem
Three parameters move	90% chance that it an engine problem
Four parameters shift in the same direction	First check for TAT error, EPR problem, or bleed system problem (compare with other engines on aircraft)
EGT fuel flow trends	+10°C EGT equivalent to +1% fuel flow (may vary with engine type)
Unexplainable trend	Investigate whether the engine was changed

Table 11-1-1. Rules of thumb for trend report parameters.

to determine the condition of the gas path and can be used to predict engine faults.

Most turbofan engines use data from both spools. Turboprop and turboshaft engines use turbine inlet temperature (TIT), N_g (gas generator speed), and fuel flow (W_f) for a given torque or horsepower to establish a trend. At a given temperature and pressure, these turboprop engines must operate within a tolerance band, either above or below charted values. Generally, the tolerance is a percentage of change. If it is too high or too low, the engine does not meet performance standards and corrective action will be needed. When a trend is established or there is a deviation from normal (original operating parameter values), this can be an indication that over operating time gas path components have deteriorated.

New engines operate either above or below charted values and within a tolerance band. They tend to deviate more from these values over time and with deterioration of gas path components. Abrupt changes, or gradual increased rate of change of the normal deviations from charted values are critical indicators of gas path component conditions. As such, changes can be detected before any drastic failure occurs.

Since there are generally three to four parameters that are monitored, the number of parameters that show a shift or trend is very important in determining the cause of the engine malfunction. As shown in Table 11-1-1, the number of parameters that shift is of great importance to predicting the probable cause.

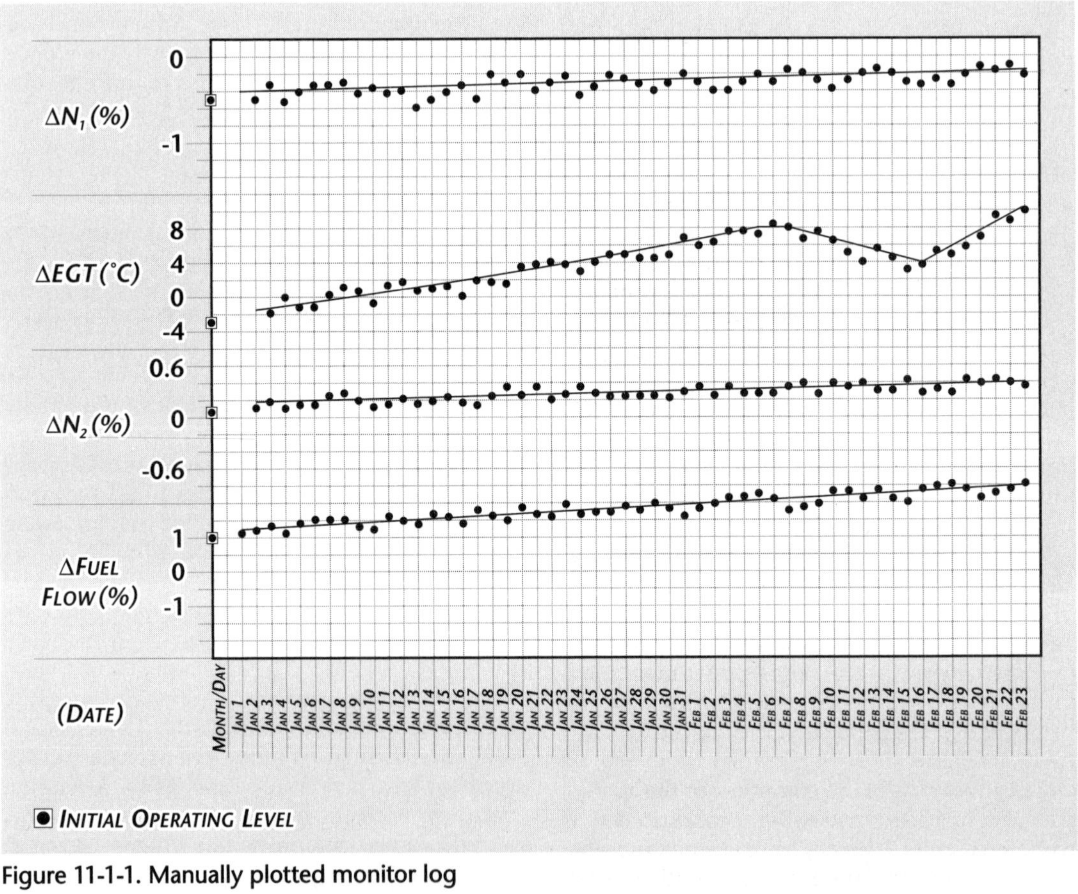

Figure 11-1-1. Manually plotted monitor log

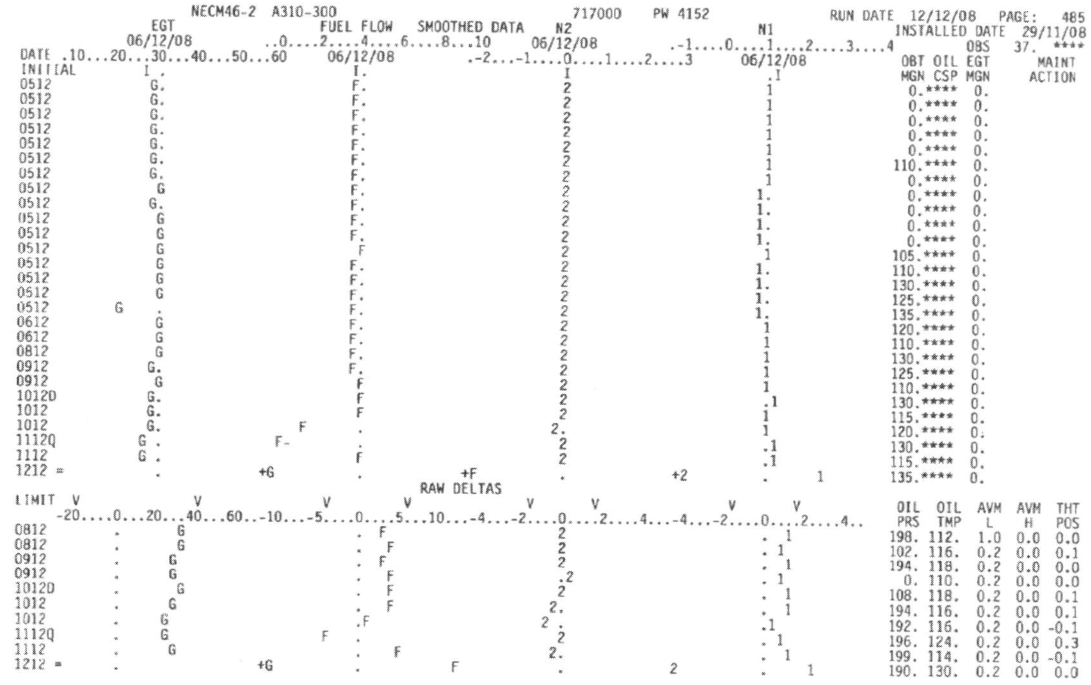

Figure 11-1-2. An example of a computer-generated trend report

The ECM system collects data inflight either automatically by the aircraft computers or manually by the flight crew. This data is written into computer files, corrected to sea level static conditions, and compared with the baseline of the particular engine. On older aircraft, the data is collected manually during cruise flight conditions and entered into a computer program or manually plotted on a graph. See Figure 11-1-1.

All aircraft engines in the fleet can be monitored easily and preventative maintenance can be planned. Figure 11-1-2 shows an example of a trend plot report. Up until December 12 all parameters had been trending consistently however all parameters start moving up on December 12, indicating an engine problem. Technicians checked the Electronic Centralized Aircraft Monitoring System (ECAM) and found a message indicating that there had been a W_3 harness circuit failure that caused the station 2.5 bleed to go to the failsafe (full open) position. By finding this condition early, fuel consumption and engine wear can be reduced.

The monitoring system should be introduced when engines are new or newly overhauled. The baseline parameters for each engine are derived during a test procedure in a test cell and are entered in the engine documentation. This creates a performance baseline before any deterioration takes place in the engine.

During every flight the computer or flight crew collect data during cruise flight conditions. The technician enters the engine parameters into a chart or computer program and will have an indication of the performance of the engine. Troubleshooting charts such as Table 11-1-2 are used in engine performance monitoring and fault isolation.

Engine Diagnostics and Trend Analysis

Gas turbine engine troubleshooting has improved dramatically with the advent of fault-detection and recording devices. Built-in test equipment (BITE) systems record EGT information, spool speeds, fuel flow, EPR and other engine parameters, which can then be displayed for both flight deck and maintenance personnel. These data collection methods are often referred to as engine condition monitoring, engine health monitoring or trend-condition monitoring.

Maintenance personnel may observe changes and degradation of performance over many flight hours, often preventing small problems from becoming major maintenance issues. Precise and consistent patterns for recording the required information are critical to this process and are often done automatically with new-generation equipment.

The engine diagnostic data can be transmitted to the maintenance engineering department during flight, and the engine parameters can be continuously monitored by the maintenance staff. Often, technicians will meet an aircraft at the gate with replacement parts when an engine malfunction has occurred.

ENGINE PARAMETERS	PROBABLE CAUSE	ACTION REQUIRED	REMARKS
All parameters UP	• AC/engine indicating systems	Inspect	Repair as required
	• Air inlet door blocked	Inspect	Repair as required
	• Bypass door or ice vane misrigged	Inspect	Repair as required
	• Compressor FOD, rub, erosion	Inspect and/or repair	Remove engine if limits are exceeded
	• Compressor contaminated/dirty	Wash compressor	
	• Bleed valve open	Inspect	Repair as required
	• $P_{2.5}$ air leaks from engine/airframe system	Inspect	Repair as required
	• PT stator vanes burned/flow area increased. PT blade tip oxidation/rub.	Inspect	Repair as required
	• Hot start	Inspect hot section and check log book	Do applicable overtemperature inspection
All parameters DOWN	• Aircraft/engine indicating system	Inspect	Repair as required
Fuel nozzle deterioration	• Inspect	Clean as required	
N_g UP or DOWN T_5, W_f constant	• Aircraft/engine indicating system	Inspect	Repair as required
W_f UP or DOWN T_5, N_g, constant	• Aircraft/engine indicating system	Inspect	Repair as required
W_f, T_5 UP N_g down	• CT stator vanes burned/flow, area increased. CT blade tip oxidation/rub.	Inspect CT stator and CT blades	If limits exceeded, do a hot section inspection
	• Normal hot section deterioration	Do a hot section inspection if T_5 limit exceeded	
W_f, T_5 UP, N_g constant	• P_3 leaks from AC/engine system	Inspect	Repair as required
	• Gas generator case cracked at fuel nozzle or P_3 bleed pads. Diffuser exit ducts cracked or loose.	Inspect	Replace engine if detect confirmed
	• Leaking gas generator drain valves. C flange, fuel nozzle gasket, or T_5 harness seal	Inspect	Replace engine if detect confirmed
	• Concurrent hot section and compressor deterioration	Inspect CT stator and CT blades, and compressor	Do hot section inspection or send engine for overhaul

Note 1 *An increase in T_5 without other parameter shilfts may be the result of defective fuel nozzles or a deteriorating combustion chamber liner altering combustion profile and gas path temperature distribution.*

Note 2 *The relationship between T_5 and the temperature in front of the CT stator may change due to hot section component deterioration altering combustion profile and/ or gas path temperature distribution. This may affect the T_5 trim and the indicated T_5, and the relationship between T_5 and the temperature in front of the CT stator used for engine certification. A T_5 turn verification on-wing or in a test cell will confirm a shift in the indicated temperature.*

Table 11-1-2. Sample turbine engine troubleshooting guide

Onboard diagnostics. Newer engine designs use onboard diagnostic systems for real-time monitoring using multiple sensors as shown in Figure 11-1-3:

- Engine pressure ratio - EPR
- Low pressure compressor rotor speed - N_1
- Engine exhaust temperature - EGT
- High pressure compressor rotor speed - N_2
- Fuel flow - FF
- Oil pressure - Oil press
- Oil temperature - Oil temp
- Oil quantity - Oil qty
- Vibration - VIB

Engine sensors supply data through the Electronic Engine Control (EEC) to the engine diagnostic system and reports of engine sensor data for ground-based engine conditioning monitoring can be downloaded to a

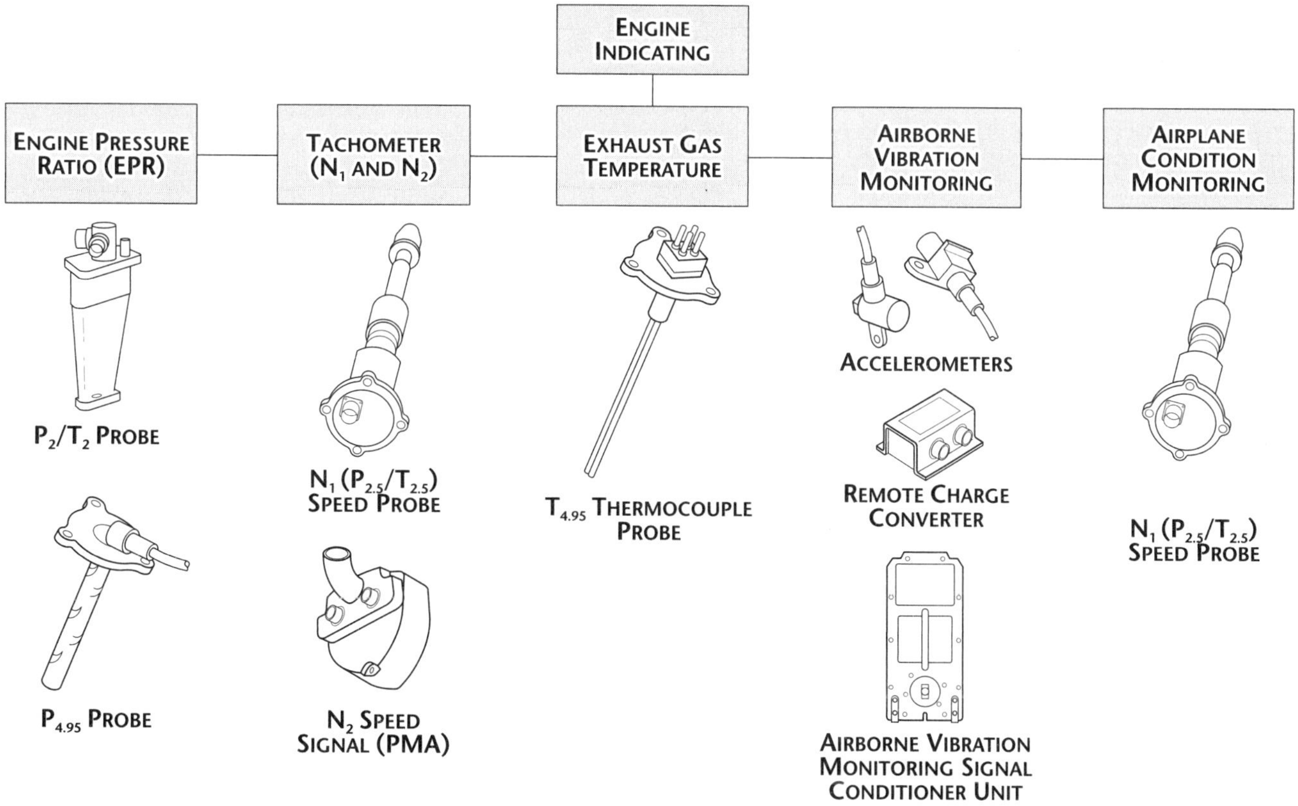

Figure 11-1-3. Engine sensors used for engine diagnostics and trend analysis

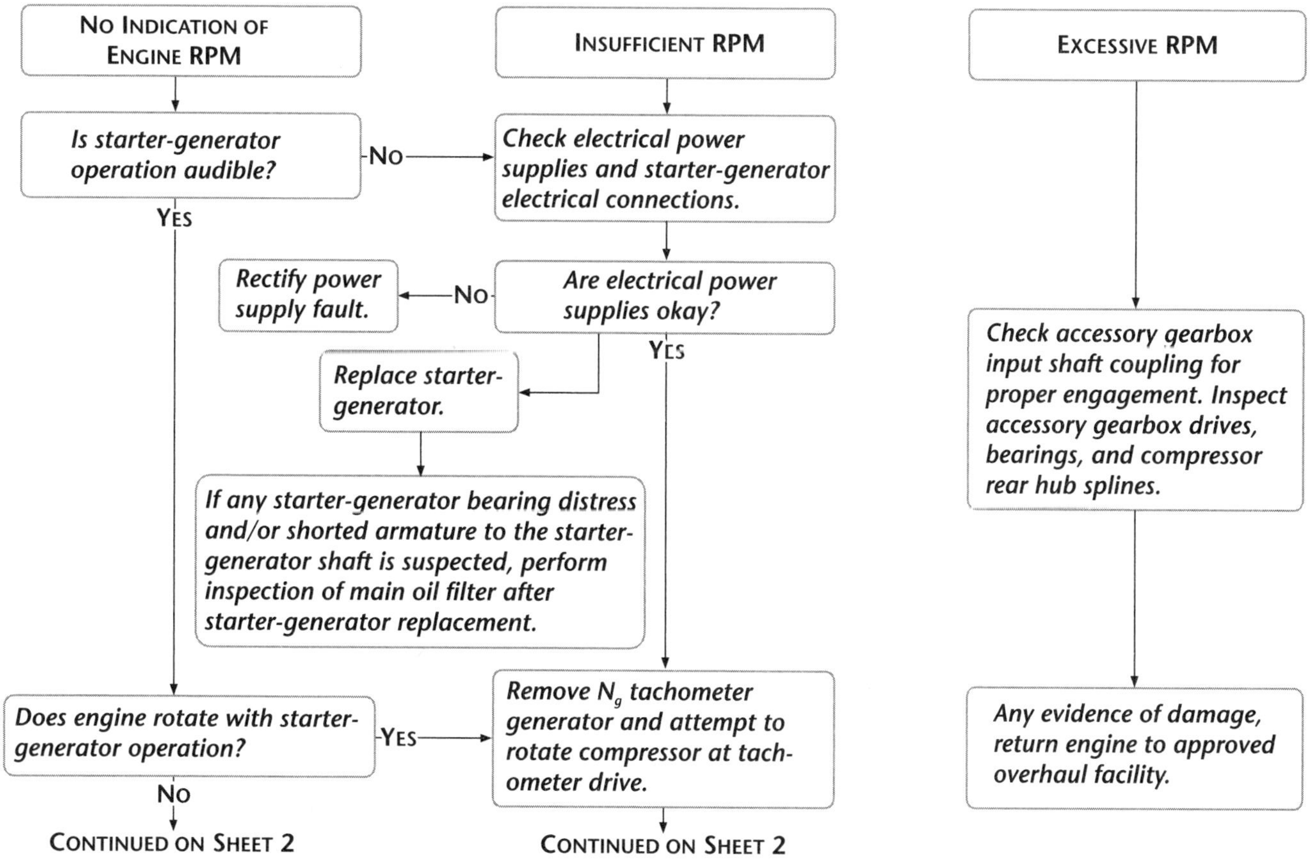

Figure 11-1-4. A troubleshooting flow chart helps to locate and solve problems.

WARNINGS?/ MALFUNCTIONS	CFDS FAULT MESSAGES				FAULT ISOLATION PROCEDURE
	SOURCE	MESSAGE	ATA	C	
ENG 1 FADEC	EIU1FAD	REV LVDT CHA/HC/EEC1	783248	2	783000 P 211 T 810 805
ENG 1 FADEC	EIU1FAD	REV LVDT CHB/HC/EEC1	783248	2	783000 P 211 T 810 805
ENG 1 FADEC	EIU1FAD	REV SL SENSCHA/HC/EEC1	783115	2	783000 P 211 T 810 805
ENG 1 FADEC	EIU1FAD	REV SL SENSCHB/HC/EEC1	783115	2	783000 P 211 T 810 805
ENG 1 FADEC	EIU1FAD	STARTER VALVE/HC/EEC1	801351	2	783000 P 211 T 810 805
ENG 1 FADEC	EIU1FAD	TCA VLV SOL/HC/EEC1	752352	2	783000 P 211 T 810 805
ENG 1 FADEC	EIU1FAD	TCA VLV/HC/EEC1	752352	2	783000 P 211 T 810 805
ENG 1 FADEC	EIU1FAD	TCA VLV/SOL/EEC1 associated with TCA VLV SOL/HC/EEC1	752351 752352	2	783000 P 211 T 810 805
ENG 1 FADEC	EIU1FAD	TCA VLV/SOL/EEC1	752351	2	783000 P 211 T 810 805
ENG 1 FADEC	EIU1FAD	TCA VLV/SOL/EEC1 associated with TCA VLV/HC/EEC1	752351 752352	2	783000 P 211 T 810 805
ENG 1 FADEC	EIU1FAD	TLA SENS/HC/EEC1	761100	2	783000 P 211 T 810 805
ENG 1 FADEC	EIU1FAD	T2.5 SENS/HC/EEC1	732218	2	783000 P 211 T 810 805
ENG 1 FADEC	EIU1FAD	VSV ACT/HC/EEC1	753241	2	783000 P 211 T 810 805
ENG 1 FADEC	EIU1FAD	10TH BLD VLV SOL/HC/EEC1	753253	2	783000 P 211 T 810 805
ENG 1 FADEC	EIU1FAD	10TH SV BLD SOL/HCEEC1	753252	2	753000 P 283 T 810 825
EFF: MXZ	ALL		**77-ECAM**		

Figure 11-1-5. Fault indication from the aircraft maintenance manual

computer and used for trend analysis and predicting upcoming failures. The engine diagnostic system is an important tool of on-condition monitoring and saves time and money.

Failure Modes and Troubleshooting

The procedure for locating a fault is called troubleshooting. The objective is for quick and accurate diagnosis of the problem and to prevent changing parts or engines unnecessarily. The basic principle of troubleshooting is to carefully study the reported problem and use a logical and systematic method of diagnosis. The reported problems are often indicated on the flight deck instruments which should be checked before proceeding.

The detection of failure modes for older engines is usually accomplished with fault isolation charts, such as the example in Figure 11-1-4. These fault isolation charts are flow charts that aid the technician in troubleshooting engine malfunctions. Engine faults can be obvious or hidden. If hidden faults are not detected, serious damage may occur to the engine. For this reason it is essential to have a thorough knowledge of correct turbine gas temperature and other important details of engine operation. Before attempting to locate a fault or difficulty, or to work on an engine which has malfunctioned during flight, consult the maintenance log and any other available data.

Modern transport category aircraft are usually equipped with a fault detection system which can display information and communicate with the built-in test equipment (BITE) of the various electronic systems and initiate tests from the Multipurpose Control Display Unit (MCDU)

Troubleshooting Manual

TASK 75-30-00-810-821
Failure of the VSV Actuator on Engine 1

1. Possible Causes

- ACTUATOR VSV (4022KS)
- Wiring from the VSV Actuator 4022KS to the EEC 400KS
- EEC (4000KS)
- FMU(400 KC)
- PUMP HP/LP FUEL (2001 EM)

2. Job set up information

A. Referenced Information

REFERENCE		DESIGNATION
AMM	24-41-00-861-002	Energize the Aircraft electrical circuits from the external power
AMM	24-41-00-862-002	De-energize the aircraft electrical circuits supplied from the external power
AMM	31-60-00-860-002	E18 Stop procedure
AMM	70-23-15-912-010	Connection of Electrical Connectors
AMM	71-00-00-710-013	Test no 11: High power assurance test
AMM	71-13-00-410-010	Closing of the Fan Cowls 437AL (447AL), 438AR (448AR)
AMM	71-50-00-210-010	Wire harness visual inspection - all power plant electrical cables
AMM	73-12-41-000-010	Removal of the LP/HP fuel pump
AMM	73-12-41-400-010	installation of the LP/HP fuel pump
AMM	73-22-34-000-010	removal of the electronic engine control (eec) (4000ks)
AMM	73-22-52-000-010	removal of he fuel metering unit (FMU)
AMM	73-22-52-400-010	installation of the fuel metering unit (FMU)
AMM	75-32-41-000-010	Removal of the variable stator vane (VSV) actuator (4022ks)
AMM	75-32-42-200-010	Inspection of the VSV mechanism
AMM	78-32-00-410-010	closing the thrust reverser halves
ASM	73-25/13	
ASM	73-25/18	
75-30-00-991-007		Fig 207

F: ALL | **75-30-00** | 267

3. Plant confirmation

A. Job Set-up

(1) Energize the aircraft electrical circuits (Ref AMM TASK 24-41-00-861-002)

(2) On the panel 50VU, release the ENG FADEC GND PWR 1 and 2 push button switches.

B. Test

(1) On the panel 50VU, push the ENG FADEC GND PWR 1 push button switch and then release it.
NOTE: This action resets the FADEC memory

(2) Do the test no 11 high power assurance test ref AMM task 71-00-00-710-013

(3) Read the last leg report of the FADEC (1A and 1B menu on the make ref 70-00-00 p block 301) and make a record of the maintenance message.

4. Fault Isolation

(Ref Fig. 207/TASK 75-30-00-991-007)
A. If the test give the maitenance message VSV ACT/HC/EEC1:- examine the harness (Ref. AMM TASK 71-50-00-210 010) from the EEC (400KS to the VSV actuator (4022KS) (Ref. ASM 73-25/18).

(1) If the fault continues:
- disconnect the connectors from the VSV actuator 4022ks
- examine the connectors and receptacles ref. AMM task 71-50-00-210-010- connect the connectors to the VSV actuator 4022ks ref AMM task 70-23-15-912-010

(2) If the fault continues:
- replace the actuator VSV 4022k8 ref AMM task 75-32-41-400-010 and ref AMM task 75-32-41-400-010

(3) If the fault continues:
- do an inspection of the VSV mechanism ref AMM task 75-32-42-200 010

(4) If the fault continues:
- read the alphanumerical code shown on the flight data and ground data of the FADEC 1A and 1 b menu on the MCDU ref 70-00-00 p block 301
- make a record of the complementary information

Figure 11-1-6. The troubleshooting procedure in the manual can save time.

located in the cockpit. Warnings and fault messages will be displayed and post-flight reports can be printed out or downloaded to a computer.

Troubleshooting an aircraft with onboard diagnostic equipment. The two types of faults are listed below:

- Faults indicated by onboard diagnostic systems - Diagnostic systems onboard the aircraft monitor many engine parameters and indicate fault messages. The system stores data in its memory, which can later be accessed for troubleshooting purposes. Diagnostic systems can identify the malfunction and direct maintenance personnel to the correct solution. Complete maintenance instructions similar to the aircraft maintenance manual can be accessed onboard the aircraft. See Figures 11-1-5 and 11-1-6.
- Faults observed by crew or maintenance technicians, which are not detected by onboard diagnostic systems - Examples include structural damage like cracks or oil leaks or foreign object damage (FOD).

These malfunctions are detected during walk around inspections and regular scheduled engine inspections like A, B or C checks.

Adjustments to engine components. On many engines the maintenance technician can make adjustments to engine fuel trimming components to correct an engine malfunction. Typically, the engine idle speed, maximum r.p.m., acceleration and deceleration times, and compressor bleed valve operation can be adjusted. Adjustments of an engine should only be made if the technician is certain that no other malfunction exists that could cause the problem.

Adjusters are usually equipped with a form of locking device such as locknuts, lockplates or safety wire. Some engines have the provision for installing remote adjustment equipment so that adjustments can be made during the ground run.

Often, maintenance technicians need to perform a ground run after engine maintenance to check the performance and mechanical integrity of the engine and to verify that the engine malfunction has been successfully repaired. Ground runs are required after an engine change, for troubleshooting which requires a running engine to duplicate the malfunction and testing of aircraft systems such as hydraulics or power generation.

Section 2

Vibration

Airborne Vibration Monitoring System

Aircraft manufacturers use varying terminology to refer to vibration diagnostic equipment. Boeing uses the term Airborne Vibration Monitoring System (AVM) and Airbus calls the system the

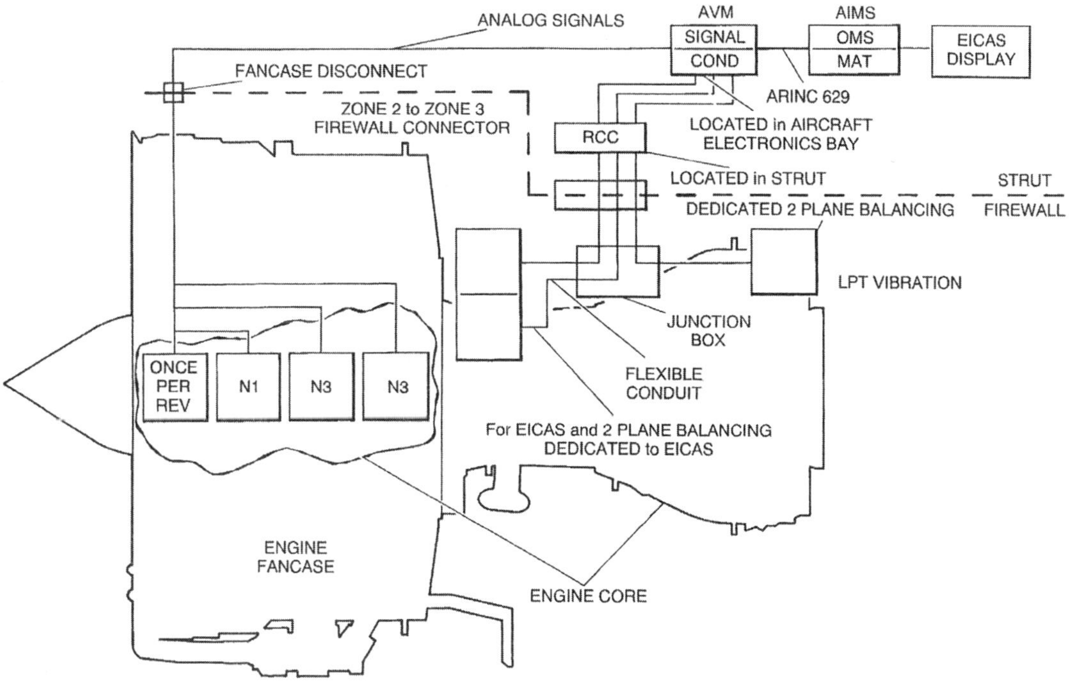

Figure 11-2-1. Vibration system

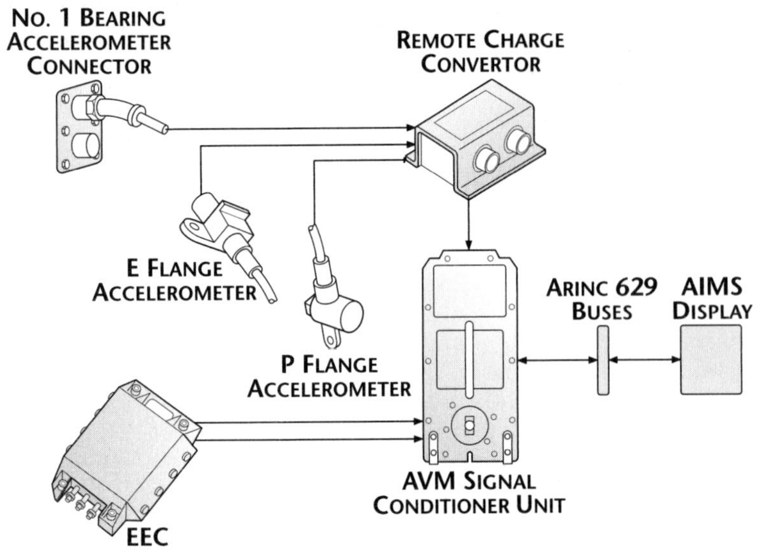

Figure 11-2-2. Airborne vibration monitoring (AVM) system

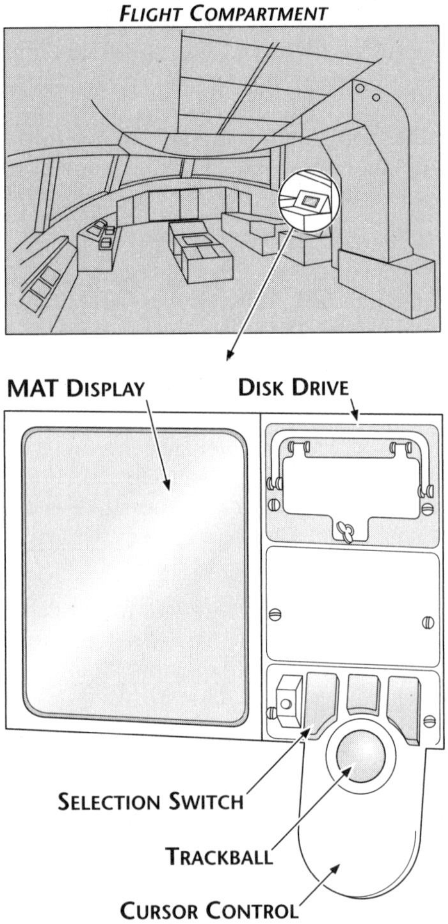

Figure 11-2-3. Maintenance access terminal (MAT)

Engine Vibration Monitoring Unit (EVMU). These systems are similar in design, but we will discuss the system used on the B777 aircraft equipped with the PW4000 engine. See Figure 11-2-1.

Most of the vibrations in large turbine engines are generated by the fan and the compressor rotors (N_1 and N_2). The airborne vibration monitoring system monitors and records the engine vibration levels. The AVM can help a technician pinpoint a disk imbalance or a worn bearing as the source of the vibration, before it results in a catastrophic failure.

There is usually one AVM system per engine. The system has three components: the accelerometer, remote charge converter (RCC) and the AVM signal conditioner unit which is shown in Figure 11-2-2.

The accelerometers send signals that are proportional to engine vibration. Each accelerometer signal goes to the RCC for signal conversion and amplification.

The RCC sends amplified vibration signals to the AVM signal conditioner unit. The AVM signal conditioner unit uses these vibration signals and the N_1 and N_2 speed signals to calculate the vibration levels for each rotor. The signal conditioner unit sends the vibration data to the airplane information management system (AIMS). The AIMS shows the vibration data on the primary display system.

The signal conditioner unit also keeps in memory the vibration data needed by the engine balancing system (EBS). The EBS is a function of the signal conditioner unit and the AIMS. It is accessed through the Maintenance Access Terminal (MAT).

Accelerometers use piezoelectric crystals to get input from engine vibration and they send it to remote charge converter. The AVM signal conditioner unit uses vibration and speed signals from engine sensors to calculate engine vibration levels. The signal conditioner unit performs the following functions as well:

- Compares the N_1 and N_2 vibration levels to find which is the highest
- Keeps in memory the vibration data for the last six flight legs

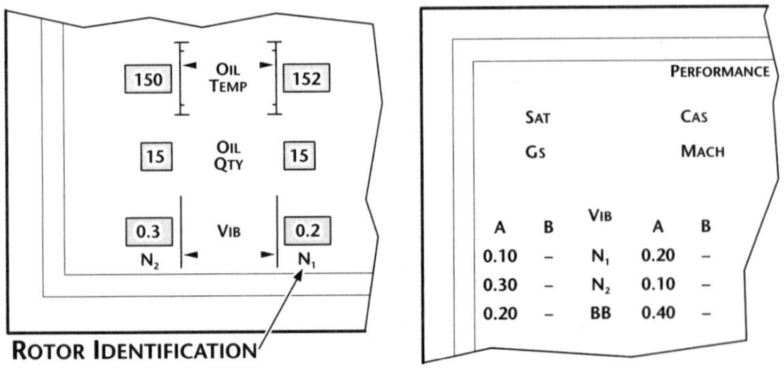

Figure 11-2-4. Secondary engine display

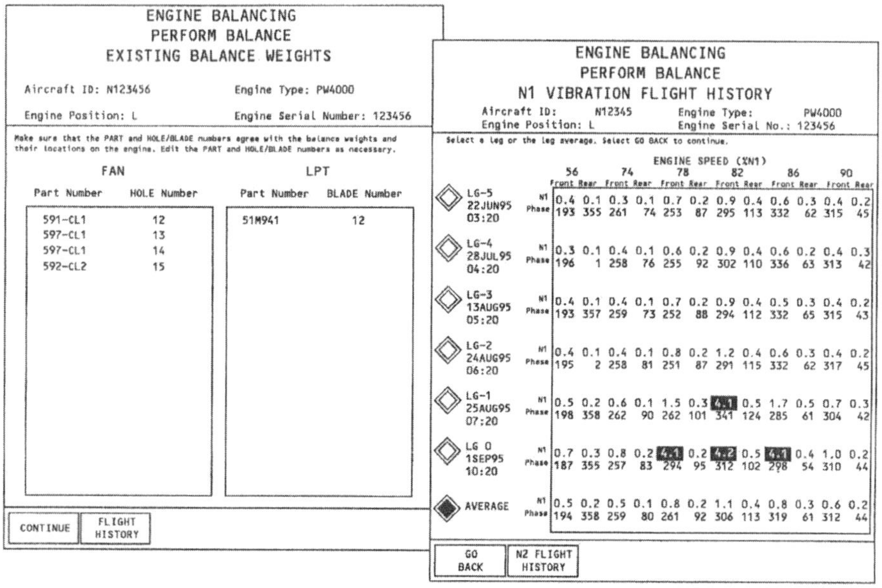

ENGINE BALANCING
PERFORM BALANCE
EXISTING BALANCE WEIGHTS

Aircraft ID: N123456 Engine Type: PW4000
Engine Position: L Engine Serial Number: 123456

Make sure that the PART and HOLE/BLADE numbers agree with the balance weights and their locations on the engine. Edit the PART and HOLE/BLADE numbers as necessary.

FAN Part Number	FAN HOLE Number	LPT Part Number	LPT BLADE Number
591-CL1	12	51M941	12
597-CL1	13		
597-CL1	14		
592-CL2	15		

CONTINUE | FLIGHT HISTORY

ENGINE BALANCING
PERFORM BALANCE
N1 VIBRATION FLIGHT HISTORY

Aircraft ID: N12345 Engine Type: PW4000
Engine Position: L Engine Serial No.: 123456

Select a leg or the leg average. Select GO BACK to continue.

ENGINE SPEED (%N1)

Leg		56 Front	56 Rear	74 Front	74 Rear	78 Front	78 Rear	82 Front	82 Rear	86 Front	86 Rear	90 Front	90 Rear
LG-5 22JUN95 03:20	N1	0.4	0.1	0.3	0.1	0.7	0.2	0.9	0.4	0.6	0.3	0.4	0.2
	Phase	193	355	261	74	253	87	295	113	332	62	315	45
LG-4 28JUL95 04:20	N1	0.3	0.1	0.4	0.1	0.6	0.2	0.9	0.4	0.6	0.2	0.4	0.3
	Phase	196	1	258	76	255	92	302	110	336	63	313	42
LG-3 13AUG95 05:20	N1	0.4	0.1	0.4	0.1	0.7	0.2	0.9	0.4	0.5	0.3	0.4	0.2
	Phase	193	357	259	73	252	88	294	112	332	65	315	43
LG-2 24AUG95 06:20	N1	0.4	0.1	0.4	0.1	0.8	0.2	1.2	0.4	0.6	0.3	0.4	0.2
	Phase	195	2	258	81	251	87	291	115	332	62	317	45
LG-1 25AUG95 07:20	N1	0.5	0.2	0.6	0.1	1.5	0.3	4.1	0.5	1.7	0.5	0.7	0.3
	Phase	198	358	262	90	262	101	341	124	285	61	304	42
LG 0 1SEP95 10:20	N1	0.7	0.3	0.8	0.2	4.1	0.2	4.2	0.5	4.1	0.4	1.0	0.2
	Phase	187	355	257	83	294	95	312	102	298	54	310	44
AVERAGE	N1	0.5	0.2	0.5	0.1	0.8	0.2	1.1	0.4	0.8	0.3	0.6	0.2
	Phase	194	358	259	80	261	92	306	113	319	61	312	44

GO BACK | N2 FLIGHT HISTORY

Figure 11-2-5. Engine balance information

- Calculates engine balance solutions
- Self-test

The AVM signal conditioner unit has a maintenance connector, which supplies alternative access for the engine balancing system (EBS) and for data loading. These functions are accessed through the Maintenance Access Terminal (MAT). See Figure 11-2-3.

The secondary engine display shows the highest vibration level for each engine. The rotor identification is shown below the vibration data. See Figure 11-2-4. If the N_1 or N_2 speed signal fails, the rotor identification shows broadband (BB) vibration. If the vibration level is equal to or more than 4.0 scalar units, the vibration unit will show in reverse video format (black numbers on a white background). The performance maintenance page shows all the engine vibration data.

Engine Balancing System

The engine balancing system (EBS) enables an AMT to select which balance weights on the engine to change or to decrease engine vibration. The 'perform balance' feature of the EBS calculates a balance solution that corrects high engine vibration. The solution identifies the balance weights that should be removed and installed in the aft spinner or on the low pressure compressor blades. Figure 11-2-5 indicates that the vibration for N_1 at 82% N_1 speed on August 25 was more than 4 scalar units and the engine needs to be balanced by adding or removing weights. The vibrations for N_1 increased more on the next flight as is evident in Figure 11-2-5.

Section 3

Materials and Manufacturing Defects

Aircraft turbine engines are high-performance machines in which components operate under conditions close to the limits of their materials' capabilities. Continuing advances in modern engine design and technology are placing ever-increasing demands on these materials, forcing the development of superalloys to meet new applications.

Engine Materials

Advances in performance hinge on a new engine's ability to operate at higher temperatures. At higher temperatures combustion is more efficient, which results in lower specific fuel consumption. However, engines that run hotter place greater stress combinations on critical engine parts, particularly hot section turbine discs, as seen in Figure 11-3-1.

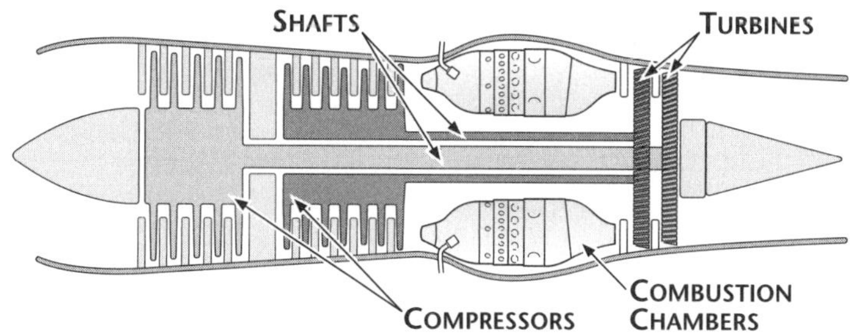

Figure 11-3-1. Engine hot sections are made with high-temperature alloys.

COMPONENT	MATERIAL TYPE
FAN BLADES	Superplastically formed titanium alloy skin diffusion bonded to a titanium honeycomb core
COMPRESSOR VANES, DISCS AND BLADES	With increasing temperature materials change from titanium alloys to 12% chromium steel to nickel-based superalloys
COMBUSTOR	Nickel-based superalloys
TURBINE BLADES, DISCS AND VANES	Nickel-based superalloys
SHAFTS	Heat treated steel
CASINGS	Aluminium alloys and composites

Table 11-3-1. Superalloys are used throughout the engine and are tailored for the specific operating environment in that section.

The materials used in turbine engines are shown in Table 11-3-1. The choices of material are mainly related to the different operating temperatures in the engine. In the cold section, where the temperature is low to medium, titanium parts are often used. In the hot section areas, nickel-based superalloys and some ceramics are used. Aluminum and composite materials are used for the engine outer casings where the temperature is relatively low.

Component Materials

Nickel-based superalloys. Nickel-based superalloys are used in the combustor and turbine sections of the engine where elevated temperatures are maintained during operation. Nickel-based superalloys typically constitute 40% to 50% of the total weight of an aircraft engine. Initially, cast-and-wrought nickel-based superalloys were developed for increased temperature and strength capability.

In the early 1970s, the emphasis was placed on powder-metallurgy (P/M) alloys for even higher temperature and strength applications. More recently, nickel-based superalloy developments have been driven toward improved damage tolerance through highly optimized fatigue-crack-growth properties. Nickel-based superalloys were developed from Ni-Cr heating elements. See Figure 11-3-2.

Nickel-based superalloys possess high strength and toughness at high temperature, creep

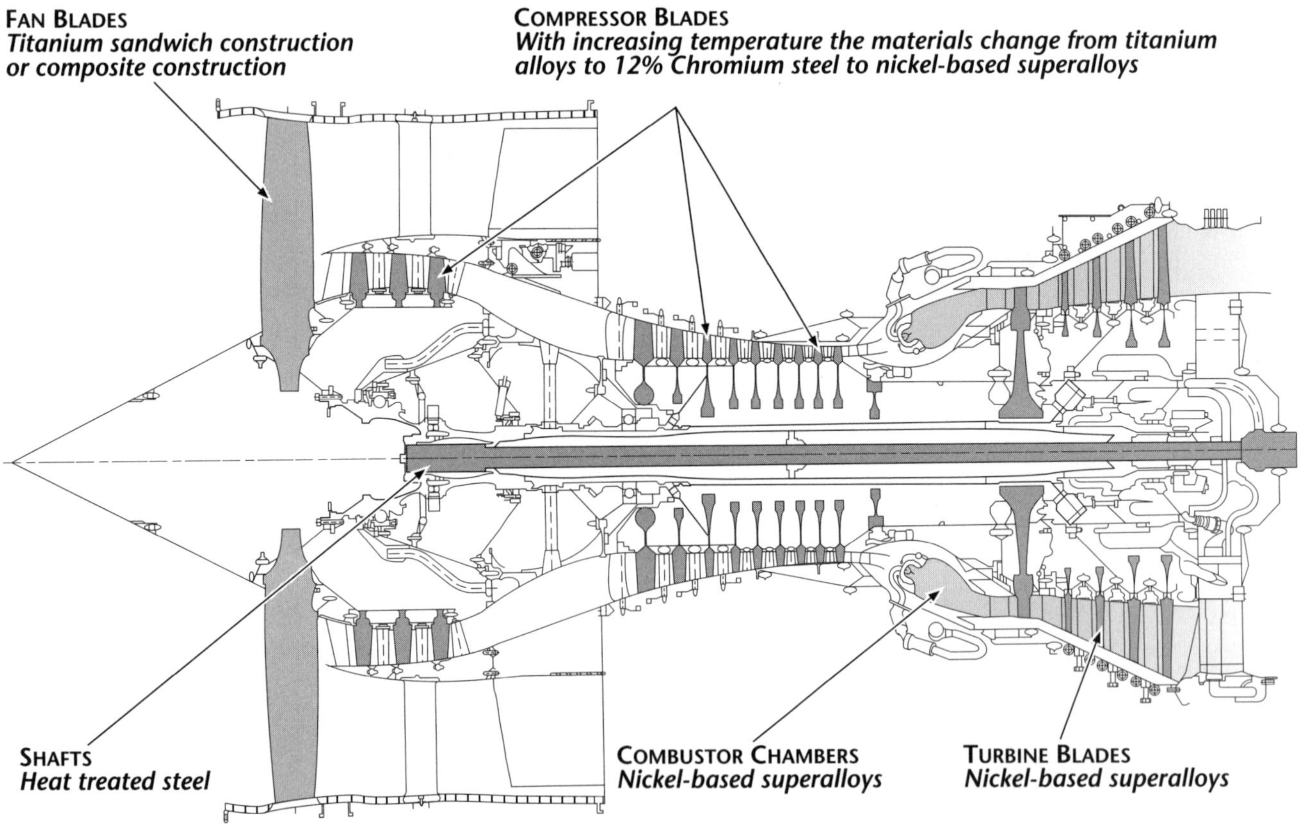

Figure 11-3-2. Turbine engine materials

resistance up to 1,000°C and corrosion resistance making them ideal materials for turbine engines.

Although superalloys retain strength up to temperatures near 1,000°C, they tend to be susceptible to environmental attack because of the presence of reactive alloying elements (which provide their high-temperature strength). Surface attack includes oxidation, hot corrosion, and thermal fatigue. In the most demanding applications, such as turbine blade and vanes, superalloys are often coated to improve thermal resistance.

Fan blade material. The V2500 engine uses unique wide chord, shroudless, hollow blades designed and developed by Rolls-Royce. These are manufactured by placing a 3D machined piece of honeycomb material between two sheets of pre-machined titanium. These fan blades can be seen in Figure 11-3-3.

Figure 11-3-3. Rolls-Royce developed titanium blades for the V2500 engine.

At high temperatures a diffusion bond is formed between the three pieces of material such that the finished blade is effectively a hollow, single-piece, structure. This lightweight blade is extremely strong with a leading edge that is robust and can resist damage due to foreign object impact.

The wide-chord nature of the blade centrifuges runway debris and dust into the by-pass duct, reducing engine removals due to foreign object damage (FOD) by a factor of four when measured against conventional narrow blades.

The GE90 turbine engine uses composite fan blades which are pictured in Figure 11-3-4. The fan blades are made from carbon-reinforced epoxy, which means no wrinkles or voids in the fibers. A composite fan blade is typically lighter than one made from titanium. The lightweight blade allows for a lighter containment system because there is less energy to absorb if a blade breaks off from the rotor. Because of the reduced weight of the composite blade, a lighter fan disc can be used to hold the fan blades in place.

Figure 11-3-4. General Electric developed composite fan blades for many of their larger engines.

Weight can be reduced in other areas of the engine that depend on blade-out load requirements such as fan casings. Fan casings made of triaxial carbon braid are introduced as an alternative to aluminum for fan containment cases for turbine engines. The braided fan case has a toughness superior to aluminum and is significantly lighter.

The process requires modeling of the composite process, advanced sensor and data acquisition systems, data-to-information conversion technologies, compression molding presses, autoclaves and small-scale molds to simulate processes.

Turbine Blade Design

First stage turbine blades are subjected to very high temperatures and could operate at 1,400°C. They are required to have a service life of 10,000 to 20,000 hours. This is possible due to:

- The use of nickel-based superalloys
- The blades are cast as a single crystal. This means that there are no grain boundaries within the structure.
- The blades are internally cooled to allow increased operating temperatures.
- The blades are coated to increase oxidation resistance.

Turbine blade coatings. The majority of gas turbine components such as turbine blades are made from nickel-based alloys. However, current running temperature of the gas turbine (1,350°C) is often higher than the melting point of these nickel alloys (1,200 to 1,315°C). Two methods have been developed to allow a higher turbine blade temperature. One is sophisticated cooling of the blades, using air that bypasses the combustion chamber after the compressor and the second is low thermal conductivity coatings on the surface of the blade.

Gas turbines obviously require protection to prevent the nickel alloy melting at high temperature but also require protection to prevent corrosion at high temperature.

The corrosion process is accelerated by high temperature and impurities present in the air due to the combustion of fuel in the engine. Therefore, coating the gas turbine blades will protect against both kinds of attack; i.e. high temperature and corrosion. Two types of coatings are used for turbine blades:

- Nickel coatings containing chromium (Cr), aluminum (Al) and yttrium (Y) called "NiCrALY Coatings" have been developed to combat high temperature corrosion and oxidation. These coatings contain 18% chromium, 22% cobalt, 12% aluminum and 0.5% yttium, and perform well in corrosive environments. The reason for the improved durability of the coatings is due to the formation of a thick, protective, and chemically stable alumina scale on the surface upon exposure to the environment. NiCrALY coatings can be applied by a variety of techniques including vacuum plasma spraying, low pressure plasma spraying, air plasma spraying, argon shrouded plasma spraying, high velocity oxygen fuel spraying, vapor phase deposition and electron beam physical phase deposition.
- Thermal barrier coating (TBC) - The ceramic coating provides a thermal barrier between the superalloy and the hot combustion gas while the metallic coating provides oxidation and corrosion protection and provides a surface for the ceramic layer to adhere to. TBCs aim to prevent extreme high temperature. NiCrALY coatings are being used in combination with ceramic (zirconia, ZrO_2) coatings, where the NiCrALY is acting as a bond coat for the ZrO_2 coating. These coatings are used to extend the life of metal components by creating a temperature drop across the coating, permitting the underlying metal to operate at a reduced temperature. Future gas turbines will use TBC technology to permit the simultaneous increase of turbine inlet temperature and the reduction of turbine cooling air, thereby increasing efficiency.

Manufacturing Defects

Engineers and technicians rely heavily on visual inspection methods to assess the condition of coated structures such as turbine blades. As a result, in-service condition monitoring and repair decisions focus on deterioration at the coating/gas-path interface. Improved non-destructive evaluation methods would provide information on when the coating must be removed and on the extent of base-metal attack.

The presence of rare metallurgical or manufacturing anomalies in aircraft turbine engines account for approximately 40% of uncontained engine failures. A probabilistic methodology has been developed to quantify the risk of fracture and the influence of periodic inspection on overall risk, supplementing the current safe life approach of maintenance. Simulation-based computer software programs such as DARWIN (Design Assessment of Reliability with INspection) are used to predict the probability of fracture of rotors and disks in commercial aircraft gas turbine engines.

Analysis of specific accidents and incidents has shown that the primary inherent failure modes result from the presence of material and manufacturing anomalies that can degrade the structural integrity of high-energy turbine rotors. Engineers use simulation-based software to predict the probability of fracture of rotors and disks in commercial aircraft gas turbine engines to avoid occurrence of uncontained engine failures.

Spectrographic Oil Analysis Program

The periodic analysis of oil samples taken from an aircraft's engine and gearboxes can be a valuable condition-monitoring tool because these engines are subject to continual wear. Because most parts in an engine are manufactured from various alloys, it is possible to judge the wear rates of individual parts. By graphing the test results obtained from different inspections, a visual wear rate of engines internal parts can be observed.

Spectrometric oil analysis programs (SOAP) can provide an early warning of abnormal wear, not only from internal distress such as a failing bearing, but also from external factors such as operating in a dusty environment without adequate filtering of intake air. Many turbine engine manufacturers mandate SOAP in certain of their turbine engine maintenance schedules.

Analysis of the oil condition in the engine can be divided into two areas: the first test determines the amount of wear metals in the oil sample, whereas the second test identifies the larger contaminants. Wear metals are very small particles of metal that have been worn away as the engine operates. By identifying each wear metal and noting the quantity present in the oil, the laboratory processing the oil sample can generally determine if this amount of wear metal is excessive and what part of the engine it has come from.

Common wear materials include: Aluminum (Al), Silver (Ag), Chromium (Cr), Copper (Cu), Iron (Fe), Nickel (Ni), Magnesium (Mg), Manganese (Mn), Sodium (Na), Lead (Pb), Silicon (Si), Tin (Sn), Titanium (Ti).

The larger contaminant particles are trapped and retained by the filter. The analysis of these larger particles is another important part of the oil analysis process.

The two most common oil analysis tests performed by a laboratory are: the atomic absorption and optical emission spectrometry tests. The atomic absorption test is more accurate than the optical emission spectrometry test but it can detect only one type of wear material at a time and the process is time consuming. Optical emission spectrometry can detect all wear materials in about one minute.

- To be effective, SOAP must be carried out in accordance with a detailed procedure. That procedure must detail samples being taken at regular intervals from the same position within the engine and analyzed by the same laboratory.
- SOAP is ineffective if one sample is taken from the middle level of the oil tank/ sump and the next is taken from the filler neck after adding fresh oil. A sample taken upstream or downstream of a filter will produce different results for certain tests such as particle counts.
- Different laboratories analyzing SOAP samples can each provide widely variable results from the same oil sample. Shopping around for the best price at each sample period will result in trend reports that make no sense. This makes the program ineffective.
- Ensure that clean sample kits are used (see Figure 11-3-5) and the appropriate equipment/component information is recorded, including history of the oil

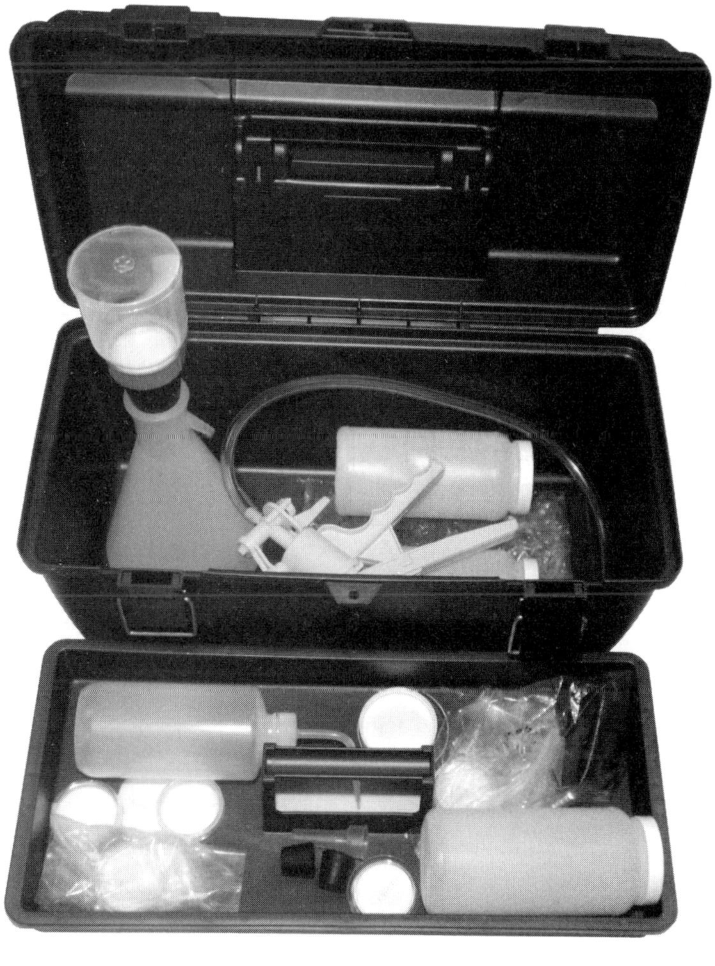

Figure 11-3-5. Oil analysis kit

AVIATION LABORATORIES

910 MARIA STREET
KENNER, LOUISIANA 70062
(504) 469-6751

ANALYSIS RESULTS

DATE: 10/31/08

OIL ANALYSIS CUSTOMER
ATTN: CHIEF MECHANIC
PO BOX 100

ANYTOWN, USA

ENGINE S/N:PCE81175M
ENGINE MODEL:PT6A-41
AIRCRAFT:BE 200
S/N:BC12
TAIL NO.:N88A-LH

** CURRENT RESULT ** SAMPLE APPEARS NORMAL, SEND NEXT SAMPLE AT THE NORMAL INTERVAL.

SAMPLE DATE: 9/21/08
ANALYSIS DATE:10/31/08
SAMPLE NUMBER: 31
TSN:
TSO: 3957
OIL HRS: 620
FILTER HRS: 620
OIL ADDED: 4.0
FILTER MGS: 9
FLASHPOINT:

*** FILTER ANALYSIS RESULTS ***

MATL:	ST ST	CB ST	AL ST	M50	COPPER	SILVER	MAGNS	ALUM	GRIT	MISC
AMOUNT:		TR						TR	MA	
TYPE:										
FORM:										

*** OIL ANALYSIS RESULTS ***

Iron	Copper	Nickel	Chromium	Silver	Magnesium	Aluminum	Lead	Silicon	Titanium	Tin	Moly	Tan
0.3	0.3	0.1	0.2	0.1	0.1	0.1	0.0	8.2	0.1	0.0	0.1	

COMMENTS: PACTEC. MORE

** PREVIOUS 1 RESULT ** SAMPLE APPEARS NORMAL, SEND NEXT SAMPLE AT THE NORMAL INTERVAL.

SAMPLE DATE:10/18/08
ANALYSIS DATE:10/31/08
SAMPLE NUMBER: 32
TSN:
TSO: 4034
OIL HRS: 698
FILTER HRS: 698
OIL ADDED:
FILTER MGS: 14
FLASHPOINT:

*** FILTER ANALYSIS RESULTS ***

MATL:	ST ST	CB ST	AL ST	M50	COPPER	SILVER	MAGNS	ALUM	GRIT	MISC
AMOUNT:		TR					TR	TR	MA	
TYPE:										
FORM:										

*** OIL ANALYSIS RESULTS ***

Iron	Copper	Nickel	Chromium	Silver	Magnesium	Aluminum	Lead	Silicon	Titanium	Tin	Moly	Tan
0.5	0.3	0.1	0.2	0.1	0.1	0.2	0.0	7.9	0.1	0.0	0.0	

COMMENTS: PACTEC. MORE

** PREVIOUS 2 RESULT ** SAMPLE APPEARS NORMAL, SEND NEXT SAMPLE AT THE NORMAL INTERVAL.

SAMPLE DATE: 7/09/08
ANALYSIS DATE:10/01/08
SAMPLE NUMBER: 04
TSN:
TSO: 3841
OIL HRS: 505
FILTER HRS: 505
OIL ADDED: 2.0
FILTER MGS: 5
FLASHPOINT:

*** FILTER ANALYSIS RESULTS ***

MATL:08	ST ST	CB ST	AL ST	M50	COPPER	SILVER	MAGNS	ALUM	GRIT	MISC
AMOUNT:		TR						TR	MA	
TYPE:										
FORM:										

*** OIL ANALYSIS RESULTS ***

Iron	Copper	Nickel	Chromium	Silver	Magnesium	Aluminum	Lead	Silicon	Titanium	Tin	Moly	Tan
0.2	0.1	0.0	0.2	0.1	0.2	0.2	.2	0.5	0.0	0.0	0.1	

COMMENTS: PACTEC - MORE

Figure 11-3-6. Oil analysis report

(operating hours or mileage on equipment and the oil, volume and frequency of top-ups, as well as changes in oil type).

- Act immediately upon the data findings. If a report warns of impending failure, the report is useless unless actions are taken to remedy the potential problem.

Trend Analysis

A SOAP program begins with the first sample being taken, preferably early in the engine's life. The results obtained from the first sample become the baseline. Subsequent sample results are then compared to that baseline. During the life of the engine, the particle count will increase but after every oil change the particle count will go down and then increase again. A sudden increase in metal particle concentration is cause for further investigation. Make sure that the sample is labeled properly so that the data can be compared to historical data. A SOAP test report is shown in Figure 11-3-6.

Field analysis. Portable oil analysis equipment is becoming increasingly popular. This equipment will quickly analyze the oil at the maintenance facility and will identify the condition of the oil. The onsite oil analysis program can be an effective screening tool for obtaining a general indication of the quality or condition of the lubricant or equipment. Onsite methods and test equipment do not have the same accuracy and/or repeatability as the more sophisticated methods and equipment found in an off-site laboratory. Most off-site equipment has lower detection limits and provides earlier notice of a developing problem.

Minimum Equipment List

The Minimum Equipment List (MEL) is intended to permit operation of an aircraft with inoperative items of equipment for a period of time until repairs can be made. It is important that repairs be accomplished at the earliest possible opportunity. In order to maintain an acceptable level of safety and reliability, the MEL establishes limitations on the duration of and conditions for operation with inoperative equipment.

When an item of equipment is discovered to be inoperative, it is reported by making an entry in the Aircraft Maintenance Record/Logbook as prescribed by Federal Aviation Regulations (FAR). The item is then repaired immediately or the repair may be deferred until a later time. MEL conditions and limitations do not relieve the operator of the responsibility for determining that the aircraft is in a condition for safe operation when items of equipment are inoperative.

All users of a MEL approved under FAR 121, 125, 129 and 135 must effect repairs of inoperative systems or components, deferred in accordance with the MEL, at or prior to the repair times established by the following letter designators:

- Category A - items in this category shall be repaired within the time interval specified in the remarks column of the operator's approved MEL.
- Category B - Items in this category shall be repaired within three consecutive calendar days, excluding the day the malfunction was recorded in the aircraft maintenance record/logbook.
- Category C - Items in this category shall be repaired within ten consecutive calendar days, excluding the day the malfunction was recorded in the aircraft maintenance record/logbook.
- Category D - Items in this category shall be repaired with one hundred and twenty consecutive days, excluding the day the malfunction was recorded in the aircraft maintenance log and/or record.

Chapter 12

TURBINE engine manufacturing

Section 1

Superalloy Casting

Learning Objectives:

- *Casting*
- *Welding*
- *Thermal Coatings*
- *Heat Treatment*
- *Composites*
- *Quality Control*

Casting is a cost-effective method for making a complex shape by the solidification of molten metal in a mold. The casting process is used to manufacture complex shapes. See Figure 12-1-1. It is used with a variety of materials such as titanium, nickel base superalloys, cobalt base superalloys, steel, aluminum and magnesium. The casting process does not provide optimal properties as compared to a forging process. A variety of casting flaws can occur with the casting process such as:

- Poor grain control
- Inclusions
- Shrink holes
- Poor alloy mix
- Improper grain orientation

Typical examples of cast products are illustrated in Figure 12-1-2. Several different casting processes are used in the aerospace industry.

Sand Casting

This technique is used for low production volume processes. Sand molds are created using various materials. The sand must be bonded together using either synthetic compounds or clay and water and molds must be rebuilt after each casting.

The design of molds is very complicated. In general, they are filled by gravity without the need for any pressure differential or mechanical action.

Left: **Before this engine was mounted on the airframe, it went through an extensive manufacturing process.**

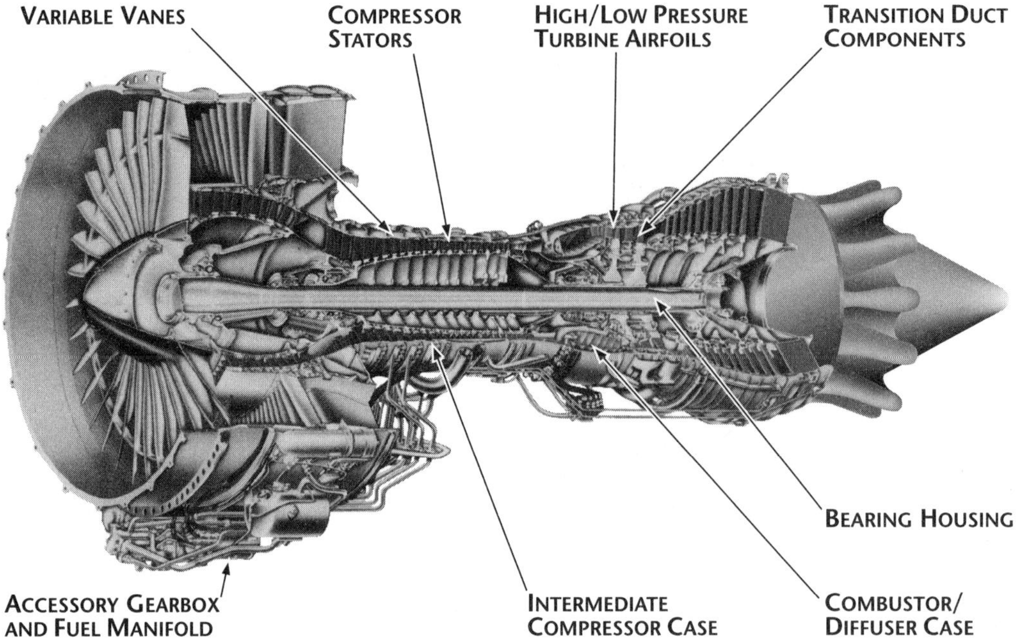

Figure 12-1-1. Cast components for a typical engine *Image courtesy of Pratt & Whitney*

Die-casting

Molds used for die-casting are permanent and made of either cast iron or steel. The three modes of die-casting are the high-pressure, low pressure and gravity modes.

High-pressure die-casting. This is the most commonly used process in which molten aluminum is injected at high-pressure into a metal mold by a hydraulically powered piston. The machinery needed for the process is very costly. This high-pressure die-casting is economical only when used for high-volume production.

Low-pressure die-casting. Low-pressure die-casting uses a die, which is filled from a pressurized crucible underneath. The process is particularly suited to the production of rotationally symmetrical products.

Gravity die-casting. Gravity die-casting is suitable for mass production and for fully mechanized casting.

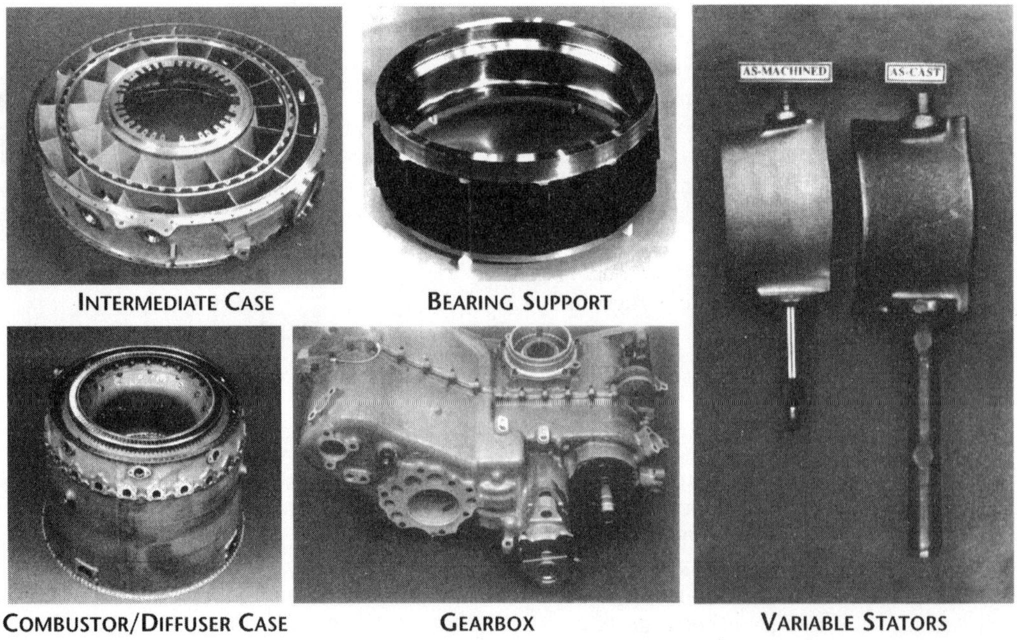

Figure 12-1-2. Selection of typical cast products *Photos courtesy of Pratt & Whitney*

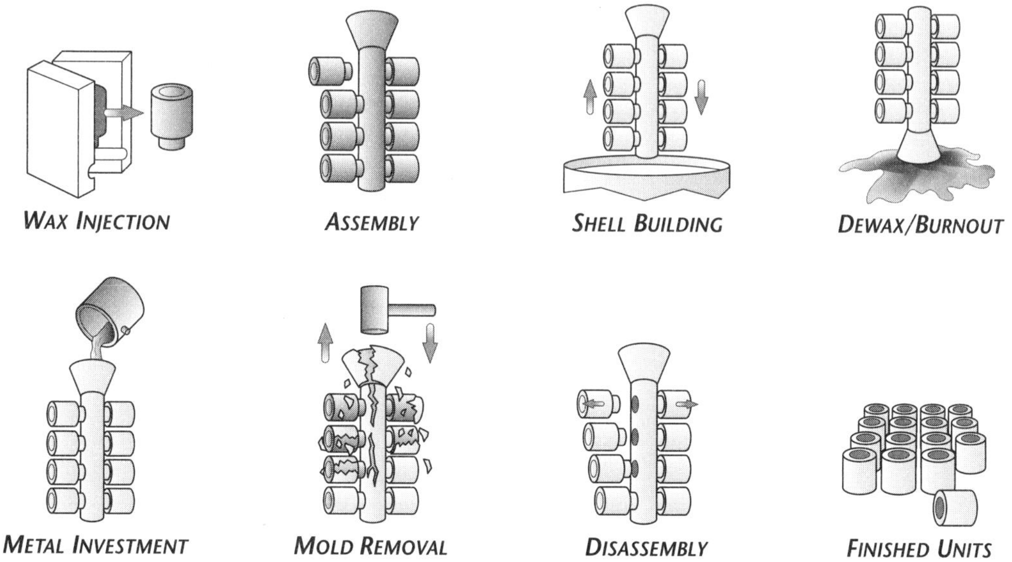

Figure 12-1-3. The investment casting process

Investment Casting

Single crystal turbine blades are produced from high-temperature nickel alloys that are cast by the investment casting or lost wax technique. The mold-making process starts with a wax pattern that will eventually be melted away. This wax pattern is dipped in refractory slurry, which coats it and forms a skin. This is dried and the process of dipping in the slurry and drying is repeated until a robust thickness is achieved. After this, the entire pattern is placed in an oven and the wax is melted away. This leaves a mold that may then be filled with molten metal. See Figure 12-1-3.

Because the mold is formed around a one-piece pattern which does not have to be pulled out from the mold as in the traditional sand casting process, very intricate parts and undercuts can be cast. The wax pattern itself is made by duplicating using a stereo lithography model (or similar) which has been fabricated using a computer solid model master. The mold must be broken up to remove the cast metal inside. This process can achieve geometries that are impossible with other casting methods. A secondary benefit is that investment casting can achieve high finish quality without post-finishing.

Forging

Forging is the plastic deformation of metals into desired shapes by compression with or without a die. The basic principle of forging is that material flows in the direction of least resistance. The simplest type of forging is called upsetting, which compresses the metal between two flat parallel platens. More complicated geometries can be achieved using dies. The two basic categories of forging are open-die and closed-die. Drop hammers supply energy through the impact of a falling weight to which the upper die is attached. Another type of forging uses the mechanical press.

In jet turbine engines iron-based, nickel-based and cobalt-based superalloys are forged into components such as discs, blades, buckets, couplings, manifolds, rings, chambers and shafts. Further improvements to the fatigue life of forged turbine disks and other high-strength components can be achieved by creating a residual compressive stress on the surface of the disk by shot peening. The peening process causes a uniform plastic deformation due to the impact of the shot, creating a microscopic dimpling of the surface. See Figure 12-1-4.

Figure 12-1-4. The forging process enhances the properties of the disk material.

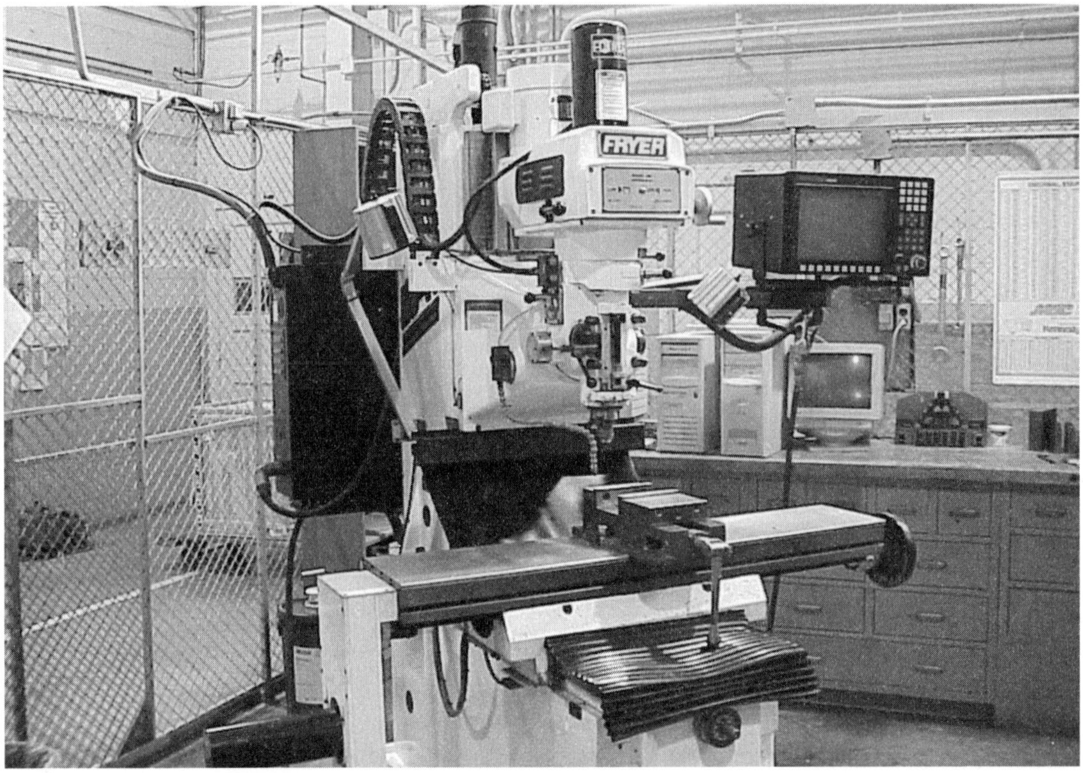

Figure 12-2-1. CNC machining equipment *Photo courtesy of Purdue University*

Section 2

High-speed CNC Machining and Welding

Many components of a turbine engine are machined using five axis computer numerically controlled (CNC) equipment. See Figure 12-2-1. Billets of raw material or extrusions can be machined to precise tolerances. High-speed machining equipment can create monolithic and thin-walled parts from aluminum alloys, titanium and nickel-based alloys, stainless steels and composites. High-performance machining strategies are under development to reduce costs and speed up production of high-quality parts.

Figure 12-2-2. A vertical turning machine produces a nearly finished part.

The machining center which can mill, drill, bore and hone complex parts, is frequently used in the aerospace industry.

Large vertical turning machines (see Figure 12-2-2) are used to manufacture ring-shaped components from Inco 718, Waspaloy, 6-4 Titanium, HR120 as well as other materials.

Welding

Welding processes are used frequently in the manufacture and repair of gas turbine engine components. The types of welding processes used are spot and seam welding, gas metal arc welding (GMAW), gas tungsten arc welding (GTAW), plasma arc, electron beam welding and friction stir welding.

The welder should be aware that the welding process will affect the heat treatment process of the welded part and often parts must be heat-treated after the welding is completed.

Basic weldment failure modes:

- Welding flaws may result in a variety of

failure modes, the most common being fatigue as a result of a stress concentration or a loss of material properties.

- The loss of strength in a weld joint could result in rupture or excessive creep.
- Distortion of a part due to welding could lead to improper fits and function relative to other parts.
- The distortion could also cause excessive levels of stress that could cause a structural failure.

Inert Gas Welding (Fusion Welding)

Gas metal arc welding (GMAW). This was formerly called MIG. During GMAW the electrode is consumed and becomes the filler material; therefore it must be of the same material as the material being welded. GMAW welding is not done in an enclosed chamber, or envelope. The shielding gas used with GMAW is either Argon or Helium. See Figure 12-2-3.

Gas tungsten arc welding (GTAW). GTAW was formerly called TIG. It uses a non-consumable tungsten electrode and filler material is fed into the weld area in the same manner as in oxyacetylene welding.

A pure tungsten electrode (green band) is used with alternating or direct current to weld aluminum or, in the case of alternating current, to weld magnesium. Thoriated tungsten (red band) and ceriated (yellow band) tungsten electrodes are used with direct current for all other alloys. See Figure 12-2-4.

The shielding gas used with GTAW can be either helium or argon, but argon is preferred due to a lower rate of diffusion with the atmosphere. Argon is also more economical than helium. Sometimes a welding chamber or durable clear plastic envelope is used in the welding process to avoid contamination of the weld area. GTAW welding is often used to repair cracks in jet engine parts.

Steady state plasma arc welding (SSPAW). Plasma Arc is in effect a GTAW arc modified by constriction of the arc column to produce a collimated gas stream of highly energized gas or plasma. It is this columnar arc of high-energy value which produces the characteristic narrow bead with deep penetration.

The high-temperatures of fusion welding and subsequent air cooling give higher hardness and lower ductility in many materials. As a result, there is a tendency toward cracking in the weld zone. This effect is greatly reduced by employing a stress-relief process after welding which is necessary for most materials.

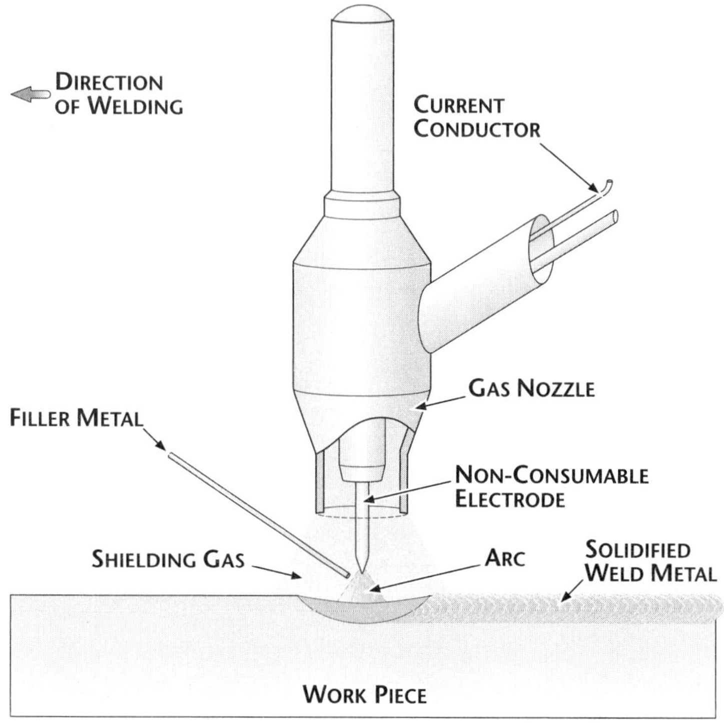

Figure 12-2-3. GMAW welding process

Electron Beam Welding

Assemblies are processed using a beam of electrons to generate heat at the joint and cut a keyhole into which the molten metal flows. The high energy density of the electron beam and the vacuum environment result in narrow heat-affected zones, deep welds with little distortion and high-quality welds with very little porosity or contaminants. An electron beam welder is

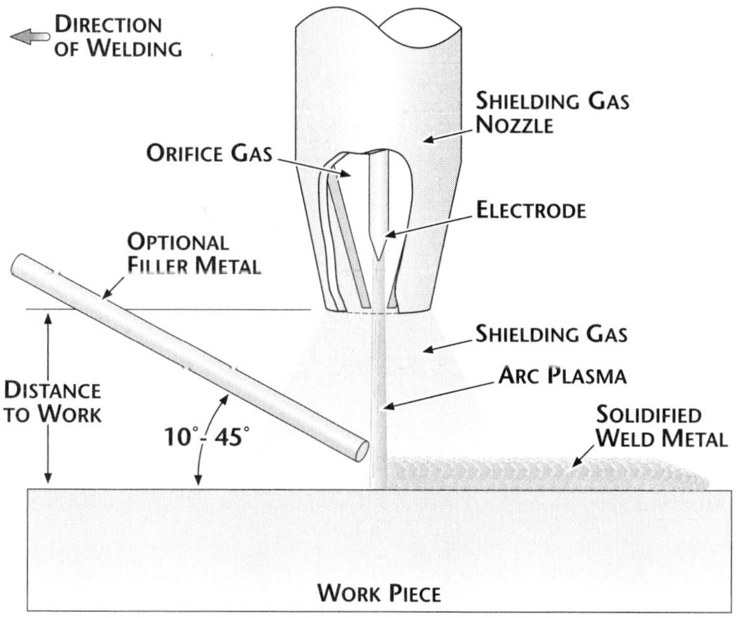

Figure 12-2-4. Plasma welding process

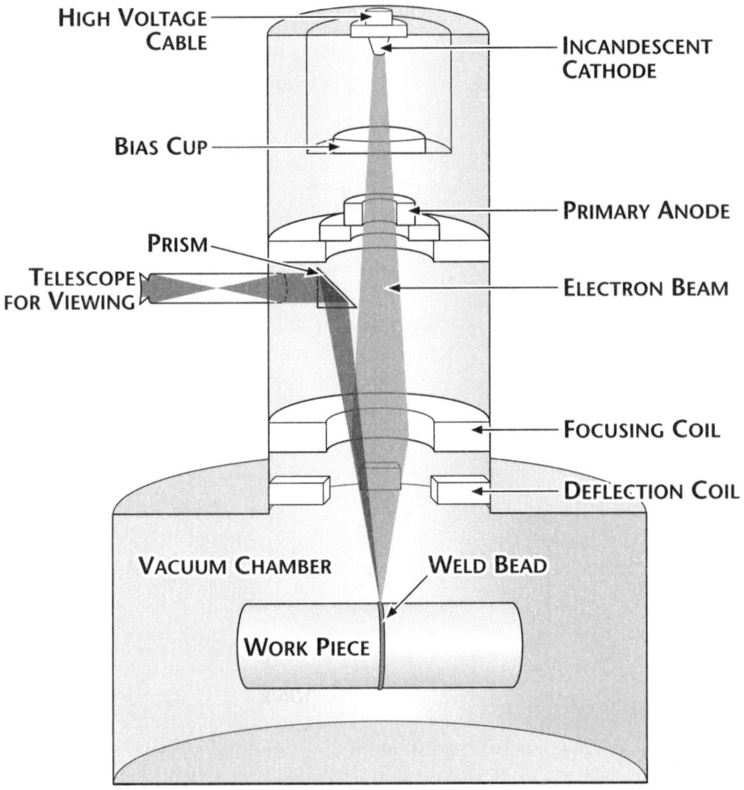

Figure 12-2-5. Electron beam welding process

shown in Figure 12-2-5. This can be used to join reactive and refractory metals, high thermal conductivity metals, dissimilar materials and large sections or complex joint designs, with or without filler metal.

Advantages of electron beam welding include:

- A reduced heat affected zone, may minimize heat treatment requirements or effects
- Deep penetration (several inches thick)
- No filler material is required
- High-speed application

Disadvantages include:

- High cost
- Must be done in a vacuum environment

Friction Stir Welding

This technology uses frictional heat generated by a rotating spindle traveling along a joint to weld two components together. See Figure 12-2-6. Friction stir welded joints are characterized by low distortion, low porosity, no shrinkage and superior mechanical properties due to their refined microstructure. A friction stir welder is shown in Figure 12-2-7.

Laser Welding

Laser beam welding is a process that produces coalescence. It uses the heat from a concentrated coherent light beam which impinges on the joint. The light beam produced by the laser device results from the transition of stimulated electrons or molecules to lower energy levels.

Laser welding can be used for welding, cladding and precise cutting of flat sheets or 3-D parts and offers many advantages. It creates a narrow heat-affected zone having little distortion and smooth cut edges that do not require post-pro-

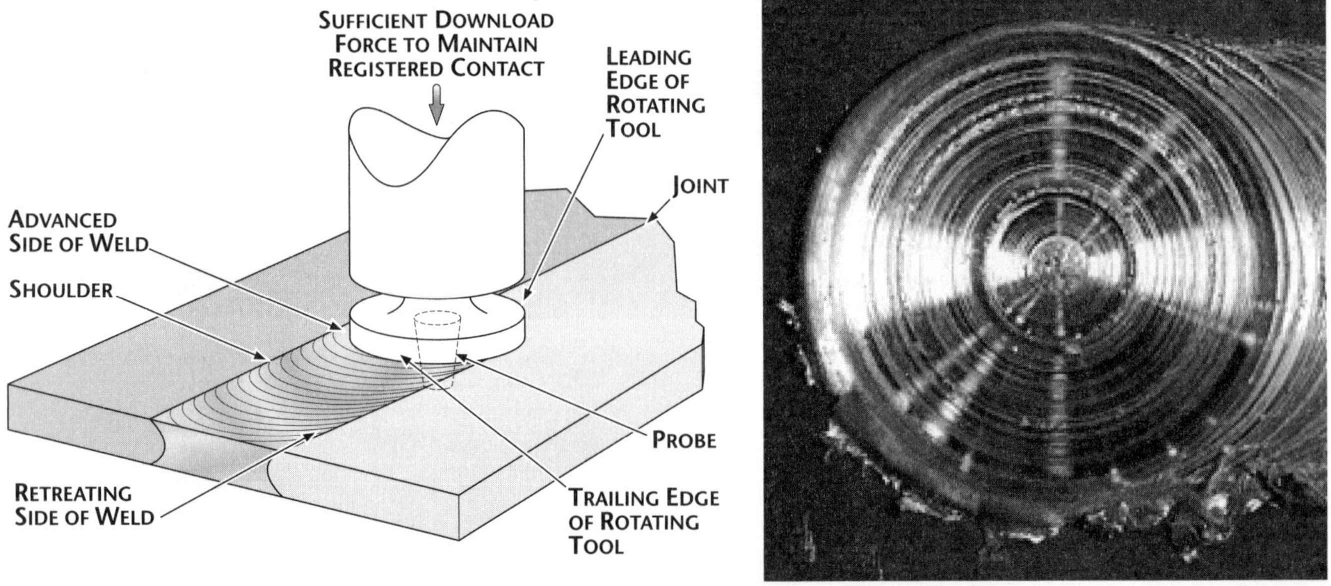

Figure 12-2-6. (A) Friction stir welding principle (B) Friction stir welding bead in aluminum material. *Purdue University photo*

cessing treatment. This is due to the high-energy density of the laser beam. Laser welding is faster and more precise than conventional methods as well as flexible, highly automated and easily integrated into other processes.

Electro-chemical Machining

Electro-chemical machining (ECM) is used for etching or to create unstressed, high-precision parts. Electrochemical machining is a way of machining metal using electrolysis techniques.

A preshaped tool with the inverse of the required detail is set up as the cathode and the workpiece is set up as the anode. A high amperage and low voltage direct current is passed between the tool and workpiece. Metal at the surface of the anode (the workpiece) is dissolved into ions and the tool is slowly lowered, maintaining a constant distance between it and the workpiece.

Electro-discharge Machining

Electrical discharge machining (EDM) is a highly-accurate manufacturing process for creating shapes within components and assemblies. EDM connects a metal workpiece to a power supply and uses a shaped tool or electrode to erode material in order to form the desired geometry or pattern. The electrical discharge is of very short duration and high current density.

The two basic types of EDM machines are wire and probe. Wire machines pre-drill a hole in the workpiece and then feed an electrode through the hole. Sinker machines cut workpieces without pre-drilling holes and use a machined graphite or copper electrode. To create a potential difference between the part and the electrode, the workpiece is often immersed in a circulating dielectric fluid.

Chemical Milling

Chemical milling is the process of removing large amounts of metal by means of chemical etching. All metal types and shapes are candidates for chemical milling, especially contoured parts which are not easily machined. The best applications for chemical milling involve the reduction in weight of contoured parts.

Chemical milling is a simple process, although a number of subtle control requirements exist which need constant attention.

- The parts to be etched are first cleaned and then masked with a synthetic rubber paint which protects the part from being etched where no etching is desired.
- Using a template to define the pattern, the rubber mask is scribed using a knife or laser.
- Areas to be etched are peeled back and the parts are submerged in the etchant. The rate of material removal is proportional to the compositional strength of the etching solution, temperature and amount of time in the tank.
- Using an ultrasonic thickness tester, the thickness is monitored until drawing dimensions are achieved.
- Parts are stripped of maskant then cleaned and touched up as necessary by hand polishing or deburring.

Laser Drilling

Laser drilling offers an alternative to mechanical drilling, punching, broaching and wire EDM. It is especially adaptable for small holes with large depth-to-diameter ratios. With laser drilling, a wide range of hole diameters are obtainable. Material such as steel, nickel alloys, aluminum, copper, brass, borosilicate glass, quartz, ceramic, plastic and rubber can be successfully laser drilled. The laser drilling process

Figure 12-2-7. Friction stir welding equipment

Photo courtesy of Transformation Technologies Inc.

is so fast and the results so reliable that it is ideal for the high production volumes associated with fully automated or semi-automated tooling applications.

The nature of the laser beam used in laser drilling allows holes to be drilled in the hardest aerospace alloys. Through the use of laser drilling, holes can be created even in coated materials. The control of the hole created with laser drilling is exceptionally precise. The programmable nature of lasers allows for very high-speed drilling applications where thousands of holes are required in short cycle times.

Thermal Spray Coatings

Plasma coatings. Plasma coatings are one group of metallic and / or ceramic coatings that are applied to the surface of parts. Other surface coatings exist that are somewhat similar and are referred to terms that can be misunderstood or misused. The purpose of this introduction is to explain the differences that distinguish one group of coatings from another and to define terms. The four basic groups of thermal spray coatings are:

- Gaseous fuel and oxygen flame process - Processes such as flame spray, powder spray and wire spray refer to a combustion process which uses a gaseous fuel and oxygen flame to melt and propel molten metal onto the surface of parts. The metal can be supplied to the gun in wire or powder form. Although variations exist in combustion equipment, the basic principle is the same and the heat available is the limiting factor. Typically, metals with relatively low melting points can be applied in this manner.
- Detonation process - This process uses a cannon-like device enclosed in a large soundproof room with an external control area. An explosive mixture of fuel gas and oxygen is ignited in the combustion chamber and erupts from the open barrel end. As escaping gases pass out of the barrel, metallic powder is melted by a shock wave and propelled by the pressure wave that follows. This process is used to apply hard

Figure 12-2-8. These shafts have just been removed from heat treatment and are ready to be quenched.

coatings with relatively high density which is attained by the high velocity at impact.

- Plasma spray process - The plasma spray process uses a high-intensity electric arc that heats an inert gas or gaseous mixture to an R ionized state. Powdered materials are injected into the hot high velocity gas, melted and propelled onto the substrate. The plasma spray process can apply many types of metals, ceramics, cermets and composites. Plasma equipment is readily available and requires a moderately sized work area.
- Dual wire electric arc process - This process creates an electric arc between two feed stock wires. The arc causes the wires to melt and high-pressure gas propels the molten metal to the substrate.

Heat Treatment

Most aerospace alloys such as aluminum, titanium and steel can be strengthened or softened by heat treating processes. Common methods used are:

- Solution heat treatment – this process makes the alloy stronger. The alloy is heated in a furnace for a specified time and temperature and is then rapidly cooled (quenched).
- Artificial aging – Some alloys do not age naturally and need an additional heat treatment to age to the desired strength.
- Annealing – This process is used to make the alloy softer for forming and to relieve stresses in the alloy.

Solution heat treatment. To take advantage of the precipitation-hardening reaction, it is necessary to first produce a solid solution. This process is referred to as solution heat-treating. The objective is to take into solid solution the maximum practical amounts of the soluble hardening elements in the alloy. The process consists of soaking the alloy at a high enough temperature high and for a long enough time to achieve a nearly homogeneous solid solution. Solutionizing temperatures vary with alloy composition, but the specific temperature must be carefully controlled within ±10°F. This first step is shown in Figure 12-2-8.

If the solution temperature is lower than required, insufficient solute will be dissolved and the final aging treatment will not reach the desired hardness. If the material is overheated, low melting point phases called eutectics at the grain boundaries will liquefy and ruin the material.

The time at the nominal solution heating temperature is called soak time and is a function of microstructure before heat-treatment, the thickness of the material being heated and the loading of the furnace being used. The time at temperature must be sufficient to completely dissolve the solute phases and homogenize the solid solution.

Quenching. To avoid the types of precipitation which are detrimental to strength or corrosion resistance, the solid solution formed during solutionizing must be quenched rapidly and without interruption to produce a supersaturated solution at room temperature. Most frequently, parts are quenched by immersion in cold water. Large aluminum production facilities use water spray quenching. For parts with complex shapes and abrupt changes in thickness, somewhat slower cooling may be required to prevent cracking. In these instances, boiling water or an aqueous solution of polyalkaline glycol is used.

Some forgings and castings, which require maximum dimensional stability, are air-cooled. The hardening response of these parts is limited but satisfactory for the applications.

The transfer time from furnace to quenching media, which is referred to as quench delay must be quite short. Generally, load transfer time should not exceed fifteen seconds. This is to prevent precooling to a critical temperature range in which rapid precipitation of unwanted phases takes place. The extent of the temperature range varies with alloy composition, but 750°F to 500°F should be avoided for virtually all aluminum alloy quenches.

Precipitation hardening. High-strength superalloys need further heat treatment to obtain the maximum strength properties. After quenching, the material is a supersaturated solid solution of alloying elements dissolved in the base metal. This is an unstable condition. The chemical balance of the material is out of equilibrium and the elements suspended in solid solution have a tendency to precipitate in order to restore the equilibrium.

When this precipitation occurs at room temperature it is referred to as natural aging. Depending upon the alloy, this process can take from one hour to many years to achieve. Alloys which require years to age naturally would require further heat treatment.

The heat energy required to drive the chemical reactions in these more sluggish alloys is supplied by artificial aging heat treatments.

With both natural and artificial aging, the precipitates harden the material by setting up submicroscopic strains throughout the aluminum matrix. The secondary phases that fall out of solution actually crowd and stretch the surrounding material. This serves to reduce the elasticity or ductility of the metal, which in turn increases hardness and structural strength.

There is an optimum particle size, neither too small nor too large, which imparts the best compromise between strength and corrosion properties.

Annealing. The softest, most ductile and workable condition of both non-heat-treatable and heat-treatable wrought alloys is produced by the annealing process. The heat-treatable alloys are annealed by thoroughly precipitating the solutes into coarse, widely spaced particles. This removes the effects of heat treatment and prevents natural age hardening.

Stress relief. Local stress-relief is the application of a heat treatment cycle by a portable heating system to a part that has been weld repaired, usually without disassembly.

Local heat treatment can be used on static parts where permitted by the authorizing repair document.

Local heat treatment is easy to do because very little fixturing is necessary to stress-relieve minor areas of large components.

Composites

The use of composite materials in the aerospace industry depends on the manufacture of cost-effective and high-quality composite structures. Fiberglass was the first successful composite material used in turbine engines but nowadays carbon fiber and boron fibers are more popular due to superior strength properties. New high-temperature composite materials are under development that could withstand the high-temperatures in the engine gas path.

The use of composites in turbine engines is restricted by the maximum temperature they can withstand. The maximum temperature for carbon fiber components is 350 °F. Composite materials are used in the manufacture of:

- Fan blades
- First stage compressor blades
- Intake ducts
- Engine cowlings

Currently, the autoclave in Figure 12-2-9 is the principal equipment for producing such high-quality parts. It can be used to bond composites and produce large aircraft components such as wing and fuselage components. It can also process a wide variety of materials, including thermosets and thermoplastics, as well as parts with complex shapes.

Plating

The principle of electroplating is that the coating metal is deposited from an electrolyte onto the base material. The object to be plated is maintained at a negative potential (cathode) relative to an inert positive counter-electrode (anode). The electroplating solution contains a reducible form of ion of the desired metal.

The purpose of plating is to secure a surface with properties or dimensions different from those of the base metal. Several processes are used in the aviation industry:

- Cadmium plating - Used to provide corrosion resistance to metal parts.
- Chromium plating, hard deposit - Used on ferrous parts to increase abrasion resistance, increase tool and die life, maintain accuracy of gages, recondition worn or undersized parts and increase corrosion resistance.
- Copper plating - Used to provide an anti-seize surface, prevent carburizing of surfaces on which carburizing is neither necessary or permitted, prevent decarburization or to provide a source of copper for furnace brazing.
- Electroless nickel plating of titanium - Used to provide hard, wear-resistant and corrosion-resistant surfaces on titanium alloys that operate at temperatures up to 900°F (482°C).
- Electroless nickel–thallium–boron plating - Used to provide hard, wear-resistant surfaces for operation at temperatures up to 900°F(482°C) and to provide uniform buildup on complex shapes.
- Nickel plating - Used to provide moderate corrosion and oxidation resistance to metal parts.

Quality Control

The Federal Aviation Administration (FAA) defines individual manufacturing approvals through its Federal Aviation Regulations (FARs) and laws mandating compliance.

An engine manufacturer must submit to the FAA data describing the inspection and test procedures necessary to ensure that each engine or engine part that is produced conforms to the type design and is in a condition for safe operation, including as applicable:

- A statement describing assigned responsibilities and delegated authority of the quality control organization, together with a chart indicating the functional relationship of the quality control orga-

Figure 12-2-9. Autoclave *Photo courtesy of Sergey Dubikovsky*

nization to management and to other organizational components and indicating the chain of authority and responsibility within the quality control system.

- A description of inspection procedures for raw materials, purchased items and parts and assemblies produced by manufacturer's suppliers, including methods used to ensure acceptable quality of parts and assemblies that cannot be completely inspected for conformity and quality when delivered to the prime manufacturer's plant.
- A description of methods used for production inspection of individual parts and complete assemblies including the identification of any special manufacturing process involved, the means used to control the processes and the final test procedure for the completed products.
- An outline of the materials review system, including the procedure for recording review board decisions and disposing of rejected parts.
- An outline of a system for informing company inspectors or current changes in engineering drawings, specifications and quality control inspection stations.

Each manufacturer shall provide information to the FAA regarding all delegation of authority to suppliers to make major inspections of parts or assemblies for which the prime manufacturer is responsible. FAA inspectors are assigned to engine manufacturers and repair stations facilities and they have surveillance over the engine manufacturer's quality control system.

Many companies are certified to the ISO 9001 quality standard or the aerospace AS9100 quality standard which is based on ISO 9001 quality standards.

The AS9100 quality standards are divided into three parts:

- AS9100 - Original Equipment Manufacturer (OEM) and Part Supplier Requirements - AS9100 is the quality management standard established for aerospace OEMs and part suppliers. It includes aerospace requirements applied to and integrated with ISO 9001, but with nearly 100 additional requirements specific to aerospace.
- AS9110 – Maintenance Organizations Requirements - Based on ISO 9001, AS9110 includes specific aerospace quality management system requirements of a maintenance repair and overhaul organization. It focuses on controlling repair schemes and maintenance plans, configuration management as well as the skill and qualifications necessary to perform Maintenance, Repair and Overhaul (MRO) tasks within the aerospace industry.
- AS9120 – Stocklist Distributor Requirements - This standard focuses on the quality management system requirements of a distributor. It includes specific aerospace requirements for distributors of aerospace related material, hardware and components. It focuses on verification of approved parts, chain of custody, traceability, record control and part availability.

Index

A

B

C

D

E

F

G

H

I

N

O

P

Q

R

S

T

U

V

W

X

Z